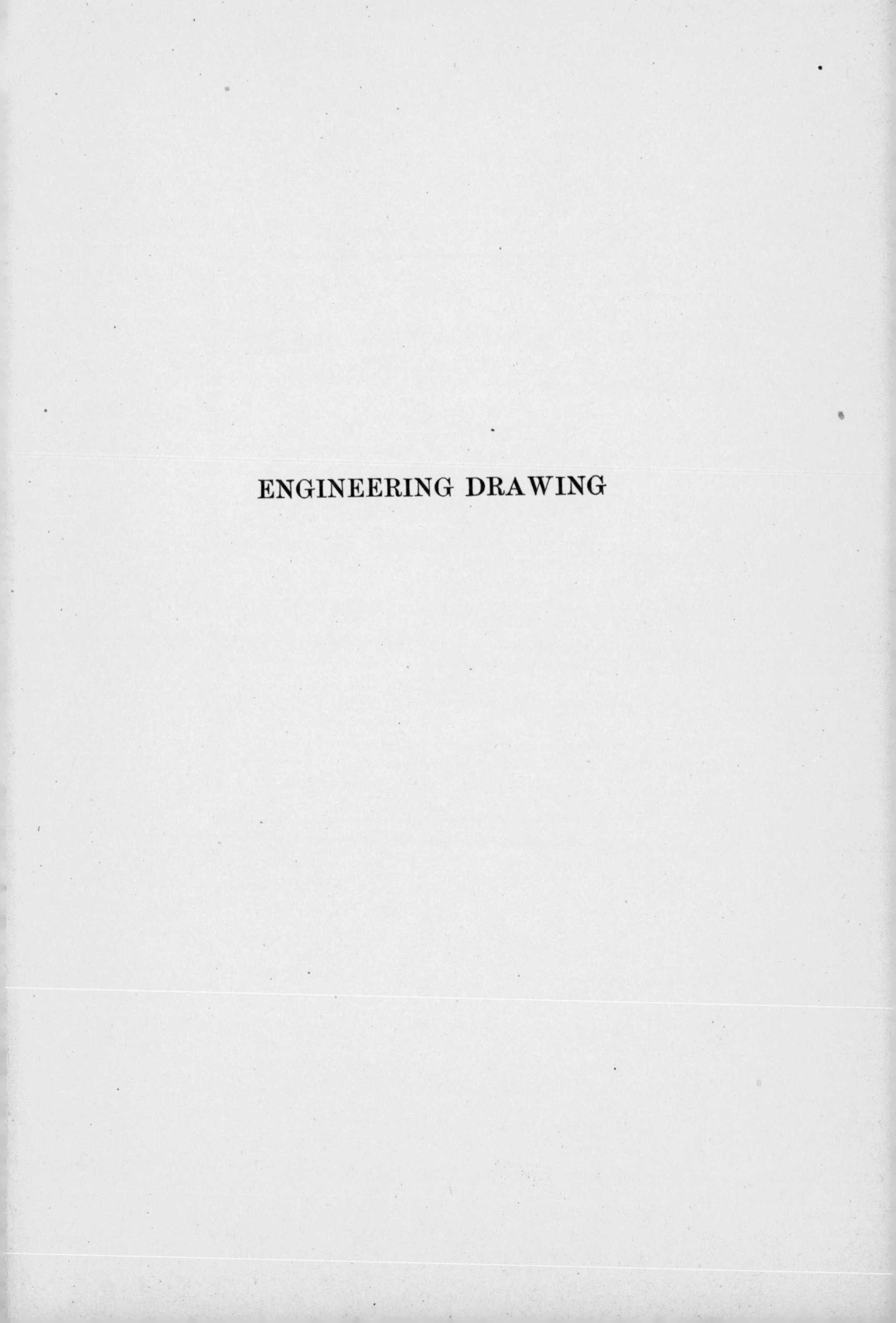

ENGINEERING DRAWING

THE
FRENCH DRAWING SERIES

FRENCH—
ENGINEERING DRAWING
FIFTH EDITION
481 pages, 6 × 9, 811 illustrations

FRENCH AND TURNBULL—
LESSONS IN LETTERING
BOOK I—Vertical Lettering
40 pages, 9 × 6
BOOK II—Inclined Lettering
40 pages, 9 × 6

FRENCH AND SVENSEN—
MECHANICAL DRAWING FOR HIGH SCHOOLS
THIRD EDITION
265 pages, 6 × 9, 535 illustrations

FRENCH AND IVES
AGRICULTURAL DRAWING AND THE DESIGN OF FARM STRUCTURES
130 pages, 7½ × 10, 182 illustrations

FRENCH AND MEIKLEJOHN—
ESSENTIALS OF LETTERING
94 pages, oblong, 9 × 6, 120 illustrations

A MANUAL
OF
ENGINEERING DRAWING
FOR
STUDENTS AND DRAFTSMEN

BY

THOMAS E. FRENCH, M.E., D.Sc.

Professor of Engineering Drawing, The Ohio State University
Member American Society of Mechanical Engineers
Society for the Promotion of Engineering
Education, Etc.

FIFTH EDITION
SIXTH IMPRESSION

McGRAW-HILL BOOK COMPANY, INC.
NEW YORK AND LONDON
1935

First Edition
First Printing, August, 1911.

Second Edition
First Printing, July, 1918.

Third Edition
First Printing, May, 1924.

Fourth Edition
First Printing, June, 1929.

Fifth Edition
Fourth Printing, December, 1935.

Fifth Edition
Sixth Printing, February, 1937.

PRINTED IN THE UNITED STATES OF AMERICA

THE MAPLE PRESS COMPANY, YORK, PA.

PREFACE TO THE FIFTH EDITION

In the successive editions of this book the aim has been to keep abreast of modern engineering practice, each time adding new material in text and problems. A course in drawing consists essentially of a series of problems given in connection with assigned study of the text. The value of the course lies in the selection, arrangement, and method of presentation of these problems, each chosen to illustrate and apply some particular teaching point. In this edition the favorite problems of the previous edition have been retained and more than a hundred new ones added, all representing current design.

The need for the present revision is indicated in that the American Standards Association has just completed its Standards for Drawings and Drafting Room Practice (Z14.1,1935). These and other pertinent A.S.A. Standards which have been adopted since the last edition was published are given in the book and the illustrations and drawings are made to conform to them.

There has been some rearrangement of chapters, meeting the preference of a majority of the users; a new chapter on sections and conventions has been made; a number of problems have been redimensioned to larger size, and the chapter on dimensioning has been expanded, illustrating the new standards and including an explanation of allowances and tolerances. The new material in text and appendix will, it is hoped, make not only a better work book for the class room but also a more valuable permanent reference book for the engineer's technical library.

The author is indebted to the teachers of drawing over the country, many of whom are his personal friends, for helpful suggestions and reassuring comment. He would also record with appreciation the assistance of his colleagues in the department, especially that of Mr. C. D. Cooper and Mr. Gilbert Coddington; the work of Mr. Paul Machovina on the drawings, and above all the able collaboration of Professor John M. Russ.

T.E.F.

COLUMBUS, OHIO,
April, 1935.

PREFACE TO THE FIRST EDITION

There is a wide diversity of method in the teaching of engineering drawing, and perhaps less uniformity in the courses in different schools than would be found in most subjects taught in technical schools and colleges. In some well-known instances the attempt is made to teach the subject by giving a series of plates to be copied by the student. Some give all the time to laboratory work; others depend principally upon recitations and home work. Some begin immediately on the theory of descriptive geometry, working in all the angles; others discard theory and commence with a course in machine detailing. Some advocate the extensive use of models; some condemn their use entirely.

Different courses have been designed for different purposes, and criticism is not intended, but it would seem that better unity of method might result if there were a better recognition of the conception that drawing is a real language, to be studied and taught in the same way as any other language. With this conception it may be seen that except for the practice in the handling and use of instruments, and for showing certain standards of execution, copying drawings does little more in the study as an art of expression of thought than copying paragraphs from a foreign book would do in beginning the study of a foreign language.

And it would appear equally true that good pedagogy would not advise taking up composition in a new language before the simple structure of the sentence is understood and appreciated; that is, "working drawings" would not be considered until after the theory of projection has been explained.

After a knowledge of the technic of expression, the "penmanship and orthography," the whole energy should be directed toward training in constructive imagination, the perceptive ability which enables one to think in three dimensions, to visualize quickly and accurately, to build up a clear mental image, a requirement absolutely necessary for the designer who is to represent his thoughts on paper. That this may be accomplished more readily by taking up solids before points and lines has been demonstrated beyond dispute.

It is then upon this plan, regarding drawing as a language, the universal graphical language of the industrial world, with its varied forms of expression, its grammar and its styles, that this book has been built. It is not a "course in drawing," but a text-book, with exercises and problems in some variety from which selections may be made.

Machine parts furnish the best illustrations of principles, and have been used freely, but the book is intended for all engineering students. Chapters on architectural drawing and map drawing have been added, as in the interrelation of the professions every engineer should be able to read and work from such drawings.

In teaching the subject, part of the time, at least one hour per week, may profitably be scheduled for class lectures, recitations, and blackboard work, at which time there may be distributed "study sheets" or home plates of problems on the assigned lesson, to be drawn in pencil and returned at the next corresponding period. In the drawing-room period, specifications for plates, to be approved in pencil and some finished by inking or tracing, should be assigned, all to be done under the careful supervision of the instructor.

The judicious use of models is of great aid, both in technical sketching and, particularly, in drawing to scale, in aiding the student to feel the sense of proportion between the drawing and the structure, so that in reading a drawing he may have the ability to visualize not only the shape but the size of the object represented.

In beginning drawing it is not advisable to use large plates. One set of commercial drafting-room sizes is based on the division of a 36″ × 48″ sheet into 24″ × 36″, 18″ × 24″, 12″ × 18″, and 9″ × 12″. The size 12″ × 18″ is sufficiently large for first year work, while 9″ × 12″ is not too small for earlier plates.

Grateful acknowledgment is made of the assistance of Messrs. Robert Meiklejohn, O. E. Williams, A. C. Harper, Cree Sheets, F. W. Ives, W. D. Turnbull, and W. J. Norris of the staff of the Department of Engineering Drawing, The Ohio State University, not only in the preparation of the drawings, but in advice and suggestion on the text. Other members of the faculty of this University have aided by helpful criticism.

The aim has been to conform to modern engineering practice, and it is hoped that the practical consideration of the draftsman's needs will give the book permanent value as a reference book in the student's library.

The author will be glad to cooperate with teachers using it as a textbook.

T.E.F.

Columbus, Ohio,
June 6, 1911.

CONTENTS

ENGINEERING DRAWING

CHAPTER I

INTRODUCTORY

1. By the term Engineering Drawing is meant drawing as used in the industrial world by engineers and designers, as the language in which are expressed and recorded the ideas and information necessary for the building of machines and structures; as distinguished from drawing as a fine art, as practiced by artists in pictorial representation.

The artist strives to produce, from either the model or landscape before him or through his creative imagination, a picture which will impart to the observer something as nearly as may be of the same mental impression as that produced by the object itself, or as that in the artist's mind. As there are no lines in nature, if he is limited in his medium to lines instead of color and light and shade, he is able only to suggest his meaning and must depend upon the observer's imagination to supply the lack.

The engineering draftsman has a greater task. Limited to outline alone, he may not simply suggest his meaning but must give exact and positive information regarding every detail of the machine or structure existing in his imagination. Thus drawing to him is more than pictorial representation; it is a complete graphical language, by whose aid he may describe minutely every operation necessary and may keep a complete record of the work for duplication or repairs.

In the artist's case the result can be understood, in greater or less degree, by anyone. The draftsman's result does not show the object as it would appear to the eye when finished; consequently his drawing can be read and understood only by one trained in the language.

Thus as the foundation upon which all designing is based, engineering drawing becomes, with perhaps the exception of mathematics, the most important single branch of study in a technical school. Every engineering student must know how to make and how to read drawings. The subject is essential in all types of engineering practice. The drafting room is often the entering gateway into industry, but even one who may expect never to make drawings must be able to interpret them and to know whether or not a drawing is correct. An engineer without a working knowledge of the engineers' language would be professionally illiterate.

2. When this language is written exactly and accurately, it is done with the aid of mathematical instruments and is called mechanical drawing.[1] When done with the unaided hand, without the assistance of instruments or appliances, it is known as freehand drawing, or technical sketching. Training in both these methods is necessary for the engineer, the first to develop accuracy of measurement and manual dexterity, the second to train in comprehensive observation, and to give control and mastery of form and proportion.

Our object then is to study this language so that we may write it, may express ourselves clearly to one familiar with it and may read it readily when written by another. To do this we must know the alphabet, the grammar and the composition, and be familiar with the idioms, the accepted conventions and abbreviations.

This new language is entirely a graphical or written one. It cannot be read aloud but is interpreted by forming a mental picture of the subject represented; and the student's success in it will be indicated not alone by his skill in execution, but by his ability to interpret his impressions, to visualize clearly in space.

It is not a language to be learned only by comparatively few draftsmen, who will be professional writers of it but, as already indicated, should be understood by all connected with or interested in technical industries, and the training its study gives in quick, accurate observation and the power of reading description from lines is of a value quite unappreciated by those not familiar with it.

In this study we must first of all become familiar with the technique of expression, and, as instruments are used for accurate work, the first requirement is the ability to use these instruments correctly. With continued practice will come a facility in their use which will free the mind from any thought of the means of expression. Under technique is included the study of lettering, usually the first work taken up in a technical course.

[1] The term "mechanical drawing" is often applied to all constructive graphics and, although an unfortunate misnomer, has the sanction of long usage. The whole subject of graphic representation of solids on reference planes comes under the general name of *descriptive geometry*. That term, however, has by common acceptance been restricted to a somewhat more theoretical treatment of the subject as a branch of mathematics. This book may be considered as an ample preparation for that fascinating subject, with whose aid many difficult problems may be solved graphically.

CHAPTER II

THE SELECTION OF INSTRUMENTS

3. In the selection of instruments and material for drawing the only general advice that can be given is to secure the *best* that can be afforded. For one who expects to do work of professional grade it is a great mistake to buy inferior instruments. Sometimes a beginner is tempted by the suggestion to get cheap instruments for learning, with the expectation of getting better ones later. With reasonable care a set of good instruments will last a lifetime, while poor ones will be an annoyance from the start and will be worthless after short usage. As good and poor instruments look so much alike that an amateur is unable to distinguish them, trustworthy advice should be sought before buying.

This chapter will be devoted to a short description of the instruments usually necessary for drawing. Mention of some others not in everyday use but convenient for special work will be found in Chapter XXIII.

4. Checklist of Instruments and Materials.

1. Set of drawing instruments, in morocco case, including at least: 6″ compasses, with fixed needle-point leg, pencil, pen and lengthening bar; 6″ hairspring dividers; two ruling pens; three bow instruments; box of hard leads.
2. Drawing board.
3. T-square.
4. 45° and 30°–60° triangles.
5. 12″ mechanical engineer's scale of proportional feet and inches (three flat or one triangular).
6. Slide rule.
7. One dozen thumb tacks.
8. Drawing pencils, 6H, 2H and F.
9. Pencil pointer.
10. Pencil eraser.
11. Bottle of drawing ink.
12. Penholder, pens for lettering and penwiper.
13. French curves.
14. Drawing paper to suit.
15. Tracing paper.

To these may be added:

16. Art gum or cleaning rubber.
17. Dusting cloth.
18. Bottle holder.
19. Erasing shield.
20. Lettering triangle.
21. Protractor.
22. 2′ or 4′ rule.
23. Sketch book.
24. Hard Arkansas oil stone.
25. Piece of soapstone.
26. Sharp pocket knife (for sharpening pencils).

The student should mark all his instruments and materials plainly with initials or name, as soon as purchased and approved.

(1) **The Case Instruments.**—All modern high-grade instruments are made with some form of "pivot joint," originally patented by Theodore Alteneder in 1850 and again in 1871. Older instruments (and some cheap modern ones) were made with tongue joints, in which the wear of the tongue on the pin results in a lost motion which after a time renders the instrument unfit for use. In the pivot joint the wear is on adjustable conical points. Several modifications of the original are made, as shown in Fig. 1.

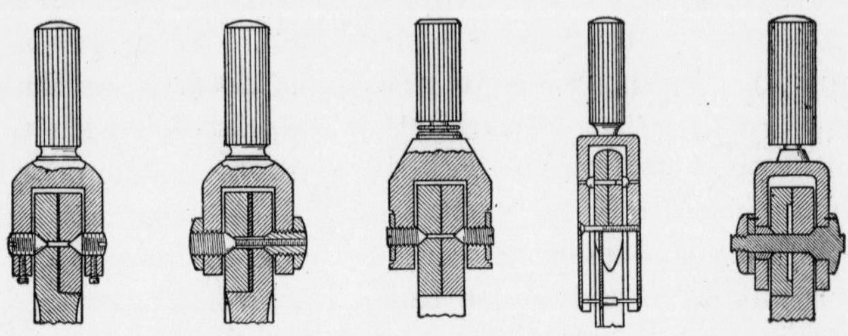

Fig. 1.—Sections of pivot joints.

The handle attached to the yoke, while not essential to the working of the joint, is very convenient. Not all instruments with handles, however, are pivot joint instruments. Several straightener devices for keeping the handle erect have been devised but by many draftsmen they are not regarded with favor.

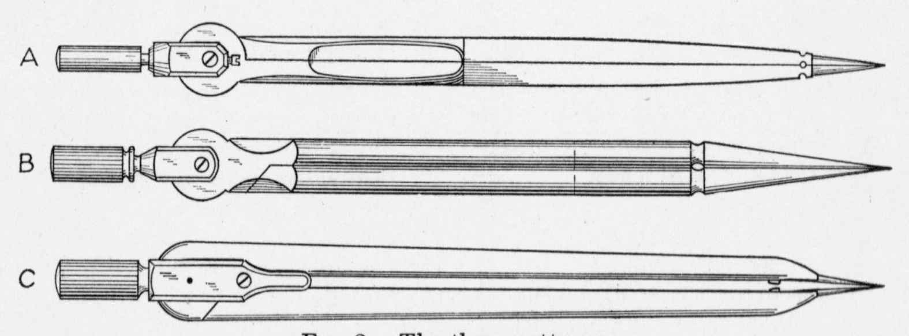

Fig. 2.—The three patterns.

There are three different patterns or shapes in which modern compasses are made; the beveled, or American (*A*), the round (*B*) and the flat (*C*), Fig. 2. The choice of shapes is entirely a matter of personal preference. After one has become accustomed to the balance and feel of a certain instrument, he will not wish to exchange it for another shape.

Compasses may be tested for accuracy by bending the knuckle joints and bringing the points together, as in Fig. 3. If out of alignment, they should not be accepted. The standard compasses are six inches long, but a favorite additional instrument with draftsmen is the four-inch size with fixed pencil leg and its companion with fixed pen leg.

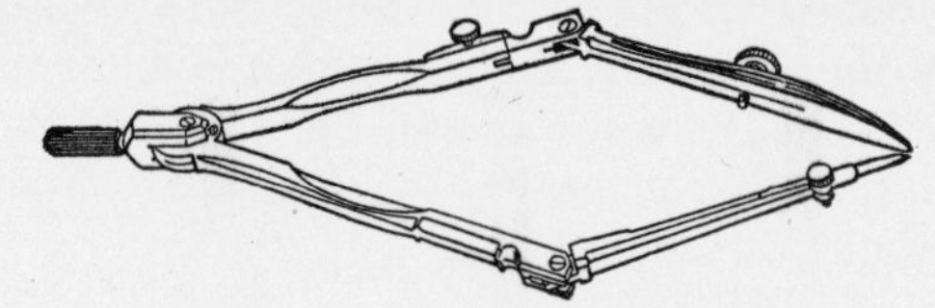

Fig. 3.—Test for alignment.

Dividers are made either "plain" as those in Fig. 2, or "hairspring" as shown in Fig. 4. The latter form, having a screw for fine adjust-

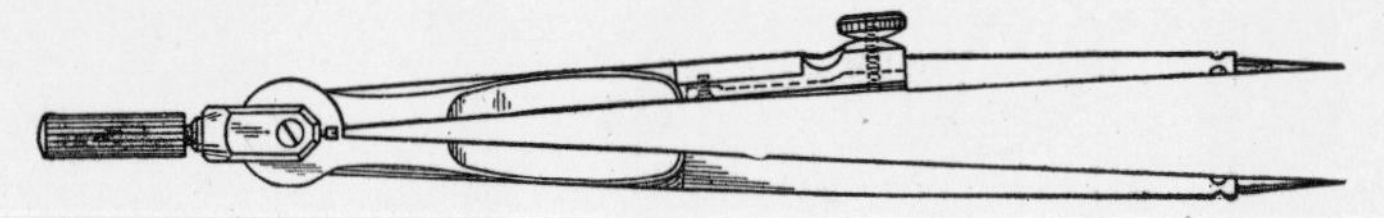

Fig. 4.—Hairspring dividers.

ment, is occasionally of convenience and should be preferred. Compasses may be had also with hairspring attachment on the needle-point leg.

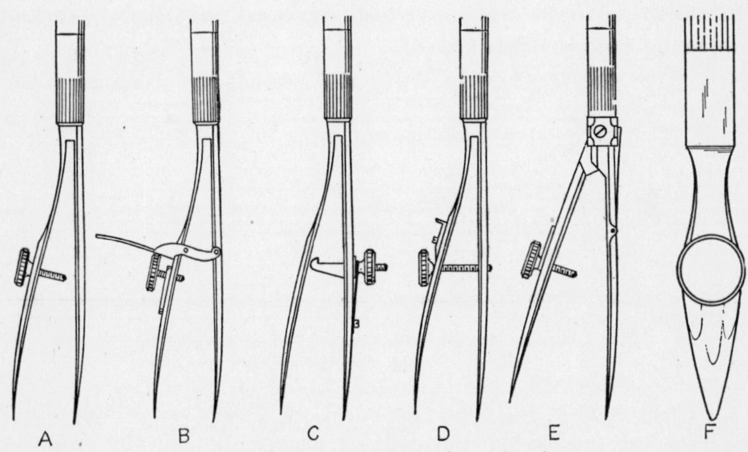

Fig. 5.—Ruling pens, opened for cleaning.

Ruling pens are made in a variety of forms, Fig. 5. The two most popular ones are the spring blade (*A*), which opens sufficiently wide for cleaning, and the jack-knife (*E*), which may be cleaned without changing the setting. The form shown at (*F*) is known as a detail pen or Swede pen, which for large work is a very desirable instrument. The nibs of the pen should be shaped as shown in Fig. 33. Pens sometimes come from the factory poorly sharpened and must be dressed as described on page 22 before they can be used.

The set of three spring bow instruments includes bow points or spacers, bow pencil and bow pen. There are several designs and sizes.

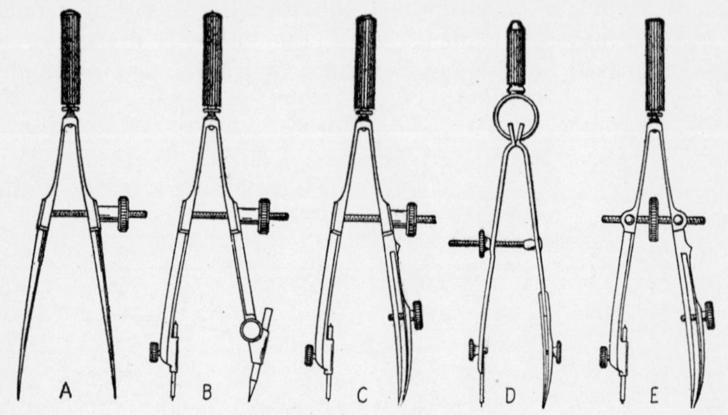

Fig. 6.—Spring bow instruments.

The standard shapes of side-screw bow instruments are shown in Fig. 6, *A*, *B*, *C*. At *D* is illustrated the hook or ring spring type, sometimes called "Richter" bows. Both standard and Richter types are made as side-screw bows and also as center-screw instruments, illustrated by the center-screw bow pen at *E*, which are becoming increas-

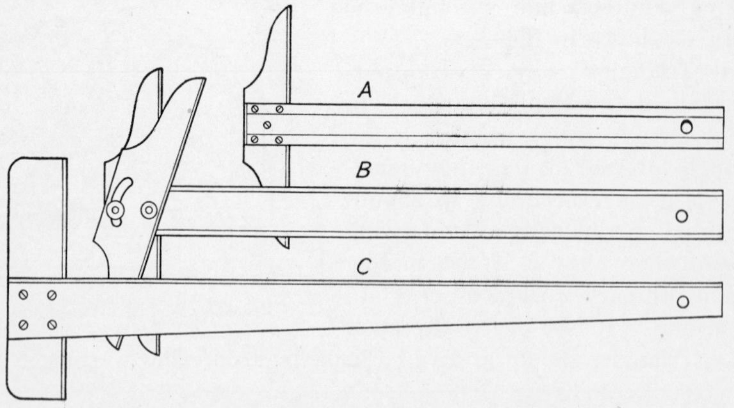

Fig. 7.—T-squares: fixed head, adjustable and English forms.

ingly popular among draftsmen. The springs of the side-screw bows should be strong enough to open to the full length of the screw but not so stiff as to be difficult to pinch together. The hook spring bow usually has a softer spring than the flat spring type.

(2) **Drawing boards** should be made of clear white pine, cleated to prevent warping. Care should be taken in their selection, and the working edge tested with a steel straight-edge.

(3) The **T-square** with fixed head, Fig. 7 *A*, is used for all ordinary work. It should be of hard wood and the blade perfectly straight. The transparent edge blade is much the best. A draftsman will have several fixed head squares of different lengths and will find an

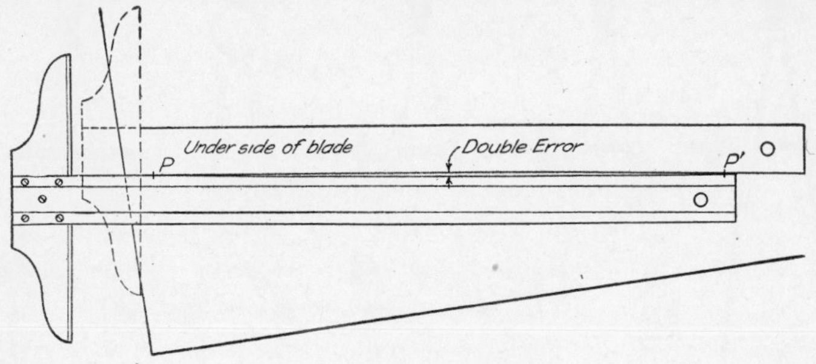

Fig. 8.—To test a T-square.

adjustable head square (*B*) of occasional use. The form shown at *C* is the English type with tapered blade and beveled edge. In a long square it has an advantage in balance and rigidity but has the objection that the lower edge is apt to disturb the eyes' sense of perpendicularity. A T-square blade may be tested for straightness by drawing a sharp line through two points, then turning it over and with the same edge drawing another line through the points, as shown in Fig. 8.

(4) **Triangles** made of transparent celluloid (fiberloid) are much to be preferred over wooden ones. Through internal strains they sometimes lose their accuracy so should be tested periodically by drawing perpendicular lines as shown in Fig. 9. For ordinary work a 6″ or 8″-45 degree and a 10″-60 degree are good sizes. Triangles should always be kept flat to prevent warping.

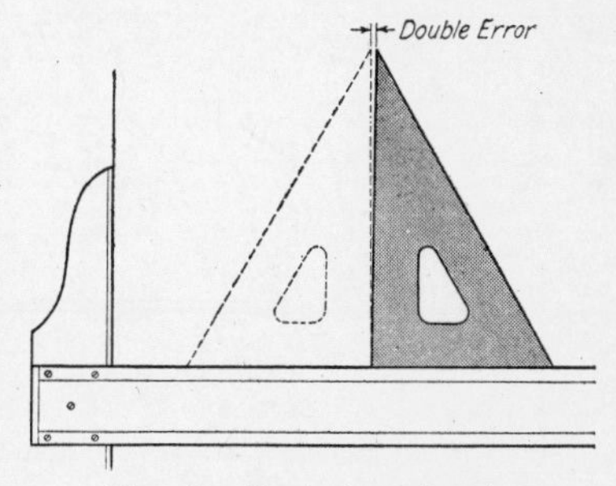

Fig. 9.—To test a triangle.

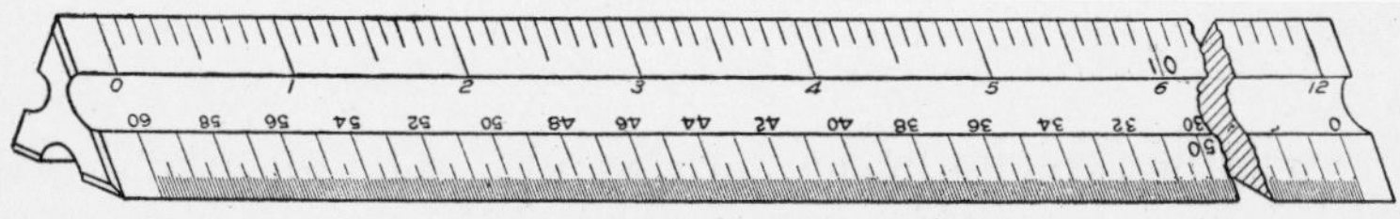

Fig. 10.—Civil engineers' scale.

(5) **Scales.**—There are two general kinds of scales, the civil engineers' scale of decimal parts, with divisions of 10, 20, 30, 40, 60

and 80 to the inch, Fig. 10; and the mechanical engineers' or architects' scale of proportional feet and inches, Fig. 11. The former is used for plotting and map drawing and in the graphic solution of problems, the latter for all machine and structural drawings. Scales are usually

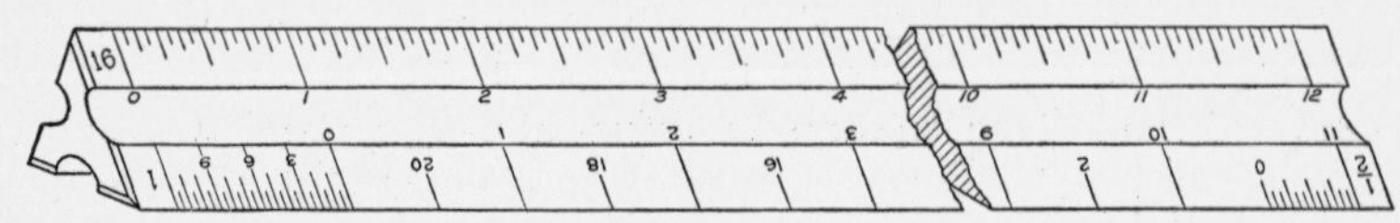

FIG. 11.—Mechanical engineers' or architects' scale.

made of boxwood, sometimes of metal or paper, and of shapes shown in section in Fig. 12. The triangular form, either *A* or *B*, is the commonest. Its only advantage is that it has more scales on one stick than the others, but this is offset by the delay in finding the scale wanted. Three flat scales are the equivalent of one triangular scale. The "opposite bevel" scale *E* is easier to pick up than the regular form *D*. Many professional draftsmen use a set of six or eight scales, each graduated in one division only. A very popular scale among machine draftsmen at the present time is the new opposite bevel "full divided" flat scale with full size on one edge and half size on the other, Fig. 13, and a second with quarter size and eighth size.

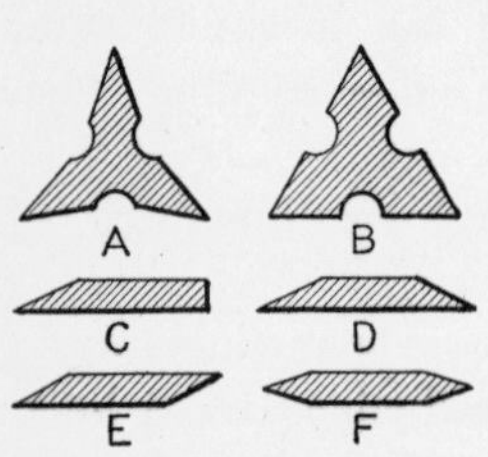

FIG. 12.—Scale sections.

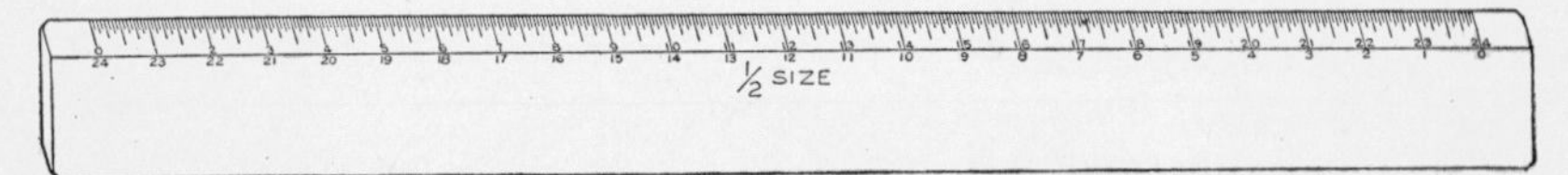

FIG. 13.—A full- and half-size scale.

(6) **Slide Rules.**—The slide rule, while not a drawing instrument, is essentially an engineer's instrument, and proficiency in its use is a requirement in every modern drafting room. A good way for a beginner to learn to use a slide rule is in connection with a drawing course. Its use facilitates the rapid calculation of volumes and weights of castings, an essential part of a draftsman's work. Of the several varieties of slide rules, those recommended for prospective engineers are a "Polyphase Duplex,"* a "Log Log Duplex"* or a "Log Log Trig,"* in ten-inch size.

(7) The best **thumb tacks** have a thin head with a steel point screwed into it. Cheaper ones are made by stamping. Tacks with comparatively short tapering pins should be chosen.

* Registered Trademark.

(8) **Drawing pencils** are graded by letters from 6B (very soft and black), 5B, 4B, 3B, 2B, B, HB, F, H, 2H, 3H, 4H, 5H, 6H to 9H (extremely hard). Some draftsmen prefer a holder using standard size drawing lead fillers.

(9) A sandpaper **pencil pointer** or flat file should always be at hand for sharpening pencil and compass leads.

(10) The Ruby **pencil eraser** is the favorite at present. One of large size, with beveled end, is preferred. This eraser is much better for ink than a so-called ink eraser, as it will remove the ink perfectly without seriously damaging the surface of paper or cloth. A piece of art gum or soft rubber is useful for cleaning paper.

(11) **Drawing ink** is finely ground carbon in suspension, with shellac added to render it waterproof. The non-waterproof ink flows more freely but smudges very easily. Chinese ink in stick form, rubbed up for use with water in a slate slab is used in making wash drawings, and for very fine line work.

(12) The **penholder** should have a cork grip, small enough to enter the mouth of a drawing ink bottle. An assortment of pens for lettering, grading from coarse to fine, may be chosen from those listed in Chapter IV. A **penwiper** of lintless cloth or thin chamois skin should always be at hand for both writing and ruling pens.

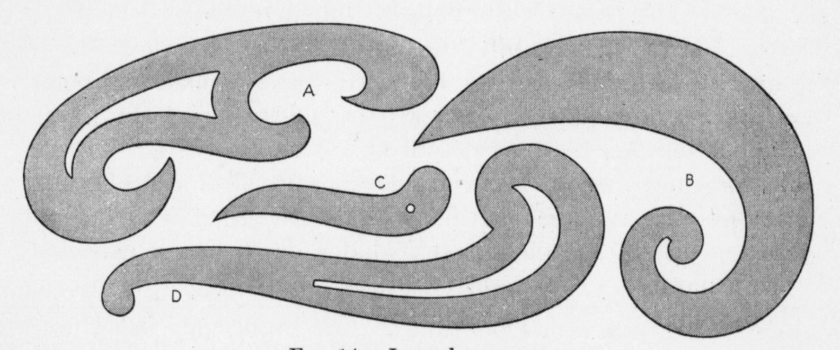

Fig. 14.—Irregular curves.

(13) **Curves.**—Curved rulers, called irregular curves or French curves, are used for curved lines other than circle arcs. The patterns for these curves are laid out in parts of ellipses and spirals or other mathematical curves in various combinations. For the student one ellipse curve of the general shape of Fig. 14 *A* or *D*, and one spiral, either a log spiral *B* or one similar to the one used in Fig. 45, will be sufficient. (The curve of the logarithmic spiral is a closer approximation to the cycloid and other mathematical curves than any other simple curve.)

(14) **Drawing paper** is made in a variety of qualities, white for finished drawings and cream or buff tint for detail drawings. It may be had in either sheets or rolls. In general, paper should have sufficient grain or "tooth" to take the pencil, be agreeable to the eye and have good erasing qualities. Good paper should hold a surface upon which a clean-cut inked line can be drawn after several inked lines have been erased. Tracing cloth should stand the same test. For wash drawings Whatman's paper should be used, and for fine line work for reproduction Reynolds Bristol board. These are both English papers in sheets, whose sizes may be found listed in any dealer's catalogue. Whatman's is handmade paper in three finishes, H, C.P. and R, or hot pressed, cold pressed and rough; the first for fine line drawings, the second for either ink or color and the third for water-color sketches. The paper in the larger sheets is heavier than in the smaller sizes; hence it is better to buy large sheets and cut them up. Bristol board is a smooth paper, made in different thicknesses, 2-ply, 3-ply, 4-ply, etc.; 3-ply is generally used. For working drawings the cream or buff detail papers are much easier on the eyes than are white papers. The cheap manila papers should be avoided. A few cents more per yard is well spent in the increased comfort gained from working on good paper. In buying in quantity it is cheaper to buy roll paper by the pound. For maps or other drawings which are to withstand hard usage, mounted papers, with cloth backings are used. Drawings to be duplicated by blue printing are made on bond or ledger papers, or traced on tracing paper or tracing cloth. Tracing and duplicating processes are described in Chapter XXI.

The foregoing instruments and materials are all that are needed in ordinary practice and are as a rule, with the exception of such supplies as paper, pencils, ink, erasers, etc., what a draftsman is expected to take with him into a commercial drafting room.

There are many other special instruments and devices not necessary in ordinary work, but with which the draftsman should be familiar, as they may be very convenient in some special cases and are often found as part of a drafting room equipment. Some are described in Chapter XXIII.

CHAPTER III

THE USE OF INSTRUMENTS

5. In beginning the use of drawing instruments, particular attention should be paid to correct method in their handling. Read carefully the instructions given, and observe strictly all the details of the technique.

Facility will come with continued practice, but from the outset *good form* must be insisted upon. One might learn to write fairly, holding the pen between the fingers or gripped in the closed hand, but it would be poor form. It is just as bad to draw in poor form as to write in poor form. Bad form in drawing is distressingly common and may be traced in every instance to lack of care or knowledge at the beginning, and the consequent formation of bad habits. These habits when once formed are most difficult to overcome.

All the mechanical drawing we do serves incidentally for practice in the use of instruments, but it is best for the beginner to make a few drawings solely to become familiar with their handling and "feel" so that in working a drawing problem there may be no loss of time on account of faulty manipulation. Later the correct, skillful use of the instruments will become a subconscious habit.

The two requirements are *accuracy* and *speed*, and in commercial work neither is worth much without the other. Accurate penciling is the first consideration. Inking should not be attempted until real skill and proficiency in penciling have been attained. A good instructor knows that it is a mistaken kindness to the beginner to accept faulty or careless work. The standard held at the start will be carried through his professional life, and the beginner should learn that a good drawing can be made just as quickly as a poor one. Erasing is expensive and mostly preventable. The student allowed to continue in a careless way will grow to regard his eraser and jack-knife as the most important tools in his kit. The draftsman, of course, erases an occasional mistake, and instructions in making corrections should be given, but the beginner's sheets should be without blemish or inaccuracy.

6. Preparation for Drawing.—The drawing table should be set so that the light comes from the left, and adjusted to a convenient height for standing, that is, from 36 to 40 inches, with the board inclined at a slope of about 1 to 8. One may draw with more freedom standing than sitting. Wipe table and instruments with dust cloth before starting to draw.

7. The Pencil.—The pencil must be selected with reference to the kind of paper used. For line drawing on paper of good texture, a pencil as hard as 5H or 6H may be used, while on Bristol, for example, a softer one used with lighter touch would be preferred. In every case the pencil chosen must be hard enough not to blur or smudge, but not so hard as to groove the paper under reasonable pressure. Sharpen it to a long conical point by removing the wood with the pen-knife

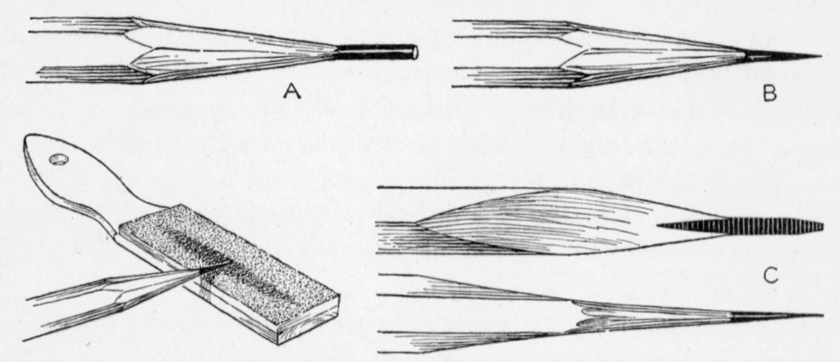

Fig. 15.—Sharpening the pencil.

as shown in Fig. 15 *A* and sharpening the lead as at *B* by rubbing it on the sandpaper pad. A flat or wedge point *C* will not wear away in use as fast as a conical point and on that account is preferred for straight line work by some draftsmen. The long wedge point illustrated is made by first sharpening as at *A*, then making the two long cuts from opposite edges, as shown, flattening the lead on the file or sandpaper and finishing by touching the corners to make the wedge point narrower than the diameter of the lead. A softer pencil (H or 2H) should be at hand, sharpened to a long conical point for sketching and lettering. Have the sandpaper pad within reach and *keep the pencils sharp.* A convenient way is to hang the pad on a cord attached to the table. When drawing long lines with a conical point rotate the pencil so as to keep the line sharp. Pencil lines should be made lightly, but sufficiently firm and sharp to be seen distinctly, without eyestrain, for inking and tracing. The beginner's usual mistake in using a hard pencil is to cut tracks in the paper. Dust off excess graphite from the pencil drawing occasionally. Too much emphasis cannot be given to the importance of clean, careful, accurate penciling. Never permit the thought that poor penciling may be corrected in inking.

8. The T-square.—The T-square is always used with the head on the left edge of the drawing board. (An exception to this is made in the case of a left-handed person, whose table should be arranged with the light coming from the right and the T-square used on the right edge.)

Since the T-square blade is more rigid near the head than toward the outer end, the paper, if much smaller than the size of the board, should be placed close to the left edge of the board (within an inch or so) with its lower edge several inches from the bottom. With the T-square against the left edge of the board, square the top of the paper approximately, hold in this position, slipping the T-square down from the edge, and put a thumb tack in each upper corner, pushing it in up to the head; move the T-square down over the paper to smooth out possible wrinkles and put thumb tacks in the other two corners.

The T-square is used manifestly for drawing parallel horizontal lines. These lines should always be drawn from left to right; consequently points for their location should be marked on the left side; vertical lines are drawn with the triangle set against the T-square, always with the perpendicular edge nearest the head of the square and toward the light. These lines are always drawn up from bottom to top; consequently their location points should be made at the bottom.

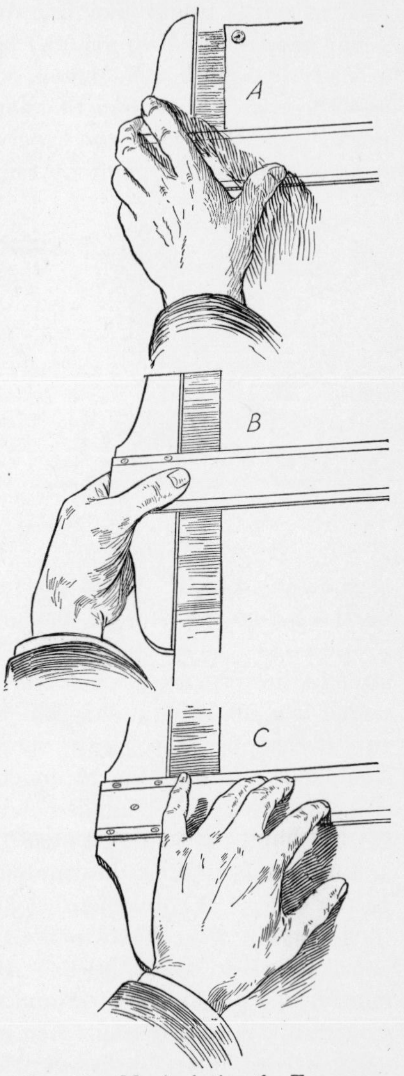

Fig. 16.—Manipulating the T-square.

In drawing lines great care must be exercised in keeping them accurately parallel to the T-square or triangle, holding the pencil point lightly, but close against the edge, and not varying the angle during the progress of the line.

The T-square is manipulated by sliding the head along the left edge of the board with the fingers against the end of the head as shown at *A*, Fig. 16, making close adjustments with the thumb above and the fingers touching the board as at *B*, or oftener with the fingers on the blade and the thumb on the board as shown in *C* of the same figure. In drawing vertical lines the T-square is held in position against the left edge of the board, the thumb on the blade, while the fingers of

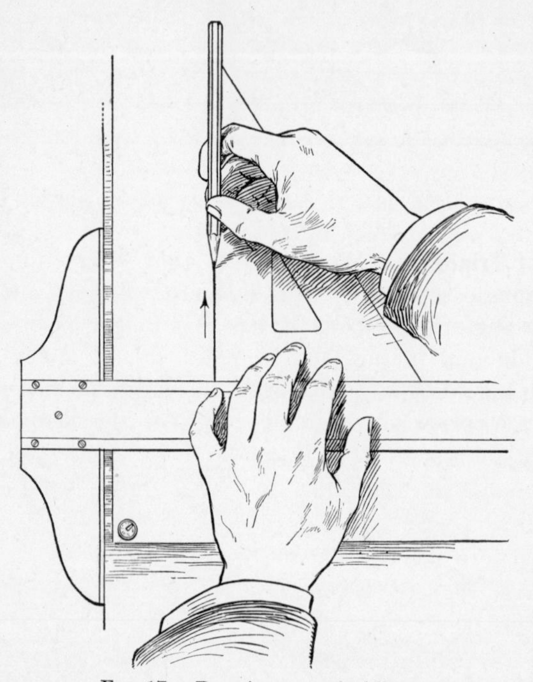

Fig. 17.—Drawing a vertical line.

the left hand adjust the triangle, as illustrated in Fig. 17. One may be sure the T-square is in contact with the board by hearing the little double click as it comes against it.

9. Laying Out the Sheet.—The paper is usually cut somewhat larger than the desired size of the drawing and is trimmed to size after the work is finished. Suppose the finished size is to be 11″ × 17″ with a ½″ border inside. Lay the scale down on the paper close to the lower edge and measure 17″, marking the distance with the pencil, at the same time marking ½″ inside at each end for the border line. Always use a short dash forming a continuation of the division on the scale in laying off a dimension. Do not make a dot, or bore a hole with the pencil. Near the left edge mark 11″ and ½″ border line points. Through these four marks on the left edge draw horizontal lines with the T-square, and through the points on the lower edge draw vertical lines with the triangle against the T-square.

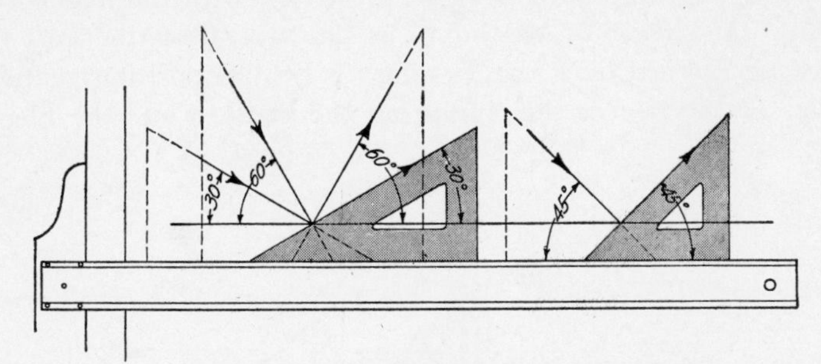

Fig. 18.—To draw angles of 30°, 45° and 60°.

10. Use of Triangles.—We have seen that vertical lines are drawn with the triangle set against the T-square, Fig. 17. Generally the 60-degree triangle is used, as it has the longer perpendicular. In both penciling and inking, the triangles should always be used in contact with a guiding straight-edge. To insure accuracy never work to the extreme corner of a triangle, but keep the T-square below the base line.

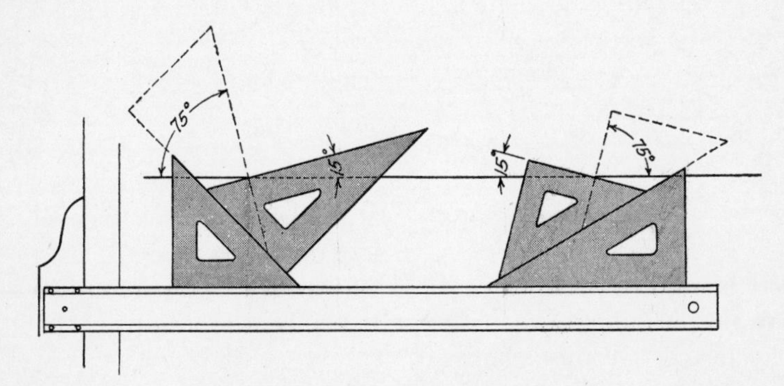

Fig. 19.—To draw angles of 15° and 75°.

With the T-square against the edge of the board, lines at 30, 45 and 60 degrees may be drawn as shown in Fig. 18, the arrows indicating the direction of motion. The two triangles may be used in combination for angles of 15, 75, 105 degrees, etc., Fig. 19. Thus any multiple of 15 degrees may be drawn directly, and a circle may be divided with the 45-degree triangle into 4 or 8 parts, with the 60-degree triangle into 6 or 12 parts, and with both into 24 parts.

In using the triangles always keep the T-square at least a half inch *below* the starting line.

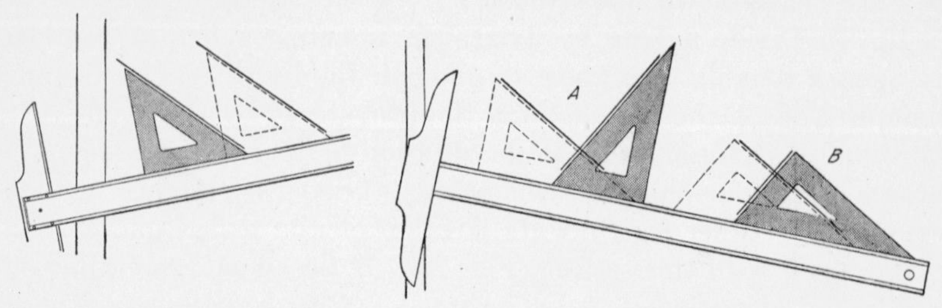

Fig. 20.—To draw parallel lines.

Fig. 21.—To draw perpendicular lines.

To draw a line parallel to any line, Fig. 20, adjust to it a triangle held against the T-square or another triangle, hold the guiding edge in position and slip the first triangle on it to the required position.

To draw a perpendicular to any line, Fig. 21 *A*, fit the hypotenuse of a triangle to it, with one edge against the T-square or another triangle, hold the T-square in position and turn the triangle until its other side is against the edge; the hypotenuse will then be perpendicular to the line. Move it to the required position. *Or*, a quicker method, set the triangle with the hypotenuse against the guiding edge, fit one side to the line, slide the triangle to the required point and draw the perpendicular as shown at *B*.

Never attempt to draw a perpendicular to a line by merely placing one leg of the triangle against it.

11. Use of Dividers.—Facility in the use of this instrument is most essential, and quick and absolute control of its manipulation must be gained. It should be opened with one hand by pinching the chamfer with the thumb and second finger. This will throw it into correct position with the thumb and forefinger on the outside of the legs and the second and third finger on the inside, with the head resting just above the second joint of the forefinger, Fig. 22. It is thus under perfect control, with the thumb and forefinger to close it and the other two to open it. This motion should be practiced until an adjustment to the smallest fraction can

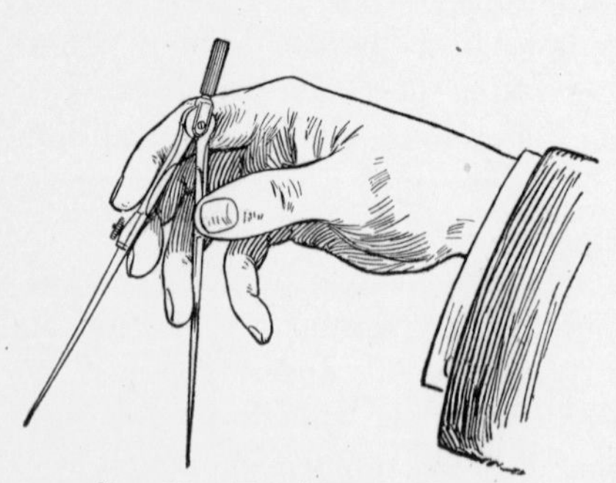

Fig. 22.—Handling the dividers.

be made. In coming down to small divisions the second and third fingers must be gradually slipped out from between the legs while they are closed down upon them.

12. To Divide a Line by Trial.—In bisecting a line the dividers are opened roughly at a guess to one-half the length. This distance is stepped off on the line, holding the instrument by the handle with the thumb and forefinger. If the division be short the leg should be thrown out to one-half the remainder, estimated by the eye, without removing the other leg from its position on the paper, and the line spaced again with this setting, Fig. 23. If this should not come out exactly the operation may be repeated. With a little experience a line may be divided rapidly in this way. Similarly, a line may be divided into any number of equal parts, say five, by estimating the first division, stepping this lightly along the line, with the dividers held vertically by the handle, turning the instrument first in one direction and then in another. If the last division fall short, one-fifth of the remainder should be added by opening the dividers, keeping the one point on the paper. If the last division be over, one-fifth of the excess should be taken off and the line respaced. If it is found difficult to make this small adjustment accurately with the fingers, the hairspring may be used. It will be found more convenient to use the bow spacers instead of the dividers for small or numerous divisions. Avoid pricking unsightly holes in the paper. The position of a small prick point may be preserved if necessary by drawing a little ring around it with the pencil. For most work and until one is very proficient it is best to divide a line into a number of parts with the scale as explained on page 57.

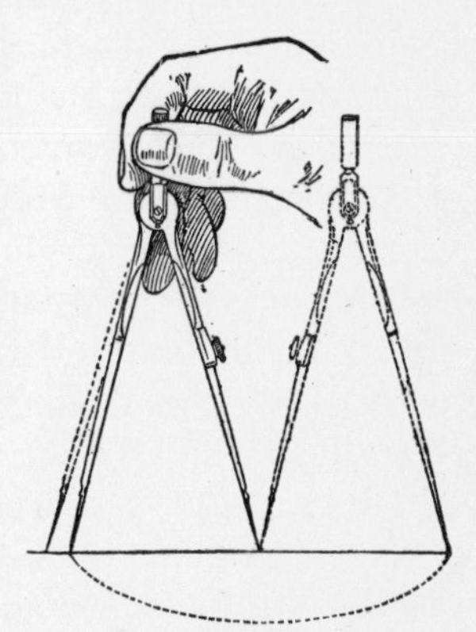

Fig. 23.—Bisecting a line.

13. Use of the Compasses.—The compasses have the same general shape as the dividers and are manipulated in a similar way. First of all the needle should be permanently adjusted. Insert the pen in place of the pencil leg, turn the needle with the shoulder point out and set it a trifle longer than the pen, Fig. 24, replace the pencil leg, and sharpen the lead to a long bevel, as in Fig. 25, and adjust it to the needle point.

To draw a circle measure and mark the radius on the paper, place the needle point at the center, guiding it with the left hand, Fig. 26, and adjust the pencil to the radius, setting the compasses with one hand as in Fig. 22. When the lead is adjusted to pass exactly through the mark, raise the right hand to the handle and draw the circle clockwise in one sweep, rolling the handle with the thumb and forefinger, inclining the compasses slightly in the direction of the line, Fig. 27. The position of the fingers after the revolution is illustrated in Fig.

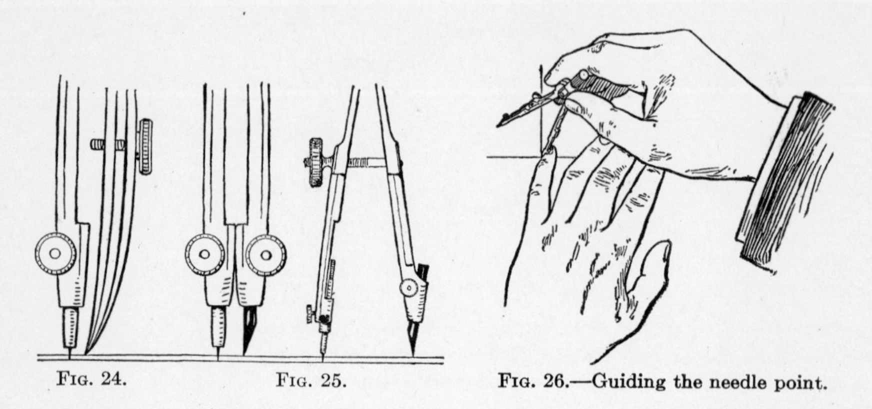

Fig. 24. Fig. 25. Fig. 26.—Guiding the needle point.

28. The pencil line may be brightened if necessary by going back over it in the reverse direction (this is one exception to a caution at the end of the chapter). Circles up to perhaps three inches in diameter

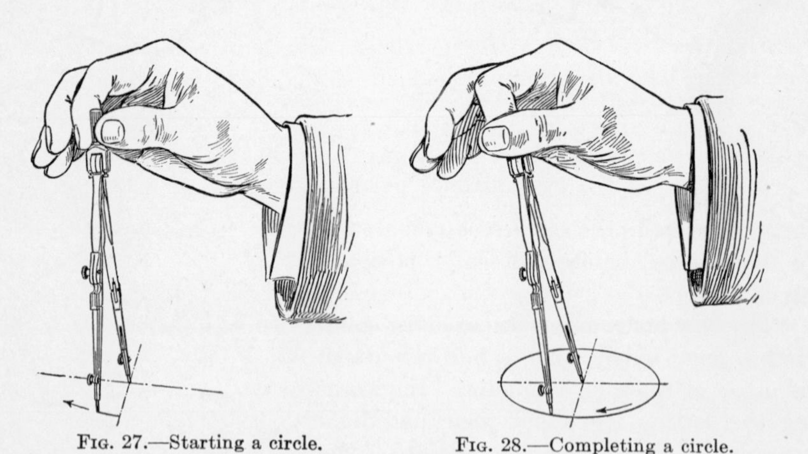

Fig. 27.—Starting a circle. Fig. 28.—Completing a circle.

may be drawn with the legs straight but for larger sizes both the needle-point leg and the pencil or pen leg should be turned at the knuckle joints so as to be perpendicular to the paper, Fig. 29. The 6-inch compasses may be used in this way for circles up to perhaps ten inches in diameter; larger circles are made by using the lengthening bar, as illustrated in Fig. 30, or the beam compasses. In drawing

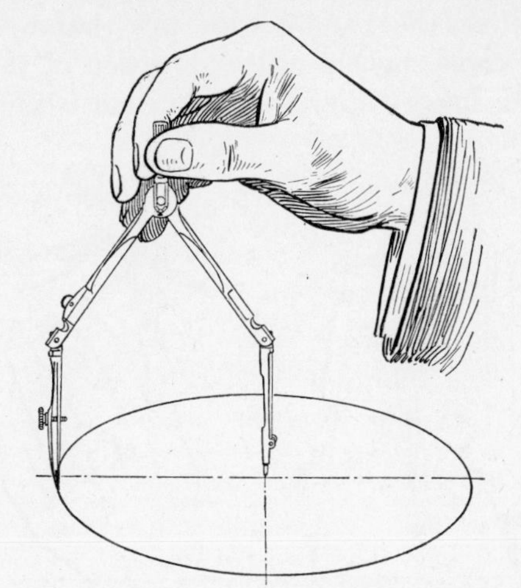

Fig. 29.—Drawing a large circle.

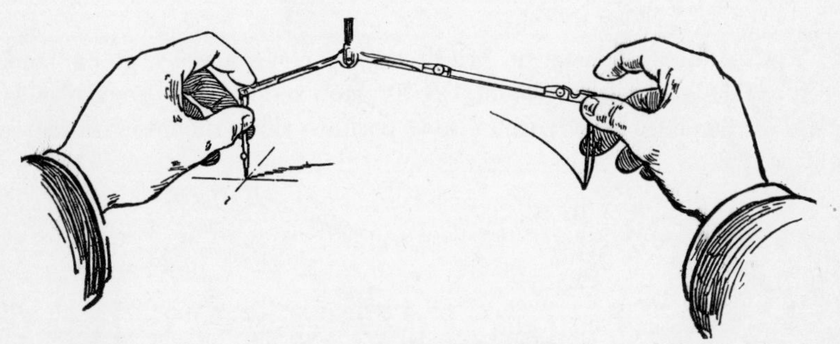

Fig. 30.—Use of lengthening bar.

concentric circles the *smallest* should always be drawn *first*, before the center hole has become worn.

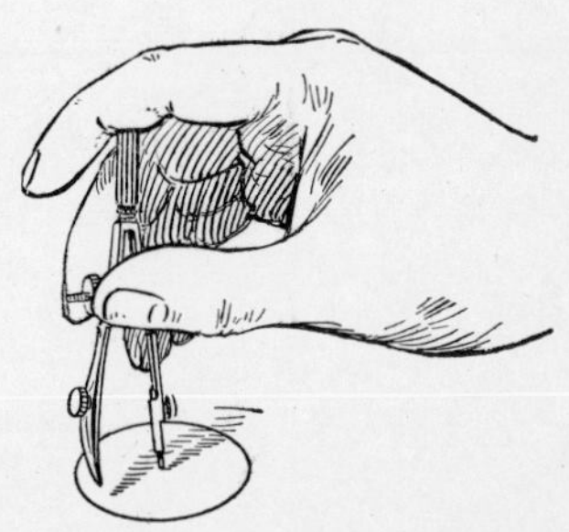

Fig. 31.—Adjusting the bow pen.

The **bow instruments** are used for small circles, particularly when a number are to be made of the same diameter. In changing the setting, to avoid wear and final stripping of the thread, the pressure of the spring against the nut should be relieved by holding the points in the left hand and spinning the nut in or out with the finger. Small adjustments should be made with one hand, with the needle point in position on the paper, Fig. 31.

14. Use of the Scale.—In representing objects which are larger than can be drawn to their natural or full size it is necessary to reduce dimensions on the drawing in some regular proportion, and for this purpose the mechanical engineers' (or architects') scales are used. The first reduction is to what is commonly called "half size," or, correctly speaking, to the scale of 6″ = 1′. This scale is used in working drawings even if the object be only slightly larger than could be drawn full size. If the draftsman does not have a half-size scale (see Fig. 13) he will use the full-size scale by considering six inches on the scale to represent one foot. Thus the half-inch divisions become full inches, each of which is divided into eighths of inches. (Do *not* use the scale of ½″ = 1′ for half-size drawings.) If this

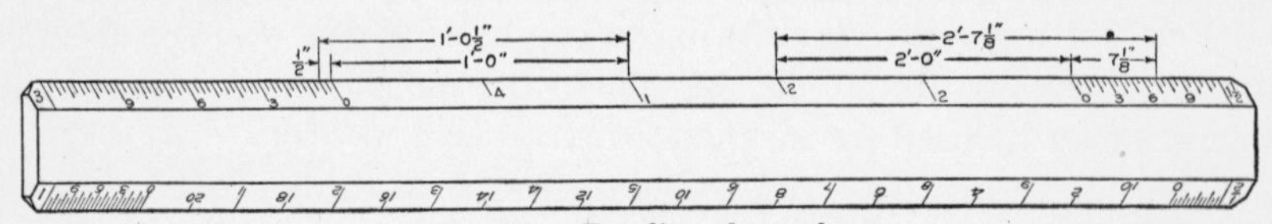

Fig. 32.—Reading the scale.

reduction is too large for the paper the drawing is made to the scale of 3″ = 1′, often called "quarter size," that is, three inches measured on the drawing is equal to one foot on the object. This is the first scale of the usual commercial set; on it the distance of three inches is divided into 12 equal parts and each of these subdivided into eighths. This distance should be thought of not as three inches but as a foot divided into inches and eighths of inches. It is noticed that this foot is divided with the zero on the inside, the inches running to the left and the feet to the right, so that dimensions given in feet and inches may be read directly, as 1′-0½″, Fig. 32. On the other end will be found the scale of 1½″ = 1′ or "eighth size," with the distance of one and one-half inches divided on the right of the zero into 12 parts and subdivided into quarter inches, and the foot divisions to the left of the zero coinciding with the marks of the 3″ scale.

If the 1½″ scale is too large for the object, the next smaller size is the scale 1″ = 1′, and so on down as shown in the following table.

Full size	Scale ¾″ = 1′
Scale 6″ = 1′ (half size)	" ½″ = 1′
" 4″ = 1′ (rarely used)	" ⅜″ = 1′
" 3″ = 1′ (quarter size)	" ¼″ = 1′
" 2″ = 1′ (rarely used)	" 3/16″ = 1′
" 1½″ = 1′ (eighth size)	" ⅛″ = 1′
" 1″ = 1′	" 3/32″ = 1′

Drawings to odd proportions such as 9″ = 1′, 4″ = 1′, etc., are not used except in rare cases when it is desired to make it difficult or impossible for a workman to measure them with an ordinary rule.

The scale ¼″ = 1′ is the usual one for ordinary house plans and is often called by architects the "quarter scale." This term should not be confused with the term "quarter size," as the former means one-fourth inch to one foot and the latter one-fourth inch to one inch.

A circle is generally given in terms of its diameter. To draw it the radius is necessary. In drawing to half size it is thus often convenient to lay off the amount of the diameter with a 3″ scale and to use this distance as the radius.

As far as possible successive measurements on the same line should be made without shifting the scale.

For plotting and map drawing the civil engineers' scale of decimal parts, 10, 20, 30, 40, 50, 60, 80, 100 to the inch, is used. This scale should never be used for machine or structural work.

The important thing in drawing to scale is to think of and speak of each dimension in its full size and not in the reduced size it happens to be on the paper.

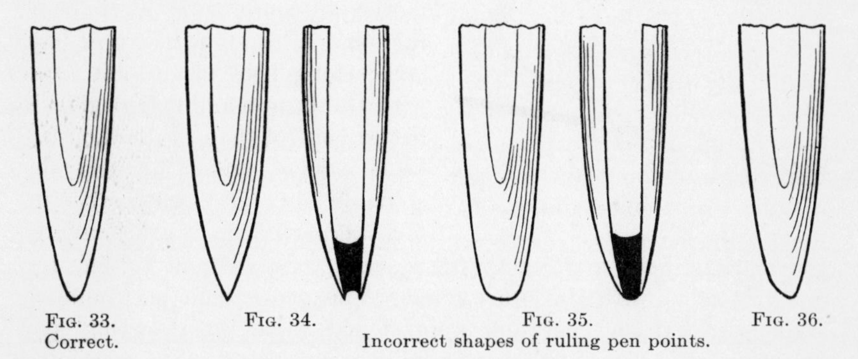

Fig. 33. Correct. Fig. 34. Fig. 35. Fig. 36.
Incorrect shapes of ruling pen points.

15. The ruling pen is for inking straight lines and non-circular curves. Several types are illustrated in Fig. 5. The important feature is the shape of the blades, which should have well-designed ink space between, and whose points should be rounded (elliptical form) equally, as in Fig. 33. If pointed, as in Fig. 34, the ink will arch up as shown and will be aggravatingly hard to start. If rounded to a blunt point as in Fig. 35, the ink will flow too freely, resulting in bulbs and over-runs at the ends of the lines. Pens in constant use become dull and worn. Figure 36 shows a worn pen. It is easy to tell whether or not a pen is dull by looking for the reflection of light that travels from the side and over the end of the point when the pen is turned in the hand. If the reflection can be seen all the way the pen is too dull. A pen in poor condition is an abomination, but a well-sharpened one is a delight to use. Every draftsman should be able to keep his pens in fine condition.

16. To Sharpen a Pen.—The best stone is a hard Arkansas knife piece, used dry. It is well to soak a new stone in oil for several days before using. The ordinary carpenter's oil stone is too coarse for drawing instruments.

The nibs must first be brought to the correct shape, as in Fig. 33, by screwing them together until they touch and, holding the pen as in drawing a line, drawing it back and forth on the stone, starting the stroke with the handle at 30° or less with the stone and swinging it up past the perpendicular as the line across the stone progresses. This will bring the nibs to exactly equal shape and length, leaving them very dull. They should then be opened slightly and each blade sharpened in turn, on the outside only, until the bright spot on the end has just disappeared, holding the pen as in Fig. 37, at a small angle with the stone and rubbing it back and forth with a slight oscillating or rocking motion to conform to the shape of the blade. A stone three or four inches long held in the left hand with the thumb and fingers gives a better control than one laid on the table. Some prefer to hold the stone in the right hand with its face perpendicular to the forearm and move it back and forth with a slight wrist motion, holding the pen against it with the other hand. The pen should be examined frequently and the operation stopped just when the reflecting spot has vanished. A pocket magnifying glass may be of aid in examining the points. The blades should not be sharp enough to cut the paper when tested by drawing a line, without ink, across it. If over-sharpened the blades should again be brought to touch and a line swung very lightly across the stone as in the first operation. When tested with ink the pen should be capable of drawing clean sharp lines down to the finest hair line. If these finest lines are ragged or broken the pen is not perfectly sharpened. It should not be necessary to touch the inside of the blades unless a burr has been formed, which might occur with very soft metal, or by using too coarse a stone or too much pressure. To remove such burr or wire edge draw a strip of detail paper between the nibs, or open the pen wide and lay the entire

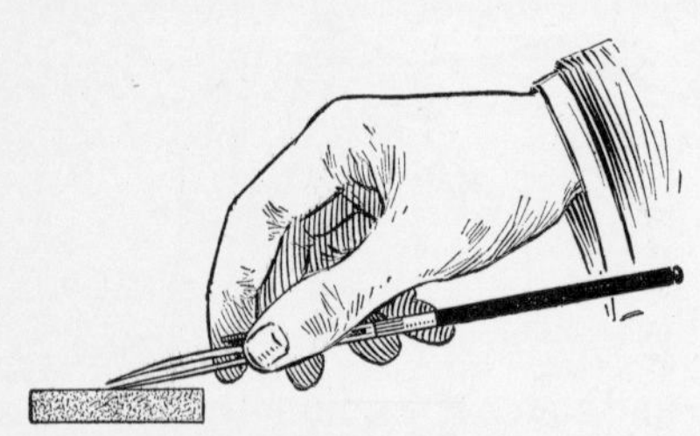

Fig. 37.—Sharpening a pen.

inner surface of the blade flat on the stone and move it with a very light touch.

The beginner had best practice by sharpening several old pens before attempting to sharpen a good instrument. After using, the stone should be wiped clean and a drop of oil rubbed over it.

17. Inking.—The ruling pen is never used freehand, but always in connection with a guiding edge, T-square, triangle, straight-edge or curve. The T-square and triangle should be held in the same positions as for penciling. *It is bad practice to ink with the triangle alone.*

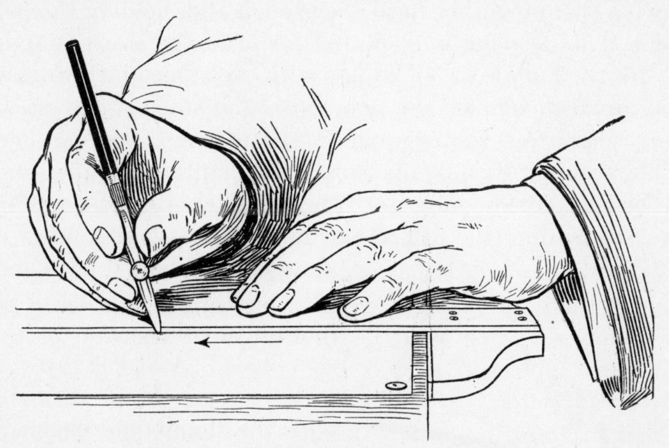

Fig. 38.—Correct position of ruling pen.

To fill the pen take it to the bottle and touch the quill filler between the nibs, being careful not to get any ink on the outside of the blades. Not more than three-sixteenths to one-fourth of an inch should be put in or the weight of the ink will cause it to drop out in a blot. The pen should be held in the finger tips as illustrated in Fig. 38, with the thumb and second finger in such position that they may be used in turning the adjusting screw, and the handle resting on the forefinger. This position should be observed carefully, as the tendency will be to bend the second finger to the position in which a pencil or writing pen is held, which is obviously convenient in writing to give the up stroke, but as this motion is not required with the ruling pen the position illustrated is preferable.

For full lines the screw should be adjusted to give a strong line, of the size of the first line of Fig. 43. A fine drawing does not mean a drawing made with fine lines, but with uniform lines, and accurate joints and tangents.

18. The pen should be held against the straight-edge with the blades parallel to it, and the screw on the outside, the handle inclined slightly to the right and always kept in a plane through the line perpendicular to the paper. The pen is thus guided by the upper edge of the ruler, whose distance from the pencil line will therefore vary with its thickness, and with the shape of the under blade of the pen, as illustrated in actual size in Fig. 39. If the pen point is thrown out from the perpendicular it will run on one blade and a line ragged on one side will result. If turned in from the perpendicular the ink is very apt to run under the edge and cause a blot.

Fig. 39.

A line is drawn with a whole arm movement, the hand resting on the tips of the third and fourth fingers, keeping the angle of inclination constant. Just before the end of the line is reached the two guiding fingers on the straight-edge should be stopped, and, without stopping the motion of the pen, the line finished with a finger movement. Short lines are drawn with this finger movement alone. When the end of the line is reached lift the pen quickly and move the straight-edge away from the line. The pressure on the paper should be light, but sufficient to give a clean-cut line, and will vary with the kind of paper and the sharpness of the pen, but the pressure against the T-square should be only enough to guide the direction.

If the ink refuses to flow it is because it has dried and clogged in the extreme point of the pen. If pinching the blades slightly or touching the pen on the finger does not start it, the pen should immediately be wiped out and fresh ink added. Pens must be wiped clean after using or the ink will corrode the steel and finally destroy them.

In inking on either paper or cloth the full lines are much wider than the pencil lines and the beginner must be very careful to have the center of the ink line cover the pencil line, as shown in Fig. 40.

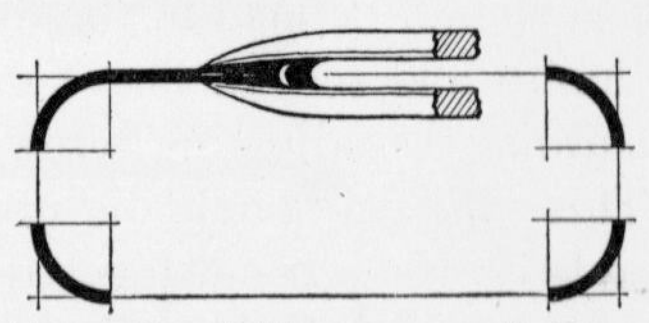

Fig. 40.—Inking a pencil line.

Instructions in regard to the ruling pen apply also to the compasses. The pen should be kept with both nibs on the paper by using the knuckle joint, and the instrument inclined slightly in the direction of the line. In adjusting the compasses for an arc which is to connect other lines the pen point should be brought down very close to the paper without touching it to be sure that the setting is exactly right.

It is a universal rule in inking that *circles and circle arcs must be drawn first.* It is much easier to connect a straight line to a curve than a curve to a straight line.

19. Tangents.—It should be noted particularly that two lines are tangent to each other when the center lines of the lines are tangent and not when the lines simply touch each other; thus at the point of tangency the width will be equal to the width of a single line, Fig. 41. Before inking tangent lines the point of tangency should be marked in pencil. For an arc tangent to a straight line this point will be on a line through the center of the arc and perpendicular to the straight line, and for two circle arcs will be on a line joining their centers. See paragraphs 51 to 57.

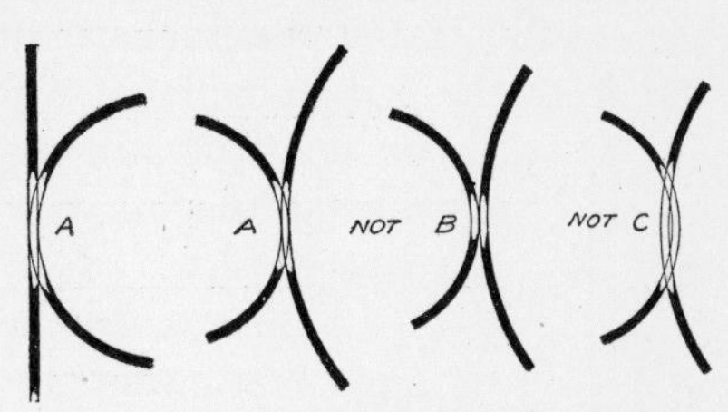

Fig. 41.—Correct and incorrect tangents.

After reading these paragraphs the beginner had best take a blank sheet of paper and cover it with ink lines of varying lengths and weights, practicing starting and stopping on penciled limits, until he feels acquainted with the pens. If in his set there are two pens of different sizes the larger one should be used, as it fits the hand of the average man better than the smaller one, holds more ink and will do just as fine work. High-grade pens usually come from the makers well sharpened. Cheaper ones often need sharpening before they can be used.

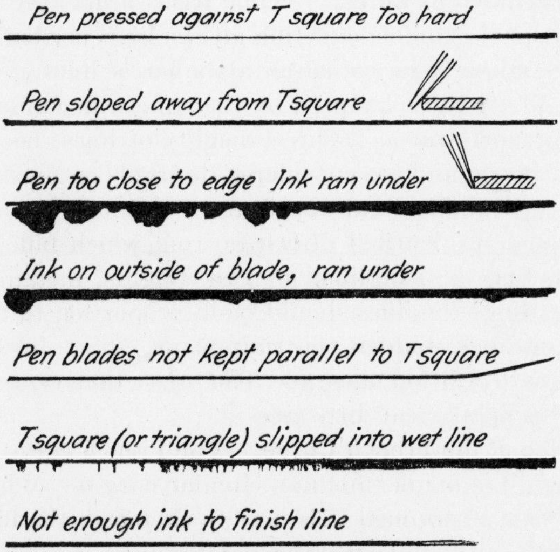

Pen pressed against T square too hard

Pen sloped away from Tsquare

Pen too close to edge Ink ran under

Ink on outside of blade, ran under

Pen blades not kept parallel to Tsquare

Tsquare (or triangle) slipped into wet line

Not enough ink to finish line

Fig. 42.—Faulty lines.

20. Faulty Lines.—If inked lines appear imperfect in any way the reason should be ascertained immediately. It may be the fault of the pen, the ink, the paper or the draftsman, but with the probabilities greatly in favor of the last. Figure 42 illustrates the characteristic

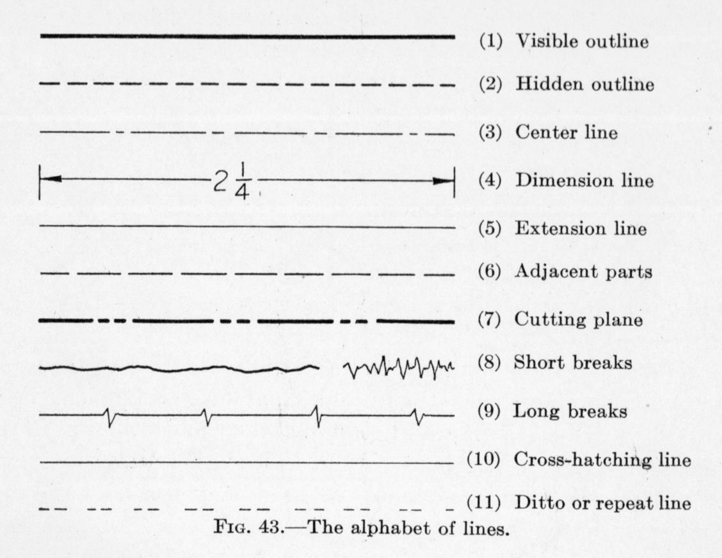

Fig. 43.—The alphabet of lines.

appearance of several kinds of faulty lines. The correction in each case will suggest itself.

21. The Alphabet of Lines.—As the basis of drawing is the line, a set of conventional symbols covering all the lines needed for different purposes may properly be called an alphabet of lines. The symbols given in Fig. 43 are those adopted by the American Standards Association, whose report states, "Three weights of lines, heavy, medium and light are shown, and are considered desirable on finished drawings in ink, both for legibility and appearance, although in rapid practice and in particular on penciled drawings from which blueprints are to be made, this may be simplified to two weights, medium and light. For pencil drawings the lines should be in proportion to the ink lines, *medium* for outlines, hidden, cutting plane, short break, adjacent part and alternate position lines, and *light* for section, center, extension, dimension, long break, and ditto lines."

22. The Use of the French Curve.—The French curve, as has been stated on page 9 is a ruler for non-circular curves. When sufficient points have been determined it is best to sketch in the line lightly in pencil freehand, without losing the points, until it is clean, smooth, continuous and satisfactory to the eye. The curve should then be applied to it, selecting a part that will fit a portion of the line most nearly, and noting particularly that the curve is so laid that the direction of its increase in curvature is in the direction of increasing curvature of the line, Fig. 45. In drawing the part of the line matched by

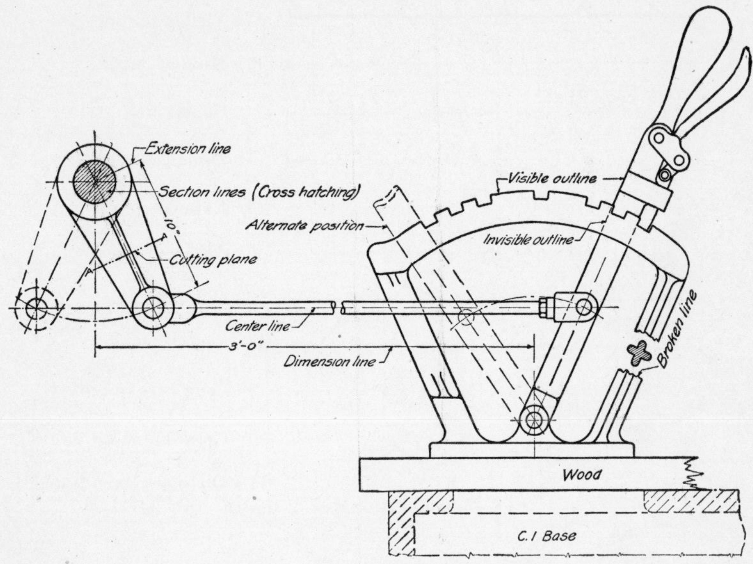

FIG. 44.—The alphabet illustrated.

the curve, *always* stop short of the distance that seems to coincide. After drawing this portion the curve is shifted to find another part that will coincide with the continuation of the line. In shifting the curve care should be taken to preserve the smoothness and continuity and to avoid breaks or cusps. This may be done if in its successive positions the curve is always adjusted so that it coincides for a little distance with the part already drawn. Thus at each joint the tangents must coincide.

If the curved line is symmetrical about an axis, after it has been matched accurately on one side, marks locating the axes may be made in pencil on the curve and the curve reversed. In such a case exceptional care must be taken to avoid a "hump" at the joint. It is often better to stop a line short of the axis on each side and to close the gap afterward with another setting of the curve.

When inking with the curve the pen should be held perpendicularly and the blades kept parallel to the edge. Inking curves will be found to be excellent practice.

Sometimes, particularly at sharp turns, a combination of circle arcs and curve may be used, as, for example, in inking a long narrow ellipse the sharp curves may be inked by selecting a center on the major axis by trial, and drawing as much of an arc as will practically coincide with the ends of the ellipse, then finishing the ellipse with the curve.

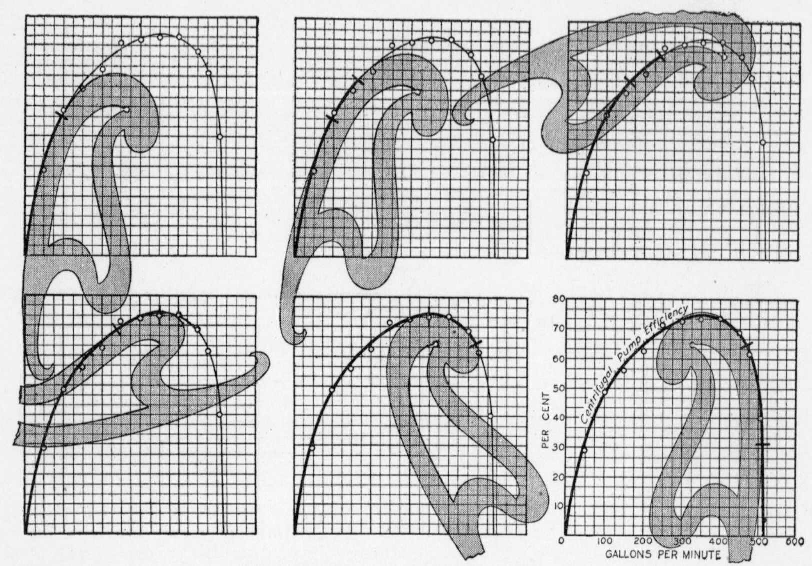

FIG. 45.—Use of the irregular curve.

The experienced draftsman will sometimes ink a curve that cannot be matched accurately, by varying the distance of the pen point from the ruling edge as the line progresses, but the beginner should not attempt it.

23. Erasing, of both pencil lines and ink lines, is best done with the Ruby pencil eraser. In erasing an ink line hold the paper down firmly and rub lightly and patiently, first along the line, then across it, until the ink is removed. When an erasure is to be made close to another line, select an opening of the best shape on the erasing shield and rub through it, holding the shield down firmly, first seeing that both of its sides are clean. Never scratch out a line or blot with a knife or razor blade. A skilled draftsman sometimes uses a sharp blade to trim a thickened spot or over-running end on a line.

24. Exercises in the Use of Instruments.—The following figures may be used, if desired, as progressive exercises for practice, either in pencil only, or afterward to be inked. The geometrical figures of Chapter V afford excellent practice in accurate penciling.

(1) **An Exercise for the T-square, Triangle and Scale.**—Fig. 46. Through the center of the space draw a horizontal and a vertical line. Measuring on these

lines as diameters lay off a 4″ square. Along the lower side and the upper half of the left side measure ½″ spaces with the scale. Draw all horizontal lines with the T-square and all vertical lines with the T-square and triangle.

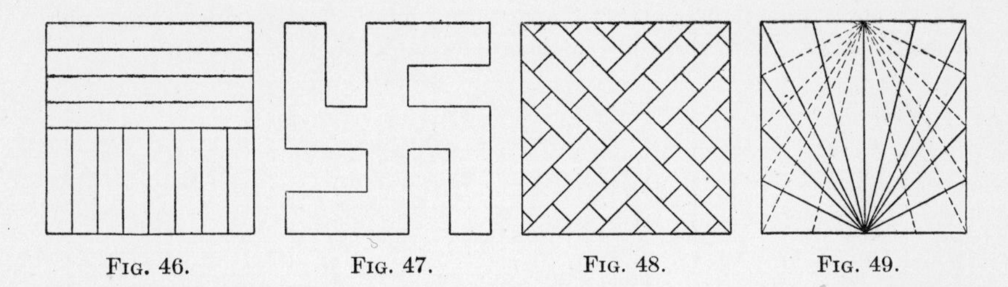

Fig. 46. Fig. 47. Fig. 48. Fig. 49.

(2) **A Swastika.**—Fig. 47. For T-square, triangle and dividers. Draw a 4″ square. Divide left side and lower side into five equal parts with dividers. Draw horizontal and vertical lines across the square through these points. Erase the parts not needed.

(3) **A Street Paving Intersection.**—Fig. 48. For 45° triangle and scale. An exercise in starting and stopping short lines. Draw a 4″ square. Draw its diagonals with 45° triangle. With the scale lay off ½″ spaces along the diagonals, from their intersection. With 45° triangle complete figure, finishing one quarter at a time.

(4) **Converging Lines.**—Fig. 49. Full and dotted. Divide the sides of a 4″ square into four equal parts. From these points draw lines to the middle points of the upper and lower sides as shown, using the triangle alone as a straightedge.

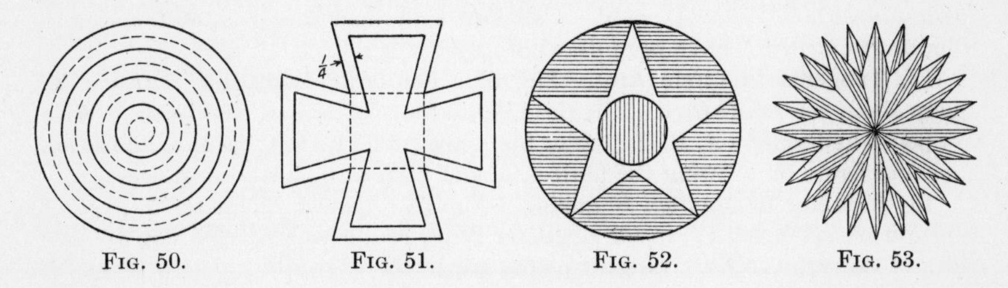

Fig. 50. Fig. 51. Fig. 52. Fig. 53.

(5) **Concentric Circles.**—Fig. 50. For compasses (legs straight) and scale. Draw horizontal line through center of space. On it mark off radii for eight concentric circles ¼″ apart. In drawing concentric circles always draw the smallest first. The dotted circles are drawn in pencil with long dashes and inked as shown.

(6) **A Maltese Cross.**—Fig. 51. For T-square, spacers and both triangles. Draw a 4″ square and a 1⅜″ square. From the corners of inner square draw lines to outer square at 15° and 75°, with the two triangles in combination. Mark points with spacers ¼″ inside each line of this outside cross, and complete figure with triangles in combination.

(7) **Air Craft Insignia.**—Fig. 52. This device is a white star with red center on a blue background. Draw a 4″ circle and a 1″ circle. Divide large circle into five equal parts with the dividers, and construct star by connecting alternate

points as shown. Red is indicated by vertical lines and blue by horizontal lines. Space these by eye approximately $\frac{1}{16}''$ apart. (Standard line symbols for colors are given in Fig. 810.)

(8) **A 24-point Star.**—Fig. 53. For T-square and triangles in combination. In a 4″ circle draw 12 diameters 15° apart, using T-square and triangles singly and in combination. With the same combinations finish the figure as shown.

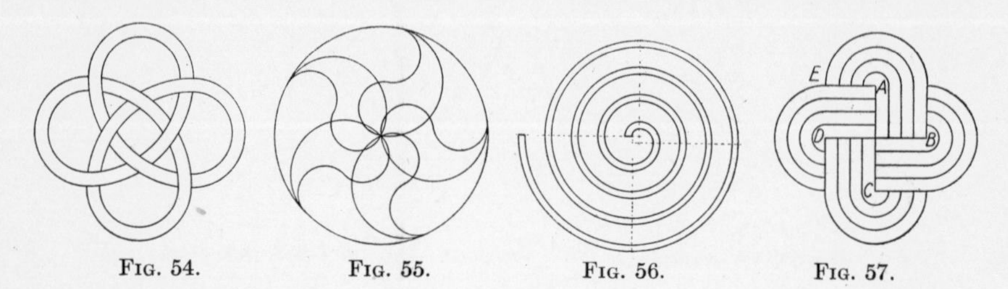

Fig. 54. Fig. 55. Fig. 56. Fig. 57.

(9) **Quarterfoil Knot.**—Fig. 54. For accuracy with compasses. On horizontal and vertical center lines draw a 2″ square. With the middle points of its sides as centers draw semi-circles 2″ and $1\frac{1}{2}''$ in diameter. With the corners of the square as centers draw quadrants to complete the figure.

(10) **Tangent Arcs.**—Fig. 55. For accuracy with compasses and dividers. Draw a circle 4″ in diameter. Divide the circumference into five equal parts by trial with dividers. From these points draw radial lines and divide each into four equal parts with spacers. With these points as centers draw the semi-circles as shown.

(11) **Four-centered Spiral.**—Fig. 56. For accurate tangents. Draw a $\frac{1}{8}''$ square and extend its sides as shown. With the upper right corner as center draw quadrants with $\frac{1}{8}''$ and $\frac{1}{4}''$ radii. Continue with quadrants from each corner in order until four turns have been drawn.

(12) **Tangents to Circle Arcs.**—Fig. 57. For bow compasses. Draw a 2″ square about center of space. Divide *AE* into four $\frac{1}{4}''$ spaces, with scale. With bow pencil and centers *A*, *B*, *C*, *D* draw four semi-circles with $\frac{1}{4}''$ radius, and so on. Complete figure by drawing the horizontal and vertical tangents as shown.

(13) **A Motor Lamination Stamping.**—Fig. 58. Outside diameter 5″; center to center of $\frac{1}{4}''$ holes 4″; inside diameter $2\frac{1}{2}''$; center to center of slot $3\frac{11}{16}''$; width of slot $\frac{9}{16}''$. Mark tangent points in pencil.

(14) **A Clutch Plate.**—Fig. 59. Outside diameter $10\frac{3}{4}''$; bore $1\frac{3}{4}''$; width of face $2\frac{1}{2}''$. The arms (extended) are tangent to a 2″ circle at the center and are $1\frac{1}{2}''$ wide at intersection with inside diameter of face. Fillets are $\frac{1}{4}''$ radius. Slots $\frac{1}{8}''$ wide. Diameter of outside rivet circle $9\frac{3}{4}''$; inside rivet circle $7\frac{3}{4}''$, for nine $\frac{1}{8}''$ holes equally spaced. On a $4\frac{3}{8}''$ and a $2\frac{3}{4}''$ circle, space six $\frac{3}{8}''$ holes each. Mark tangent points in pencil.

(15) **An Envelope Blank.**—Fig. 60. For tangents and angles. Construct accurately, full size, starting with vertical center line. Find 5° and 10° angles by dividing a 15° angle, or with protractor.

(16) **An Airfoil.**—Fig. 61. For use of French curve. This problem illustrates the standard method of plotting the outline of airfoils, as used by the National Advisory Committee for Aeronautics. Using a decimal scale, lay off the diagram and plot the points of the curve on the ordinates. Data for two profiles are given in the tables, the illustration showing the shape of the one to the right.

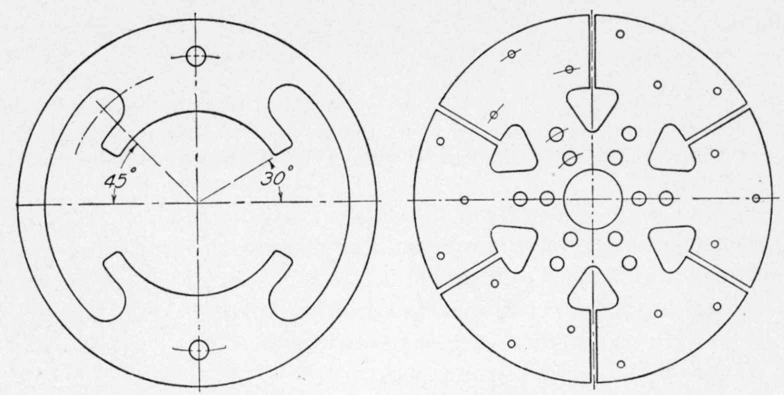

FIG. 58.—A stamping.

FIG. 59.—A clutch plate.

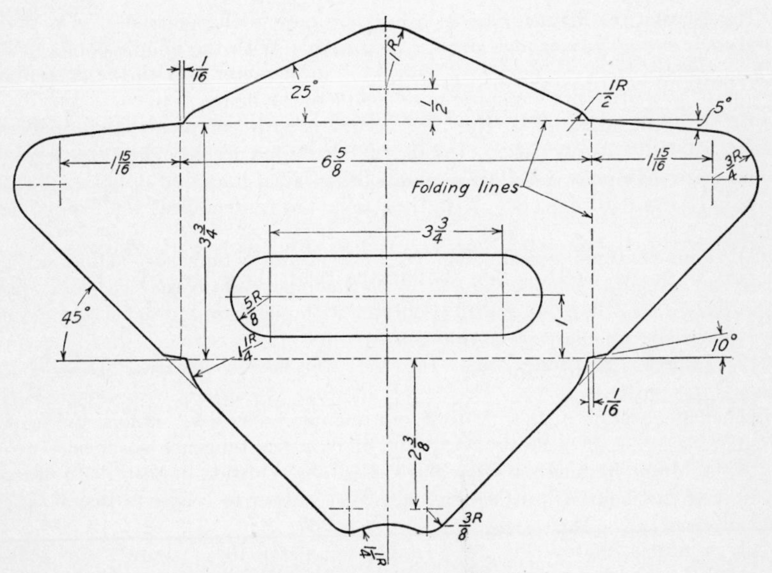

FIG. 60.—An envelope blank.

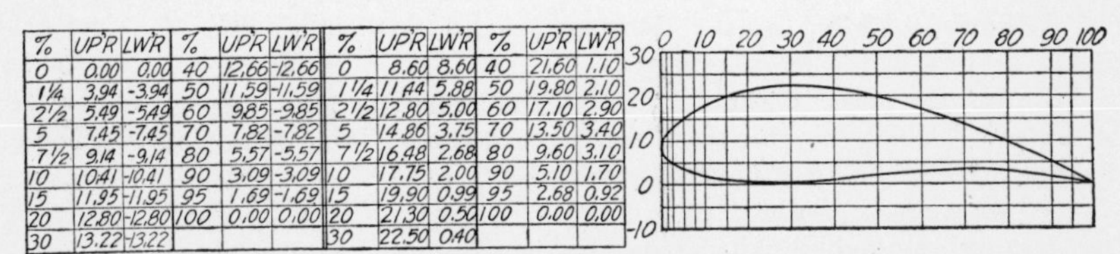

%	UP'R	LW'R	%	UP'R	LW'R	%	UP'R	LW'R	%	UP'R	LW'R
0	0.00	0.00	40	12.66	-12.66	0	8.60	8.60	40	21.60	1.10
1¼	3.94	-3.94	50	11.59	-11.59	1¼	11.44	5.88	50	19.80	2.10
2½	5.49	-5.49	60	9.85	-9.85	2½	12.80	5.00	60	17.10	2.90
5	7.45	-7.45	70	7.82	-7.82	5	14.86	3.75	70	13.50	3.40
7½	9.14	-9.14	80	5.57	-5.57	7½	16.48	2.68	80	9.60	3.10
10	10.41	-10.41	90	3.09	-3.09	10	17.75	2.00	90	5.10	1.70
15	11.95	-11.95	95	1.69	-1.69	15	19.90	0.99	95	2.68	0.92
20	12.80	-12.80	100	0.00	0.00	20	21.30	0.50	100	0.00	0.00
30	13.22	-13.22				30	22.50	0.40			

FIG. 61.—Airfoils.

A PAGE OF CAUTIONS

Never use the scale as a ruler.

Never draw with the lower edge of the T-square.

Never cut paper with a knife and the edge of the T-square as a guide.

Never use the T-square as a hammer.

Never put either end of a pencil into the mouth

Never work with a dull pencil.

Never sharpen a pencil over the drawing board.

Never jab the dividers into the drawing board.

Never oil the joints of compasses.

Never set the compasses on the scale. Mark the radius on the paper.

Never use the dividers as reamers or pincers or picks.

Never lay a weight on the T-square to hold it in position.

Never use a blotter on inked lines.

Never screw the pen adjustment past the contact point of the nibs.

Never run backward over a line with either pencil or pen.

Never leave the ink bottle uncorked.

Never hold the pen over the drawing while filling.

Never dilute ink with water. If too thick throw it away.

Never put a writing pen which has been used in ordinary writing ink, into the drawing-ink bottle.

Never try to use the same thumb-tack holes when putting paper down a second time.

Never scrub a drawing all over with an eraser after finishing. It takes the life out of the inked lines.

Never begin work without wiping off table and instruments.

Never put instruments away without cleaning. This applies with particular force to pens.

Never put bow instruments away without opening to relieve the spring.

Never fold a drawing or tracing.

Never use cheap materials of any kind.

CHAPTER IV

LETTERING

To give all the information necessary for the complete construction of a machine or structure there must be added to the "graphical language" of lines describing its shape, the figured dimensions, notes on material and finish, and a descriptive title, all of which must be lettered, freehand, in a style that is perfectly legible, uniform and capable of rapid execution. So far as its appearance is concerned there is no part of a drawing so important as the lettering. A good drawing may be ruined, not only in appearance but in usefulness, by lettering done ignorantly or carelessly, as illegible figures are very apt to cause mistakes in the work.

25. The paragraph above refers to the use of lettering on engineering drawings. In a broad sense the subject of lettering is a distinct branch of design. There are two general classes of persons who are interested in its study: first, those who have to use letters and words to convey information on drawings; second, those who use lettering in applied design, as art students, artists and craftsmen. The first class is concerned mainly with legibility and speed, the second with beauty of form and composition. Architects come under both classes, as they have both to letter their working drawings and to design inscriptions and tablets to be executed in stone or bronze.

The engineering student takes up lettering as his first work in drawing and continues its practice throughout his course, becoming more and more skillful and proficient.

In the art of lettering there are various forms of alphabets used, each appropriate for some particular purpose. The parent of all these styles is the "Old Roman" of the classic Roman inscriptions. This beautiful letter is the basic standard for architects and artists, although they have occasional appropriate use for other forms such as the gothic of the Middle Ages, popularly known as Old English. A variation known as Modern Roman is used by civil engineers in finished map and topographical drawing. For working drawings the simplified forms called commercial gothic are used almost exclusively.

In the execution of all lettering there are two general divisions, *drawn* or *built-up* letters, and *written* or *single-stroke* letters. Roman letters are usually drawn in outline and filled in; commercial gothic, except in larger size, are generally made in single stroke.

Lettering is *not* mechanical drawing. Large, carefully drawn letters are sometimes made with instruments, but the persistent use by some draftsmen of kinds of mechanical caricatures known as "geometrical letters," "block letters," etc., made up of straight lines and ruled in with T-square and triangle is to be condemned entirely.

26. General Proportions.—There is no one standard for the proportions of letters, but there are certain fundamental points in design and with the individual letters certain characteristics that must be thoroughly learned by study and observation before composition into words and sentences may be attempted. Not only do the widths of letters in any alphabet vary, from *I*, the narrowest, to *W*, the widest, but different alphabets vary as a whole. Styles narrow in their proportion of width to height are called **"COMPRESSED LETTERS"** and are used when space is limited. Styles wider than the normal are called "EXTENDED LETTERS."

The proportion of the thickness of stem to the height varies widely, ranging all the way from one-third to one-twentieth. Letters with heavy stems are called **bold face** or **black face,** those with thin stems *light face.*

27. The Rule of Stability.—In the construction of letters the well-known optical illusion in which a horizontal line drawn across the middle of a rectangle appears to be below the middle must be provided for. In order to give the appearance of stability such letters as *BEKSXZ*, and the figures 3 and 8 must be drawn smaller at the top than at the bottom. To see the effect of this illusion turn a printed page upside down and notice the letters mentioned.

28. Single-stroke Lettering.—By far the greatest amount of lettering on drawings is done in a rapid "single-stroke" letter either vertical or inclined, and every engineer must have absolute command of these styles. The ability to letter well can be acquired only by continued and careful practice, but it can be acquired by anyone with normal muscular control of his fingers who will take the trouble to observe carefully the shapes of the letters, the sequence of strokes composing them and the rules for composition; and will practice faithfully and intelligently. It is not a matter of artistic talent or even of dexterity in handwriting. Many draftsmen letter well who write very poorly.

LEONARDT 516 F: 506 F

HUNT 512: ESTERBROOK 968

Esterbrook 1000 Spencerian No. 1

Gillott 404: Gillott 303 For very fine lines Gillott 170 and 290

FIG. 62.—Pen strokes, full size.

The terms "single-stroke" or "one-stroke" do not mean that the entire letter is made without lifting the pen, but that the width of the stroke of the pen is the width of the stem of the letter. For the desired height, therefore, a pen must be selected which will give the necessary width of stroke without spreading the nibs and one that will make a uniform stroke in all directions.

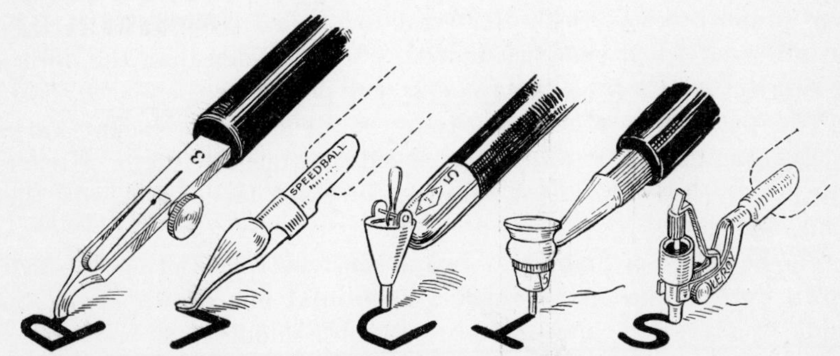

FIG. 63.—Barch-Payzant, speedball, perfection, Edco and Leroy pens.

29. Lettering Pens.—There are many steel writing pens either adaptable to or made especially for lettering. The sizes of strokes of a few popular ones are shown in full size in Fig. 62. Several special pens made in sets of graded sizes have been designed for single-stroke lettering, such as the Barch-Payzant, Speedball and Drawlet pens, Fig. 63. They are particularly useful for large work. The ink-holding reservoir of the Henry tank pen, Fig. 64, assists materially in maintaining uniform weight of line. A similar device may be made by bending a brass strip from a paper fastener, or a piece of

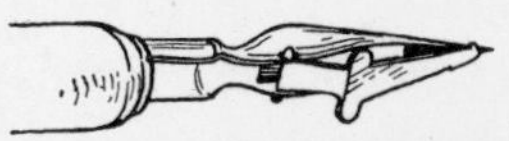

FIG. 64.—Henry tank pen.

annealed watch spring, into the shape shown in Fig. 65 and inserting it in the penholder so that the curved end just touches the nibs of the pen. The rate of feed is increased by moving the end closer to the point of the pen.

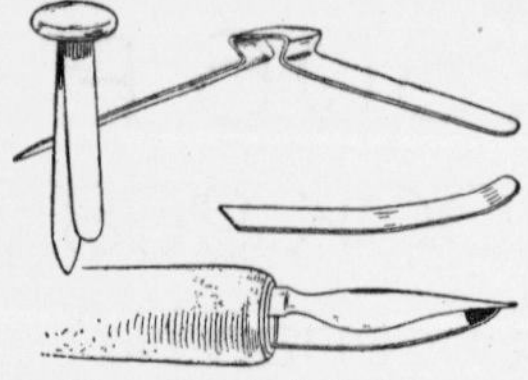

Fig. 65.—Ink holder.

Always wet a new pen and wipe it thoroughly before using, to remove the oil film. Some draftsmen prepare a new pen by holding it in a match flame for two or three seconds. A lettering pen well broken in by use is worth much more than a new one. It should be kept with care and never loaned. A pen that has been used in writing ink should never be put in drawing ink. When in use a pen should be wiped clean frequently with a cloth penwiper. The use of a ruling pen for freehand lettering is not recommended.

30. Using the Pen.—A penholder with cork grip (the small size) should be chosen and the pen set in it firmly. Many prefer to ink the pen with the quill filler, touching the quill to the under side of the pen point, rather than to dip it into the ink bottle. If the pen is dipped, the surplus ink should be shaken back into the bottle or the pen touched against the neck of the bottle as it is withdrawn. Getting too much ink on the pen is responsible for appearances of the kind shown in Fig. 66.

EHMNWTZ

Fig. 66.—Too much ink.

The first requirement in lettering is the correct holding of the pencil or pen. With the penholder in the position shown in Fig. 67 it should rest, rather than be held, in the fingers, so loosely that it could be pulled out easily with the other hand. Never tighten the grip of the fingers. The strokes of the letters should be drawn with a steady, even motion and a slight uniform pressure on the paper, not enough to cut a groove with the pencil or spread the nibs of the pen.

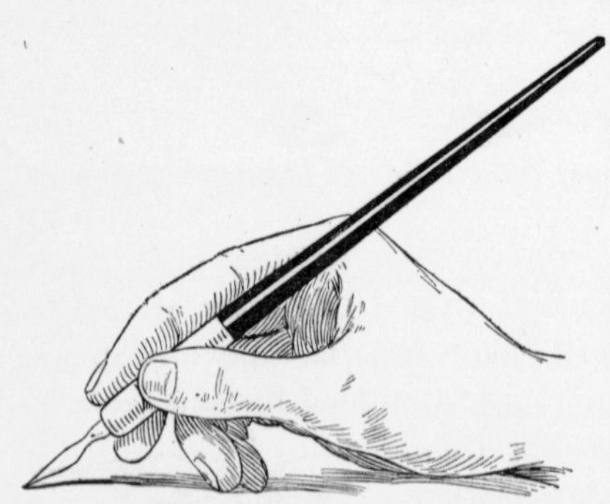

Fig. 67.—Position for lettering.

31. Guide lines for both tops and bottoms of the letters should always be drawn. Figure 68 shows the method of laying off a number of equally spaced lines of letters. Mark the height of the letters on the first line, then set the bow spacers to the distance wanted between base lines and step off the required number. With the same setting step down again from the upper point, thus obtaining points for the top and bottom for each line of letters. The Braddock-Rowe triangle, Fig. 69, and the Ames lettering instrument, Fig. 70, are convenient devices for spacing lines of letters. A sharp pencil is inserted in the countersunk holes and the instrument, guided by a T-square blade, drawn back and forth by the pencil. The holes are grouped for guide lines for capitals and lower case, the numbers indicating the height of capitals in thirty-seconds of an inch, thus No. 6 spacing means that the capitals will be $\frac{6}{32}''$, or $\frac{3}{16}''$, high.

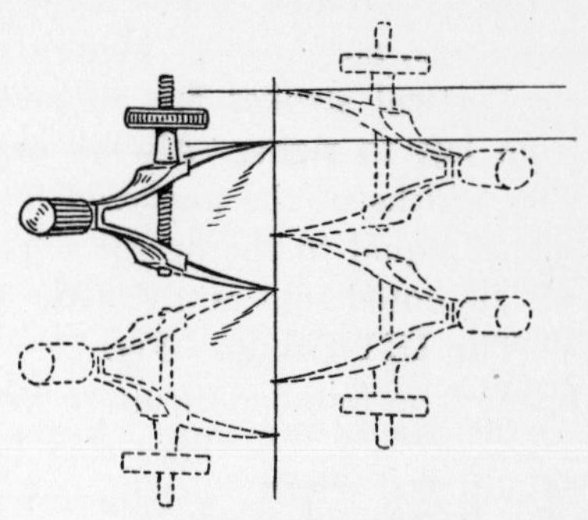

Fig. 68.—Spacing lines.

Guide lines should be drawn with a sharp hard pencil, 4H or 6H. When lettering a tracing do not attempt to use the guide lines on the pencil drawing. Always trace a new set in pencil on the cloth or paper. Letters are drawn with a softer pencil, 2H or H, with a conical point, and the habit should be formed of rotating the pencil in the fingers after every few strokes to keep the point symmetrical.

32. Single-stroke Vertical Capitals.—The vertical single-stroke commercial gothic letter is a standard for titles, reference letters, etc. In the proportion of width to height the general rule is that the

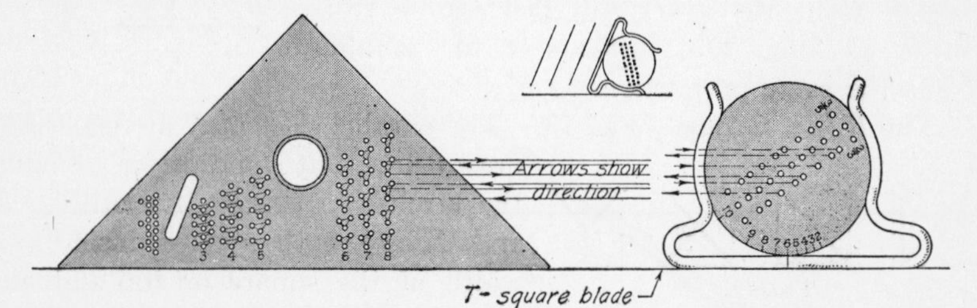

Fig. 69.—Braddock-Rowe triangle. Fig. 70.—Ames lettering instrument.

smaller the letters the more extended their width should be. A low extended letter is more legible than a high compressed one and at the same time makes a better appearance. This letter is seldom used in compressed form.

The first requirement is to learn the form and peculiarity of each of the letters. Too many persons think that lettering is simply "printing" in the childish way learned in the primary grades. There is an individuality in lettering often nearly as marked as in handwriting, but it must be based on a careful regard for the fundamental letter forms.

33. Order of Strokes.—In the following figures the vertical capitals have been arranged in family groups. The shape of each letter, with the order and direction of the strokes forming it, must be studied carefully and the letter practiced until its construction and form are perfectly familiar. The first studies should be made in pencil to large size, perhaps $\frac{3}{8}''$ high; afterward to smaller size directly in ink.

Vertical strokes are all made downward, and horizontal strokes from left to right. Always draw both top and bottom guide lines. The widths of the analyzed letters are shown in comparison with a square equal to the height. The letters are slightly extended and it will be noted that many of the letters practically fill the square.

The IHT Group.—Fig. 71. The letter *I* is the foundation stroke. It may be found difficult to keep the stems vertical; if so, direction lines may be drawn lightly an inch or so apart, to aid the eye. The *H* is nearly square and, observing the rule of stability, the cross-bar is just above the center. The top of the *T* is drawn first to the full width of the square and the stem started accurately at its middle point.

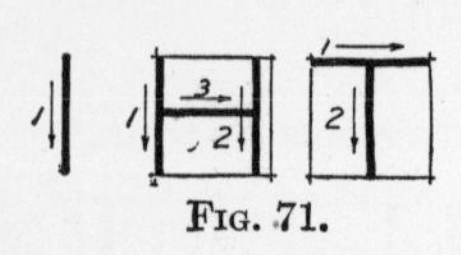

Fig. 71.

The LEF Group.—Fig. 72. The *L* is drawn in two strokes. Note that the first two strokes of the *E* are the same as the *L*, that the third or upper stroke is slightly shorter than the lower, the last stroke two-thirds as long, and just above the middle. *F* has the same proportions as *E*.

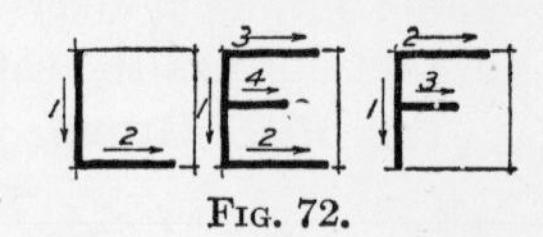

Fig. 72.

The NZXY Group.—Fig. 73. The parallel sides of *N* are generally drawn first, but some prefer to make the strokes in consecutive order. *Z* and *X* are both started inside the width of the square on top and run to full width on the bottom. This throws the crossing point of *X* above the center. The junction of the *Y* strokes is below the center.

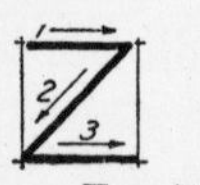

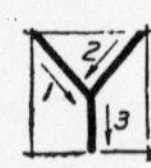

Fig. 73.

The VAK Group.—Fig. 74. *V* is slightly narrower than *A*, which here is the full width of the square. Its bridge is one-third up from the bottom. The second stroke of *K* strikes the stem one-third up from the bottom, the third stroke branches from it in a direction starting from the top of the stem.

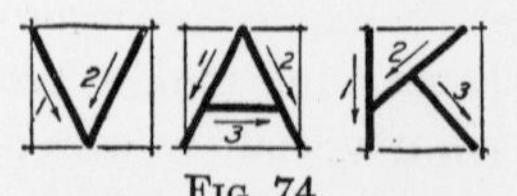

Fig. 74.

The MW Group.—Fig. 75. These are the widest letters. *M* may be made either in consecutive strokes or by drawing the two vertical strokes first, as with the *N*. *W* is formed of two narrow *V*'s. Note that with all the pointed letters the width at the point is the width of the stroke, that is, the center lines of the strokes meet at the guide lines.

Fig. 75.

The OQCG Group.—Fig. 76. In this extended alphabet the letters of the *O* family are made as full circles. The *O* is made in two strokes, the left side a longer arc than the right, as the right side is harder to draw. Make the kern of the *Q* straight or nearly straight. *C* and *G* of large size can be drawn more accurately with an extra stroke at the top, while in smaller ones the curve is drawn in one stroke. Note that the bar on the *G* is half-way up and does not extend past the vertical line.

Fig. 76.

The DUJ Group.—Fig. 77. The top and bottom strokes of *D* must be horizontal. Failure to observe this is a common fault with beginners. *U* in larger letters is formed of two parallel strokes to which the bottom stroke is added. For smaller letters it may be made in two strokes curved at the bottom to meet. *J* has the same construction as *U*.

Fig. 77.

The PRB Group.—Fig. 78. With *P*, *R* and *B* the number of strokes used depends upon the size of the letter. For large letters the horizontal lines are started and the curves added, but for smaller letters only one stroke for each lobe is needed. The middle lines of *P* and *R* are on the center line; that of *B* observes the rule of stability.

Fig. 78.

The S83 Group.—Fig. 79. The *S*, *8* and *3* are closely related in form, and the rule of stability must be observed carefully. For a large *S* three strokes may be used, for a smaller one two strokes, and for a very small size one stroke only is best. The *8* may be made on the *S* construction in three strokes, or in "head and body" in four strokes. A perfect *3* should be capable of being finished into an *8*. The *3* with flat top, sometimes seen, should not be used, on account of the danger of mistaking it for a *5*.

Fig. 79.

The 069 Group.—Fig. 80. The cipher is slightly narrower than the letter *O*. The backbones of the *6* and *9* have the same curve as the cipher, and the lobes are two-thirds the height of the figure.

Fig. 80.

The 257& Group.—Fig. 81. The secret of the *2* lies in getting the reverse curve to cross the center of the space. The bottom of *2* and the top of *5* and *7* should be straight lines. The second stroke of *7* terminates directly below the middle of the top stroke. Its stiffness is relieved by curving it slightly at the lower end. The ampersand (*&*) is made in three strokes for large letters and two for smaller ones and must be carefully balanced.

Fig. 81.

The Fraction Group.—Fig. 82. Fractions are always made with horizontal bar. The figures are two-thirds the height of the whole numbers, with a clear space above and below the bar, making the total height of the fraction five-thirds the cap height. Much practice should be given to numerals and fractions, combining them into dimensions, following the conventional rules on page 135. A useful practice sheet of figures alone may be made by designing a table of decimal equivalents. See Appendix for table.

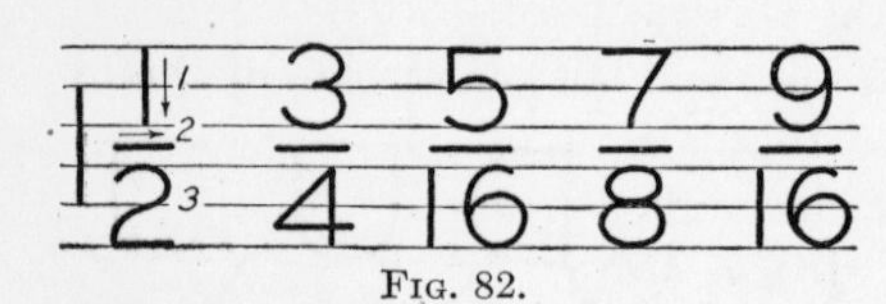

Fig. 82.

34. Vertical Lower Case.—The single-stroke vertical lower-case letter is not commonly used on machine drawings but is used extensively in map drawing. It is the standard letter for hypsography in government topographical drawing. The bodies are made two-thirds the height of the capitals with the ascenders extending to the cap line and the descenders dropping the same distance below. The basis of the letter, as used with the extended capitals just analyzed, is the combination of a circle and a straight line as shown in enlarged form in Fig. 83. The alphabet with some alternate shapes is shown in Fig. 84, which figure also gives the capitals in alphabetical order.

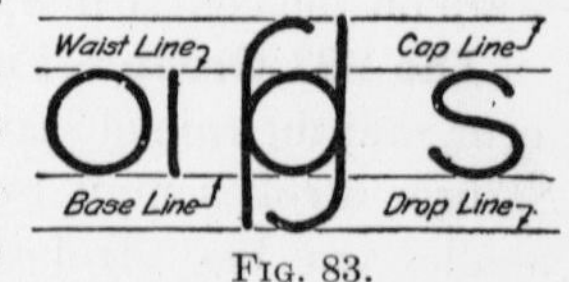

Fig. 83.

35. Single-stroke Inclined Caps.—The inclined or slant letter is used in preference to the upright by many, including the majority of structural steel draftsmen. The order and direction of strokes are the same as in the vertical form.

After ruling the guide lines, slanting "direction lines" should be drawn across the sheet to aid the eye in keeping the slope uniform.

Fig. 84.—Single-stroke vertical caps and lower case.

These may be drawn with a special lettering triangle (of about 67½°) or by setting a slope of 2 to 5 by marking two units on a horizontal line and five on a vertical line, and using T-square and triangle as shown in Fig. 85. The form taken by the rounded letters when inclined is illustrated in Fig. 86, showing that curves are sharp in all upper right-hand and lower left-hand corners and flattened in the other two corners. The snap and swing of professional work are due to three things: first, keeping a uniform slope, second, having the letters full and well shaped, third, keeping them close together. The beginner's invariable mistake is to cramp the individual letters and space them too far apart.

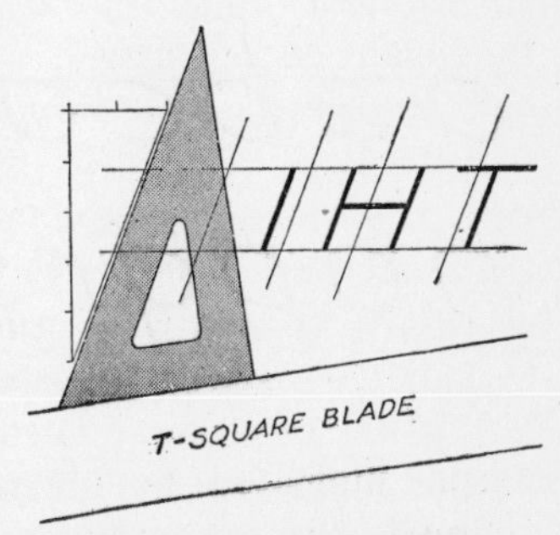

Fig. 85.—Slope guide lines.

Particular care must be observed with the letters having sloping sides as *A*, *V* and *W*. The sloping sides of these letters must be drawn so that they appear to balance about a slope guide line through their intersection as in Fig. 87. The alphabet is given in Fig. 88. Study the shape of each letter carefully.

Fig. 86. Fig. 87.

36. Single-stroke Inclined Lower Case.—The inclined lower-case letters, Fig. 88, are drawn with the bodies two-thirds the height of the capitals. This letter is generally known among older engineers as the Reinhardt letter in honor of Charles W. Reinhardt, who first systematized its construction. It is very legible and effective and after its swing has been mastered can be made very rapidly. The lower-case letter is suitable for notes and statements on drawings, for the two

Fig. 88.—Single-stroke inclined caps and lower case.

reasons indicated: first, it is read much more easily than all caps, as we read words by the word shapes, second, it can be done much faster.

All the letters of this alphabet are based on two elements, the straight line and the ellipse, and have no unnecessary hooks or appendages. They may be divided into four groups as shown in Figs. 89 to 92. The dots of *i* and *j* and the top of the *t* are on the "*t*-line," halfway between the waist line and cap line. The loop letters are made with an ellipse, whose axis is inclined about 45°, in combination with a straight line. In lettering rapidly this ellipse tends to assume a "pumpkin seed" form which should be guarded against.

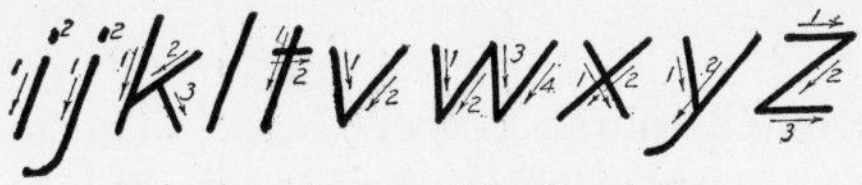

ijkltvwxyz

Fig. 89.—The straight line letters.

abdgpq

Fig. 90.—The loop letters.

ceos

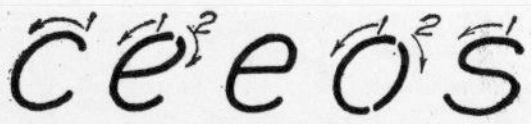

Fig. 91.—The ellipse letters.

hmnruy

Fig. 92.—The hook letters.

The *c*, *e* and *o* are based on an ellipse of the shape of the capitals, not inclined quite so much as the loop letter ellipse. In rapid small work the *o* is often made in one stroke, as are also *e*, *v* and *w*. The *s* is similar to the capital but except in letters more than one-eighth inch high is made in one stroke. In the hook letter group note the characteristic sharp turn.

The single-stroke letter may, if necessary, be very much compressed and still be clear and legible. It is also sometimes used in extended form. See Fig. 93.

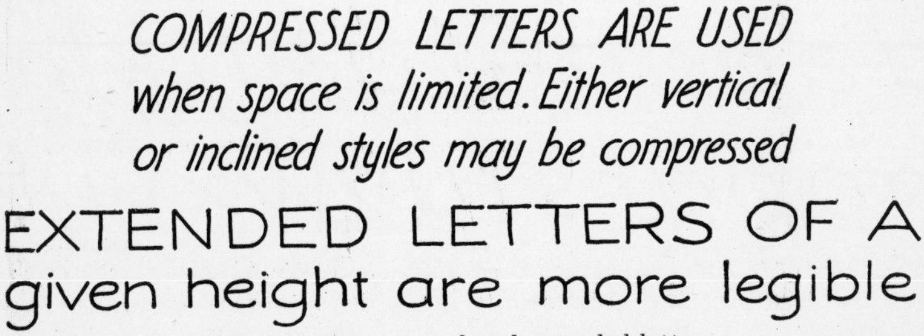

COMPRESSED LETTERS ARE USED
when space is limited. Either vertical
or inclined styles may be compressed

EXTENDED LETTERS OF A
given height are more legible

Fig. 93.—Compressed and extended letters.

37. Composition.—Composition in lettering has to do with the selection, arrangement and spacing of appropriate styles and sizes of letters. After the shapes and strokes of the individual letters have been learned the entire practice should be on composition into words and sentences, since proper spacing of letters and words does more for the appearance of a block of lettering than the formation of the letters themselves. Letters in words are not spaced at a uniform distance from each other, but so that the areas of white spaces (the irregular backgrounds between the letters) are approximately equal, making them *appear* to be spaced uniformly. Each letter is spaced with reference to its shape and the shape of the letter preceding it. Thus adjacent letters with straight sides would be spaced farther apart than those with curved sides. Sometimes combinations such as *LT* or *AV* may even overlap. The entire word or line must be studied to find what combination will set the area. It may be a word with round letters in it or a combination like *LA*. Definite rules for spacing are not successful; it is a matter of artistic judgment. Figure 94 illustrates word composition.

COMPOSITION IN LETTERING
REQUIRES CAREFUL SPACING, NOT ONLY
OF LETTERS BUT OF WORDS AND LINES

Fig. 94.—Composition.

The sizes of letters to use in any particular case may be determined better by sketching them in lightly than by judging from the guide lines alone. A finished line of letters always looks larger than the guide lines would indicate. Avoid the use of a coarse pen for small sizes, as well as one making thin wiry lines for large sizes. Before inking a line of penciled letters rub the pencil marks so the excess graphite will not "muddy" the ink.

When Caps and Small Caps are used the height of the small caps should be about four-fifths that of the caps.

In spacing words the clear distance between them should not be more than the height of the letters. The clear distance between lines may vary from one-half to one and one-half times the height of the caps. Paragraphs should always be indented.

38. Titles.—The most important problem in lettering composition which the engineering draftsman will meet is the design of titles. Every drawing has a descriptive title giving the necessary information concerning it, which is either all hand-lettered or filled in on a printed form. This information, of course, varies for different kinds of drawings (see working drawing titles, page 196; architectural titles, page 353; structural titles, page 364; map titles, page 383).

The usual form of lettered title is the *symmetrical title* which is balanced or "justified" on a vertical center line and with an elliptical or oval outline. Sometimes the wording necessitates a pyramid or inverted pyramid ("bag") form. Figure 95 illustrated several shapes into which titles might be composed. The lower right-hand corner

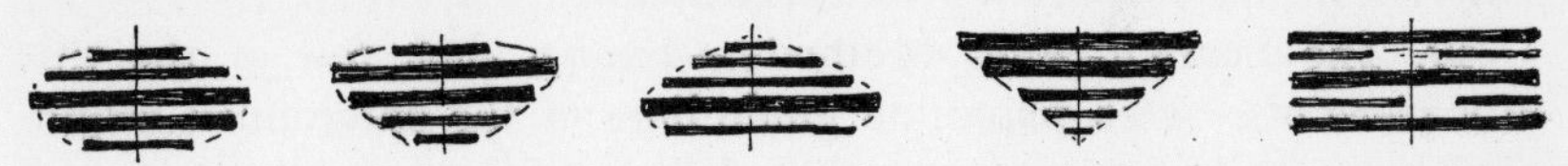

Fig. 95.—Shapes in symmetrical composition.

of the sheet is from long custom, and on account of convenience in filing, the usual location, and in laying out a drawing this corner is reserved if possible. The space given is a matter of artistic judgment depending on the size and purpose of the drawing. On an 11″ × 17″ working drawing the title might be about 3 inches long.

39. To Draw a Title.—When the wording has been determined, write out the arrangement on a separate piece of paper as in Fig. 96

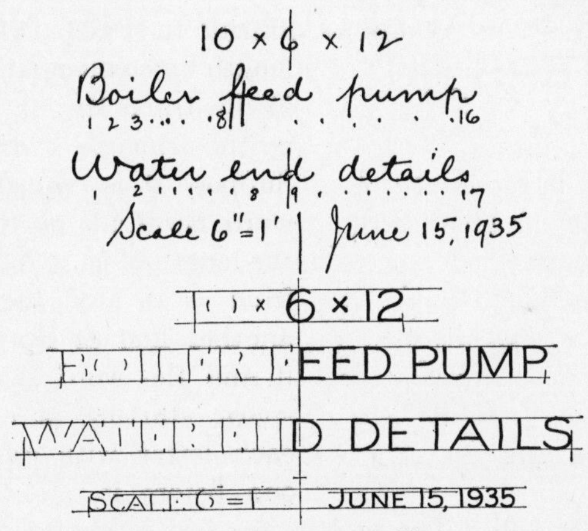

Fig. 96.—Title composition.

(or, better, typewrite it). The lines must be displayed for prominence according to their relative importance, judged from the point of view of the persons who will use the drawing. Titles are usually made in all caps. Count the letters, including the word spaces, and make a mark across the middle letter or space of each line. Draw the base line for the most important line of the title and mark on it the approximate length desired. To get the letter height divide this length by the number of letters in the line, and draw the cap line. Start at the center line and sketch very lightly the last half of the line, drawing only enough of the letters to show the space each will occupy. Lay off the length of the right half on the other side and sketch that side, working either forward or backward. When this line is satisfactory in size and spacing draw the remainder in the same way. Study the effect, shift letters or lines if necessary, and complete in pencil. Use punctuation marks only for abbreviations.

40. The Scratch-paper Methods.—Sketch each line of the title on a piece of scratch paper, on guide lines of the determined height. Find the middle point of each line, fold the paper along the base of the letters, fit the middle to the center line on the drawing and draw the final letters directly below the tentative ones. *Or* draw the letters along the edge of the scratch paper using either the upper or lower edge as one of the guide lines. *Or* letter the title on scratch paper, cut apart and adjust until satisfactory.

In making elaborate titles on tracings, such as map titles, it is customary to draw the title on a separate piece of paper and slip it under the tracing to the desired position.

41. The Proportional Method.—On account of the varying widths of Roman letters it is sometimes difficult to space a word to a given length by counting letters. Figure 97 illustrates the method of spacing by the principle of similar triangles. Suppose it is required to put the word *ROMAN* on the line and to the length of *ab*. A line *ac* is drawn from *a* at any angle (say 30°), another line *de* drawn parallel to it and the word sketched in this space, starting at *a* and spacing each letter with reference to the one before it, allowing the word to end where it will. The end of the last letter (at *c*) is connected with *b* and lines parallel to *cb* drawn from each letter, thus dividing *ab* proportionally. The height *bf* is obtained from *ce* by the construction shown, after which the word can be sketched in its final position.

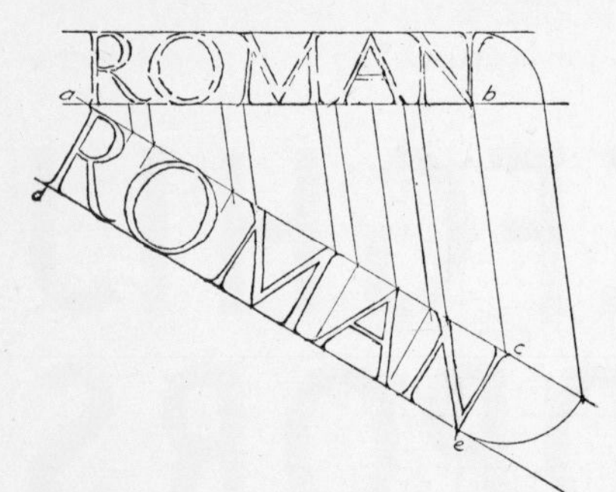

Fig. 97.—Proportional method.

Some examples of titles may be found on pages 184 and 197.

42. Outlined Commercial Gothic.—Thus far the so-called "gothic" letter has been considered only as a single-stroke letter. For sizes larger than, say, five-sixteenths of an inch, or for bold-face letters, it is drawn in outline and filled in solid. For a given size this letter is readable at a greater distance than any other style; hence it would be used in any place where legibility is the principal requirement. The stems may be from one-tenth to one-fifth of the height, and much care must be exercised in keeping them to uniform width at every point on the letter. In inking a penciled outline keep the *outside* of the ink line on the pencil line, Fig. 98; otherwise the letter will be heavier than expected.

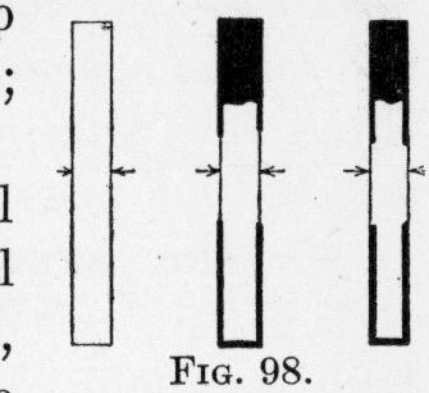

Fig. 98.

Making two strokes in place of one, the general order and direction of penciling large commercial gothic letters is similar to the single-stroke analysis, as shown in the typical examples of Fig. 99. Free ends, such as on *C*, *G* and *S*, are cut off perpendicular to the stem. The stiffness of plain letters is sometimes relieved by finishing the

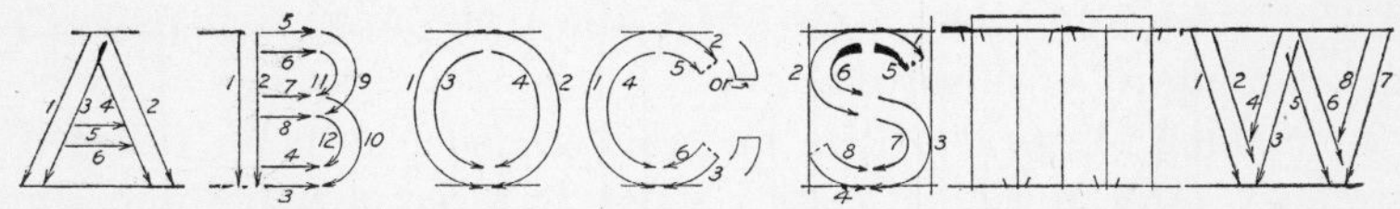

Fig. 99.—Typical construction for large commercial gothic.

ends with a slight spur as in Fig. 100. The complete alphabet in outline, with stems one-sixth of the height, is given in Fig. 101. The same scale of widths may be used for drawing lighter face letters.

ABCDEFGHIJ
KLMNOPQRS
TUVWXYZ &

Fig. 100.—Compressed commercial gothic.

Figure 100 illustrates a commercial gothic alphabet compressed to two-thirds the normal width. In this figure the stems are drawn one-seventh of the height, but the scale is given in sixths as in Fig. 101.

43. The Roman Letter.—The Roman letter has been mentioned as the parent of all the styles, however diversified, which are in use

FIG. 101.—Large commercial gothic construction.

ABCDE
FGHIJK
LMNOP
QRSTU
VWXYZ
&12345
67890

Fig. 102.—Old Roman capitals.

today. Although there are many variations of it there may be said to be three general forms: (1) the early or classic, (2) the renaissance, (3) the modern. The first two are very similar in effect and the general term "Old Roman" is used for both.

The Roman letter is composed of two weights of lines, corresponding to the down stroke and the up stroke of the broad reed pen with which it was originally written. It is an inexcusable fault to shade a Roman letter on the wrong stroke.

Rule for Shading.—All horizontal strokes are light. All vertical strokes are heavy except in *M*, *N* and *U*. To determine the heavy stroke in letters containing slanting sides trace the shape of the letter from left to right in one stroke and note which lines were made down-

Fig. 103.—Old Roman lower-case.

ward. Figure 102 is an Old Roman alphabet with the width of the body stroke one-tenth of the height of the letter and the light lines slightly over one-half this width. For inscriptions and titles it is generally used in all capitals, but sometimes the lower case, Fig. 103, is needed. This figure is drawn with the waist line six-tenths high and the width of the stems one-twelfth of the cap height.

The Old Roman is the architect's one general-purpose letter. A single-stroke adaptation of it, Fig. 104, is generally used on architectural working drawings.

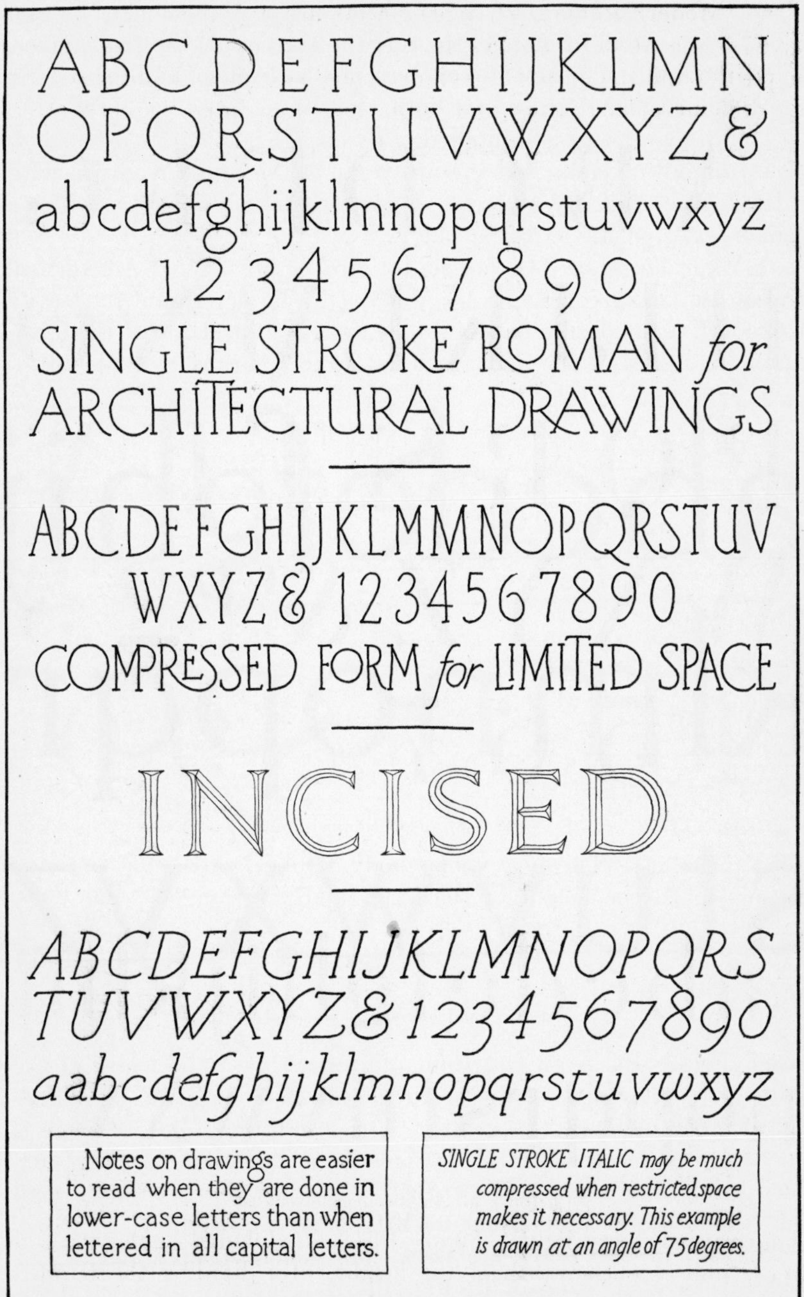

ABCDEFGHIJKLMN
OPQRSTUVWXYZ&
abcdefghijklmnopqrstuvwxyz
1234567890
SINGLE STROKE ROMAN *for*
ARCHITECTURAL DRAWINGS

ABCDEFGHIJKLMMNOPQRSTUV
WXYZ& 1234567890
COMPRESSED FORM *for* LIMITED SPACE

INCISED

ABCDEFGHIJKLMNOPQRS
TUVWXYZ& 1234567890
aabcdefghijklmnopqrstuvwxyz

Notes on drawings are easier to read when they are done in lower-case letters than when lettered in all capital letters.

SINGLE STROKE ITALIC may be much compressed when restricted space makes it necessary. This example is drawn at an angle of 75 degrees.

FIG. 104.—Single-stroke Roman and italic.

44. Modern Roman.—Civil engineers in particular must be familiar with the Modern Roman as it is the standard letter for finished map titles and the names of civil divisions, as countries and cities. It is a difficult letter to draw and can be mastered only by careful atten-

Fig. 105.—Modern Roman capitals.

tion to details. The heavy or "body strokes" are from one-sixth to one-eighth the height of the letter and the thin or "hair lines"

Fig. 106.—Modern Roman lower case.

comparatively very light. Figure 105 is an alphabet made on a scale whose unit is one-seventh of the height. By dividing the required height into seven equal parts, a small paper scale, as shown, may be made, to aid in penciling the letters. Modern lower case, Fig. 106, is used on maps for names of towns and villages. Notice the difference in the serifs of Figs. 106 and 103.

The order and direction of strokes used in drawing Roman letters are illustrated in the typical letters of Fig. 107. The serifs on the ends of the strokes extend one space on each side and are joined to the stroke

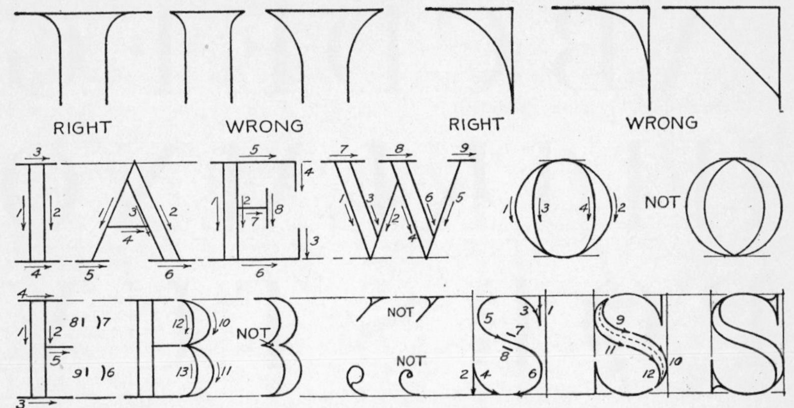

Fig. 107.—Modern Roman construction.

MAP SHOWING
IRON ORE DEPOSITS
IN THE
WESTERN STATES
SCALE-MILES 0 50 100 200 300 400

Fig. 108.—A Roman letter title.

EXTENDED ROMAN
BCGHJKLPQSUVW

COMPRESSED ROMAN-BHKTWG

Fig. 109.—Modern Roman, extended and compressed.

by small fillets. Roman letters are spoiled oftener by poor serifs and fillets than in any other way. For letters smaller than one-fourth of an inch it is best to omit the body stroke fillets altogether. It will be noticed that the curved letters are flattened slightly on their diagonals. A title in Roman letters is illustrated in Fig. 108.

The Roman letter may be extended or compressed, as shown in Fig. 109. For these a scale for widths may be made longer or shorter than the normal scale. For example, the compressed letters of Fig. 109 are made with a scale three-fourths of the height divided into sevenths.

45. Inclined Roman.—Inclined letters are used for water features on maps. An alphabet of inclined Roman made to the same proportions as the vertical of Fig. 105 is shown in Fig. 110. The slope may be from 65° to 75°. Those shown are inclined 2 to 5. The lower-case letters in this figure are known as stump letters. For small sizes their lines are made with one stroke of a fine flexible pen, while larger sizes are drawn and filled in.

A B C D E F G H I
J K L M N O P Q R
S T U V W X Y Z &
a b c d e f g h i j k l m n o
p q r s t u v or v w or w x y or y z
1 2 3 4 5 6 7 8 9 0

Fig. 110.—Inclined Roman and stump letters.

EXERCISES

46. The following exercises are designed for a 5″ × 7″ sheet or space. Lettering practice should be done in short intensive periods.

Series I. Single-stroke Vertical Caps

1. Large letters in pencil, for careful study of the shapes of the individual letters. Starting 9/16″ from top border draw guide lines for five lines of 3/8″ letters. Draw each of the straight line letters *IHTLEFNZXYVAMW* four times in pencil only, studying carefully Figs. 71 to 75. Figure 111 is a full-sized reproduction of a corner of this exercise.

2. Same as Ex. 1 for the curved line letters *OQCGDUJBPRS*. Study Figs. 76 to 79 carefully.

3. Same as Ex. 1 for figures and fractions 3 8 6 9 2 5 & ½ ¾ ⅝ 7/16 9/32. Study Figs. 80 to 82 very carefully.

4. Composition. Same layout as for Ex. 1. Read paragraph on composition, then letter the following five lines in pencil. (1) WORD COMPOSITION, (2)

TOPOGRAPHIC SURVEY, (3) TOOLS AND EQUIPMENT, (4) BRONZE BUSHING, (5) JACK RAFTER DETAIL.

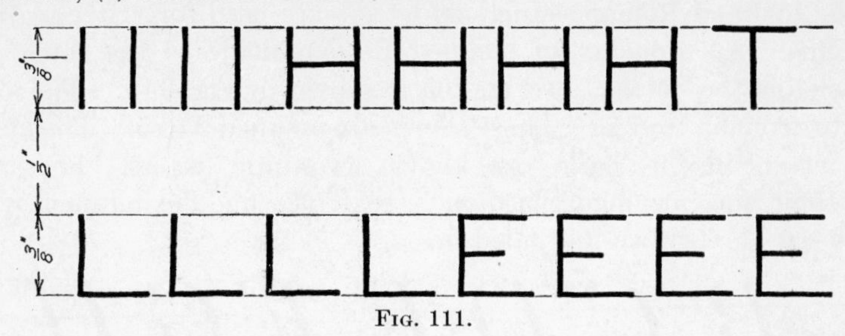

FIG. 111.

5. Quarter-inch vertical letters in pencil and ink. Starting ¼″ from top, draw guide lines for nine lines of ¼″ letters. In the group order given draw each letter first four times in pencil, then four times directly in ink, as in Fig. 112.

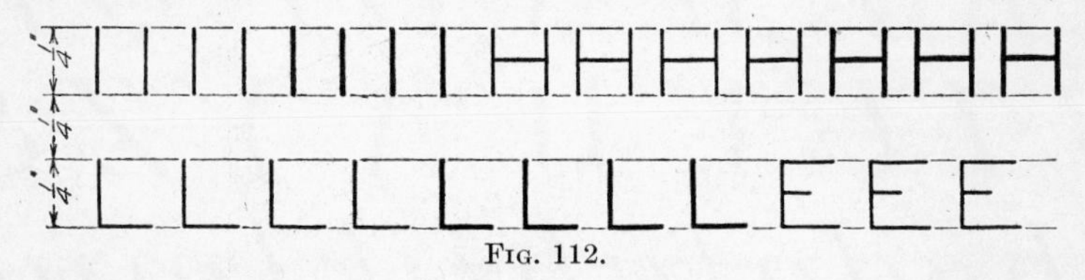

FIG. 112.

6. One-eighth inch vertical letters. Starting ¼″ from top, draw guide lines for 18 lines of ⅛″ letters. Make each letter and numeral eight times directly in ink. Fill the remaining lines with a portion of paragraph 37 on composition.

Series II. Single-stroke Inclined Capitals

7 to **14.** Same spacing and specifications as for Series I. Exercises 1 to 6 but for inclined letters. Study paragraph 35 and Figs. 85 to 88.

Series III. Single-stroke Inclined Lower Case

15. Large letters in pencil for use with ⅜″ caps. The bodies are ¼″, the ascenders ⅛″ above and the descenders ⅛″ below. Starting ⅜″ from top draw guide lines for seven lines of letters. This can be done quickly by spacing ⅛″ uniformly down the sheet and bracketing cap and base lines. Make each letter of the alphabet four times in pencil only. Study Figs. 88 to 92.

16. Lower case for 3⁄16″ caps. Starting ½″ from top, draw cap, waist and base lines for 13 lines of letters (Braddock or Ames No. 6 spacing). Make each letter six times in pencil, then six times in ink.

17. Composition. Same spacing as Ex. 16. Letter the opening paragraph of this chapter.

Series IV. Titles

18. Design a title for the assembly drawing of a rear axle drawn to the scale of six inches to the foot, as made by the Graham-Paige Motors Corporation of Detroit. The number of the drawing is C 27536. Space allowed 3″ × 5″. See page 196 for contents of a working drawing title.

19. Design a title for the front elevation of a power house drawn to quarter-inch scale by G. W. Bell, architect, for the Citizens Light and Heat Company of North Adams, Michigan. See page 353 for contents of an architectural title.

CHAPTER V

APPLIED GEOMETRY

47. With the aid of a straight-edge and compasses all pure geometrical problems may be solved. The principles of geometry are constantly used in mechanical drawing, but as the geometrical solution of problems and construction of figures differ in many cases from the draftsman's method, equipped as he is with instruments for gaining time and accuracy, such problems are not included here. For example, there are several geometrical methods of erecting a perpendicular to a given line; in his ordinary practice the draftsman equipped with T-square and triangles uses none of them. The application of these geometrical methods might be necessary occasionally in work where the usual drafting instruments could not be used, as, for instance, in laying out full-size sheet metal patterns on the floor. It is assumed that students using this book are familiar with the elements of plane geometry and will be able to apply their knowledge. If a particular problem is not remembered, it may readily be referred to in any of the standard handbooks. There are some constructions, however, with which the draftsman should be familiar as they will occur more or less frequently in his work. The constructions in this chapter are given on this account, and for the excellent practice they afford in the accurate use of instruments as well.

As an aid in recalling the names of various geometrical figures see page 71 at the end of this chapter.

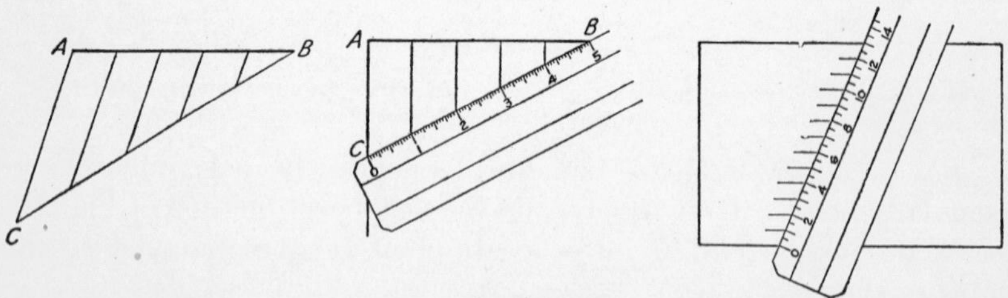

Fig. 113.—To divide a line. Fig. 14.—Scale method. Fig. 115.—Scale method.

48. To Divide a Line—Geometrical Method.—Fig. 113. To divide the line AB into (say) five equal parts, draw any line BC indefinitely, on it measure or step off five divisions of convenient length, connect the last point with A, draw lines through the points parallel to CA intersecting AB, using triangle and straight-edge as shown in Fig. 20, page 16.

Scale Method.—In the application of the foregoing principle the draftsman generally prefers the scale method, first drawing a perpendicular AC from A, then placing a scale so that five convenient equal divisions are included between B and the perpendicular, as in Fig. 114. Perpendiculars drawn with triangle and T-square through the points marked will divide the line AB as required. Figure 115 illustrates an application in laying off stair risers.

This method may be used for dividing a line into any proportional parts.

49. To Construct a Triangle Having Given the Three Sides.—Fig. 116. Given the lengths A, B and C. Draw one side A in the desired position. With its ends as centers and radii B and C draw two intersecting arcs as shown.

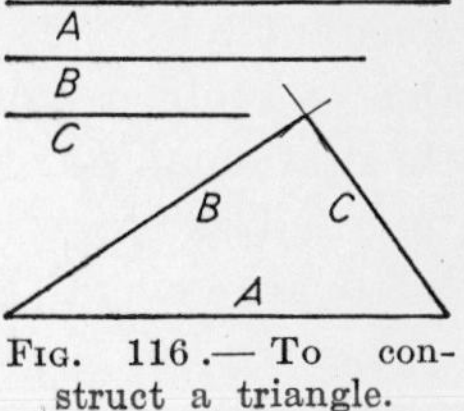

FIG. 116.—To construct a triangle.

50. To Transfer a Polygon to a New Base.—Fig. 117. Given polygon $ABCDEF$ and new position of base $A'B'$. Consider each point as the vertex of a triangle whose base is AB. With centers A' and B' and radii AC and BC describe intersecting arcs, locating the point C'. Similarly with radii AD and BD locate the point D'. Connect $B'C'$ and $C'D'$ and continue the operation, always using A and B as centers.

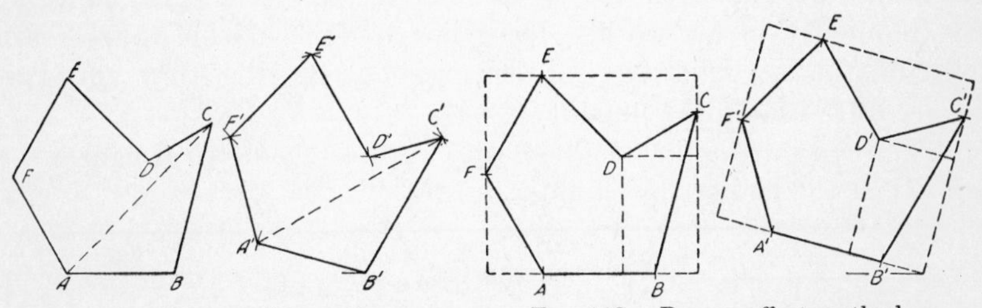

FIG. 117.—To transfer a polygon.

FIG. 118.—Box or offset method.

Box or Offset Method.—Fig. 118. Enclose the polygon in a rectangular "box." Draw the box on the new base (method of Fig. 21), locate the points $ABCEF$ on it; locate point D by rectangular coordinates as shown.

51. To Construct a Regular Hexagon.—Fig. 119. Given the distance across corners AB. Draw a circle on AB as a diameter. With the same radius and A and B as centers draw arcs and connect the points.

Second method, without using compasses. Draw lines with the 30°–60° triangle in the order shown in Fig. 120.

Third Method.—When the short diameter is given draw a circle on the short diameter and with the 30°–60° triangle draw tangents to it as in Fig. 121.

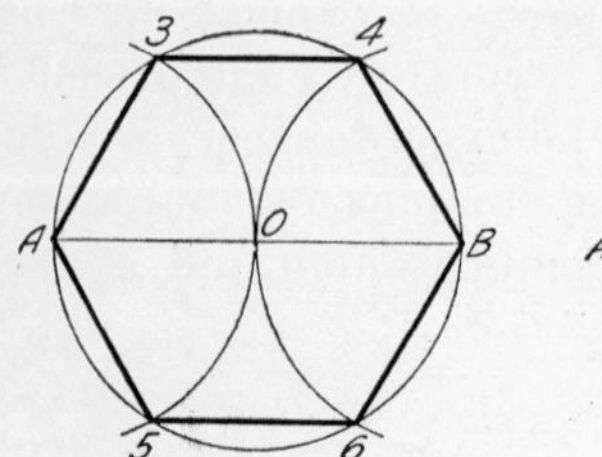

Fig. 119.—Hexagon.

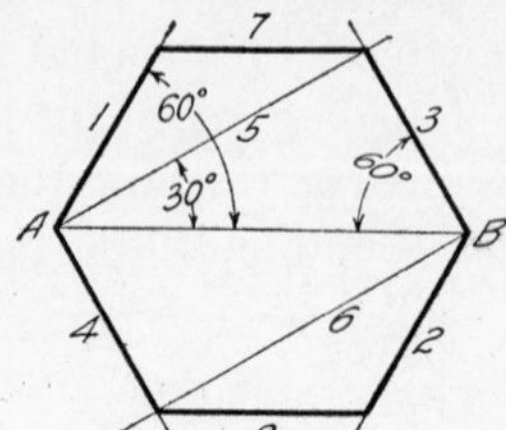

Fig. 120.—Hexagon.

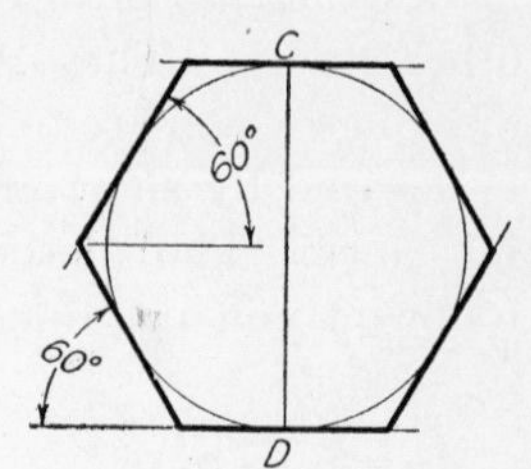

Fig. 121.—Hexagon.

52. To Inscribe a Pentagon in a Circle.—Fig. 122. Draw a diameter AB and a radius OC perpendicular to it. Bisect OB. With this point D as center and a radius DC draw arc CE. With center C and radius CE draw arc EF. CF is the side of the pentagon.

53. To Draw a Regular Octagon in a Square.—Fig. 123. Draw the diagonals of the square. With the corners of the square as centers and radius of half the diagonal draw arcs intersecting the sides of the square, and connect these points.

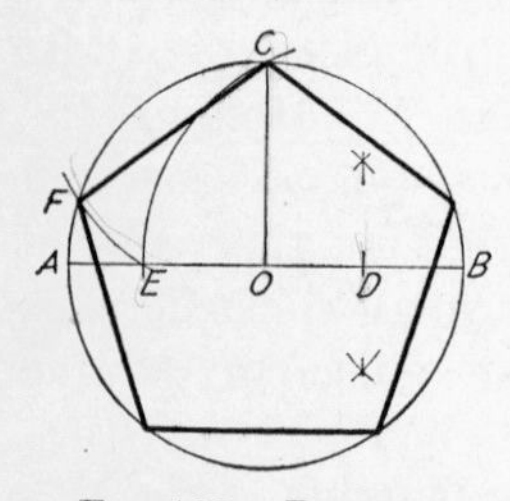

Fig. 122.—Pentagon.

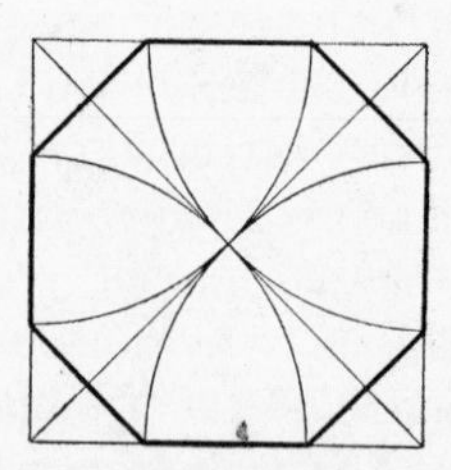
Fig. 123.—Octagon.

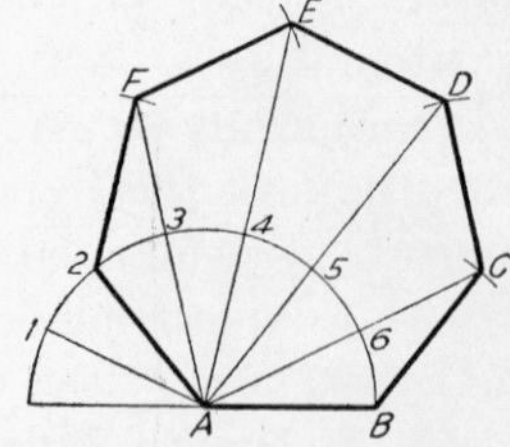

Fig. 124.—Polygon.

54. To Construct a Polygon—One Side Given.—Fig. 124. To draw a polygon of any number of sides (say seven). With the side AB as a radius and A as center draw a semi-circle and divide it into seven equal parts. Through the second division from the left draw radial line $A2$. Through points 3, 4, 5, 6 extend radial lines as shown. With AB as radius and B as center cut line $A6$ at C. With C as center cut $A5$ at D, and so on at E and F. Connect the points, *or* after $A2$ is found draw the circumscribing circle.

55. To Draw a Circle Arc through Three Given Points.—Fig. 125. Given *A*, *B* and *C*. Draw *AB* and *BC*. The intersection of the perpendicular bisectors of these lines will be the center of the required circle.

56. Tangents.—One of the most frequent geometrical operations in drafting is the drawing of circle arcs tangent to straight lines or other circles. These should be constructed accurately and on pencil drawings which are to be inked or traced the points of tangency should be located by short cross-marks to show the stopping points for the ink lines. The method of finding these points is indicated in the following constructions.

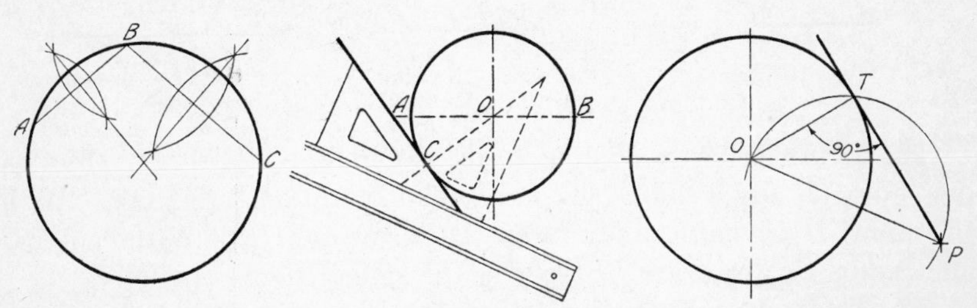

Fig. 125.—Center of arc. Fig. 126.—Drawing a tangent. Fig. 127.—Tangent from point outside.

57. To Draw a Tangent to a Circle.—Fig. 126. Given the arc *ACB*, to draw a tangent at the point *C* on the arc. Arrange a triangle in combination with the T-square (or another triangle) so that its hypotenuse passes through center *O* and point *C*. Holding the T-square firmly in place turn the triangle about its square corner and move it until the hypotenuse coincides with *C*, giving the required tangent, perpendicular to the normal *OC*. (For small constructions, or with a large triangle, this may be done a little quicker by setting the hypotenuse of the triangle on the T-square as in Fig. 21 at *B*.)

58. To Draw a Tangent to a Circle from a Point Outside.—Fig. 127. Connect the point with the center of the circle. On this line *OP* as a diameter draw a semi-circle. Its intersection with the given circle is the point of tangency. (Prove.)

59. To Draw a Tangent to Two Circles.—*First case* (open belt), Fig. 128. At center *O* draw a circle with radius R_1 minus R_2. From *P* draw a tangent to this circle by the method of Fig. 127. Extend *OT* to T_1 and draw PT_2 parallel to it. Join T_1 and T_2.

Second case (crossed belt), Fig. 129. Draw *OA* and O_1B perpendicular to OO_1. From *P* where *AB* crosses OO_1 draw tangents as in Fig. 127.

60. To Draw an Arc Tangent to Two Lines.—Fig. 130. Given the lines AB and CD, and radius R. A line parallel to AB at the distance R from it will be the locus of the centers of all circles of radius R tangent to AB. Its intersection with a similar locus parallel to

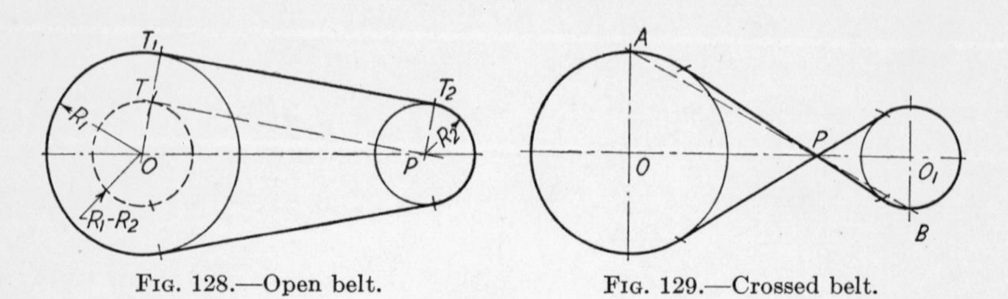

FIG. 128.—Open belt. FIG. 129.—Crossed belt.

CD will be the center of the required arc. Find the points of tangency by drawing perpendiculars from O to AB and CD. Figure 131 is the same construction with an obtuse angle. For a right angle, Fig. 132, a quicker construction is to draw an arc of radius R with B as center, cutting AB and BC at T and T'. With T and T' as centers and same radius draw arcs intersecting at O, the center for the required arc.

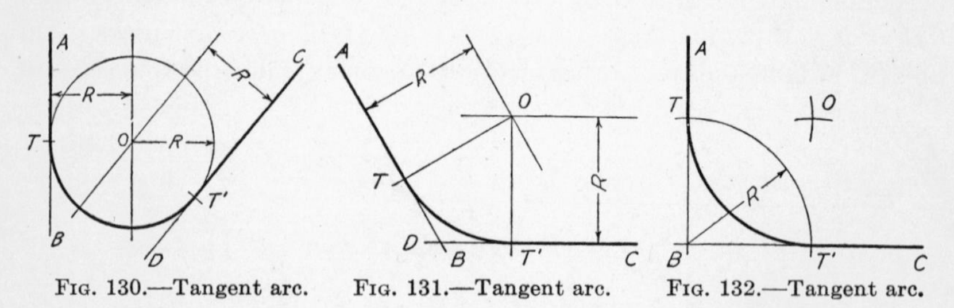

FIG. 130.—Tangent arc. FIG. 131.—Tangent arc. FIG. 132.—Tangent arc.

61. To Draw a Circle of Radius R Tangent to a Given Circle and Line.—Fig. 133. Let AB be the given line and R_1 the radius of the given circle. Draw a line CD parallel to AB at a distance R from it. With O as a center and radius $R + R_1$ swing an arc intersecting CD at X, the desired center. The tangent point for AB will be on a perpendicular to AB from X; the tangent for the two circles on a line joining their centers X and O. Note that when two circles are tangent to each other the point of tangency *must* be on the line through their centers.

62. To Draw a Circle of Radius R Tangent to Two Given Circles.—*First case*, a concave tangent. Fig. 134. Let R_1 and R_2 be the radii of the given circles having centers O and P, respectively. With O as a center and a radius $R + R_1$ describe an arc. With P as a center and a radius $R + R_2$ swing another arc intersecting the first arc at Q, which is the center sought. Mark the tangent points by cross-marks in line with OQ and QP.

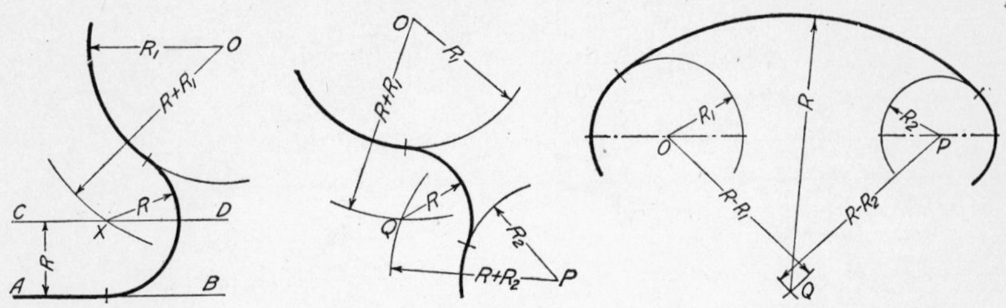

FIG. 133.—Tangent arc. FIG. 134.—Tangent arc. FIG. 135.—Tangent arc.

Second case, a convex tangent, Fig. 135. With O and P as centers and radii R minus R_1 and R minus R_2 describe arcs intersecting at the required center Q.

63. To Draw a Reverse or "Ogee" Curve.—Fig. 136. Given two parallel lines AB and CD. Join B and C by a straight line. Erect perpendiculars at B and C. Any arcs tangent to the lines AB and CD at B and C must have their centers on these perpendiculars. On line BC assume point E through which the curve is desired to pass, and

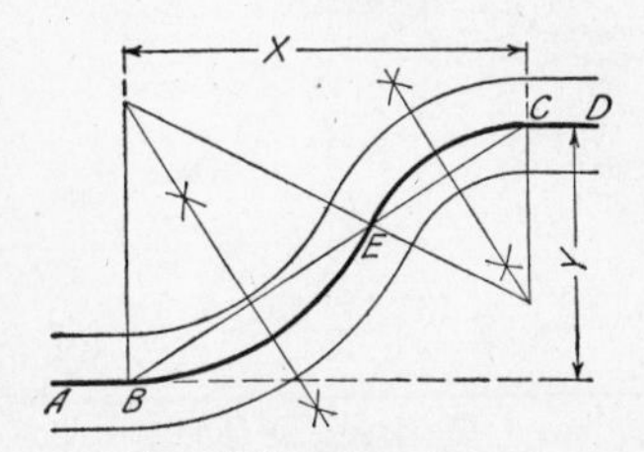

FIG. 136.—Ogee curve.

bisect BE and EC by perpendiculars. Any arc to pass through B and E must have its center somewhere on a perpendicular from the middle point. The intersection therefore of these perpendiculars with the first two perpendiculars will be the centers for arcs BE and EC. This line might be the center line for a curved road or pipe. The construction may be checked by drawing the line of centers, which *must* pass through E.

64. To Lay Off on a Straight Line the Approximate Length of a Circle Arc.—Fig. 137. Given the arc AB. At A draw the tangent

AD and chord BA produced. Lay off AC equal to half the chord AB. With center C and radius CB draw an arc intersecting AD at D, then AD will be equal in length to the arc AB (very nearly).[1] If the given arc is between 45° and 90° a closer approximation will result by making AC equal to the chord of half the arc instead of half the chord of the arc.

The usual way of rectifying an arc is to set the dividers to a space small enough practically to coincide with the arc. Starting at B step along the arc to the point nearest A, and without lifting the dividers step off the same number of spaces on the tangent, as shown in Fig. 138.

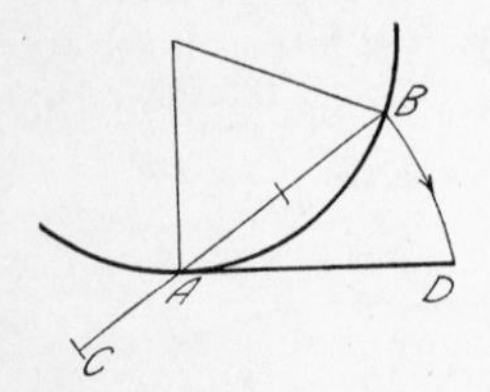

FIG. 137.—Length of arc.

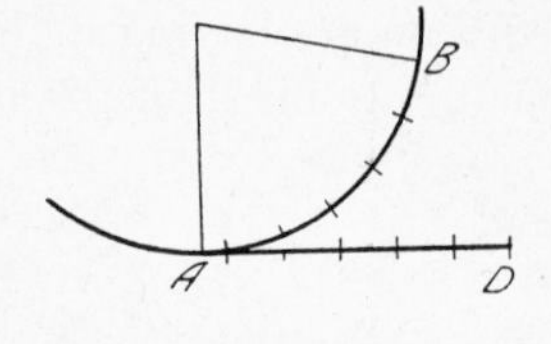

FIG. 138.—Length of arc.

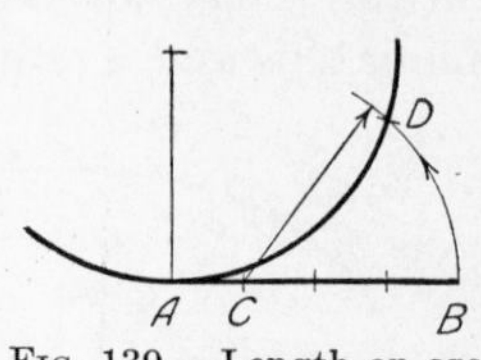

FIG. 139.—Length on arc.

65. To Lay Off on a Given Circle Arc the Approximate Length of a Straight Line.—Fig. 139. Given the line AB, tangent to the circle at A. Lay off AC equal to one-fourth AB. With C as a center and radius CB draw an arc intersecting the circle at D. The arc AD is equal in length to AB (very nearly).[1] If greater than 60° solve for one-half AB.

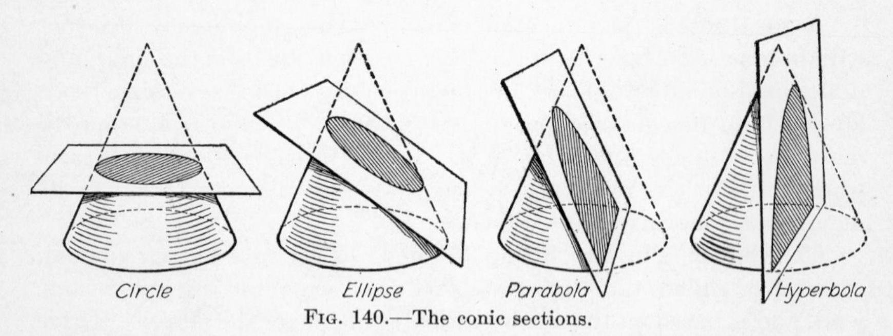

FIG. 140.—The conic sections.

66. Conic Sections.—In cutting a right circular cone by planes at different angles four curves called the *conic sections* are obtained, Fig. 140. These are the *circle*, cut by a plane perpendicular to the axis;

[1] In this (Professor Rankine's) solution, the error varies as the fourth power of the subtended angle. At 60° the line will be 1/900 part short, while at 30° it will be only 1/14,400 part short.

the *ellipse,* cut by a plane making a greater angle with the axis than the elements do; the *parabola,* cut by a plane making the same angle with the axis as the elements do; the *hyperbola,* cut by a plane making a smaller angle than the elements do. These curves are studied mathematically in analytic geometry but may be drawn without a knowledge of their equations by knowing something of their characteristics.

67. The Ellipse.—Fig. 141. An ellipse is a curve generated by a point moving so that the sum of the distances from two fixed points (F_1, F_2), called the foci, is a constant and is equal to the longest diameter, or major axis (AB).

The minor axis or short diameter (DE) is the line through the center perpendicular to the major axis. The foci may be determined by cutting the major axis with an arc having its center at one end of the minor axis and a radius equal to one-half the major axis.

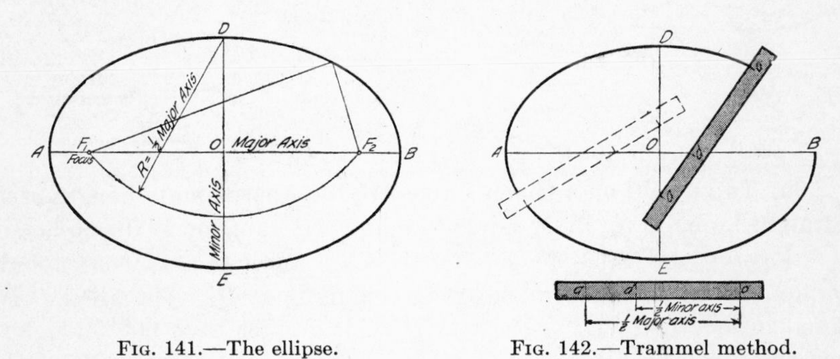

FIG. 141.—The ellipse.

FIG. 142.—Trammel method.

As an ellipse is the projection of a circle viewed obliquely, it is met with in practice oftener than the other conics, aside from the circle, and draftsmen should be able to construct it readily; hence several methods are given for its construction, both as a true ellipse and as an approximate curve made by circle arcs. In the great majority of cases when this curve is required, its long and short diameters, that is, its major and minor axes, are known.

68. Ellipse—Pin and String Method.—This well known method, sometimes called the "gardener's ellipse," is often used for large work and is based on the mathematical principle of the ellipse. Drive pins at the points D, F_1, F_2, Fig. 141, and tie an inelastic thread or cord tightly around the three pins. If the pin D be removed and a marking point moved in the loop, keeping the cord taut, it will describe a true ellipse.

69. Ellipse—Trammel Method.—Fig. 142. On the straight edge of a strip of paper, thin cardboard or sheet of celluloid, mark the distance *ao* equal to one-half the major axis and *do* equal to one-half the minor axis. If the strip be moved keeping *a* on the minor axis and *d* on the major axis, *o* will give points on the ellipse. This method will be found very convenient, as no construction is required, but for accurate results great care should be taken to keep the points *a* and *d* exactly on the axes. The ellipsograph, Fig. 788, is constructed on the principle of this method.

70. Ellipse—Parallelogram Method.—Figs. 143 and 144. This method may be used with either the major and minor axes or with any pair of conjugate diameters. On the diameters construct a parallelogram. Divide *AO* into any number of equal parts and *AG* into the same number of equal parts, numbering the points from *A*. Through these points draw lines from *D* and *E* as shown. Their intersections will be points on the curve.

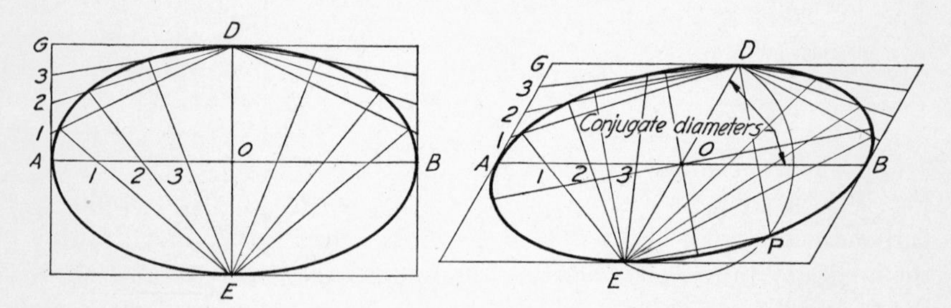

Fig. 143.—Parallelogram method.

Fig. 144.—Parallelogram method.

To Determine the Major and Minor Axes of an Ellipse, the Conjugate Axes Being Given.—Fig. 144. The property of conjugate diameters is that each is parallel to the tangent to the curve at the extremities of the other. At *O* draw a semi-circle with radius *OE*. Connect the point of intersection *P* of this circle and the ellipse with *D* and *E*. The major and minor axes will be parallel to the chords *DP* and *EP*.

71. Ellipse—Concentric Circle Method.—Fig. 145. This is perhaps the most accurate method for determining points on the curve. With *O* as center describe circles on the two diameters. From a number of points on the outer circle as *P* and *Q* draw radii *OP*, *OQ*, etc., intersecting the inner circle at *P′*, *Q′*, etc. From *P* and *Q* draw lines parallel to *OD*, and from *P′* and *Q′* lines parallel to *OB*. The intersection of the lines through *P* and *P′* gives one point on the ellipse, the intersection of the lines through *Q* and *Q′* another point, and so on. For accuracy the points should be taken closer together toward the major axis. The process may be repeated in the four quadrants and the curve sketched in lightly freehand, or one quadrant only may be constructed and the remaining three repeated by marking the French curve.

72. To Draw a Tangent to an Ellipse. 1. *At a Point P on the Curve.*—Fig. 146. Draw lines from the point to the foci. The line bisecting their exterior angle is the required tangent.

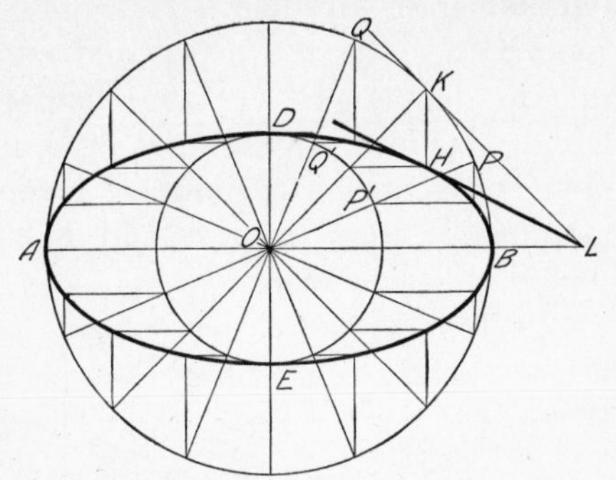

FIG. 145.—Concentric circle method.

2. When the ellipse has been drawn by the concentric circle method, Fig. 145, a tangent at any point H may be drawn by dropping a perpendicular from the point to the outer circle at K and drawing the auxiliary tangent KL cutting the major axis at L. From L draw the required tangent LH.

A Tangent Parallel to a Given Line GH.—Fig. 146. Draw F_1, E perpendicular to GH. With F_2 as center and radius AB draw an arc

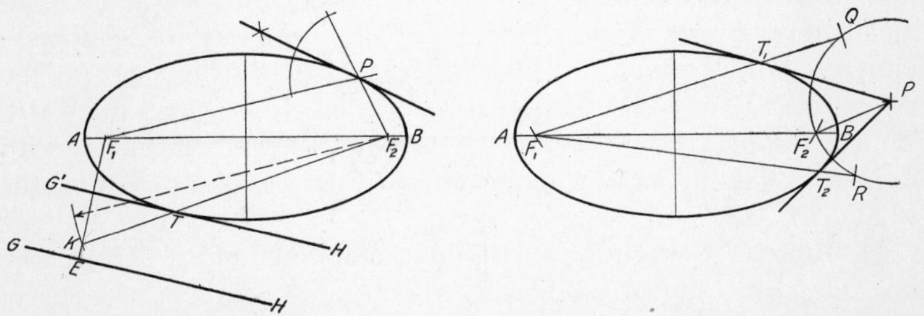

FIG. 146.—Tangents. FIG. 147.—Tangent from point outside.

cutting F_1E at K. The line F_2K cuts the ellipse at the required point of tangency T, through which draw the required tangent parallel to GH.

A Tangent from a Point Outside.—Fig. 147. Find the foci F_1 and F_2. With given point P as center and a radius PF_2 draw an arc RF_2Q. With F_1 as center and a radius AB cut this arc at Q and R.

Connect QF_1 and RF_1. The intersections of these lines with the ellipse at T_1 and T_2 will be the tangent points of tangents to the ellipse from P. (Prove.)

73. Approximate Ellipse with Four Centers.—Fig. 148. Join A and D. Lay off DF equal to AO minus DO. Bisect AF by a perpendicular which will cross AO at G and intersect DE produced (if necessary) at H. Make OG' equal to OG, and OH' equal to OH. Then G, G', H and H' will be centers for four circle arcs approximating the ellipse. Draw arcs G and G' first, then H and H', which may have to be shifted slightly to fit perfectly.

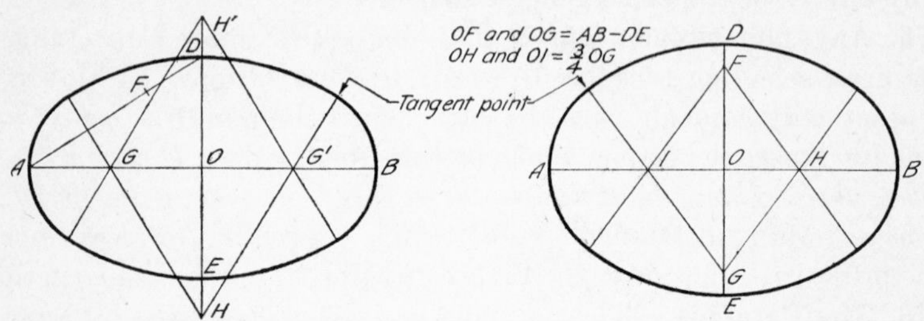

FIG. 148.—Approximate ellipse. FIG. 149.—Approximate ellipse.

Another method is shown in Fig. 149. This should be used only when the minor axis is at least two-thirds the major axis.

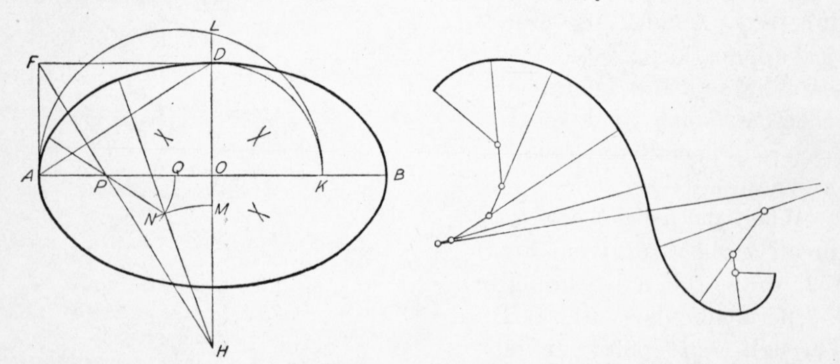

FIG. 150.—Approximate ellipse. FIG. 151.—Curve made with circle arcs.

74. Approximate Ellipse with Eight Centers.—Fig. 150. When a closer approximation is desired, the eight-centered ellipse, known in masonry as the "five-centered arch," may be constructed. Draw the rectangle $AFDO$. Draw the diagonal AD and draw from F a line perpendicular to it intersecting the extension of the minor axis at H. Lay off OK equal to OD and on AK as a diameter draw a semi-circle intersecting the extension of the minor axis at L. Make OM equal LD. With center H and radius HM draw the arc MN.

With A as center and radius OL intersect AB at Q. With P as center and radius PQ intersect the arc MN at N; then P, N and H are centers for one-half of the semi-ellipse of "five-centered oval." This method is based on the principle that the radius of curvature at the end of the minor axis is the third proportional to the semi-minor and semi-major axes, and similarly at the end of the major axis is the third proportional to the semi-major and semi-minor axes. The intermediate radius found is the mean proportional between these two radii.

It should be noted that an ellipse is changing its radius of curvature at every point, and that these approximations are not ellipses but simply curves of the same general shape.

75. Any non-circular curve may be approximated by tangent circle arcs, selecting a center by trial, drawing as much of an arc as will practically coincide with the curve, then changing the center and radius for the next portion, remembering always that, *if arcs are to be tangent, their centers must lie on the common normal at the point of tangency.* Many draftsmen prefer to ink curves in this way rather than to use irregular curves. Figure 151 illustrates the construction.

76. The Parabola.—The parabola is a curve generated by a point so moving that its distance from a fixed point, called the focus, is always equal to its distance from a straight line, called the directrix. Among its practical applications are included searchlights and parabolic reflectors, some loud speakers, road sections, certain bridge arches, etc.

When the focus F and the directrix AB are given, Fig. 152, draw the axis through F perpendicular to AB. Through any point D on the axis draw a line parallel to AB. With the distance DO as a radius and F as a center draw an arc intersecting the line, thus locating a point P on the curve. Repeat the operation with as many lines as needed.

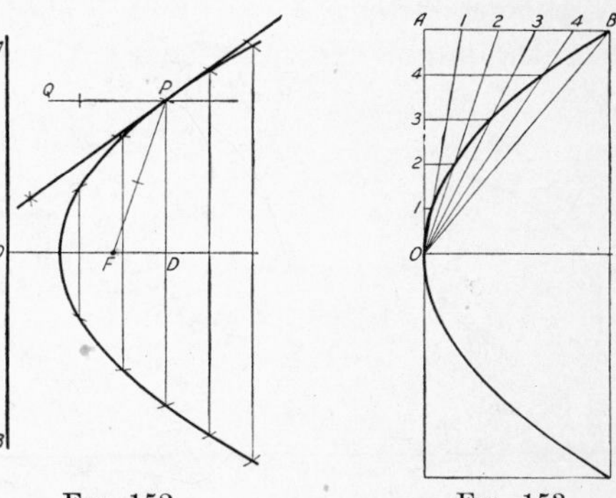

FIG. 152. FIG. 153.
Methods of drawing the parabola.

To Draw a Tangent at Any Point P.—Draw PQ parallel to the axis and bisect the angle FPQ.

77. Parabola—Parallelogram Method.—Usually when a parabola is required, the enclosing rectangle, that is, its width and depth (or span and rise), is given, as in Fig. 153. Divide OA and AB into the same number of equal parts. From the divisions on AB draw lines converging at O. The intersections of these with the corresponding lines from the divisions on OA drawn parallel to the axis will be points on the curve.

78. Parabola—Offset Method.—Given the enclosing rectangle, the parabola (Fig. 154) may be plotted by computing the offsets from the line OA. These offsets vary as the square of their distances from O. Thus, if OA be divided into four parts, DD' will be one-sixteenth of AA'; CC' (since it is twice as far from O as DD' is) will be four-sixteenths of AA', and BB' nine-sixteenths. If OA were divided into five parts the relations would be $\frac{1}{25}$, $\frac{4}{25}$, $\frac{9}{25}$, $\frac{16}{25}$, the denominator being in each case the square of the number of divisions. This method is the one generally used by civil engineers in drawing parabolic arches.

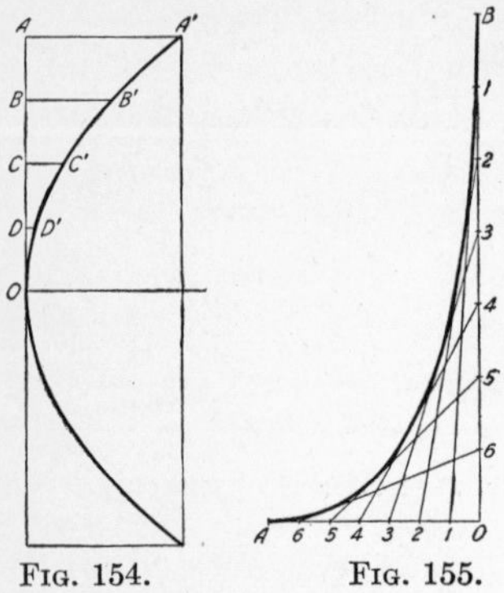

Fig. 154. Fig. 155.
Methods of drawing the parabola.

79. Parabolic Envelope.—Fig. 155. This method of drawing a pleasing curve is often used in machine design. Divide OA and OB into the same number of equal parts, numbering from O and B. Connect corresponding numbers. The tangent curve will be a portion of a parabola although its axis is not parallel to either ordinate.

80. Hyperbola.—The hyperbola is a curve generated by a point moving so that the difference of its distances from two fixed points, called the foci, is a constant. (Compare this definition with that of the ellipse.)

To draw a hyperbola when the foci F_1F_2 and the transverse axis AB (constant difference) are given, Fig. 156. With F_1 and F_2 as centers, and any radius greater than F_1B draw arcs, as F_1P. With the same centers and radius F_1P minus AB intersect these arcs, giving points on the curve. To draw a tangent as at P, bisect the angle F_1PF_2.

81. Equilateral Hyperbola.—The common case of the hyperbola of practical interest to the engineer is the equilateral or rectangular hyperbola on its asymptotes, as representing the relation between the pressure and volume of steam or gas expanding under the law $pv = c$.

To Draw the Equilateral Hyperbola.—Fig. 157. Let OA and OB be the asymptotes and P any point on the curve (this might be the point of cutoff on an indicator diagram). Draw PC and PD. Mark any points 1, 2, 3, 4 on PC, through these points draw lines parallel to

OA and through the same points lines to O. From the intersection of these lines with PD draw perpendiculars. The intersections of these perpendiculars with the corresponding horizontal lines give points on the curve.

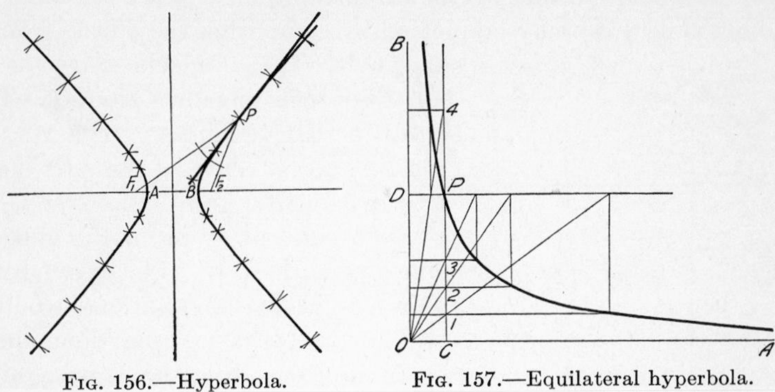

Fig. 156.—Hyperbola.

Fig. 157.—Equilateral hyperbola.

82. Cycloidal Curves.—A cycloid is the curve generated by the motion of a point on the circumference of a circle rolled along a straight line. If the circle be rolled on the outside of another circle the curve is called an epicycloid; when rolled inside it is called a hypocycloid. These curves are used in drawing one system of gear teeth.

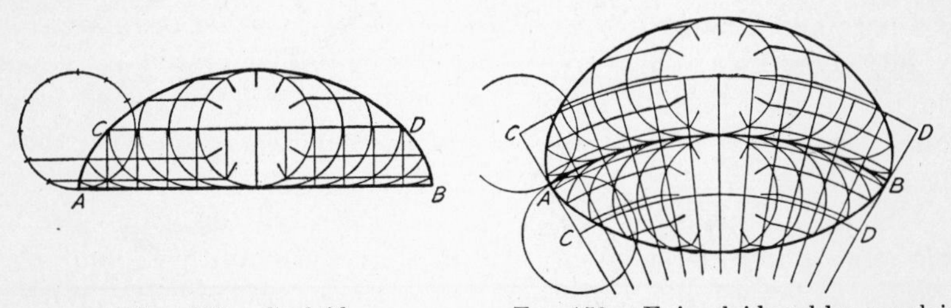

Fig. 158.—Cycloid.

Fig. 159.—Epicycloid and hypocycloid.

To Draw a Cycloid.—Fig. 158. Divide the rolling circle into a convenient number of parts (say 12), lay off the rectified length of the circumference, with these divisions, on the tangent AB. Draw through C the line of the centers CD and project the division points up to this line by perpendiculars. On these points as centers draw circles representing different positions of the rolling circle, and project across on these circles in order the division points of the original circle. These intersections will be points on the curve. The epicycloid and hypocycloid may be drawn similarly as illustrated in Fig. 159.

83. The Involute.—An involute is the spiral curve traced by a point on a cord unwinding from around a polygon or circle. Thus the involute of any polygon may be drawn by extending its sides, as in Fig. 160, and with the corners of the polygon as successive centers drawing arcs terminating on the extended sides.

In drawing a spiral in design, as, for example, in bent iron work, the easiest way is to draw the involute of a square. See Fig. 56.

A circle may be conceived as a polygon of an infinite number of sides. Thus to draw the involute of a circle, Fig. 161, divide it into a convenient number of parts, draw tangents at these points, lay off on these tangents the rectified lengths of the arcs from the point of tangency to the starting point and connect the points by a smooth curve. It is evident that the involute of a circle is the limiting case of the epicycloid, the rolling circle becoming of infinite diameter. It is the basis for the involute system of gearing.

84. The Spiral of Archimedes is a curve generated by a point moving out uniformly along a straight line while the line revolves in a plane with uniform angular velocity.

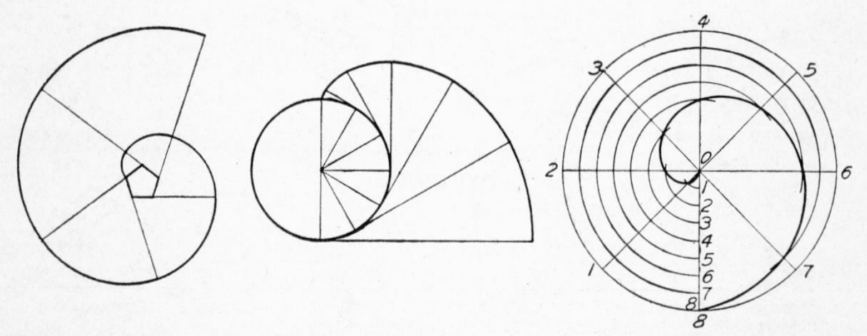

Fig. 160.—Involute of a pentagon. Fig. 161.—Involute of a circle. Fig. 162.—Spiral of Archimedes.

To draw a spiral of Archimedes making one turn in a given circle, Fig. 162, divide the circumference into a number of equal parts, drawing the radii and numbering them. Divide the radius *O*-8 into the same number of equal parts, numbering from the center. With *O* as a center draw concentric arcs intersecting the radii of corresponding numbers, and draw a smooth curve through these intersections. This is the curve of the heart cam, for converting uniform rotary motion into uniform reciprocal motion.

PROBLEMS

85. To be of value, both as drawing exercises and as solutions, geometrical problems should be worked very accurately. The pencil

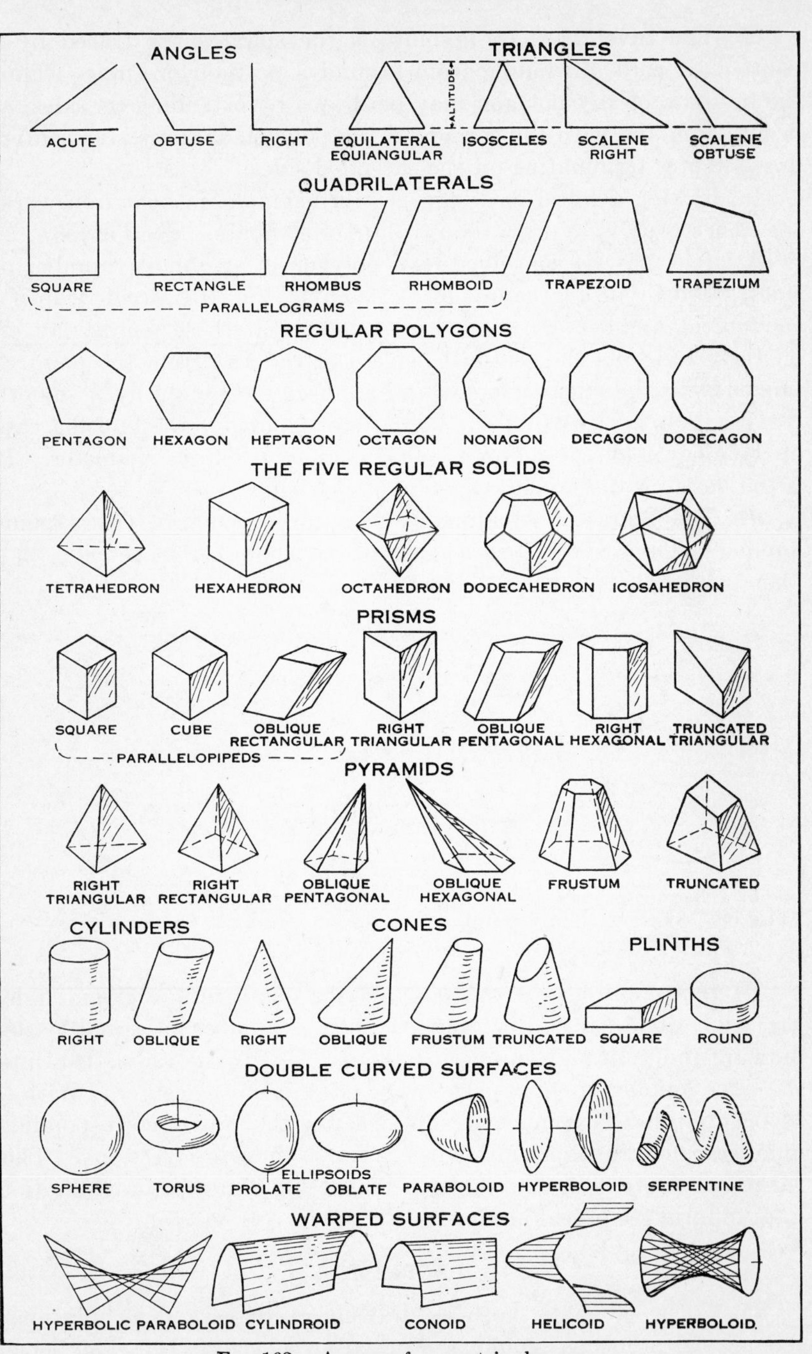

Fig. 163.—A page of geometric shapes.

must be kept very sharp, and comparatively light lines used. A point should be located by two intersecting lines and the length of a line by short dashes crossing the given line.

The following problems (except 15 and 16) are dimensioned to fit a space not over 5″ × 7″.

1. Near the center of the space draw a horizontal line 4½″ long. Divide it into seven equal parts by the method of Fig. 114.

2. Draw a vertical line 1″ from left edge of space and 3⅞″ long. Divide it into parts proportional to 1, 3, 5 and 7.

3. Construct a polygon as shown in Fig. 164, drawing the line *AK* of indefinite length ⅝″ above bottom of space. From *A* draw and measure *AB*. Proceed in the same way for the remaining sides. The angles may all be obtained by proper combinations of the two triangles.

4. Draw line *AK* making an angle of 15° with the horizontal. With this line as a base transfer the polygon of Fig. 164.

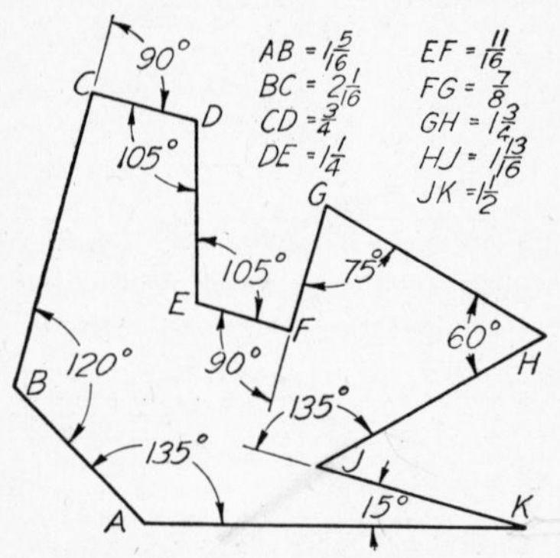

FIG. 164.—Prob. 3.

5. Draw a regular hexagon having a distance across corners of 4″.

6. Draw a regular hexagon, short diameter 3⅜″.

7. Draw a regular dodecagon, short diameter 3⅜″.

8. Construct an ogee curve joining two parallel lines *AB* and *CD* as in Fig. 136, making $X = 4''$, $Y = 2\frac{1}{2}''$ and $BE = 3''$. Consider this as the center line for a rod 1¼″ diameter and draw the rod.

9. Lay out lines *AB*, *CD* and *EF* as in Fig. 165. Draw ogee curves joining *BC*, *DE*, *BG* and *EH*.

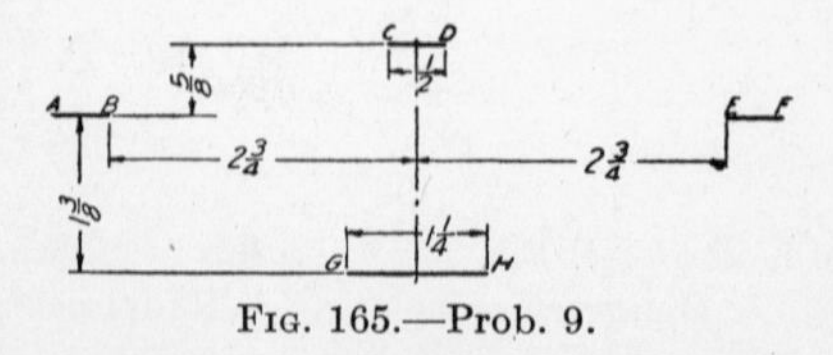

FIG. 165.—Prob. 9.

10. Draw an arc of a circle having a radius of 3 13/16″, with its center ½″ from top of space and 1½″ from left edge. Find the length of an arc of 60° by construction, and compute the length arithmetically and check the result.

Tangent Problems

These problems are given for practice in the accurate joining of tangent lines. Read carefully paragraphs 56 to 63 before beginning. Locate centers for all circle arcs geometrically. If inked, ink outlines and center lines only.

11. A *gasket*, Fig. 166. Outside diameter 4″. Inside diameter 2¾″. Two ¾″ holes, 5″ center to center. Ears ¾″ radius, 1″ fillets. Mark tangent points in pencil, as in Fig. 134.

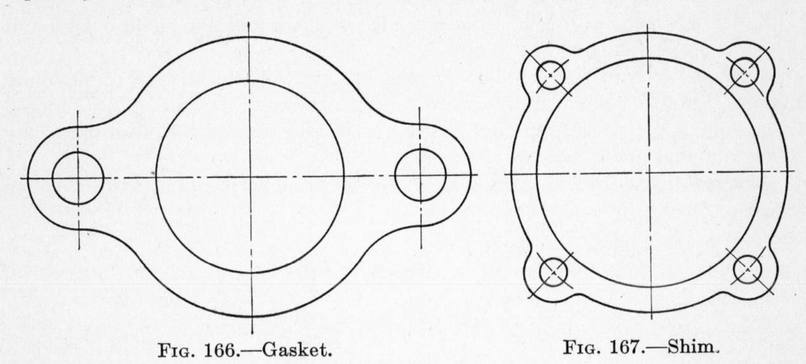

FIG. 166.—Gasket.

FIG. 167.—Shim.

12. A *shim*, Fig. 167. Outside diameter 4″. Inside diameter 3⁵⁄₃₂″. Holes 1³⁄₃₂″. Ears ⁷⁄₁₆″ radius, ³⁄₁₆″ fillets. Draw center lines and on them measure and mark radii for given diameters. Mark all tangent points in pencil, as in Fig. 134.

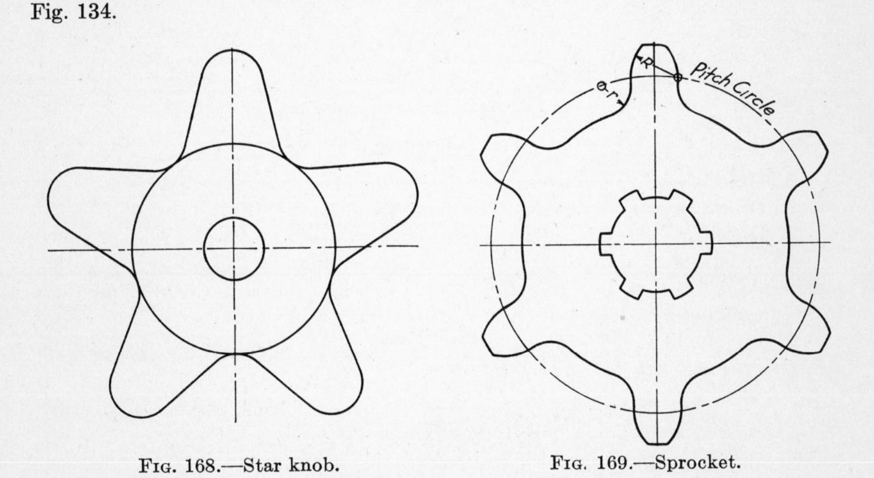

FIG. 168.—Star knob.

FIG. 169.—Sprocket.

13. Front view of a *star knob*, Fig. 168. Radius of circumscribing circle 2⅜″. Diameter of hub 2½″. Diameter of hole ¾″. Radius at points ⅜″. Radius of fillets ⅜″. Mark tangent points in pencil.

14. Front view of a *sprocket*, Fig. 169. Outside diameter 4¾″; pitch diameter 4″; root diameter 3¼″; bore 1¼″. Thickness of tooth at pitch line ⁹⁄₁₆″. Splines ¼″ wide by ⅛″ deep. Mark tangent points in pencil.

15. Front view of a *fan*, Fig. 170. Draw full size to dimensions given.

16. Front view of a *fan guard*, Fig. 171. Draw full size to dimensions given.

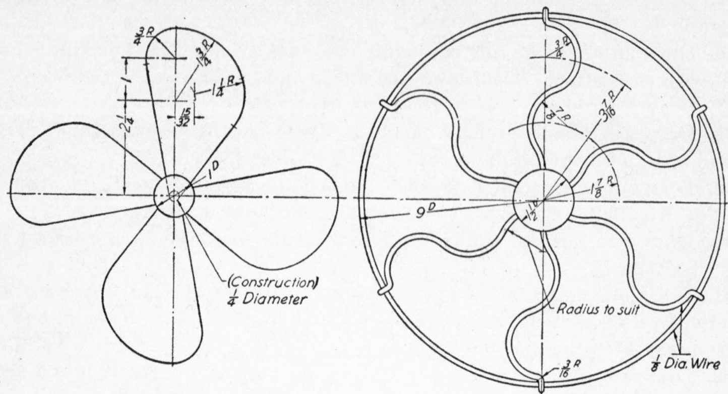

Fig. 170.—Fan.

Fig. 171.—Fan guard.

17. Combine Probs. 15 and 16 putting the guard in front of the fan.

18. Front view of a *cam*, Fig. 172.

19. Front view of a drawn metal *fan base*, Fig. 173. The curve profile is a parabolic envelope. Refer to paragraph 79.

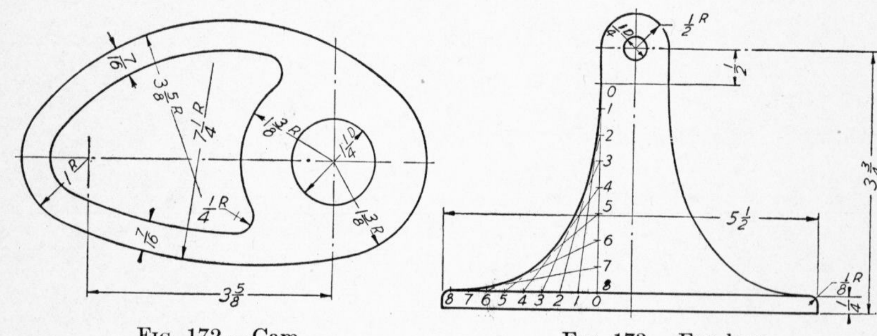

Fig. 172.—Cam.

Fig. 173.—Fan base.

Curve Problems

In locating a curve the number of points to be determined will depend upon the size of the curve and the rate of change of curvature. More points should be found on the sharp turns. For most of the following problems, points may average about one-fourth of an inch apart.

20. Draw an ellipse having a major axis of 4½″ and minor axis of 3″, using the trammel method as explained in paragraph 69.

21. Draw an ellipse having a major axis of 4⅝″ and a minor axis of 1½″, using the concentric circle method as explained in paragraph 71.

22. Draw an ellipse on a major axis of 4″. One point on the ellipse is 1½″ to the left of the minor axis and ⅞″ above the major axis.

23. Draw an ellipse whose minor axis is 2³⁄₁₆″ and the distance between foci 3¼″. Draw a tangent at a point 1⅜″ to the right of the minor axis.

24. Draw an ellipse, major axis 4″. A tangent to the ellipse intersects the minor axis $1\frac{3}{4}''$ from the center, at an angle of 60°.

25. Draw a five-centered arch with a span of 5″ and a rise of 2″. Refer to paragraph 74.

26. Draw an ellipse having conjugate axes of $4\frac{3}{4}''$ and $2\frac{3}{4}''$, making an angle of 75° with each other. Determine the major and minor axes.

27. Draw a parabola, axis vertical, in a rectangle $4'' \times 2''$.

28. Draw a parabolic arch, 6″ span, $2\frac{1}{2}''$ rise, by the offset method, dividing the half span into eight equal parts.

29. Draw an equilateral hyperbola passing through a point P, $\frac{1}{2}''$ from OB and $2\frac{1}{2}''$ from OA, reference letters corresponding to Fig. 157.

30. Draw two turns of the involute of a pentagon whose circumscribed circle is $\frac{1}{2}''$ diameter.

31. Draw one-half turn of the involute of a circle $3\frac{1}{4}''$ in diameter, whose center is 1″ from the left edge of space. Compute the length of the last tangent and compare with the measured length.

32. Draw a spiral of Archimedes making one turn in a circle 4″ in diameter.

CHAPTER VI

THE THEORY OF PROJECTION DRAWING

86. The previous chapters have been preparatory to the real subject of engineering drawing as a language. In Chapter I there was pointed out the difference between the representation of an object by the artist to convey certain impressions or emotions and the representation by the engineer to convey information. The full information required by the engineer includes the description of the *shape* of the object and the specification of the *size* of every detail in it. In this chapter we are concerned with the different methods of describing the *shape*.

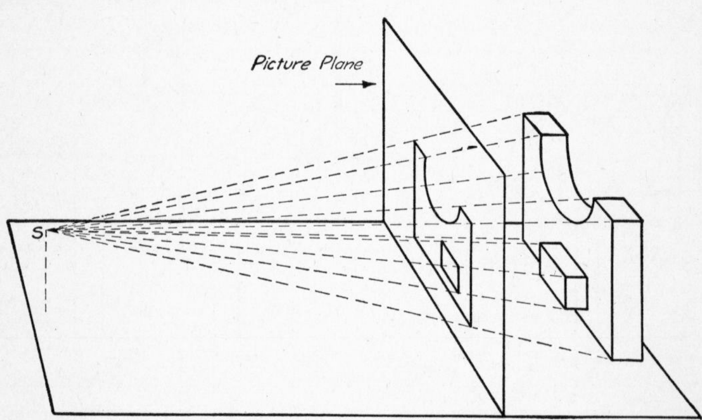

Fig. 174.—Perspective projection.

If an ordinary object be looked at from some particular station point one may usually get a good idea of its shape because (1) generally more than one side is seen, (2) the light and shadow on it tell something of its configuration, (3) looked at with both eyes there is a stereoscopic effect which aids in judging shapes and dimensions. In technical drawing the third point is never considered, but the object is drawn as if seen with one eye; and only in special cases is the effect of light and shadow rendered. In general we have to do with outline alone.

If a transparent plane be imagined as set up between an object and the station point *S* of an observer's eye, Fig. 174, the intersection with this plane of the cone of rays formed by lines from the eye to all points of the object will give a picture of the object which will be practically the same as the picture formed on the retina of the eye by the intersection of the other end (nappe) of the cone. Drawing made on this principle is known as *perspective drawing* and is the basis of all artists' work. In a technical way it is used chiefly by architects in making preliminary sketches for their own use in studying problems in design, and for showing their clients the finished appearance of a proposed building. It is entirely unsuited for working drawings as it shows the object as it appears and not as it really is.

If the observer be imagined as walking backward from the station point S until he reaches a theoretically infinite distance, the cone of rays formed by the projecting lines from his eye to the object will grow longer until it finally becomes a cylinder, with the visual rays all parallel to each other and perpendicular to the picture plane, and

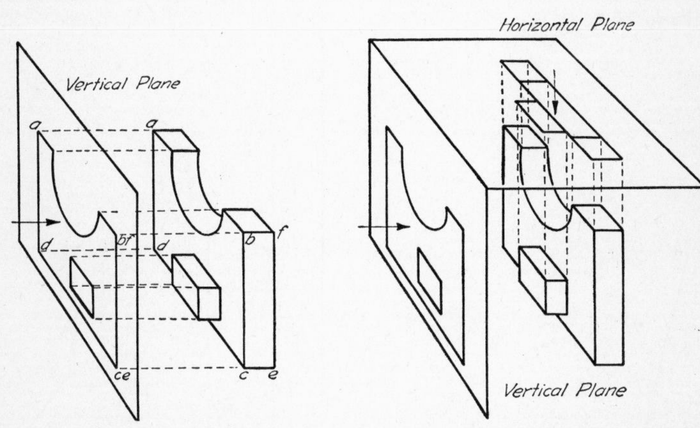

Fig. 175.—Orthographic projection. Fig. 176.—The planes of projection.

the picture becomes what is known as an *orthographic projection.* If now all of the cylinder from the picture plane to infinity be discarded, the picture can be thought of as being found by extending perpendiculars to the plane from all points of the object, Fig. 175. This picture, or projection, will evidently have the same width and height as the object itself, but it will not tell the thickness; hence more than one projection will be required to describe the object. In orthographic projection the picture planes are called *planes of projection* and the perpendiculars *projecting lines* or *projectors.*

If another transparent plane be imagined as placed horizontally above the object, as in Fig. 176, the projection on this plane, found by extending perpendiculars to it from the object, will give the appearance of the object as if viewed from directly above it and will show exactly the length and thickness. These two planes represent the paper, and if the horizontal plane be revolved as in Fig. 177 the two views will be shown in their correct relationship and together will give the three dimensions of the object. A third plane may be imagined, perpendicular to the first two, on which a third view may be projected, as described in the next chapter.

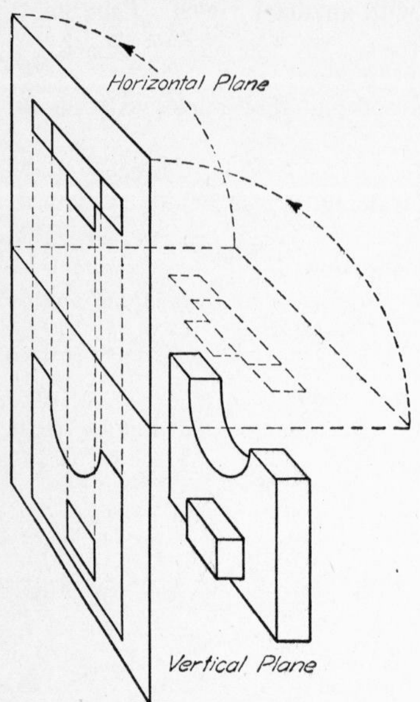

FIG. 177.—The horizontal plane revolved.

In looking at these theoretical projections, or "views," the observer should not think of them as flat but should imagine himself as looking *through* the transparent planes at the object itself.

87. One-plane Methods.—If the object, instead of being placed in its natural position parallel to the plane of projection, be imagined as turned at an angle, then tilted forward so that three of its faces would be seen, a special kind of orthographic projection known as *axonometric projection* would result. It has three subdivisions, isometric, dimetric and trimetric, all explained in Chapter XIV.

Another division in the classification of methods of projection is that the *oblique projection* in which the object is imagined as placed parallel to the plane of projection and projected to it by a system of parallel projecting lines making an angle other than 90° with the plane.

Axonometric and oblique projection are classified, along with perspective, as one-plane pictorial methods, distinguishing them from the usual orthographic projection, in which at least two planes are required to show the three dimensions of the object.

The different systems of projection are classified in tabular form on the following page, with page references to the text.

Map projection, covering the numerous and interesting methods of representing the curved surface of the earth on a plane, is not included in this table.

PROJECTION DRAWING

Orthographic Projection Projectors perpendicular to planes of projection	**Multiplanar** (Two or more planes)	**Two-view drawings** **Three-view drawings** **Drawings with auxiliary views.** *Page* 86
	Axonometric (One plane)	**Isometric projection** Three axes making equal angles with plane. *Page* 289 **Isometric drawing.** *Page* 290 **Dimetric projection** Two of the three axes making equal angles with plane. *Page* 296 **Trimetric projection** Three axes making unequal angles with plane. *Page* 296
Oblique Projection Projectors oblique to planes of projection	(One plane)	**Cavalier projection** Two axes parallel to plane, projectors making an angle of 45° with it, in any direction. *Page* 296 **Cabinet projection** Two axes parallel to plane, projectors making an angle 26° 35′ approximately. *Page* 300 **Various oblique positions.** *Page* 301 **Clinographic projection** Object turned at an angle whose tangent is ⅓. Projectors at an angle whose tangent is ⅙. *Page* 301
Perspective Projection Projectors converging to a fixed point	(One plane)	**Parallel perspective** Object with one face parallel to plane. *Page* 323 **Angular perspective** Two faces of object inclined to plane. *Page* 321 **Oblique perspective** Three faces of object inclined. (*Rarely used*)

CHAPTER VII

ORTHOGRAPHIC PROJECTION

88. The problem in engineering drawing is to reproduce the exact shape of an object with its three dimensions, length, breadth and thickness, on the surface of a sheet of paper which has only two dimensions. To do this the system of orthographic projection has been devised. Practically, this means that the drawing is made up of a set of separate views looking at the object from different positions and arranged in a definite way, each view showing two of the three dimensions. Illustrating with the block shown in Fig. 178, if the

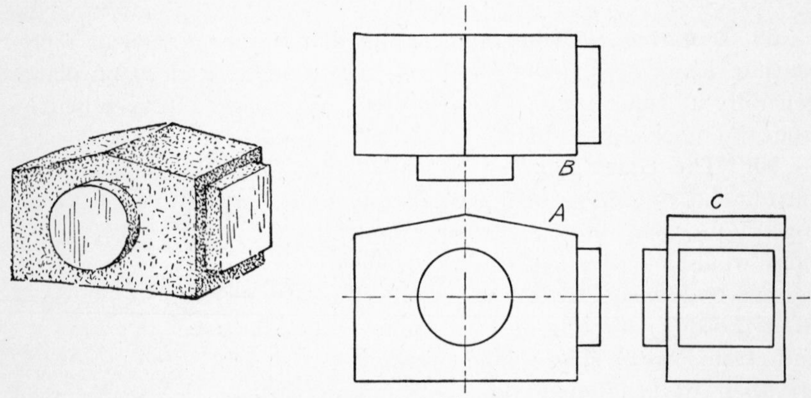

Fig. 178.—A block and its three views.

observer imagine himself as in a position directly in front (theoretically at an infinite distance, practically at a reasonable seeing distance but assuming the rays of light from each point to his eye as parallel) the front view would appear as at *A*. This view tells the length and height but not the width of the block nor what the circle represents. Then let the observer change his position so as to look down from directly above the block. He will see the top view as at *B*, giving the length and width, and showing that the circle of the front view is a projecting boss. It is necessary to have another view in this case to show the shape of the extension on the side. *C* is the right side view. These three views arranged in their natural position with the top view directly above the front view, and the side view in line with the front view, completely describe the shape of the block. *Note that in the top and side views the front of the block always faces toward the front view.*

The theory upon which this is based has been outlined in paragraph 86, and on it the following definition may be given:

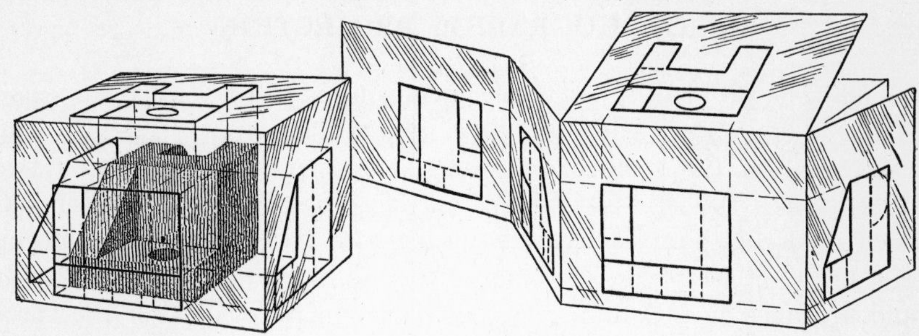

FIG. 179.—The transparent box. FIG. 180.—The box as it opens.

89. Definition.—**Orthographic projection** is the method of representing the exact shape of an object in two or more views on planes generally at right angles to each other, by dropping perpendiculars from the object to the planes.

90. "The Glass Box."—The object may thus be thought of as surrounded by a box with transparent sides hinged to each other, Fig. 179. The projections on these sides would be practically what would be seen by looking straight at the object from positions directly in front, above and from both sides. These planes are then to be thought of as opening up, as illustrated in Fig. 180, into one plane. The projection on the front plane is known as the *front view, vertical projection* or *front elevation;* that on the horizontal plane the *top view, horizontal projection* or *plan;* that on the side or "profile" plane the *side view* or *end view, profile projection, side* or *end elevation.* Figure 181 shows the relative positions of the *front, top* and *right side* views, which taken together completely describe the shape of the block. Sometimes the left side view describes an object more clearly than the right side would do. Figure 182 shows the top, front and left side views. Note again that in the side views the object is facing the front view, and

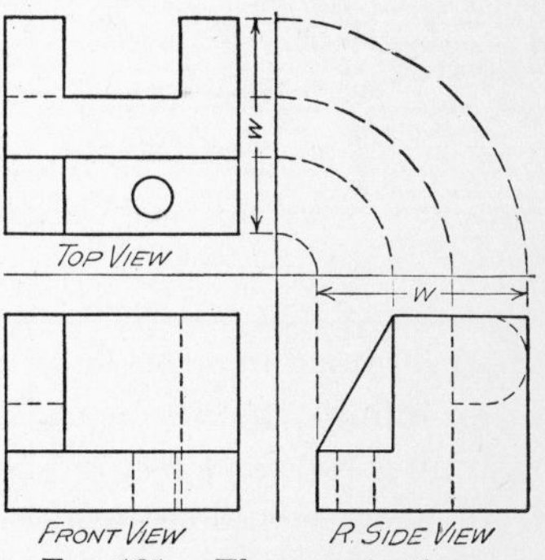

FIG. 181.—Three projections.

that thus the side view of any point will be the same distance horizontally from the front edge as its top view is back from the front edge. (The lines of intersection of the reference planes are shown in Figs. 181 and 182 to aid the beginner in seeing the relationship of the three views. In actual work these lines are never drawn.)

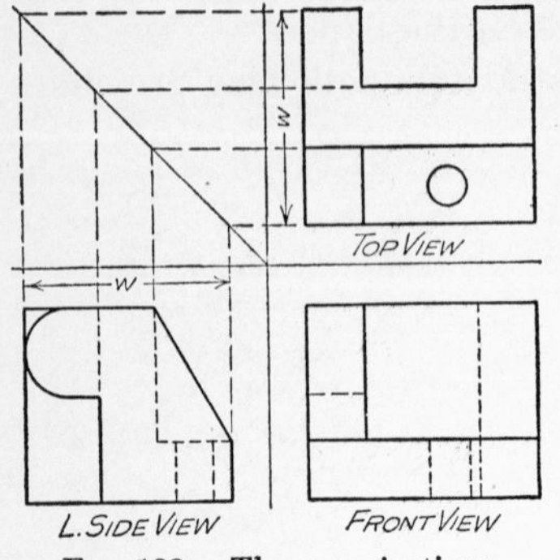

Fig. 182.—Three projections.

In comparatively rare cases a bottom view or a rear view may be required to show some detail of shape or construction. Figure 183 shows the arrangement of these views. The plane of the rear view is hinged to that of the left side view, giving it

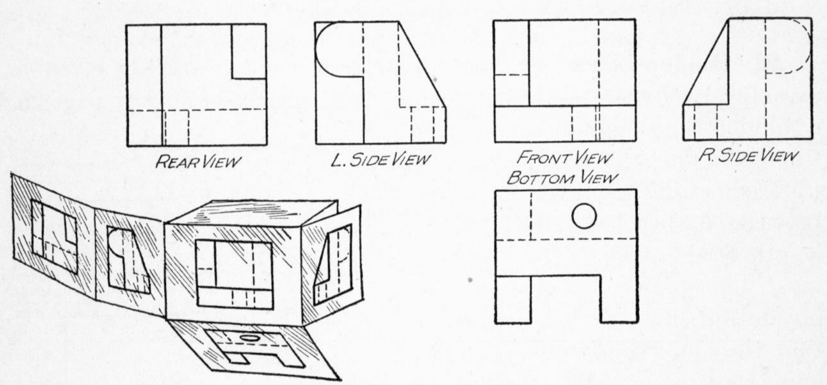

Fig. 183.—Positions of bottom view and rear view.

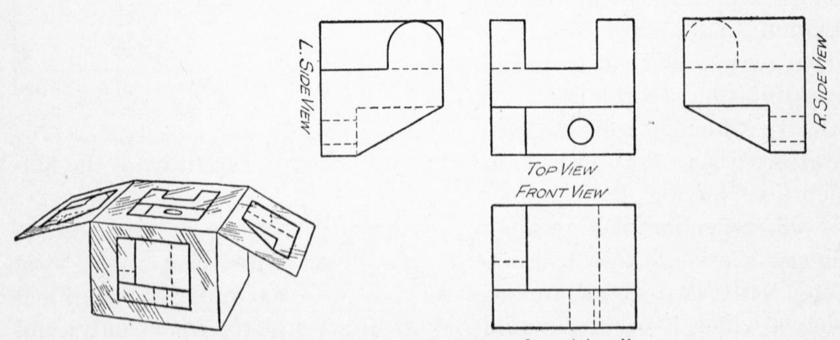

Fig. 184.—Side views in "second position."

the position recommended by the American Standards Association. Compare Figs. 183 and 181.

The ends of the box may be conceived as hinged to the top instead of the front plane, as in Fig. 184, thus placing the side views across from the top view. This arrangement is of occasional use in drawing a broad flat object, in order to save space on the paper.

91. Principles.—From the foregoing study the following principles will be noted:

1. The top view is directly over the front view.
2. The side views are in line horizontally with the front view.
3. The widths of the side views are exactly the same as the width of the top view.
4. A surface parallel to a plane of projection is shown in its true size.
5. A surface perpendicular to a plane of projection is projected as a line.
6. A surface inclined to a plane of projection is foreshortened.

Similarly,

7. A line parallel to a plane of projection will show in its true length.
8. A line perpendicular to a plane of projection will be projected as a point.
9. An inclined line will have a projection shorter than its true length.

92. Hidden Lines.—A drawing must give the location of invisible as well as visible edges. As shown in the alphabet of lines on page 26, a hidden line is indicated by a "dotted" line, that is, a line made up of short dashes, with the space between dashes less than half the length of the dash. The beginner must pay particular attention to his dotted lines, as it is important that they start and stop correctly, and that they are uniform in lengths of dashes and spaces. A hidden line always starts with a dash except when it would form a continuation of a full line. Dashes always touch at corners. An arc starts with a dash at the tangent point. Study carefully all the hidden lines on Fig. 185.

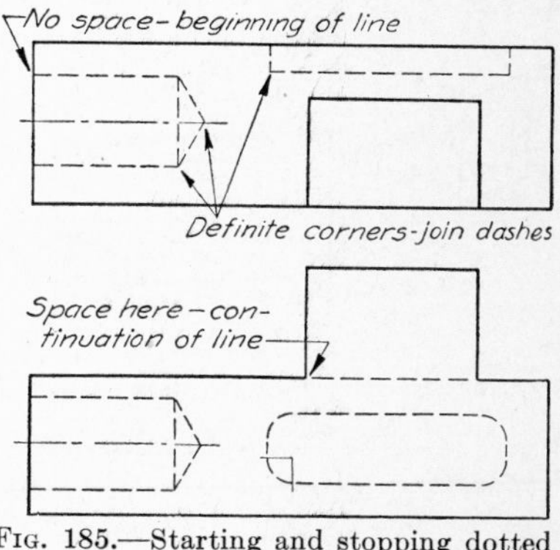

Fig. 185.—Starting and stopping dotted lines.

93. Selection of Views.—In practical work it is very important to choose the views that will describe the object in the best way. Very often only two views are necessary, as, for example, a cylindrical shape, which if vertical would require front and top views only; and if horizontal, front and side views only. On the other hand, some complicated pieces will need more than the three regular views. In general, a view is needed in each direction in which the edge shows a characteristic shape of any part of the object. Study the objects in Fig. 186 and determine why the views were so chosen.

94. Drawing in Orthographic Projection.—In beginning the study of projections it is best to draw freehand the three views of a number of simple pieces (even if three views are not always needed), developing the ability to "write" the language, and exercising the constructive imagination in seeing the object itself by reading the three projections.

As a general rule the view showing the characteristic contour or shape of a piece should be started first. Space the views so as to give a well-balanced appearance and carry them along together, projecting

Fig. 186.—Projection studies.

from one to another. Figure 182 shows a method, sometimes convenient, for obtaining the widths, or depths, of the side view by "mitering" on a 45° line from the top view.

Review the objects shown in Fig. 186, noting the application of the principles of paragraph 91. The pictures of objects in Fig. 187 should then be translated into orthographic projection by sketching their three views. Similar practice may be had by sketching the projections of any simple models or pieces with geometrical outlines, such as those of Fig. 536. Later this process should be reversed and reading practiced by making pictorial sketches from orthographic projections.

95. Reading a Drawing.—A line on a drawing always indicates either an intersection of two surfaces, as in the projection of a prism, or a contour, as in the projection of a cylinder. One cannot read a drawing by looking at one view. Each line on a view means a change

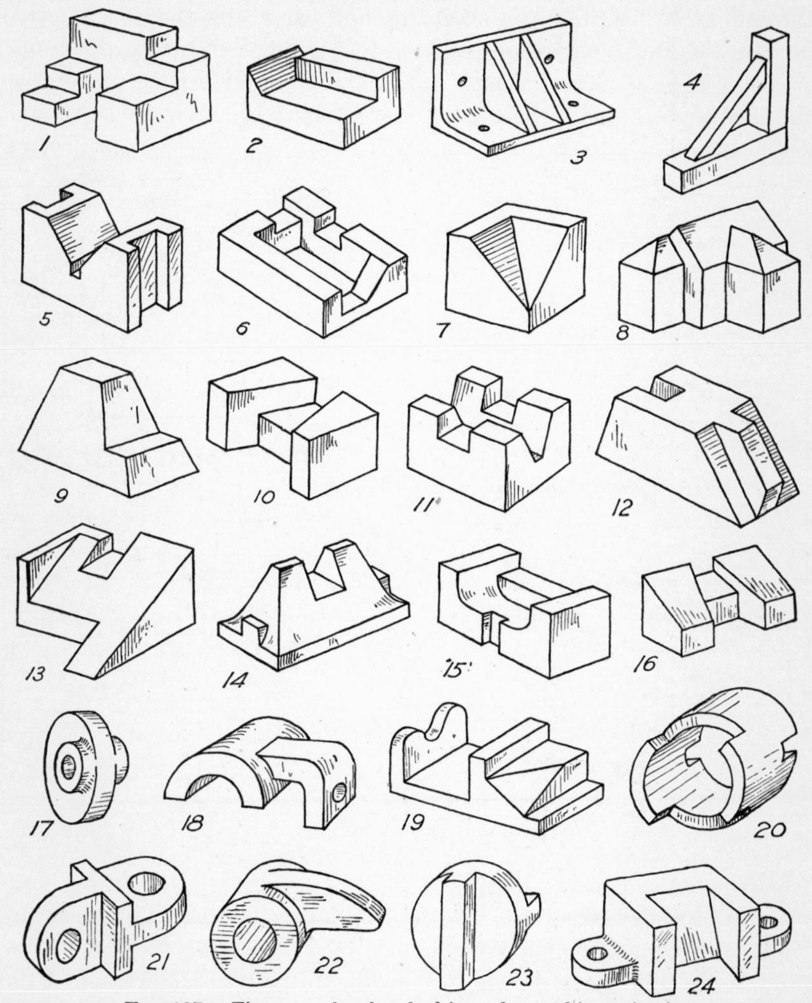

Fig. 187.—Figures to be sketched in orthographic projection.

in the direction of a surface, but the corresponding part of another view must be consulted to tell what the change is. For example, a circle on a front view, as in Fig. 178, may mean either a hole or a projecting boss. A glance at the side view or top view will show at once which it is. In reading a drawing one should first gain a general idea of the shape of the object by a rapid survey of all the views given, then should select for more careful study the view that best shows the characteristic shape, and by referring back and forth to the adjacent views see what each line represents. *In looking at any view one should always imagine that it is the object itself, not a flat projection of it, that is seen,* and in glancing from one view to another the reader should imagine himself as moving around the actual object and looking at it from the direction the view was taken.

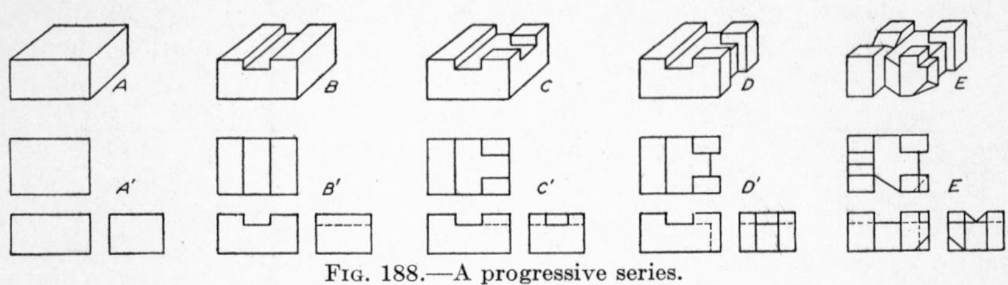

Fig. 188.—A progressive series.

Figure 188 shows successive cuts made in a block and the corresponding projections of the block in the different stages. The effort should be made to visualize the object from these projections until the projection can be read as easily as the picture. A drawing as simple as A' or B' can be read and the mental picture formed at a glance; one with more lines, as E', will require a little time for study and comparison of the different views. One cannot expect to read a

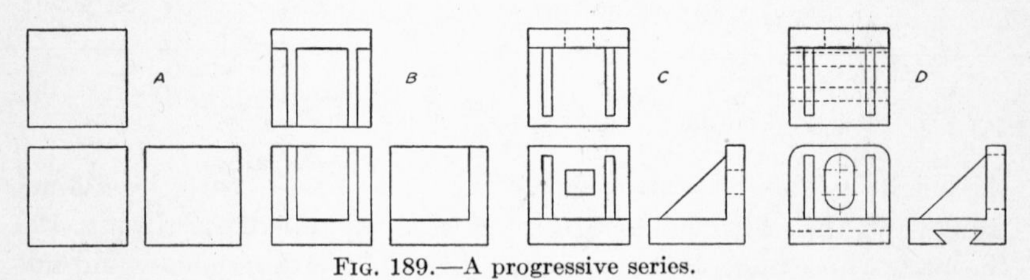

Fig. 189.—A progressive series.

whole drawing at once any more than he would think of reading a whole page of print at a glance. Figure 189 is another progressive series to be studied.

96. Auxiliary Views.—A surface is shown in its true shape when projected on a plane parallel to it. In the majority of cases the object may be placed with its principal faces parallel to the three reference planes and be fully described by the regular views. Sometimes however, the object may have one or more inclined faces whose true shape it is desirable or necessary to show, especially if irregular in outline. This is done by making an *auxiliary* view looking straight against the surface, that is, imagining a projection on an extra or auxiliary plane parallel to the inclined surface, and revolving it into the plane of the paper.

97. There are three kinds of auxiliary views: first, **auxiliary elevations,** made on planes which are perpendicular to the horizontal plane, or, in other words, the kind of views that would be seen if one walked in a horizontal circle around the object, starting to the right from the position at which the front view is seen. The front view, or front elevation, shows the height of the object. In an auxiliary elevation the observer is looking in a horizontal direction; hence

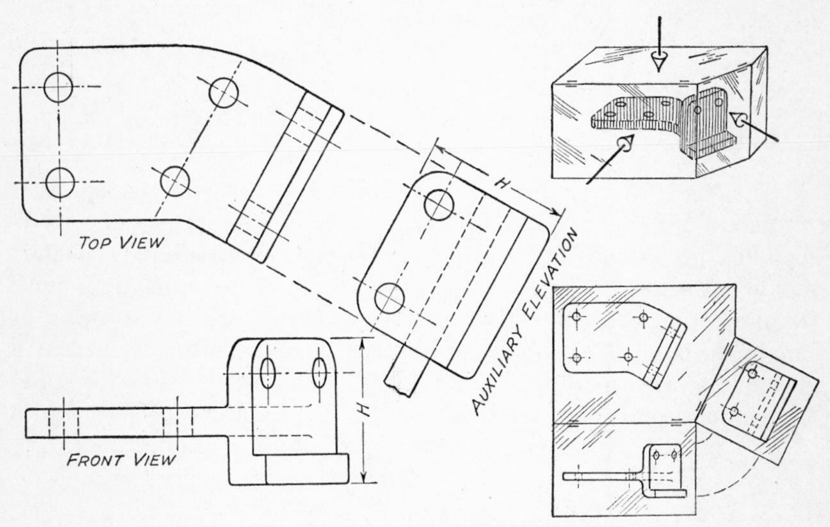

FIG. 190.—Auxiliary elevation (stop bracket).

the height will be the same as in the front view and, as with the original front view, the width will be projected from the top view. In Fig. 190 the pad, whose edge is shown at an angle in the top view, would not show in its true shape in either the front or side views. An auxiliary elevation taken as if looking directly at the pad would show the true shape. The view would be projected from the *top* view, with the heights taken from the front view, as shown at *H*. The horizontal plate is not completed in the auxiliary view as it is fully described by the front and top views.

The second kind, which occurs much more frequently, is that of **left-** and **right-auxiliary views,** made on planes perpendicular to *V* but inclined to *H*, as if the observer looked at the object from some point above (or below) the position in which the right or left side view is seen. The locus of all the view-points for left and right auxiliaries would be a frontal circle passing through the view-points of the right side, top, left side and bottom views. Thus the width of this auxiliary

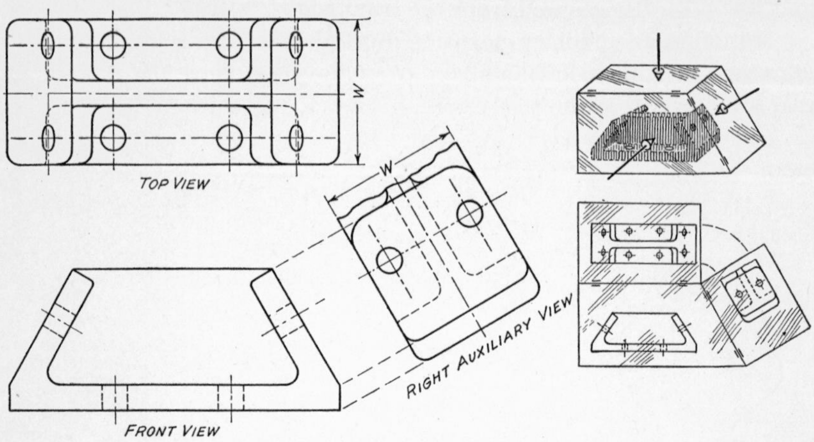

FIG. 191.—Right-auxiliary view (reverse angle bracket).

view would be the same as that of the side view or top view, showing the depth of the object from front to back. Figure 191 shows a

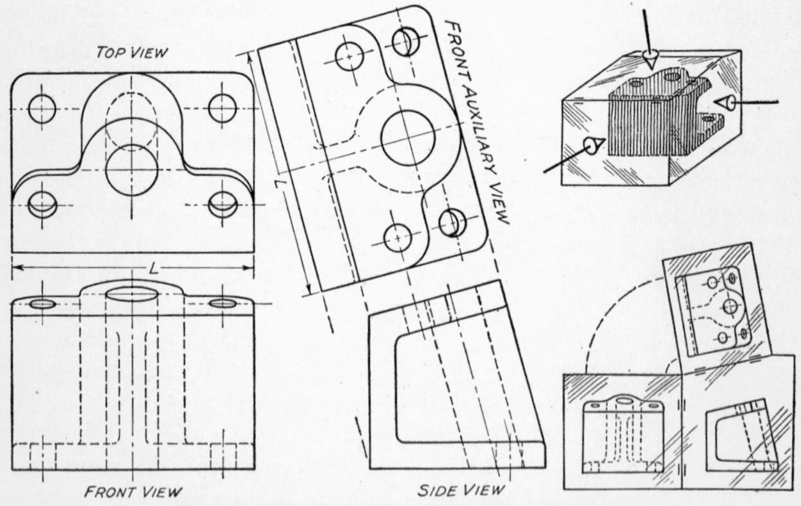

FIG. 192.—Front-auxiliary view (spacer bracket).

right-auxiliary view of the inclined surface of the angle bracket projected from the *front* view and its width W taken from the top view.

The third type is that of **front- and rear-auxiliary views,** made on planes perpendicular to the profile plane, or, for a front-auxiliary view, as if the object were viewed from a point somewhere on a circle arc between the view-point of the front view and that of the top view. Figure 192 shows a front-auxiliary view, projected from the *side* view and its width L measured from the front view.

Note that an auxiliary elevation must always be projected from the *top* view, a right or left auxiliary from the *front* view and a front or rear auxiliary from the *side* view.

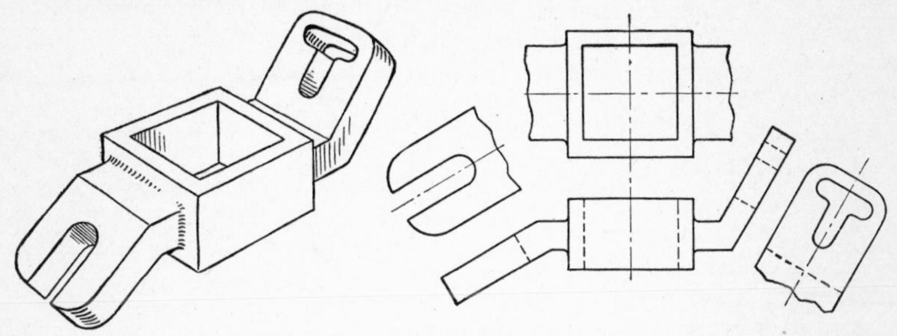

FIG. 193.—Use of partial views.

98. Use of Auxiliary Views.—An auxiliary view will not only show the shape of an inclined part to better advantage but will often save making one or more of the regular views. A second important use is in the case where a principal view cannot be completed without drawing an auxiliary view from which the foreshortened part may be projected. In practical work extensive use is made of auxiliary views. They are generally only partial views showing simply the part of the object parallel to the auxiliary plane, as in Figs. 190 and 191, where nothing would be gained by projecting the whole piece. A casting, for example, as pictured in Fig. 193, would be drawn as shown, making both the auxiliary views and the top view as partial views. In Fig. 194 the auxiliary view takes the place of a side view and also shows the true shape of the rounded surface, since it is taken perpendicular to the surface. An auxiliary view may be placed at any convenient distance from the view from which it is projected.

99. To Draw an Auxiliary View.—Auxiliary views if symmetrical are worked from center lines; if not, from reference lines, and their dimensions are directly obtainable from the other views. In drawing an *auxiliary elevation* the edge of the plane of the base is generally used as the reference line. Draw a base line for the auxiliary view perpendicular to the direction in which the view is taken, that is, parallel to the top view of the face to be shown, project each point of the object from the top view and measure its height from the base line on the front view. Transfer this to the auxiliary view measuring up from the auxiliary base line, as in Fig. 190.

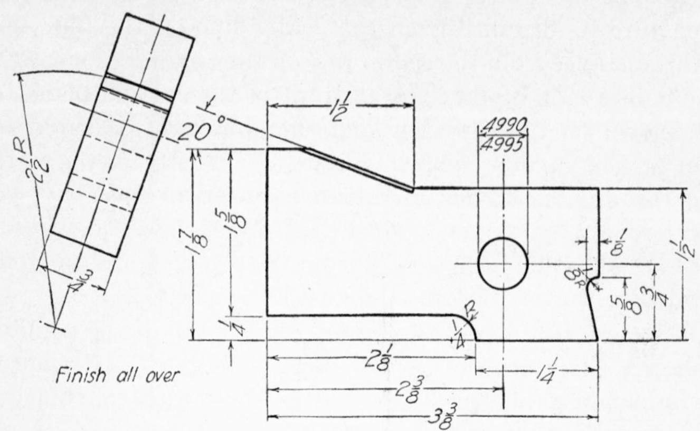

Fig. 194.—Working drawing with auxiliary view (toggle).

The method of making a *right-auxiliary view* of a symmetrical piece is shown in Fig. 195 in which the true size of the cut surface of the block is desired. Draw a center line for the auxiliary view parallel to the cut

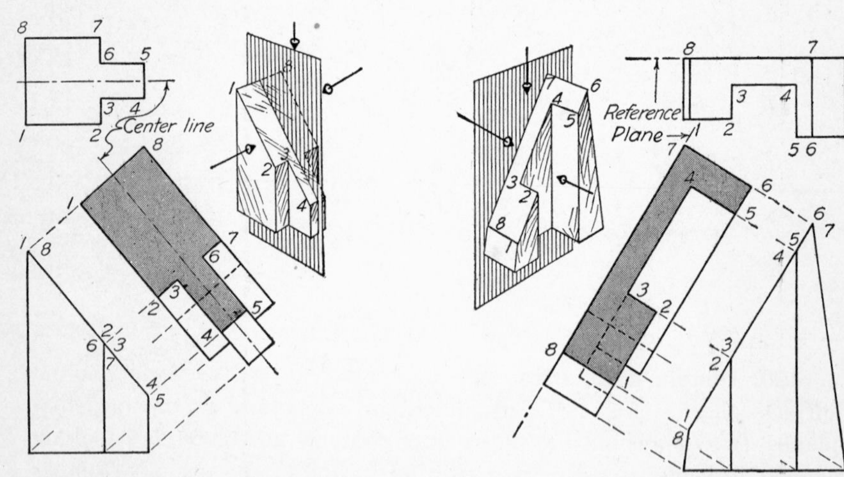

Fig. 195.—Auxiliary view, using center line.

Fig. 196.—Auxiliary view, using reference plane.

surface and at any convenient distance from it. Draw a horizontal center line on the top view. Think of these two center lines as the edge views of a vertical reference plane cutting through the piece, as illustrated in the small sketch. Project each point of the cut face by drawing projecting lines from the front view perpendicular to the auxiliary center line. The width of the auxiliary view will evidently be the same as the width, or depth, of the top view. Thus for each point measure its distance from the center line on the top view and lay off this distance from the center line on the auxiliary view. Notice that the points 1, 2, 3 and 4 are in front of the cutting plane (center line) as shown on the top view and therefore are measured toward the front on the auxiliary view. Figure 196 illustrates the method of drawing the auxiliary view of an unsymmetrical piece by working from a reference plane taken against the back of the piece, whose edges are represented by the horizontal line on the top view and the reference line parallel to the cut face for the auxiliary view.

While in practical work usually only the detail of the inclined face is necessary, such pieces as Figs. 255 and 256 make interesting problems in drawing when the entire figure is projected on the auxiliary plane, as was done in Figs. 195 and 196.

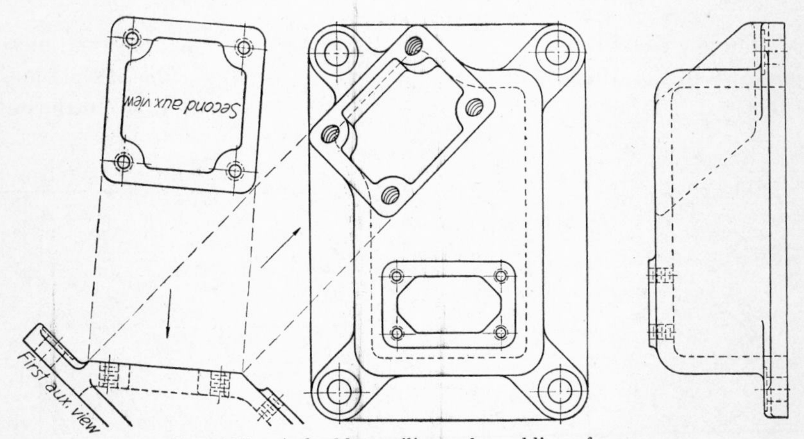

Fig. 197.—A double auxiliary of an oblique face.

100. Double Auxiliaries.—To find the true shape of an oblique surface, that is, one not perpendicular to any one of the principal planes, two operations are required. First, an auxiliary view looking against its edge in a direction parallel to one of the principal planes must be drawn, then, working with this view and the one from which it was projected as if they were regular views, a second auxiliary is made as described in paragraph 99. The process is illustrated in Fig. 197, in which an auxiliary elevation was made first, then a second auxiliary view against the inclined surface, assuming the auxiliary elevation and the top view to be two regular views, and discarding the original front view. Turning the paper or the head may assist in orienting these two views.

101. Revolution.—An object may be drawn in an oblique position by first drawing it in a simpler position, then revolving it about an axis perpendicular to one of the principal planes.

Rule for Revolution.—If an object be revolved about an axis perpendicular to a plane, (1) *its projection on that plane will change only in position, but not in shape or size.* (2) *The dimensions parallel to the axis on the other views will be unchanged.*

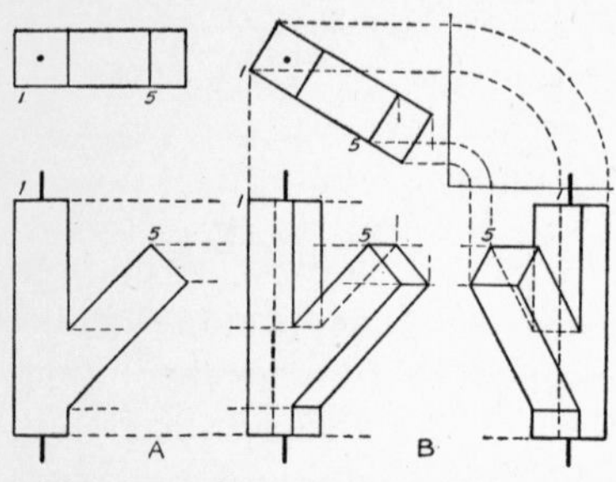

Fig. 198.—Revolution about vertical axis.

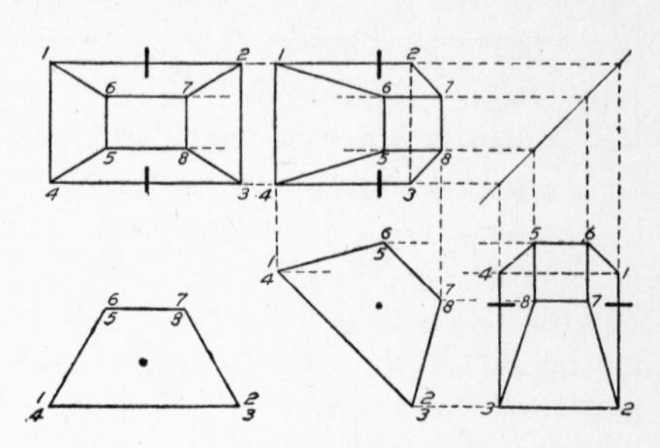

Fig. 199.—Revolution about horizontal axis.

Illustration.—If the object in Fig. 198 should be revolved from the position *A* about a vertical axis through 30° the top view would not change in shape but would take a position as shown in the top view of *B*. The vertical heights of all the points of the object remain unchanged in the revolution; thus the new front view can be found by projecting each point across from the original front view to meet a projection line dropped from the corresponding point on the new top view. The side view is then drawn by the regular methods of projection, as shown.

To avoid confusion it is well to letter or number the corresponding points on each view.

Similarly, if an object be revolved about a horizontal axis, perpendicular to the *V* plane, Fig. 199, the front view would be unchanged and would be transferred by copying it in the new position. The new top view would then be found by projecting across from the original top view and up from the new front view. The side view would be found as before.

In a revolution forward or backward about an axis perpendicular to the profile plane the side view would be the unchanged view and the new front view would be found by projecting across from the revolved side view, and obtaining the widths from the original front view.

Successive revolutions may be made under the same rules. Figure 200 is a piece revolved first about a horizontal axis through 30°, and from this position revolved about a vertical axis through 45°.

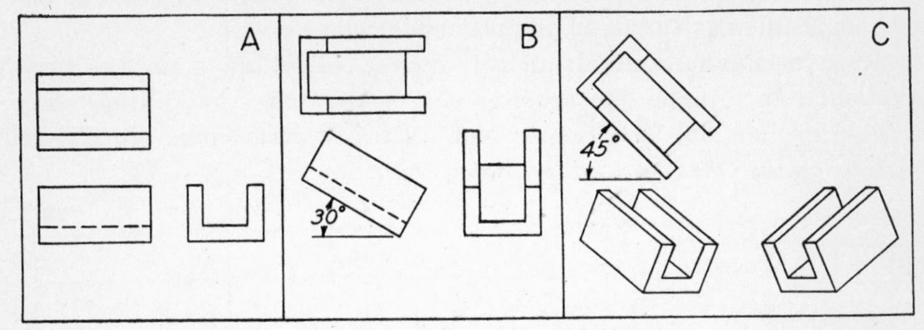

Fig. 200.—Successive revolutions.

Evidently the only difference between the methods of revolution and auxiliary projection is that in the former the object is moved while in the latter the plane of projection is moved. Although revolution has very little application in practical drafting, problems in it are an excellent aid to the student in understanding the theory of projections.

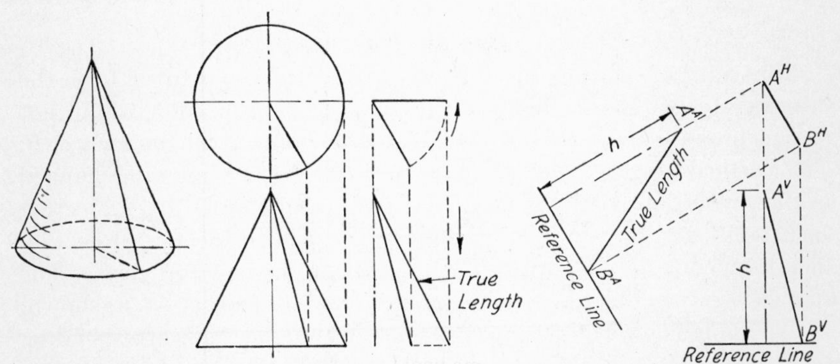

Fig. 201.—True length of a line, revolution method.

Fig. 202.—True length of a line, auxiliary view method.

102. The True Length of a Line.—An oblique line will not show in its true length in any of its views. If it be revolved into a position parallel to one of the principal planes its true length will be shown in that view. This may be easily understood by assuming the line to be an element on a cone, as in Fig. 201. The slant lines of the front view of a cone show the true lengths of its elements. If the cone be imagined as revolving about its axis each element in turn will take a position parallel to the plane of projection. Thus if the line be assumed to be on a cone as in the figure, its true length would be found by revolving the top view until the line is parallel to V, and projecting the revolved end down to meet the horizontal line corresponding to the base of the cone.

The true length of a line may also be found by making an auxiliary view of it, looking straight against the line, as in Fig. 202.

103. First Angle Projection.—The system of orthographic projection explained in this chapter is known as "third angle projection" and is the universally adopted standard in the United States.

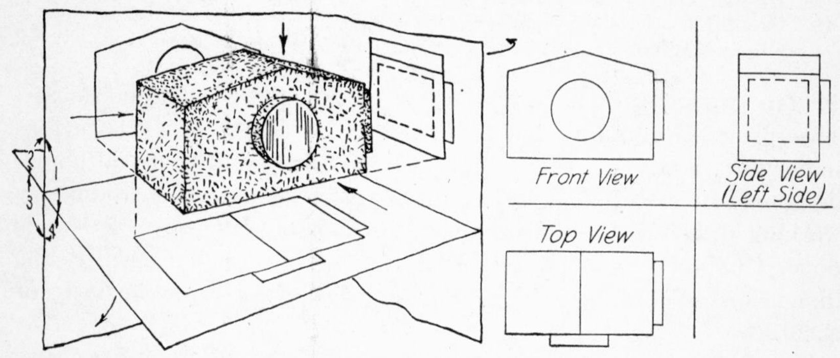

FIG. 203.—First angle projection.

If the horizontal and vertical planes are extended beyond their intersection four dihedral angles will be formed which are called respectively first, second, third and fourth angles, numbered as illustrated in Fig. 203. If the object be placed in the *first* angle, projected to the planes and the planes opened up into one plane, the top view would evidently fall below the front view, and if the profile view were added the view of the left side of the figure would be to the right of the front view. This system, known as "first angle projection," was formerly in universal use but was generally abandoned in this country some forty or more years ago and is now obsolete. The student should understand it, however, as it may be encountered occasionally in old drawings, in some book illustrations and in drawings from most foreign countries.

In England some attempt has been made to introduce the more practical third angle projection but nearly all British drawings are either first angle or with the curious combination of first angle for top and front views and third angle for the side view. Holland has adopted third angle projection as standard, but other European countries still adhere to the older method. Canadian practice is the same as American.

PROBLEMS

104. Selections from the several groups of problems following may be made for practice in projection drawing. They are intended to be drawn with instruments but will give valuable training done in freehand on either plain or coordinate paper.

The groups are as follows:

Group I. Projections from pictorial views.
Group II. Views to be supplied.
Group III. Views to be changed.
Group IV. Auxiliary views.
Group V. Double auxiliaries.
Group VI. Revolutions.
Group VII. True lengths of lines.
Group VIII. Drawing from description.
Group IX. Drawing from memory.
Group X. Volume and weight calculations (with slide rule).

The two things to be told about an object are its *shape* and its *size*. The former is given by the projections; the latter, which is just as important, is given by the dimensions. These problems, although designed primarily for *shape* description, may be drawn as introductory working drawings by adding dimension lines and figures. If this is done, Chapter IX on dimensioning must be studied carefully, the dimensions placed according to the rules given and checked for accuracy.

The first requirement of a good drawing, after the requisite views have been determined, is that the views be well spaced on the sheet and in relation to each other. Allow adequate room between views for dimensions (on account of the limits in page size many of the drawings in the book are crowded closer together than would be done on regular working drawings). Make a little preliminary freehand sketch on scratch paper for arrangement; then follow a systematic order of working. *First,* lay off the sheet and border; *second,* decide what scale to use; *third,* draw the center lines or base lines for each view and on these block in the principal dimensions; *fourth,* finish the projections, carrying the views along together, projecting from one to another.

Work lightly with sharp pencil and do not erase overrunning lines until the problem is finished. For a finished pencil drawing brighten the outlines and erase unnecessary lines. Refer to paragraph 198 with the accompanying illustration, Fig. 428, for a more detailed explanation of the order of penciling, and to paragraph 200 for the order of inking.

Group I. Projections from Pictorial Views. Probs. 1 to 30.

The approximate net space required for the problem, if drawn to the size given, is added in parenthesis after each specification.

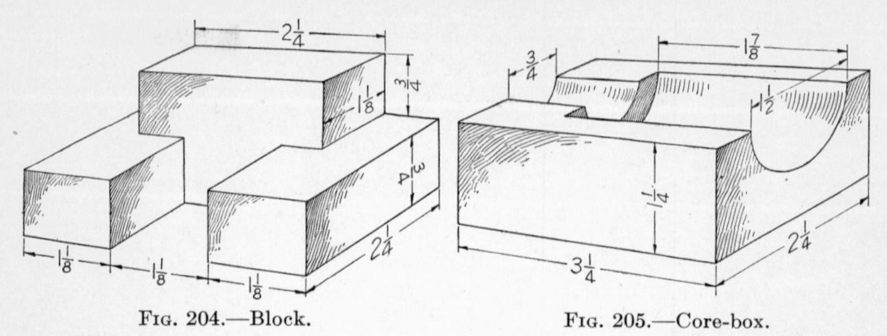

FIG. 204.—Block. FIG. 205.—Core-box.

1. Fig. 204. Draw the front, top and right side views of the block shown Full size (5 × 7 space).

2. Fig. 205. Draw front, top and right side views of core-box (5 × 7 space).

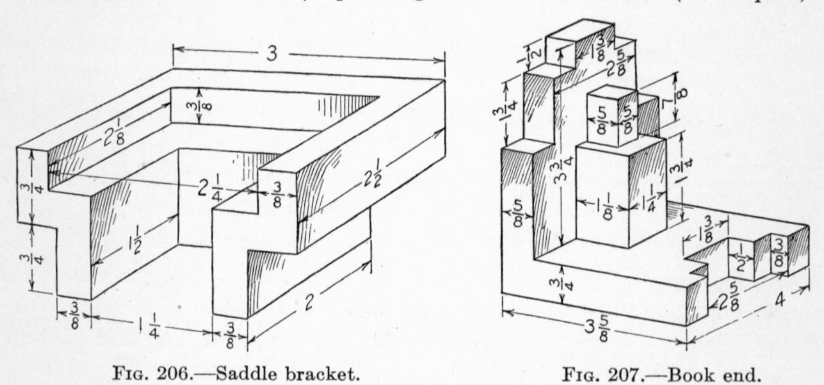

FIG. 206.—Saddle bracket. FIG. 207.—Book end.

3. Fig. 206. Draw three views of saddle bracket (5. × 7 space).

4. Fig. 207. Draw three views of book end (9 × 9 space).

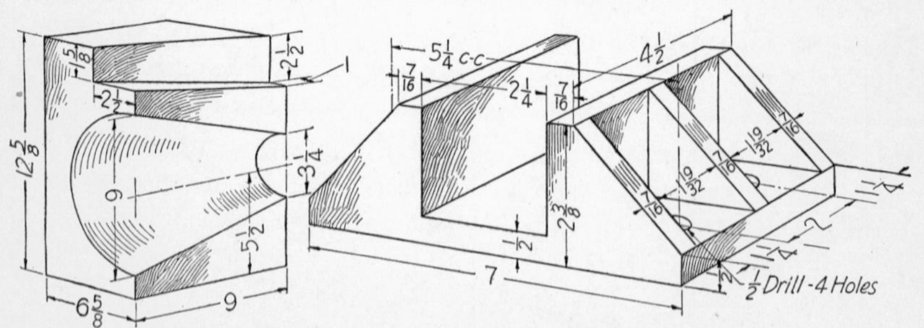

FIG. 208.—Burner block. FIG. 209.—Spring saddle guide.

5. Fig. 208. Draw three views of burner block to suitable scale. In use R & L halves fit together (9 × 11 at ½ size).

6. Fig. 209. Draw three views of spring saddle guide (8 × 12 space)

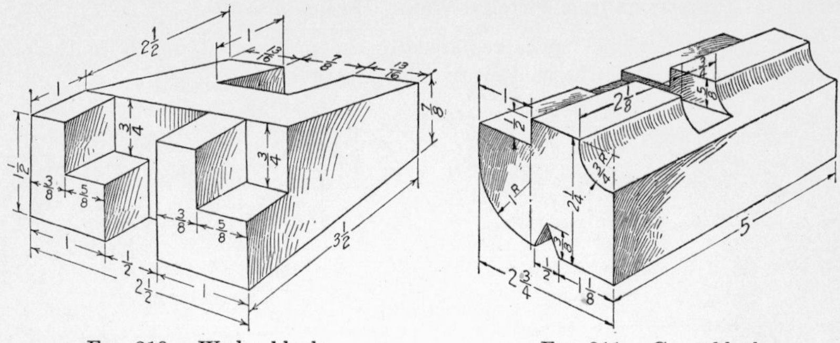

FIG. 210.—Wedge block. FIG. 211.—Cross-block.

7. Fig. 210. Draw three views of wedge block (6 × 7 space).
8. Fig. 211. Draw three views of cross-block (6 × 8 space).

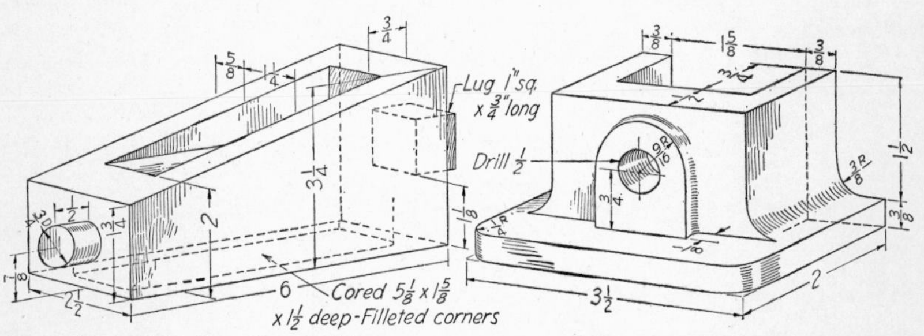

FIG. 212.—Leveling wedge. FIG. 213.—Guide base.

9. Fig. 212. Draw three views of leveling wedge (8 × 11 space).
10. Fig. 213. Draw three views of guide base (5 × 7 space).

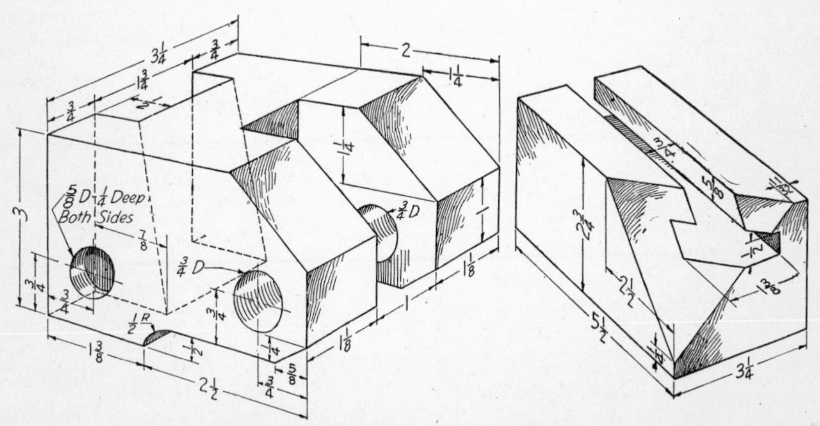

FIG. 214.—Rocker block. FIG. 215.—Clipped T-slot block.

11. Fig. 214. Draw three views of rocker block (8 × 8 space).
12. Fig. 215. Draw three views of clipped T-slot block (8 × 11 space).

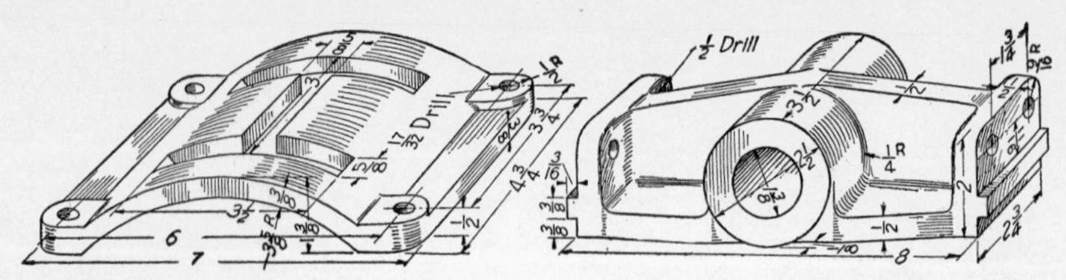

FIG. 216.—Gear shifter gate. FIG. 217.—Truss bearing.

13. Fig. 216. Draw two views of gear shifter gate (7 × 7 space).
14. Fig. 217. Draw three views of truss bearing (7 × 13 space).

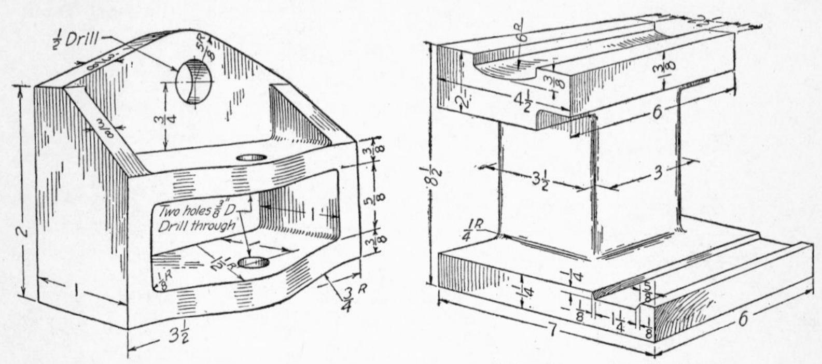

FIG. 218.—Wall bracket. FIG. 219.—Muffle base.

15. Fig. 218. Draw three views of wall bracket (5 × 7 space).
16. Fig. 219. Draw three views of muffle base (scale to suit).

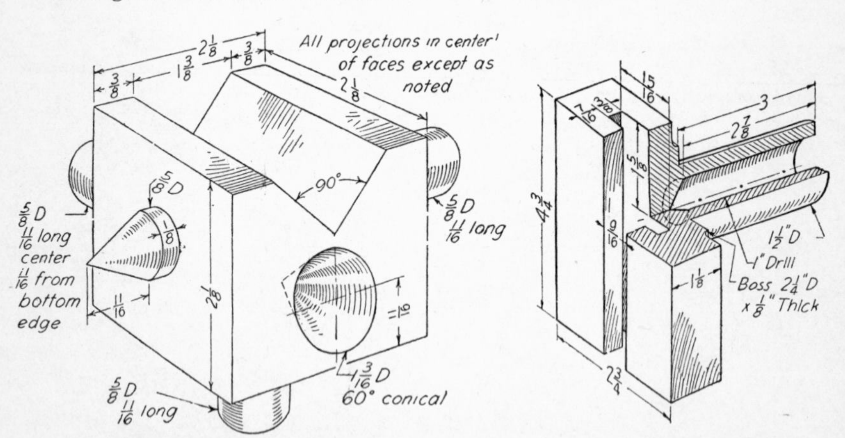

FIG. 220.—Drilling block. FIG. 221.—Slotted crank.

17. Fig. 220. Draw three views of drilling block (7 × 7 space).
18. Fig. 221. Draw three views of slotted crank (8 × 8 space).
19. Fig. 222. Draw three views of splice plate (scale to suit).
20. Fig. 223. Draw three views of buckstay clamp (6 × 7 space).

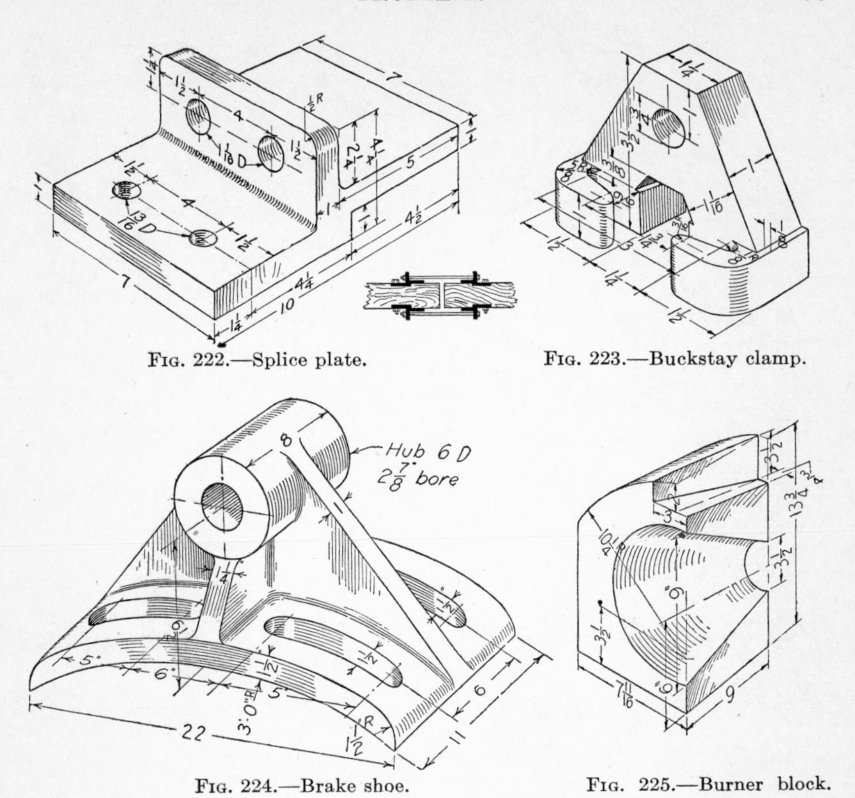

FIG. 222.—Splice plate.

FIG. 223.—Buckstay clamp.

FIG. 224.—Brake shoe.

FIG. 225.—Burner block.

21. Fig. 224. Draw two views of brake shoe (scale to suit).

22. Fig. 225. Draw three views of burner block (scale to suit). Compare this block with that of Prob. 5, Fig. 208.

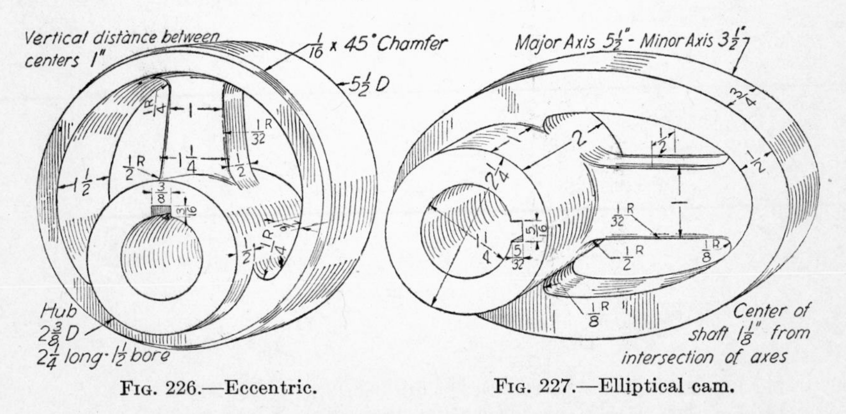

FIG. 226.—Eccentric.

FIG. 227.—Elliptical cam.

23. Fig. 226. Draw two views of eccentric (6 × 9 space).

24. Fig. 227. Draw two views of elliptical cam (6 × 9 space).

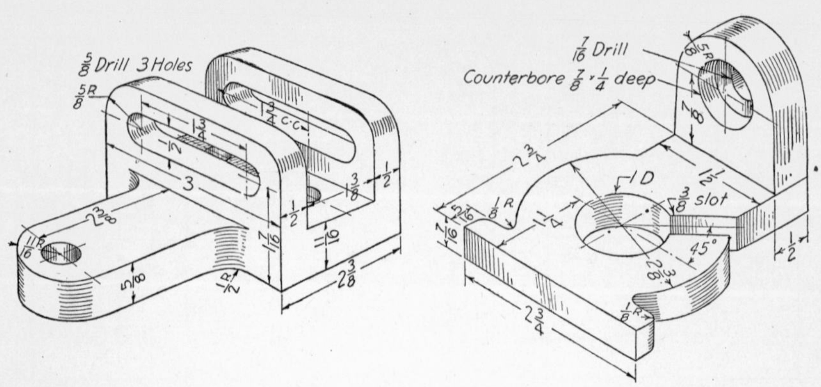

Fig. 228.—Adjusting bracket.

Fig. 229.—Switch base.

25. Fig. 228. Draw three views of adjusting bracket (6 × 9 space).
26. Fig. 229. Draw three views of switch base (5½ × 7 space).

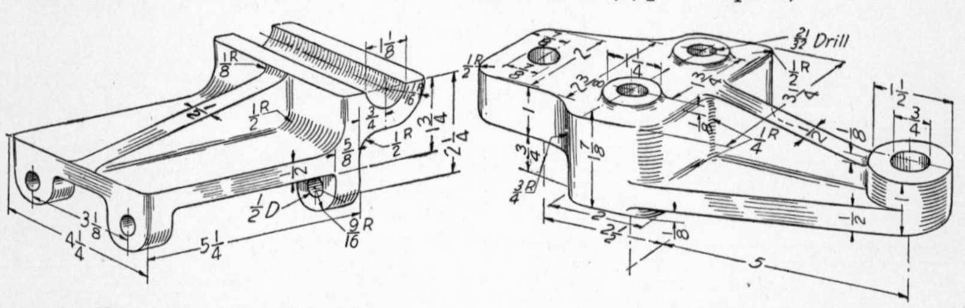

Fig. 230.—Hinged bearing.

Fig. 231.—Clamp lever.

27. Fig. 230. Draw three views of hinged bearing (9 × 12 space).
28. Fig. 231. Draw two views of clamp lever (7 × 10 space).

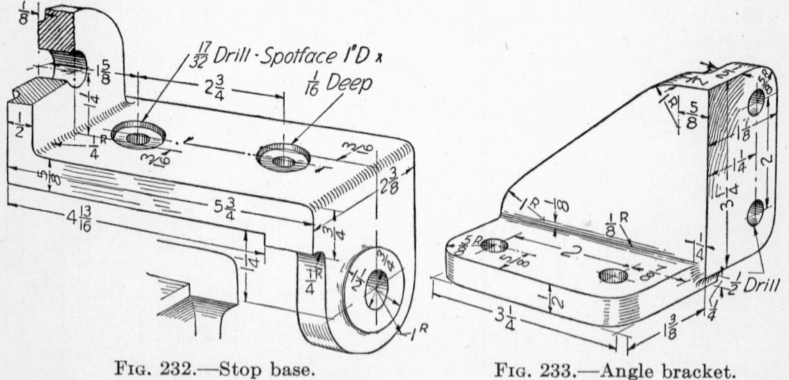

Fig. 232.—Stop base.

Fig. 233.—Angle bracket.

29. Fig. 232. Draw three views of stop base (9 × 11 space).
30. Fig. 233. Draw three views of angle bracket (8 × 8 space).

Group II. Views to Be Supplied. Probs. 31 to 43.

31. Fig. 234. Draw the views given, completing the top view from information given on front and side views.

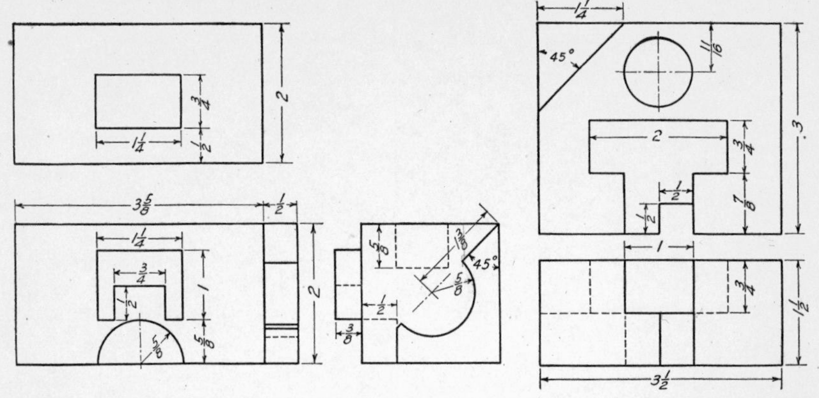

FIG. 234.—Projection study.

FIG. 235.—Projection study.

32. Fig. 235. Given top and front views of block. Required top, front and right side views. Be careful in drawing the hidden lines. See paragraph 92.

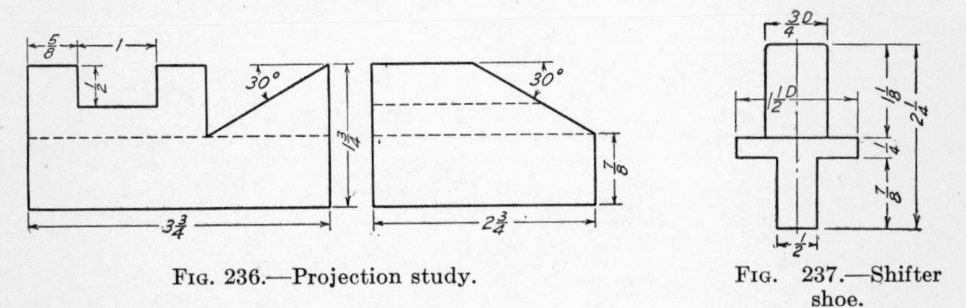

FIG. 236.—Projection study.

FIG. 237.—Shifter shoe.

33. Fig. 236. Given front and side views of block. Required front, side and top views. Try to visualize the block. See paragraph 95.

34. Fig. 237. Given front view of shifter shoe. Required front, top and side views. Note that *D* is the abbreviation for diameter.

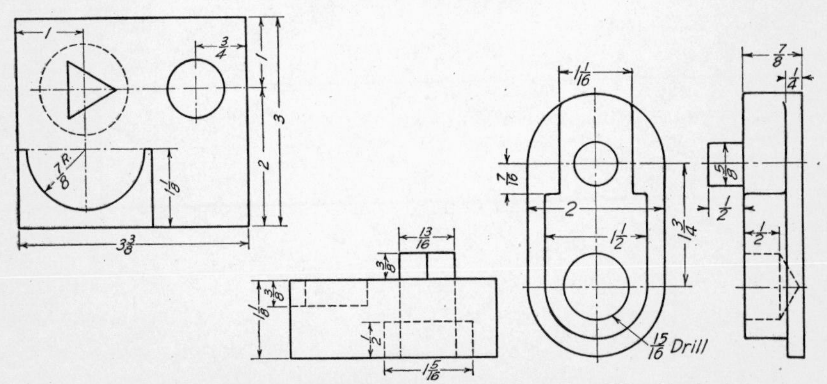

FIG. 238.—Projection study.

FIG. 239.—Lock plate.

35. Fig. 238. Given top and side views of block. Required top, front and side views. Carry the three views along together.

36. Fig. 239. Given front and side views of lock plate. Draw three views.

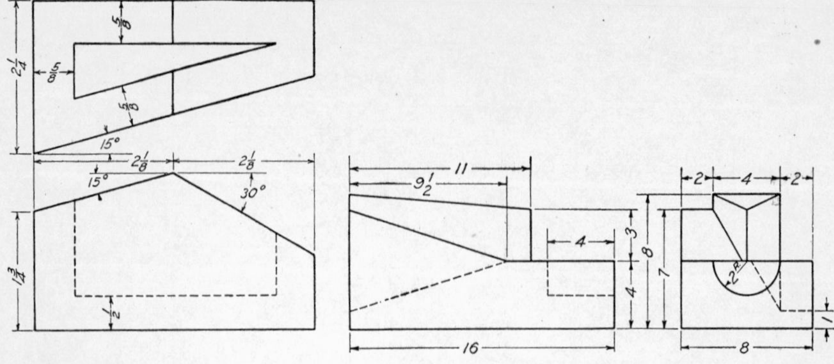

FIG. 240.—Wedge block. FIG. 241.—Bit point-forming die.

37. Fig. 240. Given top and front views of wedge block. Draw these views and from them obtain right side view.

38. Fig. 241. Draw the two views given of the bit point-forming die and from them add the top view.

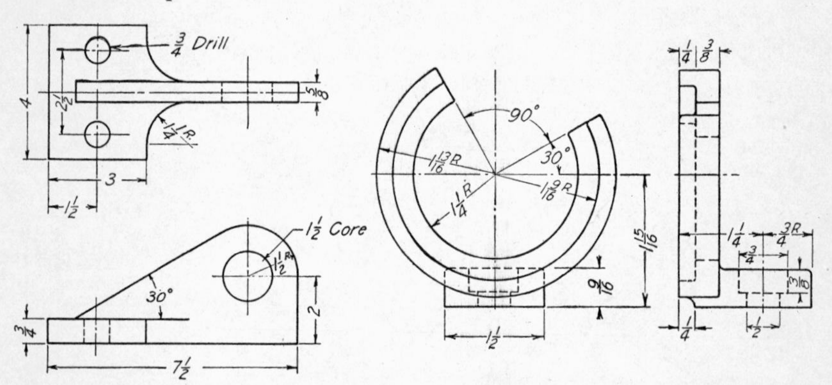

FIG. 242.—Anchor bracket. FIG. 243.—Saddle collar.

39. Fig. 242. Given front and top views of anchor bracket. Required front, top and right side views. Scale to suit.

40. Fig. 243. Given front and side views of saddle collar. Add top view.

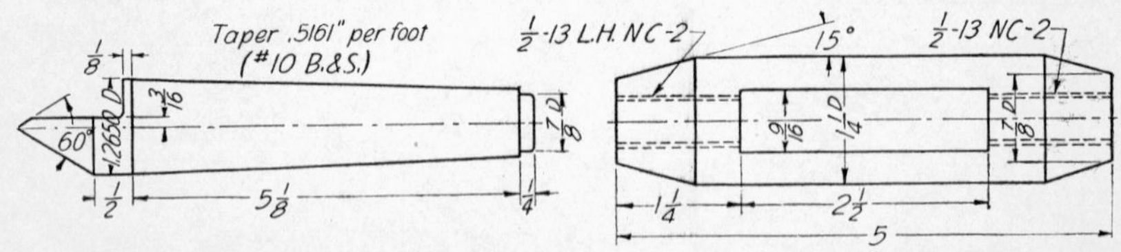

FIG. 244.—Grinder tailstock center. FIG. 245.—Turnbuckle.

41. Fig. 244. Given one view of grinder tailstock center. Required three views.

42. Fig. 245. Given one view of turnbuckle. Required three views. For thread symbols see paragraph 160, page 156.

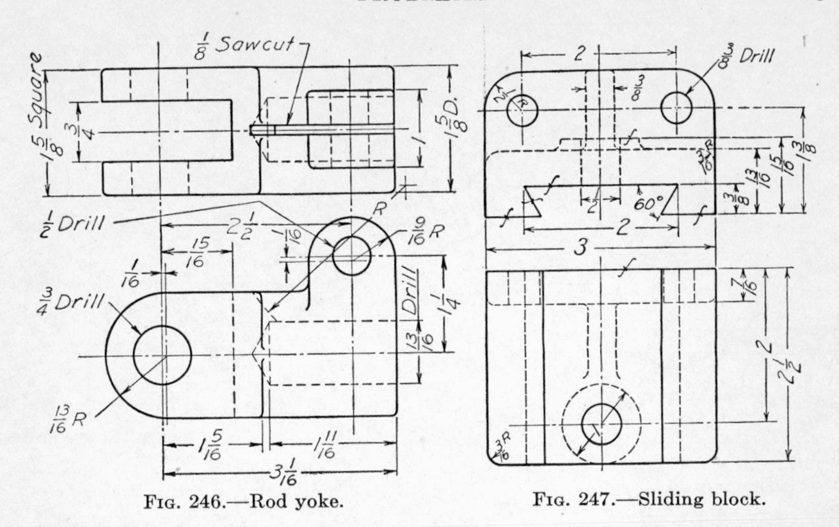

FIG. 246.—Rod yoke.

FIG. 247.—Sliding block.

43. Fig. 246. Given front and top views of rod yoke. Required front, top and right side views. Space views farther apart than in illustration.

Group III. Views to Be Changed. Probs. 44 to 50.

44. Fig. 247. Given top and front views of sliding block. Required new front, top and side views, turning the block around so that the back becomes the front. The rib contour is straight.

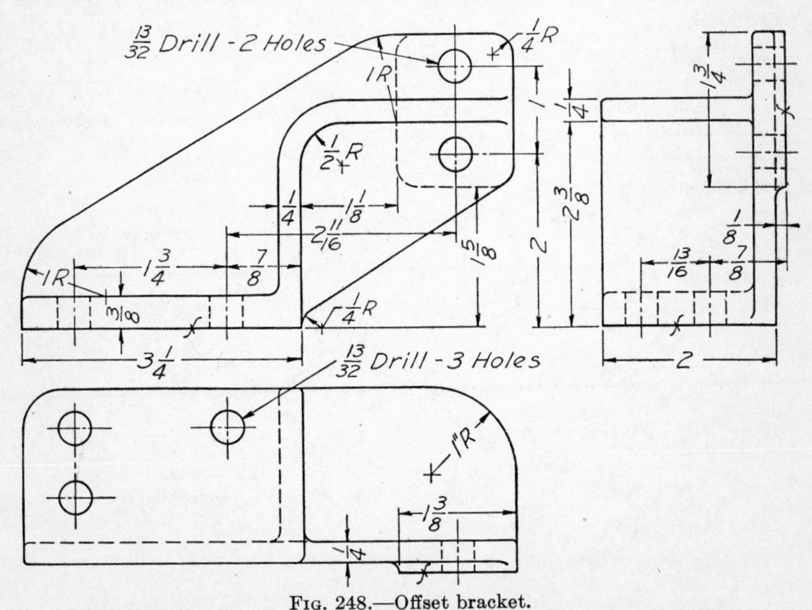

FIG. 248.—Offset bracket.

45. Fig. 248. Given front, right side and bottom views of offset bracket. Required front, top and left side views.

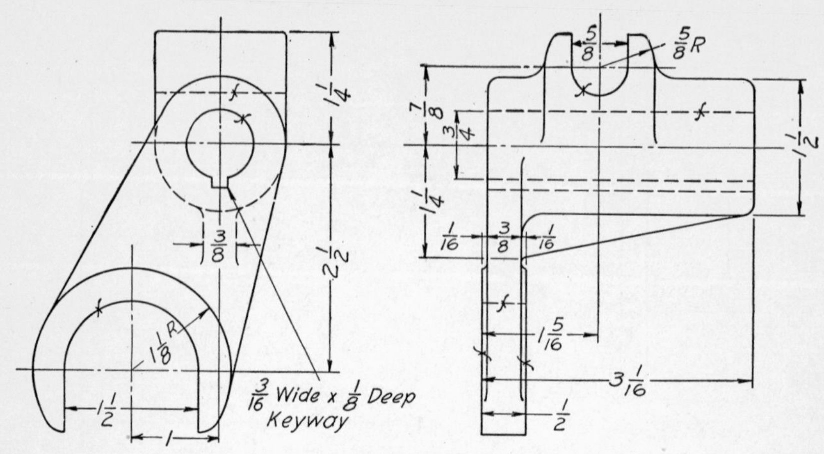

FIG. 249.—Shifter fork.

46. Fig. 249. Given front and left side views of shifter fork. Required front, right side and top views.

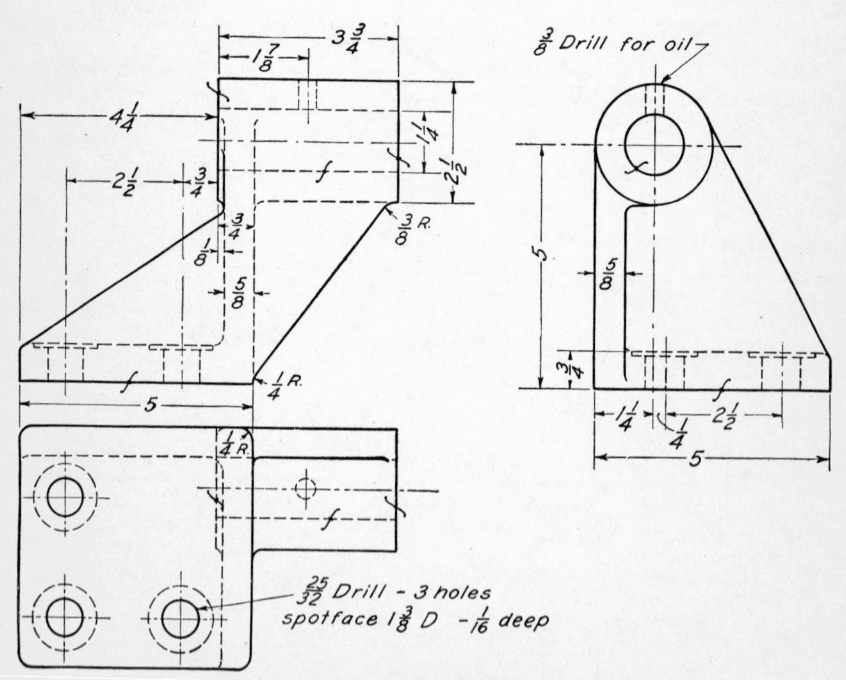

FIG. 250.—Toggle shaft bracket.

47. Fig. 250. Given rear, bottom and *left* side views of toggle shaft bracket. Required front, top and right side views.

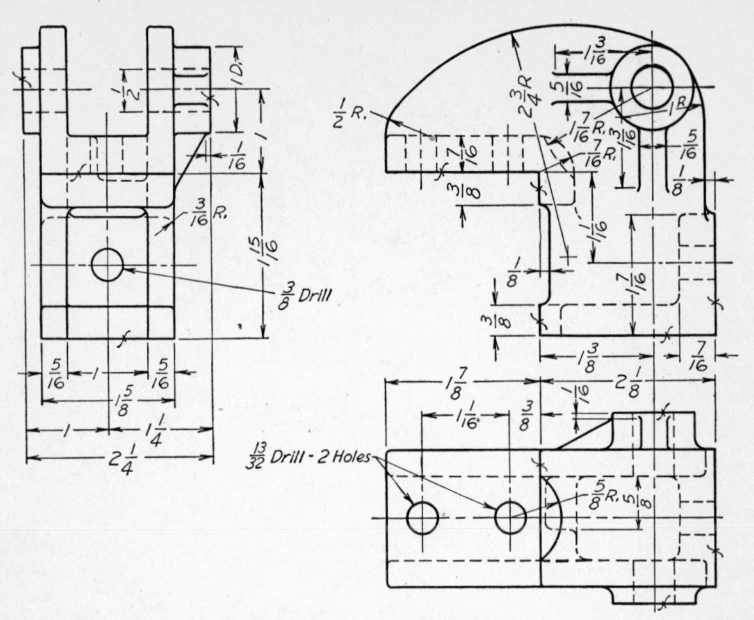

FIG. 251.—Angle bracket.

48. Fig. 251. Given front, bottom and left side views of angle bracket. Required front, top and right side views.

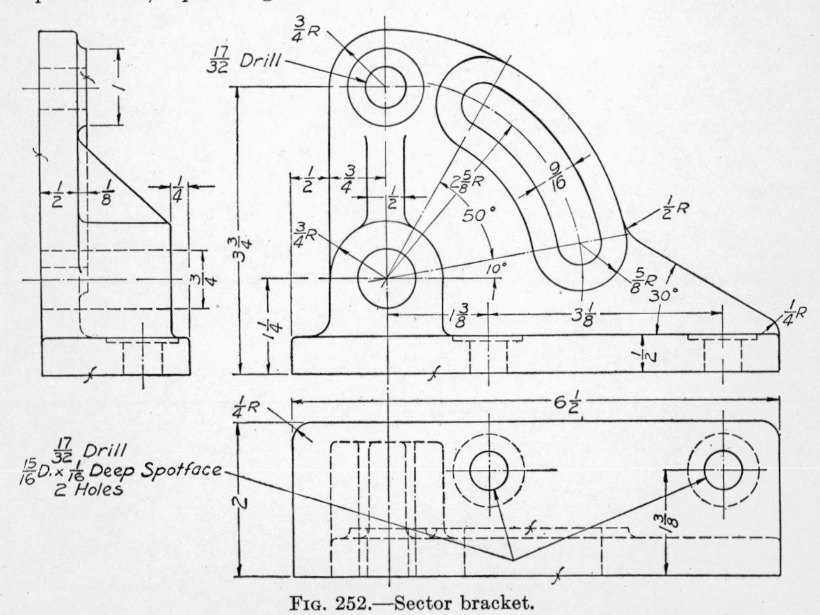

FIG. 252.—Sector bracket.

49. Fig. 252. Given front, left side and bottom views of sector bracket. Required front, right side and top views.

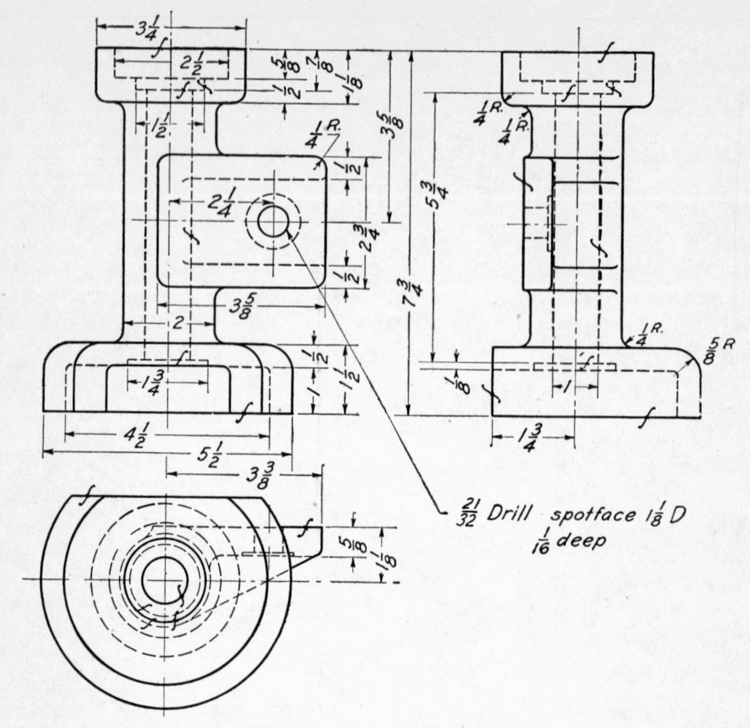

FIG. 253.—Indicator bracket.

50. Fig. 253. Given rear, bottom and *left* side views of indicator bracket. Required front, top and right side views.

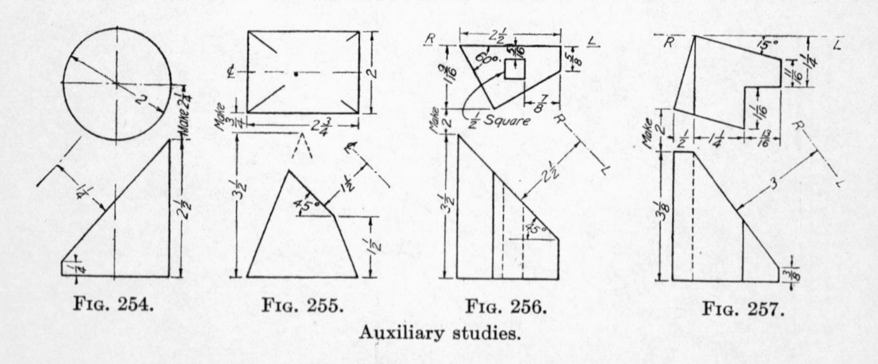

FIG. 254. FIG. 255. FIG. 256. FIG. 257.

Auxiliary studies.

Group IV. Auxiliary Views. Probs. 51 to 64.

51, 52, 53, 54. Figs. 254 to 257. Draw views given and auxiliary views on center or reference lines as indicated.

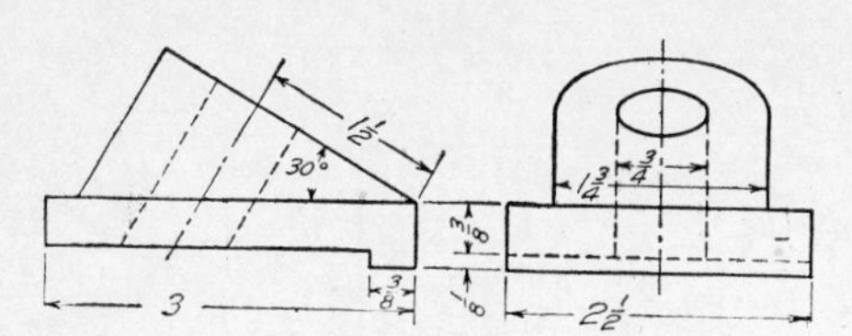

Fig. 258.—Bevel washer.

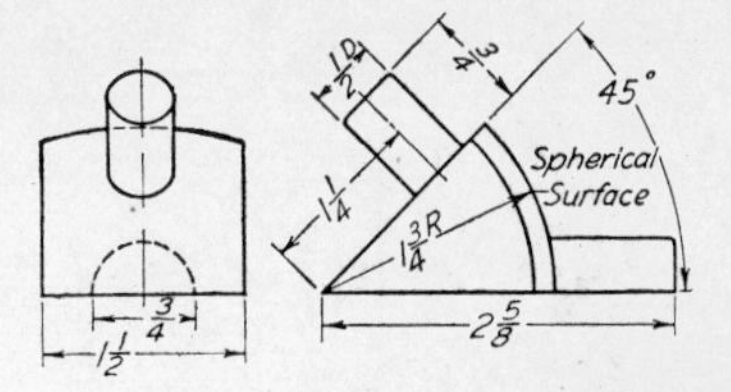

Fig. 259.—Siamese block.

55. Fig. 258. Given front and side views of bevel washer. Required front view and right-auxiliary view. Side view may be drawn if desired.

56. Fig. 259. Given front and left side views of Siamese block. Required left-auxiliary view in addition. Space views so as to avoid interference.

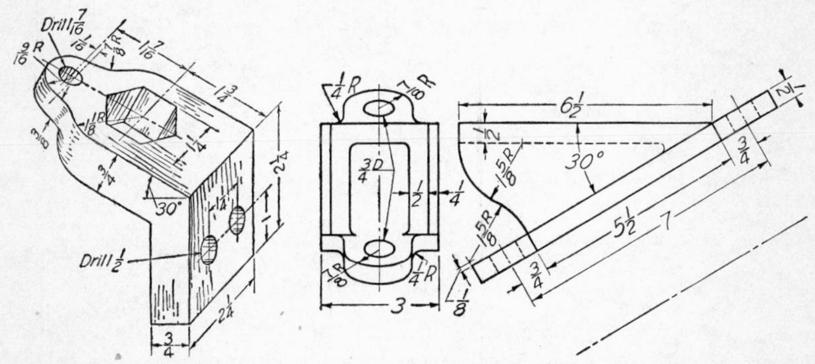

Fig. 260.—Jig angle. Fig. 261.—Angle bracket.

57, 58. Figs. 260 and 261. Determine what views and part views will best describe the piece. Submit sketch before starting the drawing.

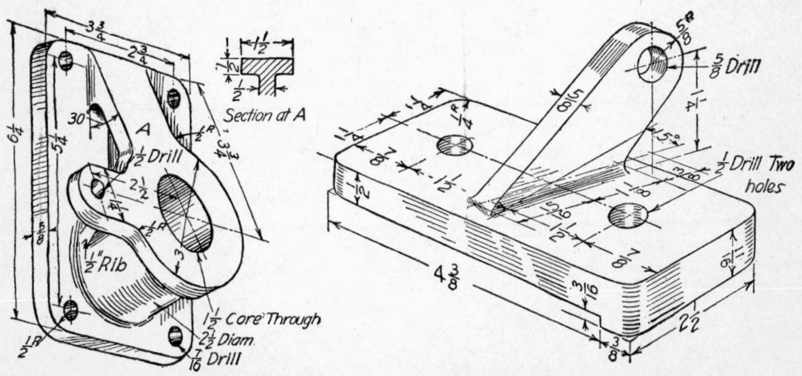

Fig. 262.—Angle shaft base. Fig. 263.—Anchor bracket.

59, 60. Figs. 262 and 263. Determine what views and part views will best describe the piece. Submit sketch before starting the drawing.

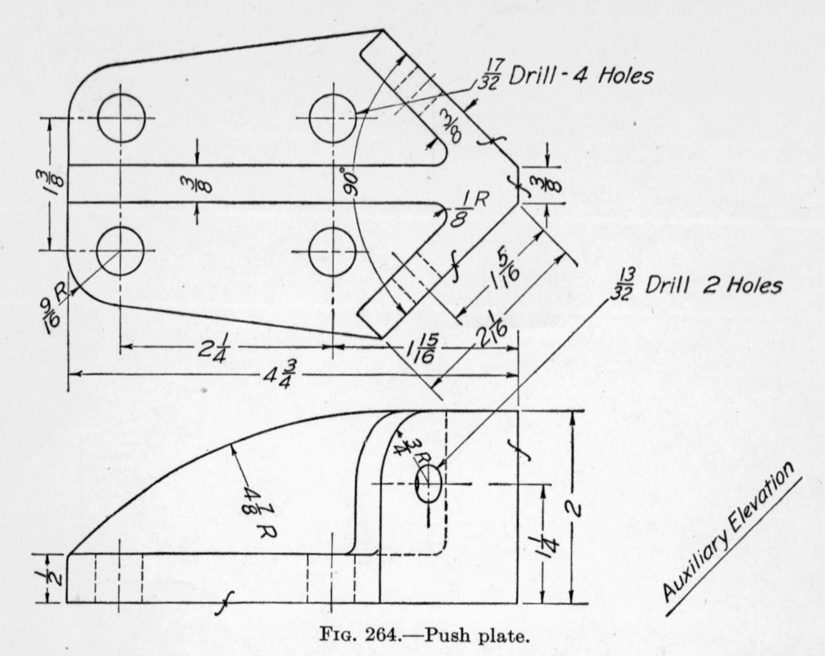

FIG. 264.—Push plate.

61. Fig. 264. Draw views given and auxiliary elevation.

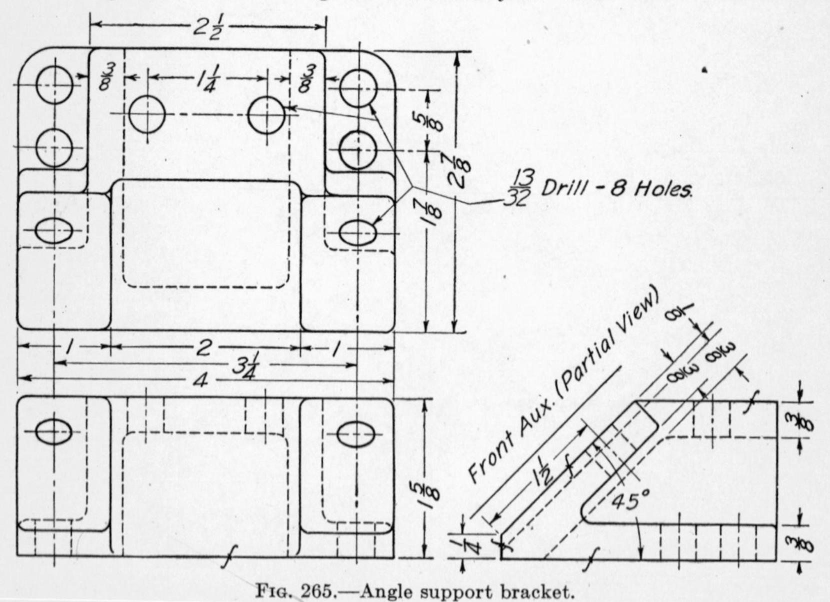

FIG. 265.—Angle support bracket.

62. Fig. 265. Draw views given and front auxiliary. Space to suit.

63. Fig. 266. Draw top, front and side views of skew slide, with auxiliary part-elevation (9 × 13 space).

64. Fig. 267. Determine best views and part views to describe the rubber

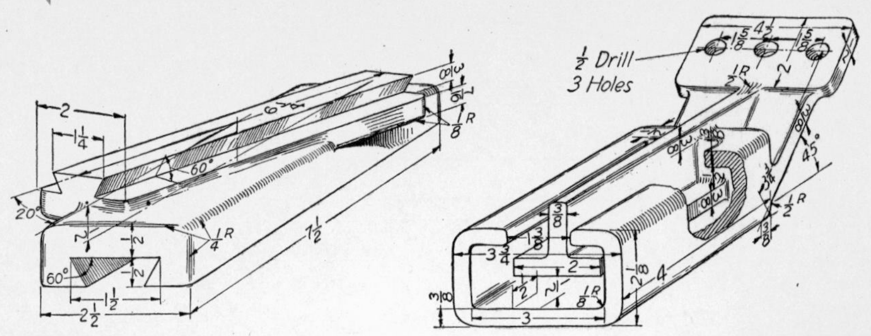

Fig. 266.—Skew slide. Fig. 267.—Rubber support anchor.

support anchor. Submit sketch before drawing (9 × 13 space).

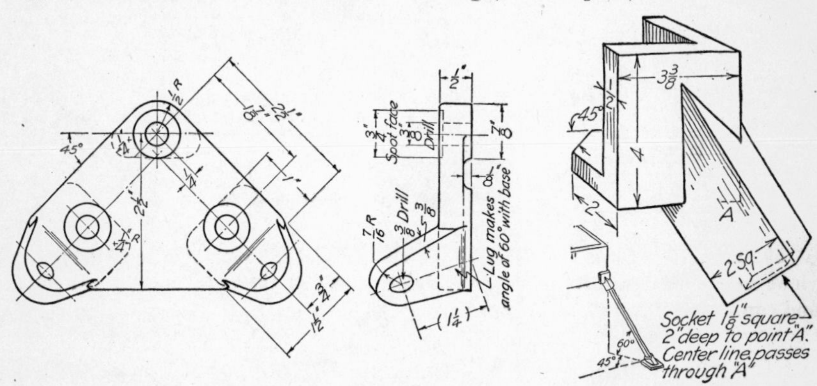

Fig. 268.—Cable anchor. Fig. 269.—Corner bracket.

Group V. Double Auxiliaries. Probs. 65 to 69.

65. Fig. 268. Draw views given by using double auxiliary method.

66. Fig. 269. Draw necessary views of corner bracket using double auxiliary method.

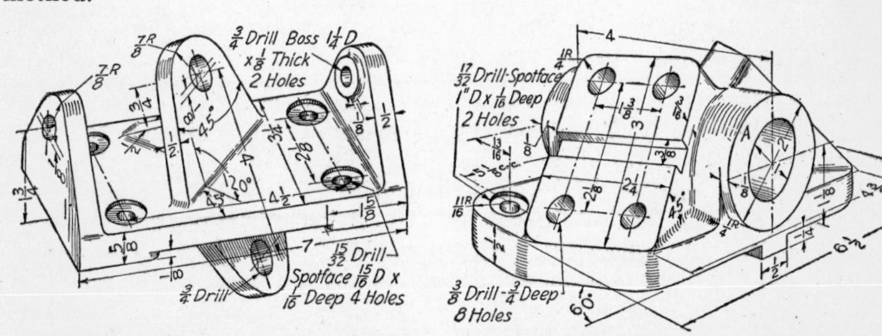

Fig. 270.—Transverse connection. Fig. 271.—Chamfer tool base.

67. Fig. 270. Draw top, front, left side (across from top), auxiliary elevation (part) and second auxiliary of transverse connection. (Start top view in upper right-hand corner of 10 × 14 space.)

68. Fig. 271. Draw top, front, auxiliary part-elevation and second auxiliary. (Start top view in upper left corner of 10 × 14 space with face *A* at the rear. The piece is symmetrical about main axis.)

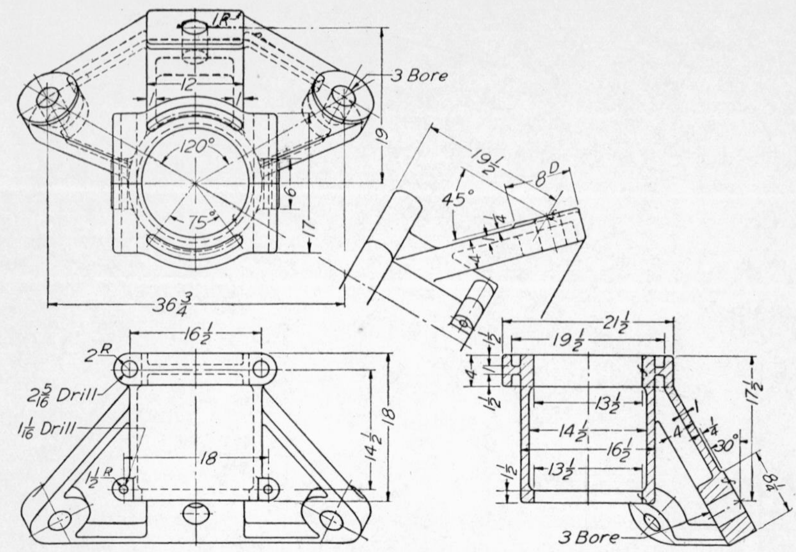

FIG. 272.—Crane mast-head collar and cap.

69. Fig. 272. Draw the layout of the views given and such additional auxiliary views as are necessary to make a working drawing of the crane mast-head collar and cap. (8½″ × 13″, to ⅛ size.)

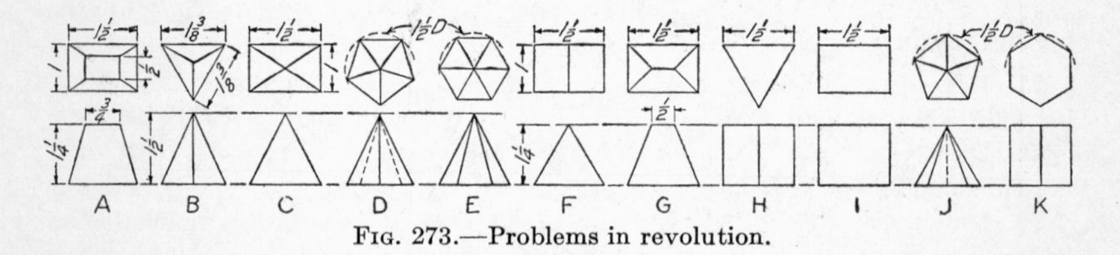

FIG. 273.—Problems in revolution.

Group VI. Revolution. Probs. 70 to 72.

70. Fig. 273. (1) Draw three views of one of the blocks *A* to *K* in the position shown. (2) Revolve from position (1) about an axis $\perp H$ through 15°. (3) Revolve from position (2) about an axis $\perp V$ through 45°. (4) Revolve from position (1) about an axis $\perp P$ forward through 30°. (5) Revolve from position (2) about an axis $\perp P$ forward through 30°. (6) Revolve from position (3) about an axis $\perp P$ forward through 30°. (4), (5) and (6) may be placed to advantage under (1), (2) and (3) so that the widths of front and top views may be projected down directly.

71. Fig. 274. The triangle *ABC* is the base of a triangular pyramid, altitude 2½″, whose apex is equidistant from *A*, *B* and *C*. Counterrevolve until the base is horizontal, and complete the figure.

72. Fig. 274. The triangle *ABC* is the base of a triangular pyramid, altitude 1¼″, whose faces make equal angles with the base. Counterrevolve in two operations, until the base is horizontal, and complete the figure.

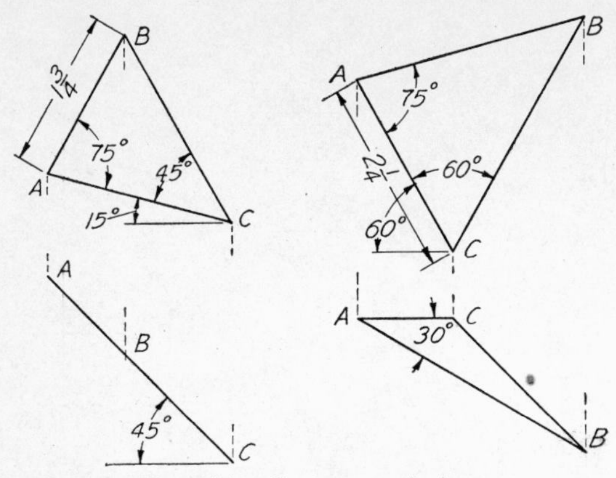

FIG. 274.—Counter revolutions.

FIG. 275.—Timber brace.

Group VII. True Lengths of Lines. Probs. 73 to 75.

73. Find the true length of the body diagonal of a $2\frac{1}{2}''$ cube.

74. Find the true length of an edge of one of the pyramids of Fig. 273.

75. Fig. 275. Find the true length of the line *AB*. Make a detail drawing of the brace.

Group VIII. Drawing from Description. Probs. 76 to 86.

76. Draw three views of a pentagonal prism, axis $1\frac{1}{2}''$ long and perpendicular to *H*, circumscribing circle of base $1\frac{1}{2}''$ diam. surmounted by a cylindrical abacus (cap) $2''$ diam., $\frac{1}{2}''$ thick.

77. Draw three views of a triangular card each edge of which is $2\frac{3}{4}''$ long. One edge is perpendicular to *P*, and the card makes an angle of 30° with *H*.

78. Draw three views of a circular card $2\frac{1}{2}''$ diam., inclined 30° to *H*, and perpendicular to *V*. (Find eight points on the curve.)

79. Draw three views of a cylinder of $1\frac{1}{2}''$ diam., $2''$ long, with hexagonal hole, $1''$ long diam., through it. Axis of cylinder parallel to *H* and inclined 30° to *V*.

80. Draw top and front views of a hexagonal plinth whose faces are $1''$ square and two of which are parallel to *H*, pierced by a square prism, two faces of which are parallel to *H*, $3''$ long, base $\frac{7}{8}''$ square. The axes coincide, are parallel to *H* and make an angle of 30° with *V*. The middle point of the axis of the prism is at the center of the plinth.

81. Draw the two projections of a line $3''$ long, making an angle of 30° with *V*, and whose *V* projection makes 45° with a horizontal line, the line sloping downward and backward to the left.

82. Draw three views of a square pyramid whose faces are isosceles triangles $1\frac{3}{4}''$ base and $2\frac{1}{4}''$ altitude, lying with one face horizontal, the *H* projection of its axis at an angle of 30° with the horizontal.

83. Draw the top and front views of a right rectangular pyramid, base $1\frac{1}{8}'' \times 2''$, altitude $1\frac{7}{8}''$, long edges of base parallel to *V*. By two revolutions place the pyramid so that the short edges are parallel to *H* and make an angle of 60° with *V* while the apex is in the same horizontal plane as one of the short edges of the base.

84. Draw three views of a triangular pyramid formed of four equilateral triangles whose sides are 2¼″. The base makes an angle of 45° with *H*, and one of the edges of the base is perpendicular to *V*.

85. Draw top and front views of a rectangular prism, base 1″ × 1¾″, whose body diagonal is 2½″ long. Find projection of prism on an auxiliary plane perpendicular to the body diagonal.

86. Draw the top and front views of a cube whose body diagonal, 2½″ long, is parallel to *V*. Make an auxiliary projection of the cube on a plane perpendicular to the body diagonal.

Group IX. Drawing from Memory.

A most valuable exercise is that of training the graphic memory in accuracy and power by drawing from memory. Select an object not previously used, such as one from Fig. 187 or Figs. 204 to 233, look at it with concentration for a certain time (from 10 seconds to a minute or more), close the book and make an accurate orthographic sketch. This practice may be varied in many ways that will suggest themselves. If continued faithfully it will strengthen wonderfully the power of observation.

Group X. Volume and Weight Calculations, with Slide Rule.

In calculating the weight of a piece from the drawings it should be divided or broken up into the geometric solids (prisms, cylinders, pyramids, cones) of which it is composed. The volume of each of these shapes should be calculated and these added, or sometimes subtracted, to find the total volume, which multiplied by the weight of the material per unit of volume will give the weight of the object.

A table of weights of materials will be found on page 464.

87. Find the weight of the cast iron block, Fig. 204.

88. Find the weight of the cast iron saddle bracket, Fig. 206.

89. Find the weight of the brass cross-block, Fig. 211.

90. Find the weight of the wrought iron drilling block, Fig. 220.

91. Find the weight of the cast iron eccentric, Fig. 226.

92. Find the weight of the block, aluminum, Fig. 236.

93. Find the weight of the fire clay burner block, Fig. 208.

These are given as examples of problems whose weights may be found. Many other problems, such as the flywheel, Fig. 460, may be used.

CHAPTER VIII

SECTIONS AND CONVENTIONS

105. Sectional Views.—The previous chapter has dealt with the method of describing the shape of an object by orthographic views, using dotted lines to indicate the invisible parts of it. If the object is very simple in its interior construction these hidden lines are not hard to read and understand. Often, however, when the interior is complicated or when several different pieces are assembled in place, the attempt to show the construction on an exterior view would result in a confusing mass of dotted lines, annoying to draw and difficult if not impossible to read clearly. In such cases one (or more) of the views is made "in section," a method of conventional representation in which for that particular view a part of the object is imagined to be cut or broken away and removed so as to expose the interior. This view is called a "sectional view," or simply a "section." It must be understood clearly that, in thus removing the front portion in order to make the sectional view, this portion is *not* removed or omitted from the other views.

When a drawing has more than one view in section, each sectional view should be considered separately without any reference to what has been cut away in other views.

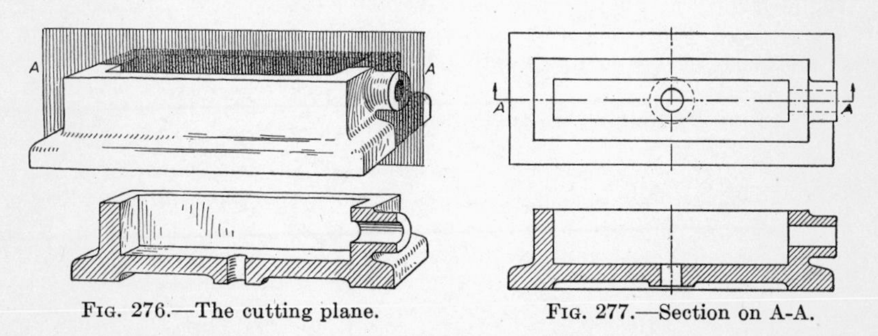

FIG. 276.—The cutting plane.

FIG. 277.—Section on A-A.

106. Figure 276 shows the picture of a casting intersected by a cutting plane and how it would appear if it had actually been sawed through by the plane and the front part removed, exposing the interior. Figure 277 shows the drawing as it would be made, with the front view in section. The edge of the cutting plane is indicated on the top view by a line symbol (line 7 in the alphabet of lines, page 26), with reference letters, and arrows showing the direction in which the view is taken.

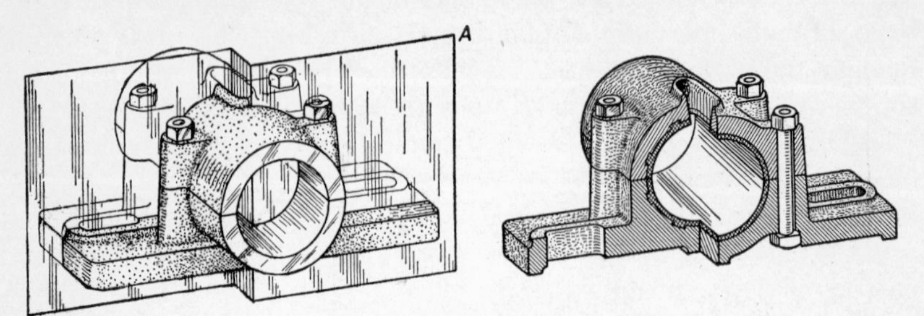

Fig. 278.—Picture of an offset cutting plane.

Wherever material has been cut by the section plane the cut surface is indicated by section lining, done with fine lines, generally at 45°, spaced uniformly to give an even tint.

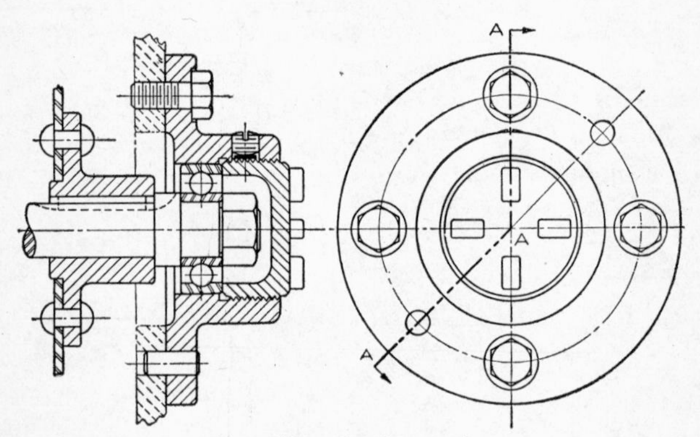

Fig. 279.—Section study.

107. Five Principles in Sectioning.

1. The cutting plane need not be a single continuous plane but may be offset or changed in direction so as to show the construction to the best advantage, Fig. 278.
2. Shafts, bolts, nuts, rods, rivets, keys and the like, whose axes occur in the plane of the section, are left in full and not sectioned, Fig. 279.
3. Invisible lines beyond the plane of the section should not be drawn unless necessary for the description of the piece.
4. Adjacent pieces are section-lined in opposite directions and are often brought out more clearly by varying the pitch for each piece, using closer spacing for the smaller pieces, Fig. 286.
5. The same piece in different views or in different parts of the same view should always be section-lined identically in spacing and in direction of lines on the paper.

108. A full section is a sectional view in which the cutting plane has cut entirely across the object, showing the whole view in section. It is usually taken straight through on the main axis or center line, as in Fig. 277, but the cutting plane may be offset or changed in direction to go through some detail not on the axis, as in Fig. 278. It is generally made in the place of the front view but may be a sectional side view or top view. Examples of full sections are shown in Figs. 480, 481, etc.

109. A half section is a view sometimes used with symmetrical objects, in which one half is drawn in section and the other half as a usual exterior view, Fig. 280. The cutting plane is imagined to extend halfway across, stopping at the axis or center line. This has the advantage of showing both the exterior and interior on one view, but a disadvantage is that inside diameters cannot be dimensioned well. Hidden lines are not drawn on either side except where necessary to describe the construction. Examples of half sections are given in Figs. 457 and 502.

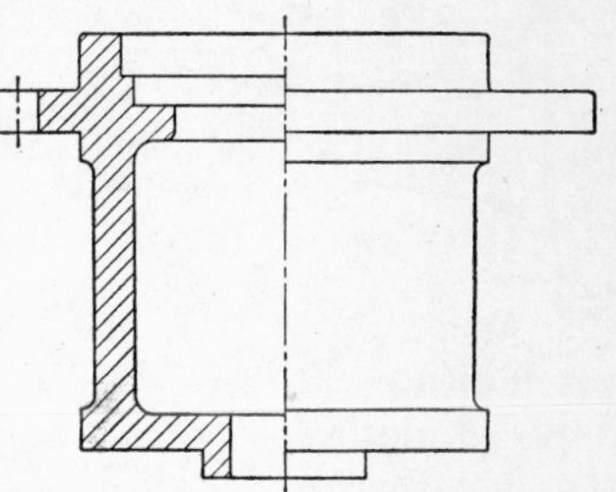

Fig. 280.—A half section.

110. A broken-out section is a partial section used on an exterior view to show some interior detail without drawing a complete full or half section. The object is imagined to be sawed by a cutting plane through the portion to be shown, and the part in front broken out, leaving an irregular break line, which, along with part of the contour of the object, will bound the broken-out section. Figures 281 and 509 show examples.

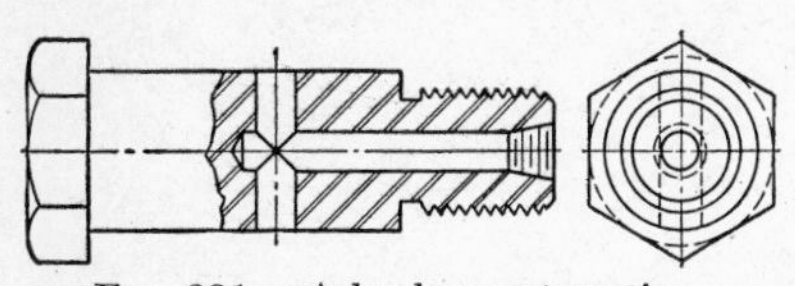

Fig. 281.—A broken-out section.

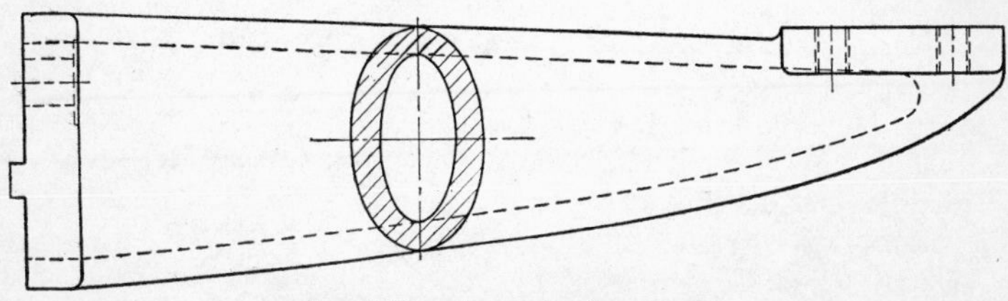

Fig. 282.—A revolved section.

111. A revolved section, made directly on an exterior view, provides a very convenient and useful method of showing the shape of the cross-section of some detail of construction such as a rib or the arm of a wheel. The cutting plane is passed perpendicular to the center line of the part to be shown and the resulting section revolved or turned up in place, Fig. 282. When the lines of the outline interfere with the section, as is sometimes the case, the piece may be broken out to leave a clear space for it. Figures 298, 460 and 514 contain some examples of revolved sections, or, as they are sometimes called, interpolated sections.

112. Detail sections, or **removed sections,** are for the same purpose as revolved sections but instead of being drawn on the piece they are set off to some adjacent place on the paper, Fig. 283. (This propeller blade is used with the hub of Fig. 493.) The cutting plane, with reference letters, should always be indicated. When the shape of a

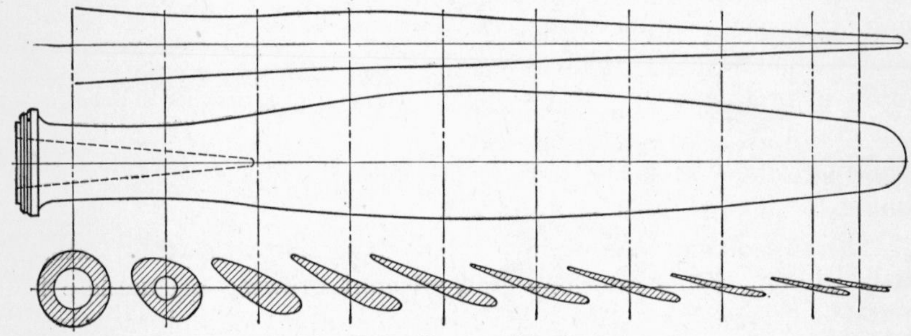

Fig. 283.—Removed sections.

piece is not uniform several of these cross-sections may be required. It is often of advantage to draw them to larger scale than that of the main drawing. Detail sections are sometimes called "separate sections" or "sliced sections." An example occurs in Fig. 502.

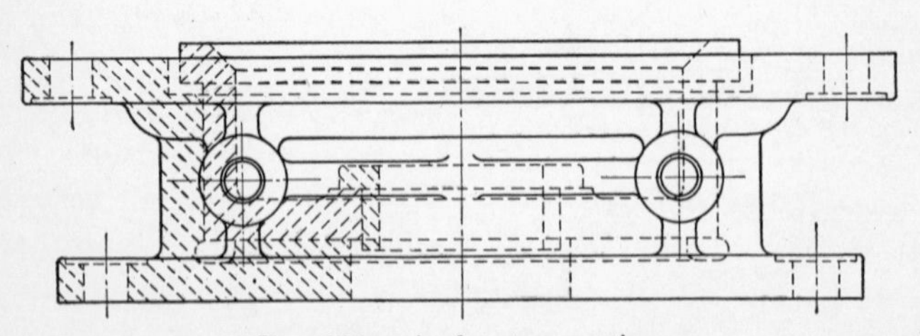

Fig. 284.—A phantom section.

113. A phantom section is an exterior view with the interior construction brought out by dotted cross-hatching, Fig. 284. It is rarely used, its only advantage being in a case where a broken-out section would cut away some detail on the outside. The term "phantom" is also used for an absent part, dotted in to show the relative position of the piece, as in Figs. 480 and 490.

114. Section Lining.—The spacing of section lines is done entirely by the eye, except when some form of mechanical section-liner is used. The pitch, or distance between lines, is governed by the size of the surface. For ordinary working drawings it will not be much less than 1/16″ and rarely over 1/8″. Very small pieces will have closer spacing. Care should be exercised in setting the pitch by the first two or three lines, and one should glance back at the first lines often in order that the pitch may not gradually increase or decrease. Nothing mars the appearance of a drawing more than poor section lining.

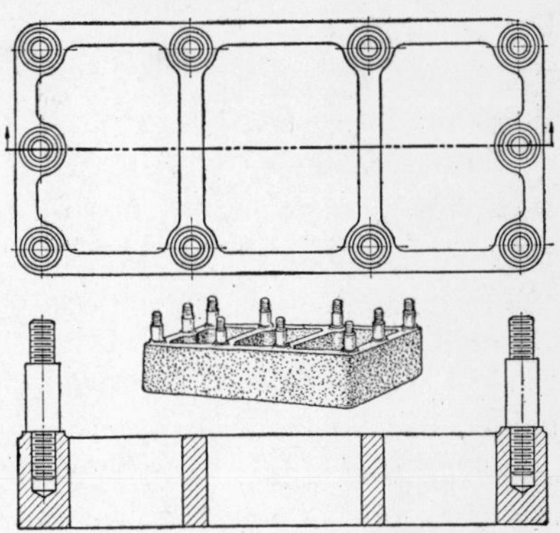

Fig. 285.—Omission of detail.

On assembly sections, shafts, bolts, nuts, screws, keys, pins, rivets, balls, rollers, etc., whose axes lie in the cutting plane have no interior parts to be shown and consequently are left in full, as if they had been removed when the section was cut, and afterward laid back in place, Fig. 279.

The usual rules of projection are generally followed in making sectional views, but confusion in reading a complicated piece may occur if all the detail behind the cutting plane is drawn. To insure clearness such detail as is not required in explaining the construction may be omitted, as in Fig. 285.

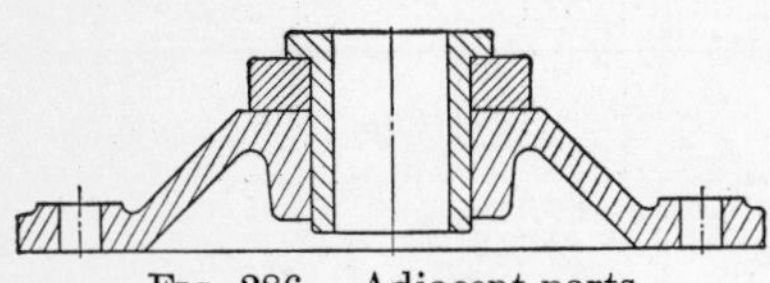

Fig. 286.—Adjacent parts.

Two adjacent pieces in an assembly section would be sectioned in opposite directions. If three pieces adjoin, one of them must be sectioned at another angle than 45°. If a piece is so shaped that 45° sectioning runs parallel or nearly so to one of its edges, another direction should be chosen, Fig. 286.

Large surfaces are sometimes sectioned only around the edge, as illustrated by the part view, Fig. 287.

Very thin sections, as sheet metal or structural steel shapes to small scale, may be shown in solid black, with white spaces between adjacent parts, Fig. 288.

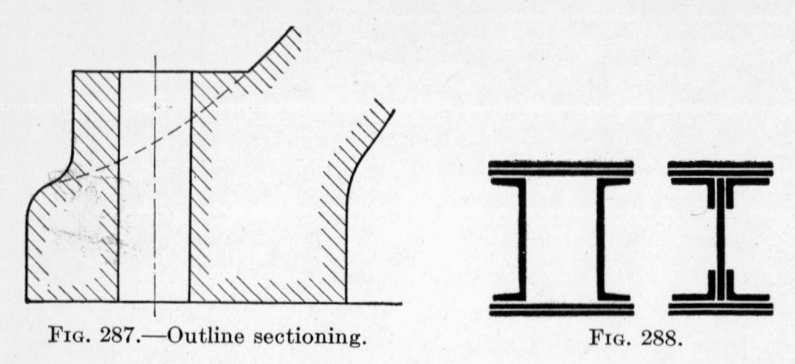

FIG. 287.—Outline sectioning. FIG. 288.

115. Conventional Sections.—Sometimes added clearness may be gained by violating strict projection. This is often found in making sectional views, as in a section through a pulley. Compare Figs. 477 and 480, one of a three-arm pulley, the other with solid web. The true projection of a section of the handwheel, Fig. 289, is unsymmetrical and misleading, therefore not good practical drawing. The preferred form is shown in the second view, where the foreshortened arm is revolved, or aligned, and neither arm section-lined.

116. Aligned Sections.—A section cut in more than a single direction may often be "aligned" or straightened out into one plane to

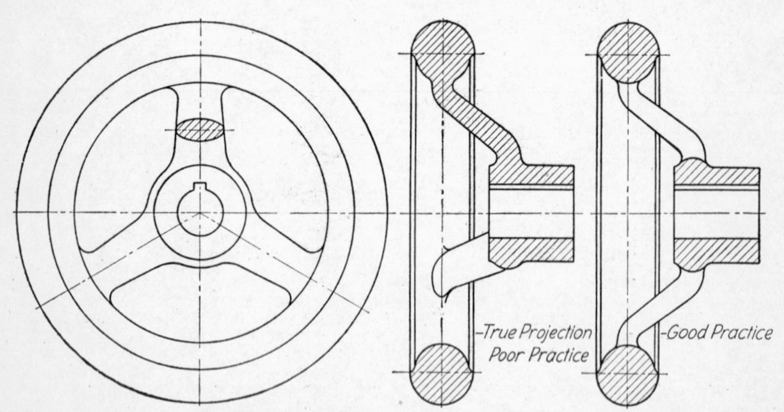

FIG. 289.—Conventional section.

good advantage. In Fig. 290 a straight section gives an unsymmetrical appearance to a symmetrical piece. In the second view the section is drawn as if the two directions of the cutting plane *A–A* were swung into a single plane.

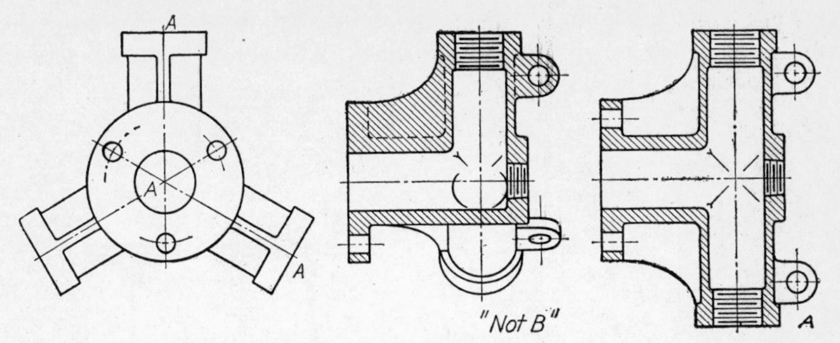

FIG. 290.—Symmetrical section.

117. Ribs in Section.—When the rib of a machine part lies in a sectional plane, if a true section be drawn the effect is heavy and misleading. The approved method is to omit the section lines from the

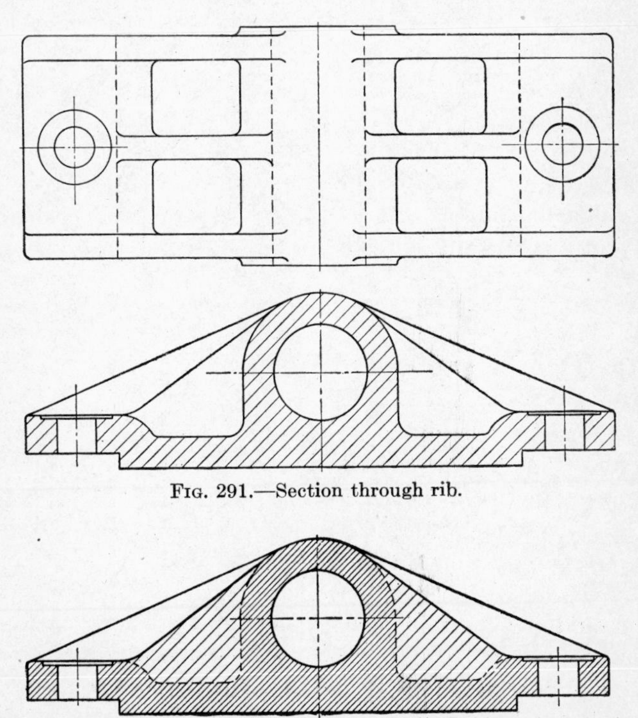

FIG. 291.—Section through rib.

FIG. 292.—Section through rib, using alternate section-lining.

rib, as if the cutting plane were just in front of it, Fig. 291. Another method, not so frequently used, is to omit alternate section lines from the rib, as in Fig. 292.

118. Drilled flanges in section should show the holes at their true distance from the center whether or not they come in the plane of the section. See Fig. 293, where the true projection is misleading. When the holes do not fall in the plane of the section they should be shown as if swung into it. This paragraph applies also to flanges in full views. Pipe fitters use the terms "one up" and "two up" to indicate whether the flange has one hole on the vertical axis or two holes across it.

119. Codes for Materials.—The American Standards Association's section line symbols for indicating different materials will be found on

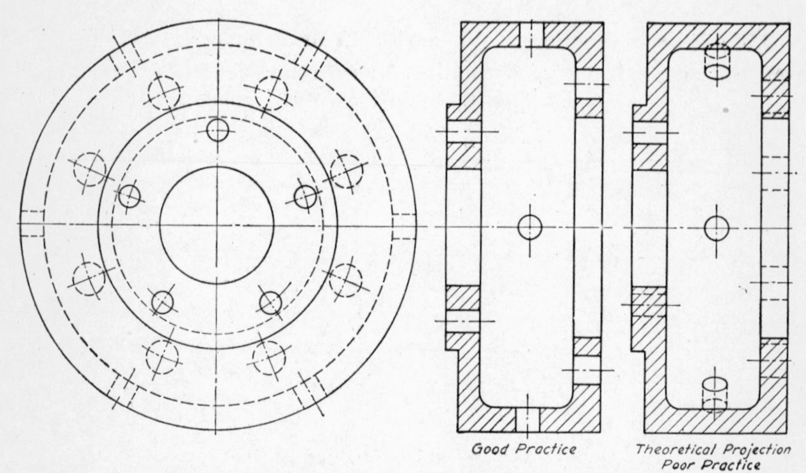

Fig. 293.—Conventional representation of drilling.

page 462. Symbolical section-lining is not commonly used on ordinary working drawings but sometimes in an assembly section it is desired to show a distinction between materials, and a recognized standard code is of obvious advantage. See Figs. 481 and 490. Code section-lining is used only as an aid in reading the drawing and is not to be taken as the official specification of the material. A note specifying the exact kind of material is always added on the detail drawing.

A common example of the use of symbolic sectioning is in distinguishing a bearing or lining metal such as Babbitt metal, poured into place hot. It is a universal practice to indicate such metal by the conventional symbol of crossed lines. The quickest way to make this symbol is to section over both the lining metal and the adjacent cast iron at once, then cross the lining metal in the other direction, but a better effect is gained by making it separately with finer pitch.

120. Conventional Practices.—There are violations of true projection in full views as well as in sectional views that are recognized as good practice because they add to the clearness of the drawing. For example, if a front view shows a hexagonal bolt head "across corners" the theoretical projection of the side view would be "across flats." In a working drawing when bolt heads occur they should be drawn across corners in both views, to show the space needed.

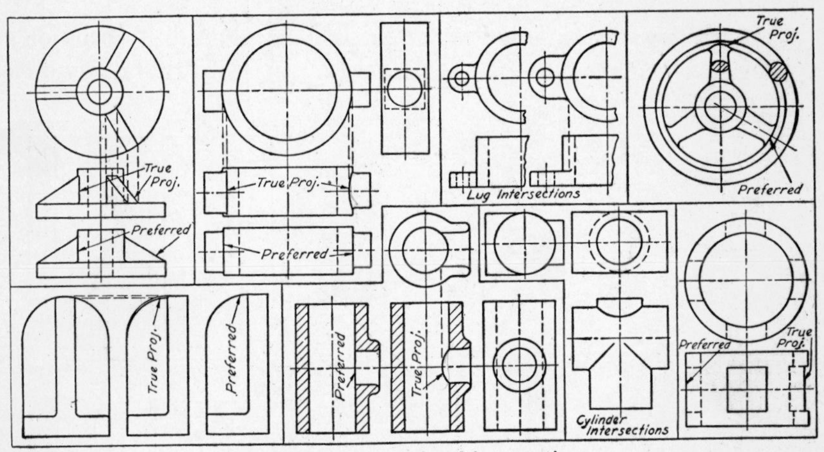

Fig. 294.—Conventional intersections.

Some typical examples, in which true lines of intersection are of no value as aids in reading the drawing and are therefore ignored, are shown in Fig. 294.

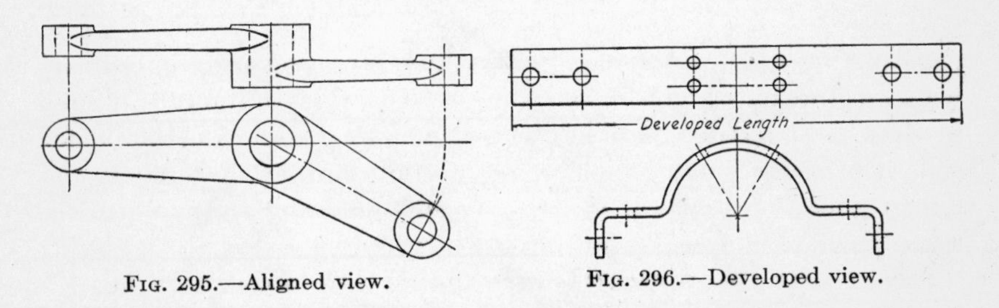

Fig. 295.—Aligned view.

Fig. 296.—Developed view.

Pieces which have parts at an angle with each other, as the lever of Fig. 295, may have their alignment straightened out in one view as shown. Similarly, bent pieces of the type of Fig. 296 should have one view made as a developed view.

Lugs or parts cast on for holding purposes, and to be machined off, are shown in phantom, in dashed lines. If in section, the section lines are dotted. Dashed lines are also used for indicating the limiting positions of moving parts and for showing adjacent parts which aid in locating the position or use of the piece.

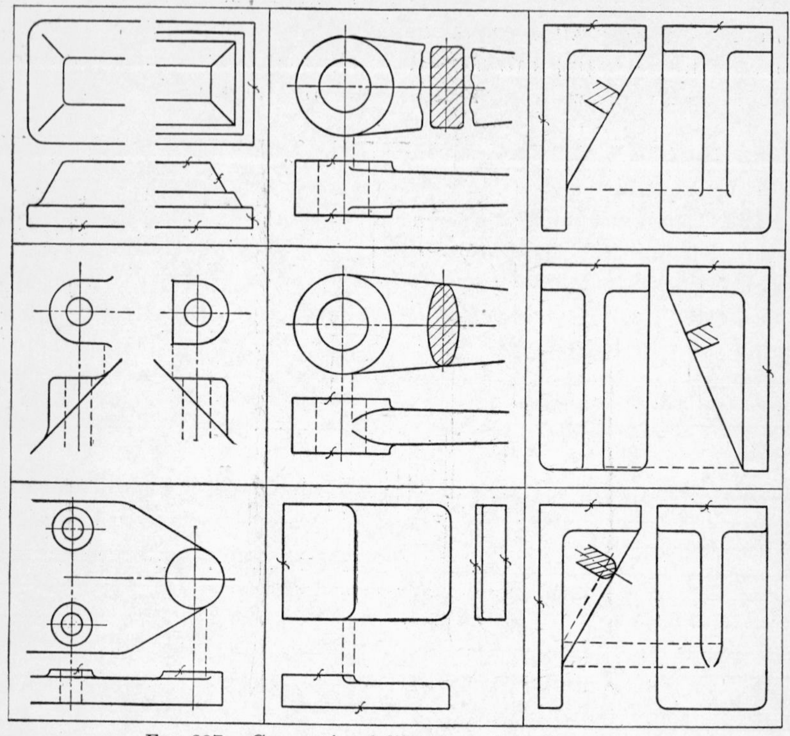

FIG. 297.—Conventional fillets, rounds and run-outs.

121. Fillets and Rounds.—In designing a casting a sharp internal angle must never be left, on account of the liability to fracture at that point. The radius of the fillet depends on the thickness of the metal and other design conditions. When not dimensioned, it is left to the pattern maker. External angles may be rounded for appearance or comfort, in radii ranging from merely removing the sharp edges to that of nearly the thickness of the piece. An edge made by the intersection of two unfinished surfaces of a casting should always be "broken" by a very small round. A sharp corner on a drawing thus indicates that one or both of the intersecting surfaces must be a finished surface. These minute rounds as well as other small fillets and "run-outs" are best put in freehand, in both pencil and ink.

Theoretically there would be no line between filleted intersections as there is no abrupt change in direction, so conventional indication is necessary. Figure 297 shows some methods of conventional representation of fillets and rounds, with the run-outs of arms and brackets intersecting other surfaces.

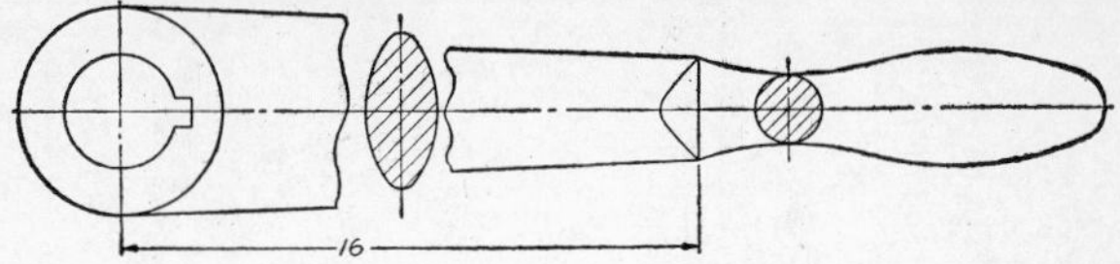

Fig. 298.—Broken out view.

122. Conventional Breaks.—In making a detail of a long bar or piece with uniform shape of section, there is evidently no necessity for drawing its whole length. It may be shown to larger scale and thus better by breaking out a piece, moving the ends together and giving the true length by a dimension as in Fig. 298. The characteristic shape of the cross-section is indicated by the break, as in Fig. 299.

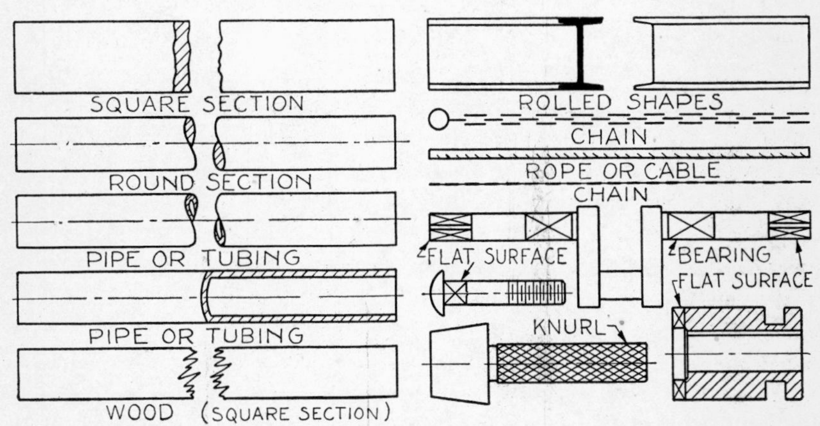

Fig. 299.—Conventional breaks and other symbols.

123. Half-views.—When space is very limited it is allowable practice to make the top or side views of a symmetrical piece as half-views. If the front view is an exterior view, the *front* half of the top or side view would be used, as in Fig. 300, but if a sectional view, the *rear* half would be used, as in Fig. 301. See Figs. 459 and 510 for examples.

124. Conventional Symbols.—Draftsmen use conventional representation for indicating many details, such as screw threads, springs, pipe fittings, electrical apparatus, etc. These have been standardized by the American Standards Association, whose code for materials in section has already been referred to in paragraph 119.

The symbol of two crossed diagonals is used for two distinct purposes: first, to indicate on a shaft the position of finish for a bearing, and, second, to indicate that a certain surface (usually parallel to the picture plane) is flat, but these two uses are not apt to be confused, Fig. 299.

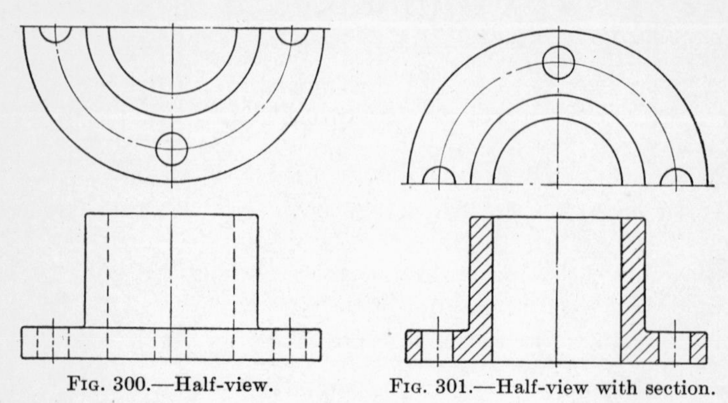

FIG. 300.—Half-view. FIG. 301.—Half-view with section.

On account of constant recurrence the representation of screw threads is one of the most important items under conventional symbols. Up to the time of their official standardization by the American Standards Association there were a dozen different thread symbols in use. Now, one regular symbol and one simplified one are adopted for American drawings, and both are understood internationally. These symbols for the indication of threads on bolts, screws and tapped holes are given in the chapter on Bolts and Screws, pages 156 and 157. The conventional representation of helical springs is discussed on page 169 and the conventional methods of representing pipe and fittings is given on page 172. Symbols for arc welding are shown on page 200.

The conventional symbols mentioned in the last paragraph are used principally in machine drawing. Architectural drawing, on account of the small scales employed, uses many conventional symbols, and topographic drawing is made up entirely of symbols. It is suggested that the reader consult the index of this book to find the symbol for some item desired.

125. References to isometric sections will be found on page 295, to architectural sections on page 346 and to masonry sections on page 366.

PROBLEMS

126. Selections from the following problems may be used either for shape description only or as working drawings by adding dimensions.

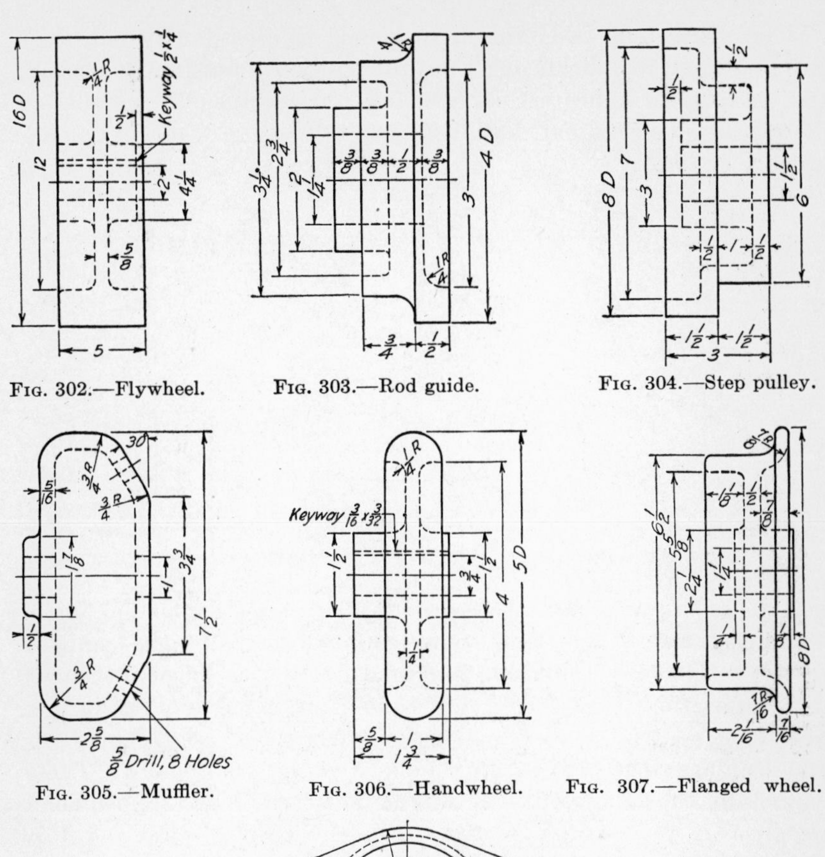

Fig. 302.—Flywheel.

Fig. 303.—Rod guide.

Fig. 304.—Step pulley.

Fig. 305.—Muffler.

Fig. 306.—Handwheel.

Fig. 307.—Flanged wheel.

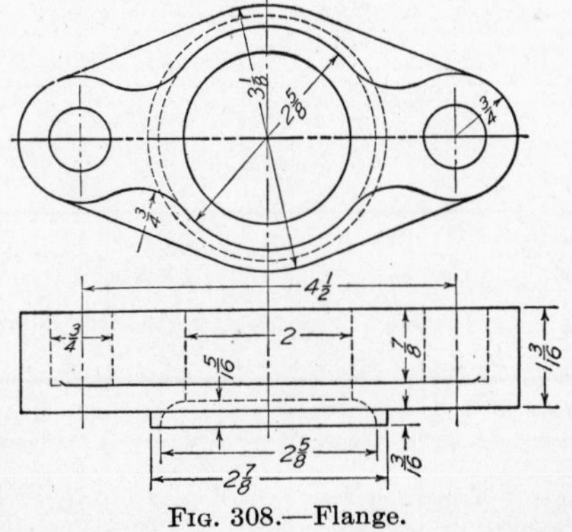

Fig. 308.—Flange.

1, 2, 3. Figs. 302, 303, 304. Draw a full front view, and a side view in section. Scale to suit.

4, 5, 6. Figs. 305, 306, 307. Draw a full front view, and a side view in section.

7. Fig. 308. Draw top view, and front view as a half section.

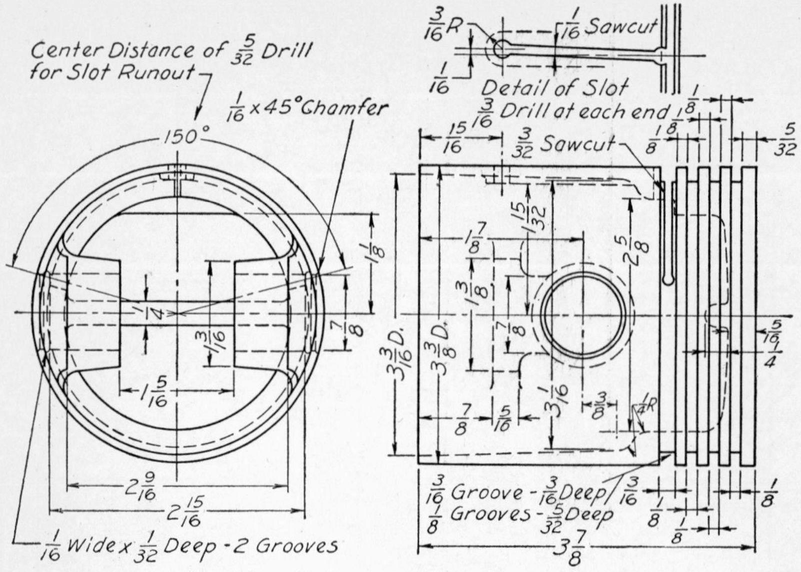

FIG. 309.—T-slot automotive piston (De Soto)

8. Fig. 309. Draw three views of automotive piston. Right half of end view to be a section on the center line of the piston pin. Lower half of front view in section. Top view to be a full section. Allow enough space between top and front views for a detail view of the slot, as shown. Some of the details of design, such as the drilling for oil return, have been omitted, to simplify the problem (11 × 10 space).

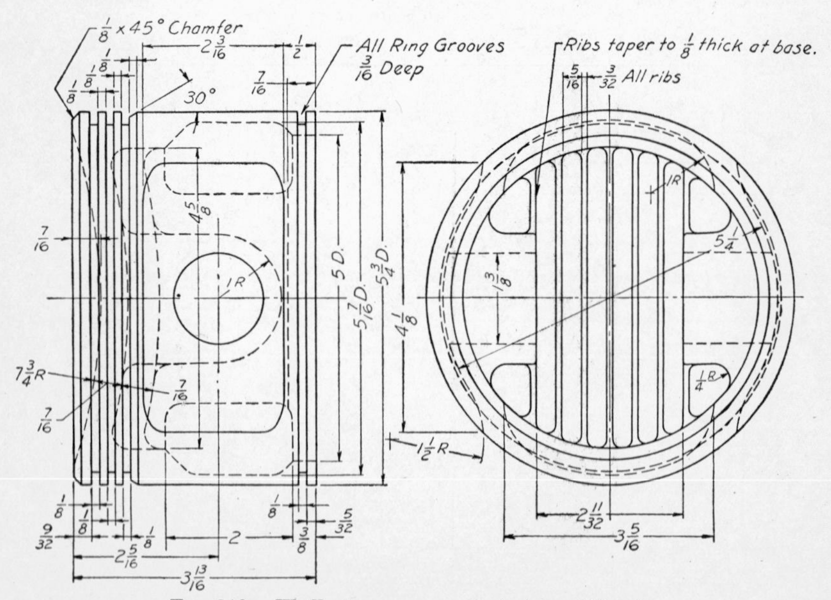

FIG. 310.—Waffle-type aeronautical piston (Wasp).

9. Fig. 310. Draw three views of aeronautical piston. Right half of end view to be a section on the center line of the piston pin. Top view and lower half of front view in section. Some details of design have been omitted, to simplify the problem ($11\frac{1}{2} \times 15$ space).

10. Fig. 311. Draw top view, and change front and side views to sectional views as indicated.

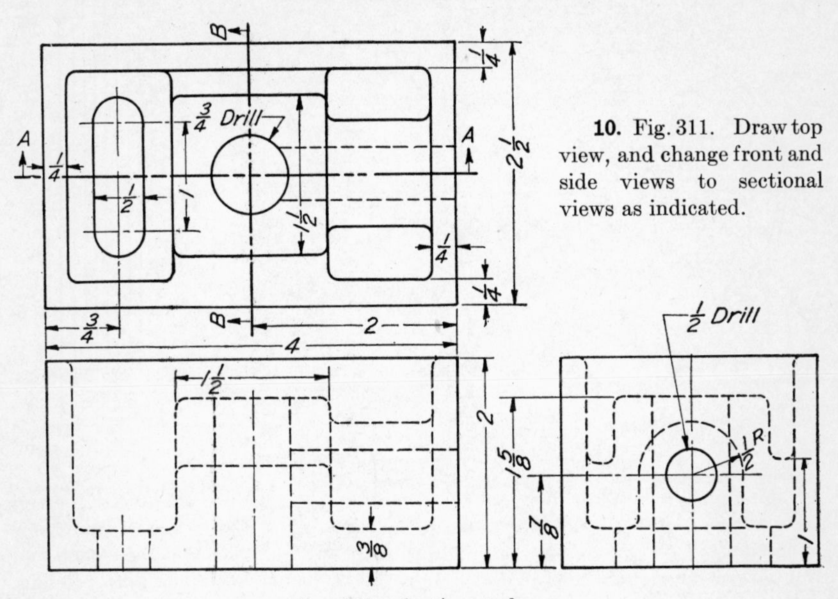

Fig. 311.—Section study.

11. Fig. 312. Draw top view, and make front and two side views in section on cutting planes indicated.

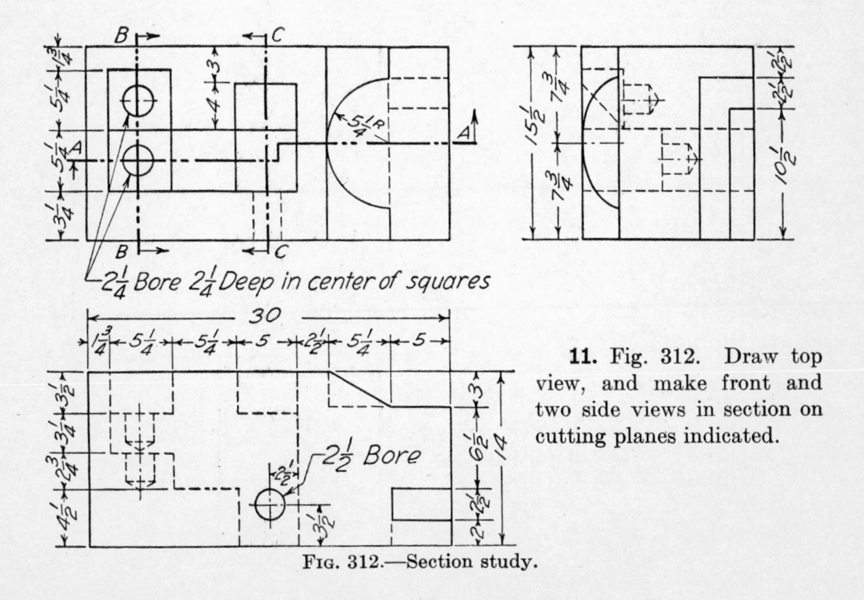

Fig. 312.—Section study.

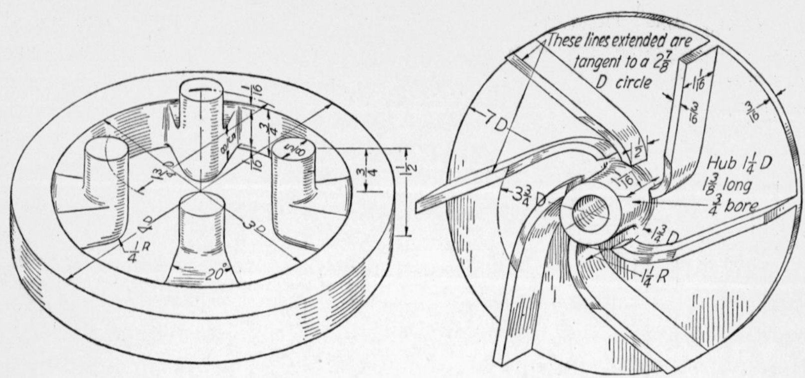

FIG. 313.—Selector ring. FIG. 314.—Impeller.

12. Fig. 313. Draw top view, and front view in conventional section (paragraph 115).

13. Fig. 314. Draw front view, and side view in conventional section (paragraph 115).

14. Fig. 315. Draw complete top view, and front view in half section.

15. Fig. 316. Select views which will best describe the piece. Submit sketch before drawing.

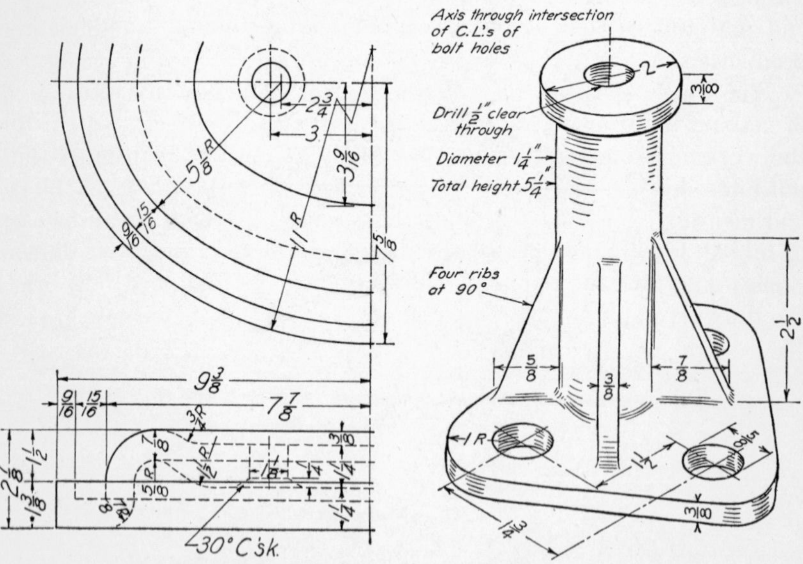

FIG. 315.—Manhole cover. FIG. 316.—Stem support.

CHAPTER IX

DIMENSIONS AND NOTES

127. After the correct representation of the object by its projections, that is, telling its *shape*, the entire value of the drawing as a working drawing lies in the dimensioning, that is, telling the *size.* Here our study of drawing as a language must be supplemented by a knowledge of shop methods. The machine draftsman to be successful must have an intimate knowledge of pattern-making, forging and machine shop practice, as well as, in some cases, sheet metal working, metal and plastic die-casting and structural steel fabrication.

The beginning student without this knowledge should not depend alone upon his instructor but should set about to inform himself regarding the elements of the pattern-maker's and founder's work, and as to the uses of the ordinary machine tools, observing work going through the shops and reading books and periodicals on methods and materials used in modern machine shop practice and machine production.

The dimensions put on a drawing are not necessarily those used in making the drawing, but those necessary and most convenient for the workmen who are to make the piece. The draftsman must thus put himself in the place of the pattern-maker, blacksmith or machinist and mentally construct the object represented, to see if it can be cast or forged or machined practically and economically, and what dimensions would give the required information in the best way. In brief, the drawing must be made with careful thought of its purpose.

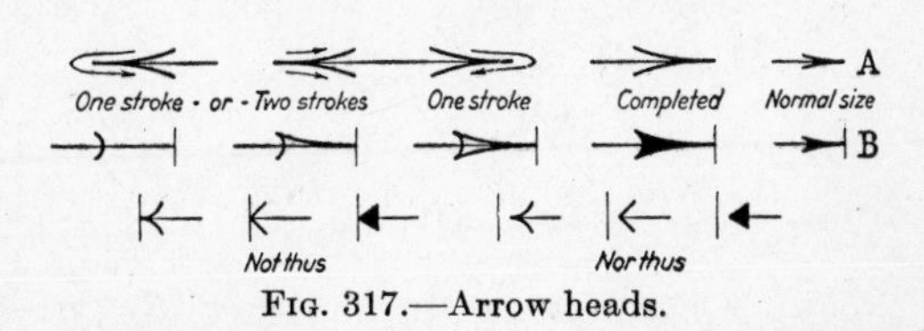

FIG. 317.—Arrow heads.

128. Lines and Symbols.—Dimension lines are made with fine full lines, so as to contrast with the heavier outline of the drawing. They are terminated by carefully made arrow heads whose tips touch the extension lines and thus indicate exactly the points to which the dimension is taken. Arrow heads are drawn with a writing pen on each dimension line just before the figures are added, making the sides either in one stroke, as shown in enlarged form in Fig. 317, or in two strokes from the point. The general preference is for the filled-in head, which is best made by first setting the length with a short curved stroke as shown at *B* in Fig. 317. The size of arrow heads varies somewhat with the size of the drawing but one-eighth inch is a good general length. The width at the base should not be more than one-third the length. All arrow heads on the same drawing should be the same size, except in restricted spaces. Avoid the incorrect shapes shown. In machine drawing practice a space is left in the line for the figures, which should always read with the line. It is universal in structural practice and is very common in architectural practice to place the figures above a continuous dimension line as in Fig. 711.

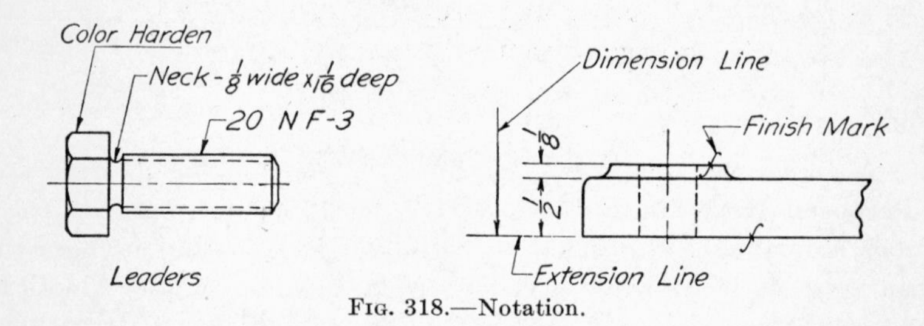

Fig. 318.—Notation.

Extension lines are fine lines extending outside the view to indicate the distance measured. They should not touch the outline but should start about 1/16″ from it and should extend about 1/8″ beyond the dimension line, Fig. 318.

Leaders are made up of fine straight ruled lines, with an arrow head touching the contour view or edge of the surface to which a note or dimension applies. When several are used they should be kept parallel if possible. The usual angle is 60°.

Figures must be carefully drawn in either vertical or inclined style and of a size to be easily readable. In an effort for neatness the beginner often gets them too small. One-eighth inch is a good general height.

Fractions must be made with the division line in line with the dimension line, and with figures two-thirds the height of the whole numbers, so that the total height of the fraction is nearly twice that of the whole number.

Feet and inches are indicated thus: 5′-6″. When there are no inches it should be so indicated, as 5′-0″, 5′-0½″. When dimensions are all in inches the inch mark is preferably omitted from all the dimensions.

129. Finish marks are used to indicate that certain surfaces of metal parts are to be machined, and that allowance must therefore be made on the casting or forging for finish. They are not necessary on parts made from rolled stock or on operations machined from the solid, as spot faces and drilled, reamed, counterbored or countersunk holes. The symbol which has been in use for many years is an italic *f* with its cross-mark intersecting the line, placed on all views which show the surface as a line, including hidden lines. If the piece is to be finished all over, the note "Finish all over" is used and the marks on the drawing omitted. Figure 319 illustrates the use of the finish mark.

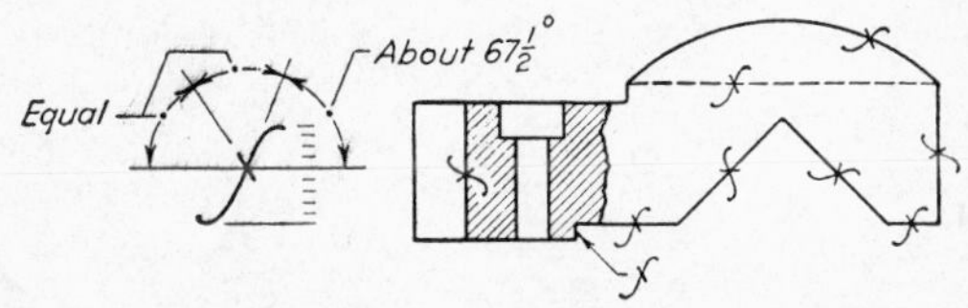

Fig. 319.—The finish mark.

Proposed New Finish Mark.—Meeting the objection that the *f* symbol is inadequate for modern manufacture and that it mars the appearance of a drawing even when made neatly, the American Standards Association is proposing a new symbol, a 60° V with its point touching the line representing the surface to be machined, and with a key number placed in the angle of the V to indicate the degree of finish required. At the present writing (1935) the sub-committee on standard finishes has not completed the details of its report on the proposed new marks.

130. Theory of Dimensioning.—Any object, even if apparently complicated, can be analyzed as made up of a combination of simple geometrical shapes, principally prisms and cylinders, with occasionally parts of pyramids and cones, now and then a double curved surface and very rarely (except for the surface of screw threads) some warped surfaces. If, *first*, each of these elemental shapes be dimensioned and, *second*, the relative location of each be given, measured from center or base lines or from each other, the dimensioning of any piece can be done systematically and simply. Dimensions may thus be classified under the divisions *Size Dimensions* and *Location Dimensions*.

131. Size Dimensions.—As every solid has three dimensions, each of the geometrical shapes making up the object must have its length, breadth and thickness indicated in the dimensioning.

The commonest shape met with is the *prism*, usually in plinth, or flat, form. The universal rule to be followed is: *Give two of the three dimensions on the view showing the contour shape, and the third on one of the other views.* Analyze Figs. 320 and 321, then Fig. 324.

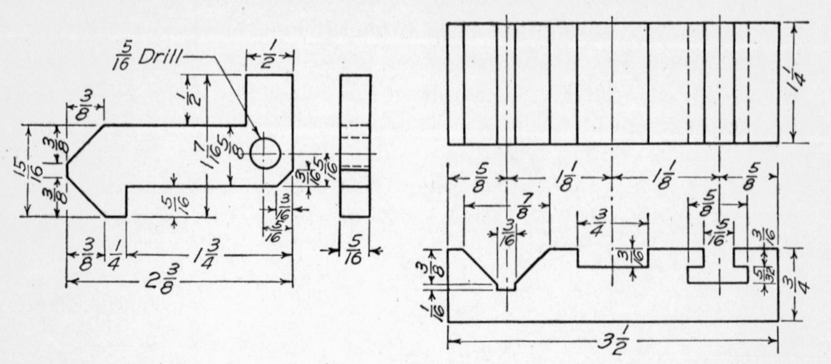

FIG. 320.—Contour rule applied (trip finger).

FIG. 321.—Contour rule applied (locating block).

The second shape is the *cylinder*, found on nearly every mechanical piece as a shaft or a boss or a hole. A cylinder obviously requires only two dimensions, diameter and length. While it cannot be given as a rule, it is good practice to give the diameter and length on the same

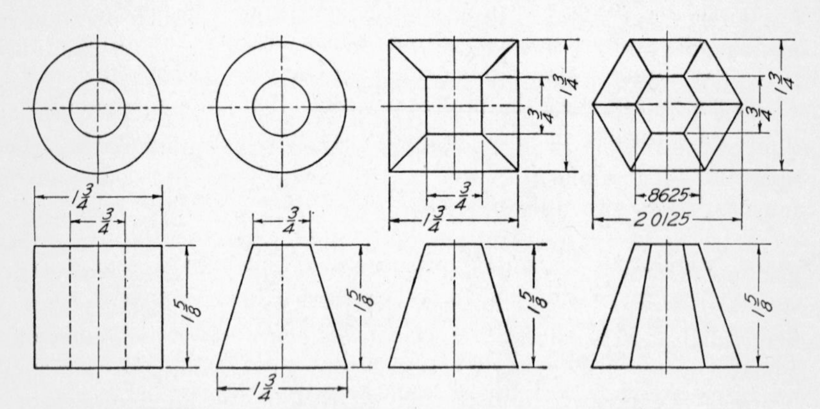

FIG. 322.—Dimensioning cylinders, cones and pyramids.

view, Fig. 322. An exception to this is in the case of "negative cylinders," or holes, in which the diameter and operation are better given together as a note on the contour view, as in Fig. 320. The contour rule also applies to all partial cylinders, such as rounded corners and fillets, whose radii must be given on the view that shows their shape.

Cones may be dimensioned with the altitude and diameters on the same view. They usually occur as frustums or as tapers.

Taper per foot means the difference in diameters or widths in one foot of length. In dimensioning a taper, when the slope of the taper is specified, the length and one diameter are given, or both diameters may be given, omitting the length of the taper, Fig. 323. See page 443 for taper dimensions.

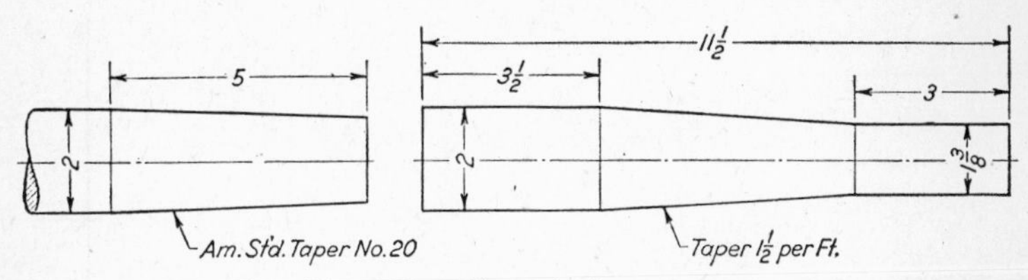

Fig. 323.—Dimensioning tapers.

Pyramids should have two of their three dimensions given on the view that shows the shape of the base.

Spheres are dimensioned by giving the diameter on the most convenient view; other surfaces of revolution by dimensioning the generating curve.

Warped surfaces are dimensioned according to their method of generation; and as their representation requires numerous sections, each of these must be fully dimensioned.

132. Location Dimensions.—The selection and placing of location dimensions require even more thought than do size dimensions. The operations of making the piece and the way it fits with other pieces must be kept constantly in mind.

After the size dimensions have been put on, take up the elementary geometric forms again one by one and locate each in the way best suited to its method of construction, its importance, the accuracy demanded and its relation to other elements of the unit or machine. Illustrating with Fig. 325, the *importance* of locating the two shaft bearings is indicated in that they were dimensioned first and in a conspicuous position; that *accuracy* is required between the two bearings is shown by locating the lower one with reference to the upper one; the *relationship* of one part to another is indicated in that the vertical location dimensions for the upper bearing and the bolt holes are taken from the under surface of the integral spline. On the drawing of the piece to which this support bracket is to be bolted, all vertical information relating to the bracket would, therefore, be given from the lower surface of the slot on which the bracket spline rests when the two pieces are assembled.

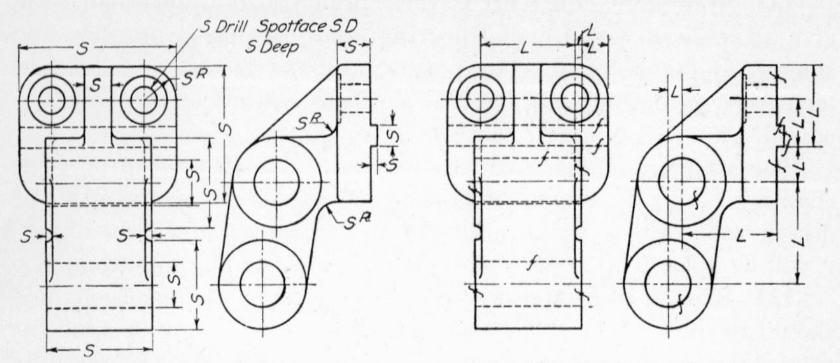

FIG. 324.—Size dimensions. FIG. 325.—Location dimensions.

Flat surfaces are located from center lines or from base lines representing the edge of finished surfaces. Every circle representing a

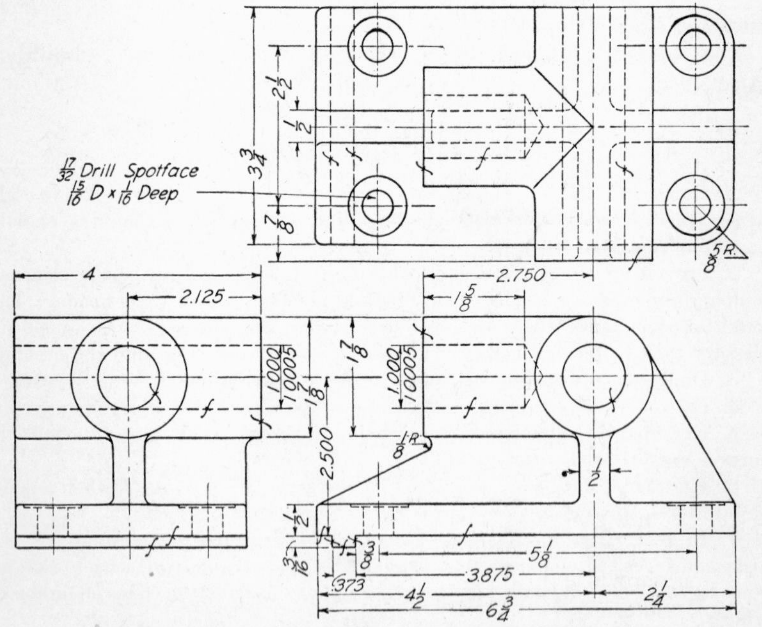

FIG. 326.—An example of dimensioning (angle shaft bracket).

cylinder will have two center lines at right angles. Locate the axis of the cylinder by dimensioning from these center lines, as in Figs. 325

and 326. In general, location dimensions are made from either a finished surface or a center line. With rough castings or forgings a basic surface should be selected or a center line assumed.

133. Systematic adherence to these principles of dimensioning will give an assurance and confidence that the drawing is properly and completely dimensioned. Not only will all the necessary dimensions have been given, but any unnecessary ones will not even have been considered.

The ability to think in three dimensions, emphasized in previous chapters, is of just as much importance in size description as in shape description. Unless one can look at the drawing and see the object, it will be difficult to apply this theory of dimensioning intelligently.

134. Placing of Dimensions.—All extension and dimension lines should be drawn before any figures are put in. Bearing in mind the convenience and ease of reading the drawing, study the piece carefully and place each dimension line where one would naturally look for it. Be careful not to crowd dimension lines. Keep them at least one-quarter inch away from the drawing and from each other. Sometimes it may be found necessary to move a size dimension in order to place a location dimension advantageously.

The following general rules, grouped for convenience, should be observed.

RULES FOR DIMENSIONING

1. Horizontal and sloping dimensions should always read from left to right, and vertical dimensions from bottom to top; that is, the drawing should be readable from the bottom and right side.

2. Preferably keep dimensions outside the view, unless added clearness, simplicity and ease of reading will result from placing some of them inside. They should for appearance's sake be kept off the cut surfaces of sections. When it is necessary they be placed there, the section lining is omitted around the numbers.

3. Dimensions should generally be placed between views.

4. Do not repeat dimensions unless there is a special reason for it.

5. Keep parallel dimension lines at equal distances apart and "stagger" the figures. See Fig. 310.

6. Figures should be halfway between the arrow heads, except when a center line interferes, or when several parallel dimensions are staggered.

7. In general give location dimensions from or across center lines, or from finished surfaces. Remember that rough castings or forgings will vary in size, and do not locate drilled holes or other machine operations from the edges of unfinished surfaces.

8. Never give dimensions to the edge of a circular part, but always from center to center.

9. If it is practical to locate a point by dimensioning from two center lines do not give an angular dimension.

10. Never use a center line as a dimension line.

11. Never use a line of the drawing as a dimension line.

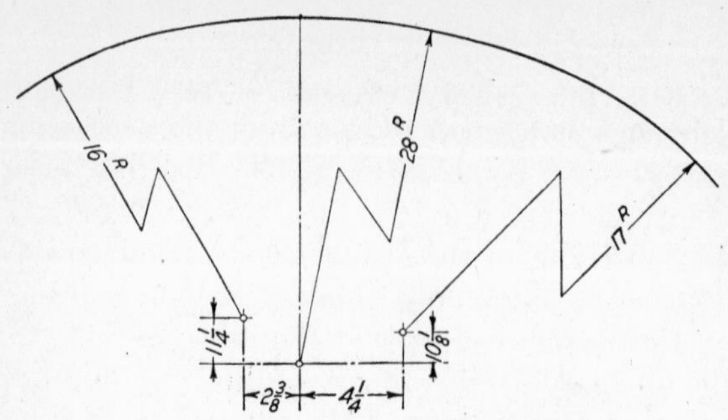

FIG. 327.—Inaccessible centers.

12. Do not allow a dimension to cross an extension line unless unavoidable.

13. For equally spaced holes in a circular flange give the diameter of the "bolt circle," with the number and size of holes. See Fig. 511.

14. Give the diameter of a circle, not the radius. It should be followed by the abbreviation *D* except when it is obvious from the drawing that the dimension is a diameter.

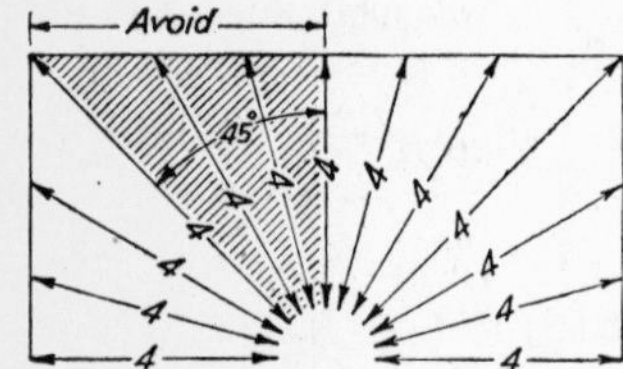

FIG. 328.—Undesirable zone.

15. Give the radius of an arc, followed by the letter *R* (a radius dimension line has no arrow head at the arc's center).

16. When locating the center of an arc lying outside the limits of the drawing, the radial dimension line is offset as in Fig. 327.

17. Avoid running dimensions in a direction included in the shaded area of Fig. 328. If this is unavoidable they should read downward with the line.

18. A number of dimensions in a row may be either continuous or staggered, continuous preferred, Fig. 329.

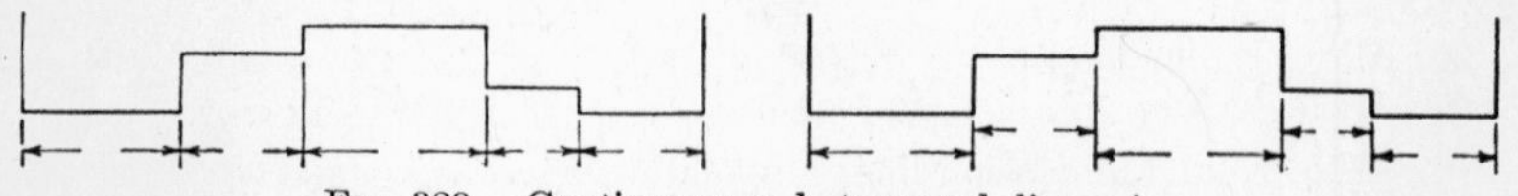

FIG. 329.—Continuous and staggered dimensions.

19. Always give the three over-all dimensions (a usual exception is with pieces having cylindrical ends, paragraph 135), placing them outside any other dimensions.

20. Never require a workman to add or subtract dimensions.

21. Never require a workman to scale a drawing.

22. Dimensions must never be crowded. If space is small, methods as illustrated in Fig. 330 may be used. If still too small, use an enlarged removed section or part view.

23. A dimension which has been changed so as not to agree with the scaled distance should be underscored with a heavy line, or indicated by one of the

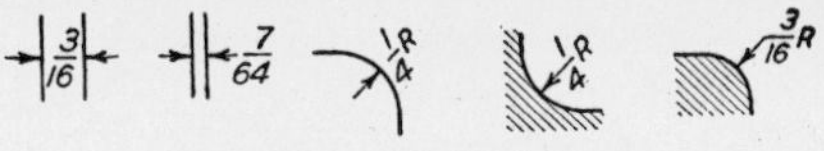

FIG. 330.—Limited space.

methods of Fig. 331. If several such changes occur on a drawing they should be listed in tabular form with reference letters.

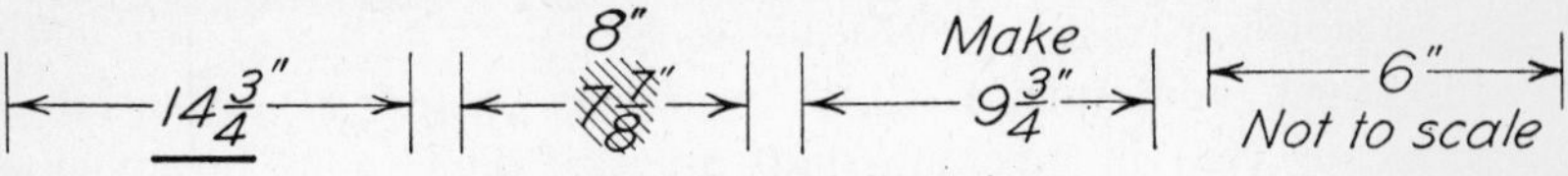

FIG. 331.—Revised dimensions.

24. The dimension for an angle should be placed horizontally on an arc as a dimension line. Exception may be made for a large angle, placing the dimension in line with the arc, Fig. 332.

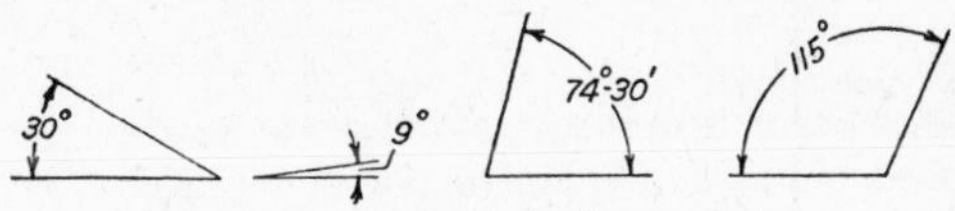

FIG. 332.—Dimensioning angles.

25. A curved line may be dimensioned either by radii or offsets, Figs. 333 and 334.

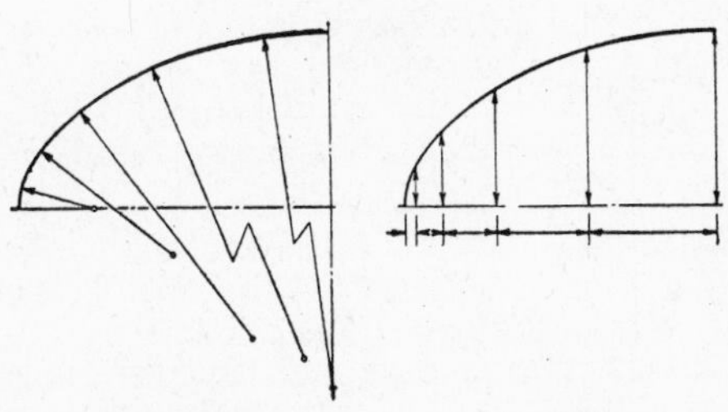

FIG. 333. FIG. 334.
Dimensioning curves.

26. All notes should read horizontally if possible.
27. Make decimal points of ample size.
28. Do not add any unnecessary dimensions.

135. Shapes with rounded ends should be dimensioned according to their method of manufacture. Figure 335 shows three similar

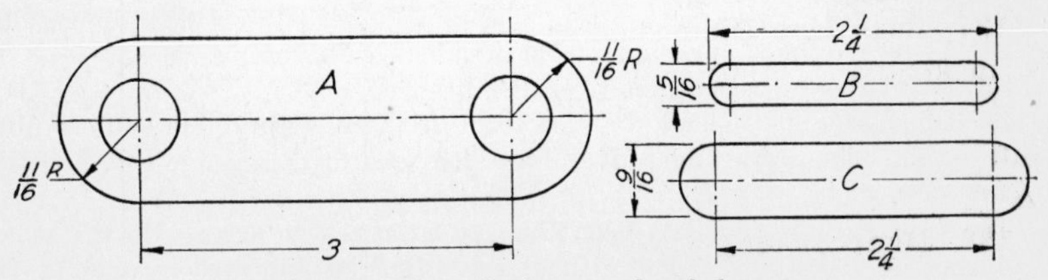

FIG. 335.—Dimensioning round end shapes.

contours differently dimensioned. The link *A* has the radius of the curve and the center distance given, as it would be laid out. *B* shows the contour view of a Pratt and Whitney key or keyway. These keys are specified by their width and over-all length, and the keyway is dimensioned to correspond. At *C*, a slot machined from the solid as with a milling machine, the given dimensions show the diameter of the cutter and travel of the table.

136. Feet and Inches.—The American Standards Association recommends that in machine shop practice dimensions be given in inches up to 72 inches. In architectural and structural work, dimensions over 12 inches are given in feet and inches.

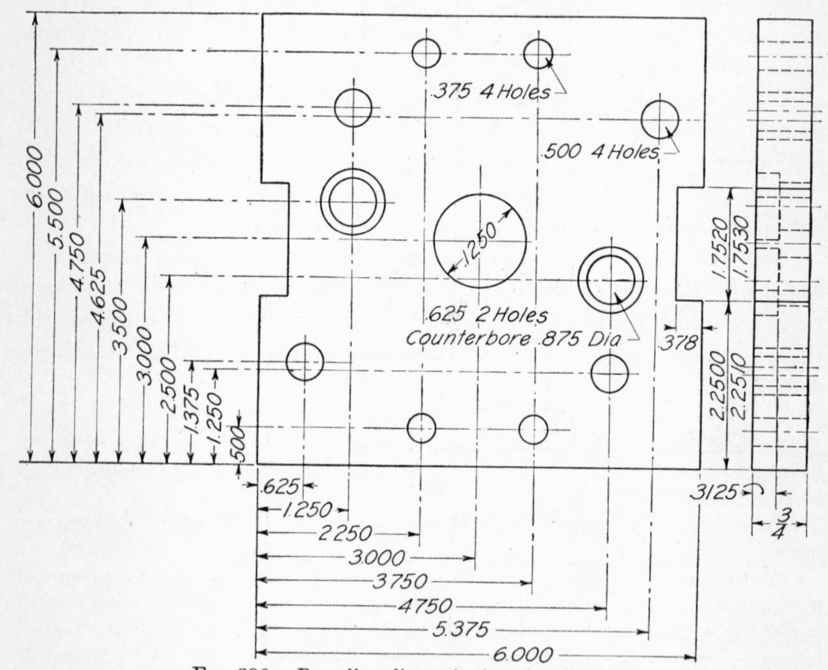

Fig. 336.—Base line dimensioning, for die work.

137. Base Line Dimensioning.—This method, principally used in die making and other precision work, takes two finished edges at right angles as base or reference lines and measures all dimensions from these lines. The jig plate, Fig. 336, is an example. The advantage of this method is that errors will not be cumulative.

138. Dimensioning Threaded Parts.—The representation, dimensioning and notation of threaded parts according to the American

Standards Association are taken up in detail in the next chapter and hence are not repeated here. See page 159 *et seq.*

139. Decimal Dimensioning.—In dimensioning any working drawing, the degree of accuracy required for various mating parts confronts the draftsman. In the ordinary dimensioning of surfaces to be machined, American practice uses as standard sizes the common fractions of an inch, as $\frac{1}{2}$, $\frac{1}{4}$, $\frac{1}{8}$, $\frac{1}{16}$, $\frac{1}{32}$, $\frac{1}{64}$. In general the limit of accuracy expected in a fraction dimension is not less than 0.010″. With closely fitting parts the old practice was to mark both parts with the same dimension and add a note such as "drive fit," "loose fit," etc., leaving the amount of allowance to the judgment of the machine shop. In modern practice the dimension for each piece is given in decimals to thousandths or ten-thousandths of an inch, the engineering department taking all the responsibility for the correctness of the kind of fit required.

Since it is not possible to work to absolute accuracy, and in the modern system of quantity production with the requirement of "interchangeable assembly," it is necessary to give these dimensions with "limits," that is, the maximum and minimum sizes within which the actual measurements must fall in order to be accepted.

140. Allowances and Tolerances.—The five terms—*nominal size*, *basic size*, *allowance*, *tolerance* and *limits* are so interconnected that their meanings should be clearly understood before the study of the theory of limit dimensioning is attempted. The American Standards Association gives the following definitions:

Nominal Size.—A designation given to the subdivision of the unit of length having no specified limits of accuracy but indicating a close approximation to a standard size.

Basic Size.—The exact theoretical size from which all limiting variations are made.

Allowance.—(Neutral zone.) An intentional difference in the dimensions of mating parts; or the minimum clearance space which is intended between mating parts. It represents the condition of the tightest permissible fit, or the largest internal member mated with the smallest external member. It is to provide for different classes of fit.

Tolerance.—The amount of variation permitted in the size of a part.

Limits.—The extreme permissible dimensions of a part.

In illustration of these terms suppose a 2″ shaft to have a free fit (class 2) in a 2″ hole. The *nominal size* is 2″. The *basic size* is the exact theoretical size of the hole, 2.0000″. (This is called the "basic hole" system, in which the minimum size of the hole is taken as a base from which all variations are made.) The A.S.A. *allowance* for a 2″ free fit is 0.0022 and the *tolerance* 0.0016. Thus the limits of the size of the hole would be a minimum of 2.0000 and a maximum of 2.0000 + 0.0016 = 2.0016. The limits for the shaft would be the basic size minus the allowance (2.0000 − 0.0022 = 1.9978) as the maximum, and this maximum minus the tolerance

$$(1.9978 - 0.0016 = 1.9962)$$

as the minimum. These limits would be put on the drawing as shown in Fig. 337. Note that the hole dimension has the min. over the max., and the shaft dimension has the max. over the min. This is for convenience in machining.

1.9978
1.9962

2.0000
2.0016

Fig. 337.

In this example the tightest fit possible (max. shaft in min. hole) would be 0.0022, and the loosest fit possible (min. shaft in max. hole) 0.0054.

Where a number of fits of the same nominal size are required on one shaft, as in line shafting, the "basic shaft" system is used instead of the "basic hole" system, using for the basic size the maximum diameter of the shaft.

Figure 338 is an example of limit dimensioning.

141. Classes of Fits.—Different allowances must be made for different kinds of fits and in various classes of machinery. When one part is to move on another the allowance is positive; if they are to be forced together it is negative; that is, the shaft would be larger than the hole and there would be an "interference" of metal.

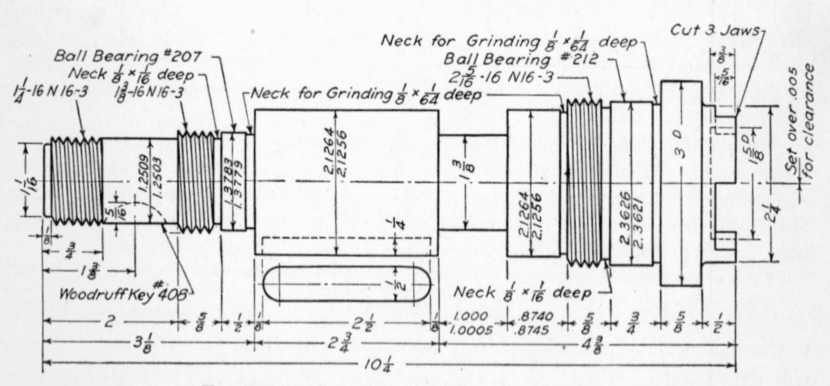

Fig. 338.—Limit dimensioning (clutch shaft).

The American Standards Association has made a classification of eight different kinds of fits and has compiled tables of limits for external and internal members for different sizes in each class. These limits are tabulated on pages 454 and 455 in the Appendix.

CLASSIFICATION OF FITS, A.S.A.

Loose Fit (**Class 1**)—**Large Allowance.**—This fit provides for considerable freedom and embraces certain fits where accuracy is not essential.

Examples: Machined fits of agricultural and mining machinery; controlling apparatus for marine work; textile, rubber, candy and bread machinery; general machinery of a similar grade; some ordnance material.

Free Fit (**Class 2**)—**Liberal Allowance.**—For running fits with speeds of 600 r.p.m. or over, and journal pressures of 600 pounds per square inch or over.

Examples: Dynamos, engines, many machine-tool parts and some automotive parts.

Medium Fit (**Class 3**)—**Medium Allowance.**—For running fits under 600 r.p.m. and with journal pressures less than 600 pounds per square inch; also for sliding fits; and the more accurate machine-tool and automotive parts.

Snug Fit (**Class 4**)—**Zero Allowance.**—This is the closest fit which can be assembled by hand and necessitates work of considerable precision. It should be used where no perceptible shake is permissible and where moving parts are not intended to move freely under a load.

Wringing Fit (**Class 5**)—**Zero to Negative Allowance.**—This is also known as a "tunking fit" and it is practically metal-to-metal. Assembly is usually selective and not interchangeable.

Tight Fit (**Class 6**)—**Slight Negative Allowance.**—Light pressure is required to assemble these fits and the parts are more or less permanently assembled, such as the fixed ends of studs for gears, pulleys, rocker arms, etc. These fits are used for drive fits in thin sections or extremely long fits in other sections and also for shrink fits on very light sections. Used in automotive, ordnance and general machine manufacturing.

Medium Force Fit (**Class 7**)—**Negative Allowance.**—Considerable pressure is required to assemble these fits and the parts are considered permanently assembled. These fits are used in fastening locomotive wheels, car wheels, armatures of dynamos and motors, and crank disks to their axles or shafts. They are also used for shrink fits on medium sections or long fits. These fits are the tightest which are recommended for cast iron holes or external members as they stress cast iron to its elastic limit.

Heavy Force and Shrink Fit (**Class 8**)—**Considerable Negative Allowance.**—These fits are used for steel holes where the metal can be highly stressed without exceeding its elastic limit. These fits cause excessive stress for cast iron holes. Shrink fits are used where heavy force fits are impractical, as on locomotive wheel tires, heavy crank disks of large engines, etc.

142. In dimensioning with limits, experience in manufacturing is needed as well as a study of the particular mechanism involved before the draftsman is able to know just the accuracy necessary and can specify proper fits and tolerances. The following quotation from the A.S.A. Standard is pertinent:

"In choosing the class of fit for manufacture, the engineer should keep in mind that cost usually increases proportionately to the accuracy required, and no finer class of fit should be chosen than the functional requirements actually demand.

It is axiomatic that the closer the fit the smaller the manufacturing tolerance, and usually the greater the cost. The length of engagement of the fit also plays an important part in the selection of the class of fit for a piece of work. It is obvious that a long engagement will tolerate more looseness than a short one, and due regard should be paid to this feature."

143. Example of Use of A.S.A. Tables.—Suppose a $1\frac{1}{4}''$ shaft is designed to run with a class 3 fit. The table (page 454) shows that the hole may vary between $+0.0000$ and $+0.0009$, and the shaft between -0.0010 and -0.0019; that is, the tolerance is 0.0009 and the allowance 0.0010. The basic size is 1.2500; thus the dimension put on the hole would be $\frac{1.2500}{1.2509}$, and on the shaft $\frac{1.2490}{1.2481}$.

This is known as the unilateral system, in which the tolerance is taken all plus or all minus from the basic size. In Fig. 339 the method shown at *A* is approved by the American Standards Association and is the method to use where gages are used and on small parts. That at *B* is sometimes used and is approved for large parts where gages are

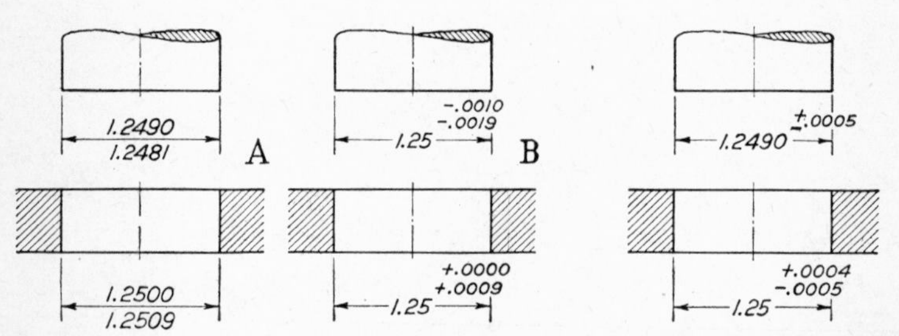

Fig. 339.—Unilateral system. Two methods.

Fig. 340.—Bilateral system.

not used, but it requires the workman to add or subtract figures. Another system known as bilateral limits is sometimes used, though not recommended. In it a dimension is written as 2. ± 0005, meaning that the total tolerance is 0.001, one-half of which may be above and one-half below the theoretical size, Fig. 340.

144. The Ford Decimal System.—After two years of successful trial and use the Ford Motor Company in December, 1934, released for publication the story of the new decimal system employed in the Ford plants for dimensioning of drawings and in the manufacturing operations following.

This new system abandons the cumbersome common fractions of quarters, eighths, sixteenths, etc., and uses decimal divisions for all subdivisions of the inch. It thus secures one of the principal advantages claimed for the metric system, without the disadvantages which have prevented the universal adoption of that system.

The American designer thinks in inches. The only change required of him in adopting the Ford system is that he discard thinking in terms of eighths and sixteenths and begin to think in terms of tenths, working with a decimal scale instead of his present one of inches and sixteenths. In the engineering department and the various shops throughout the Ford plant all scales marked in common fractions were replaced by scales based on tenths of an inch, which, to facilitate reading, have the smallest divisions fiftieths instead of hundredths. Figure 341 shows a portion of one of the scales used. Notice the arrangement of lengths of the division marks.

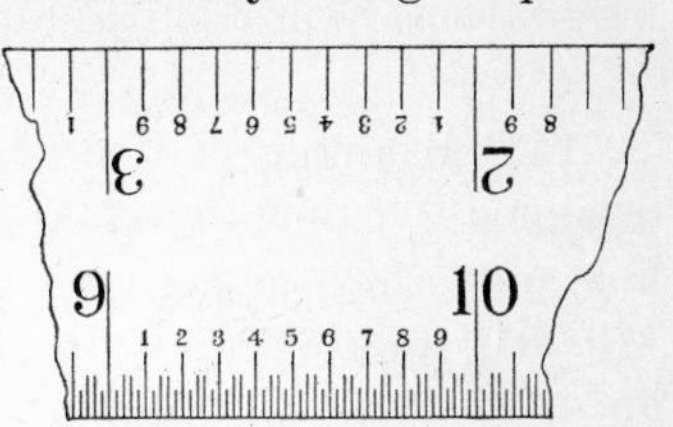

Fig. 341.—Ford scale.

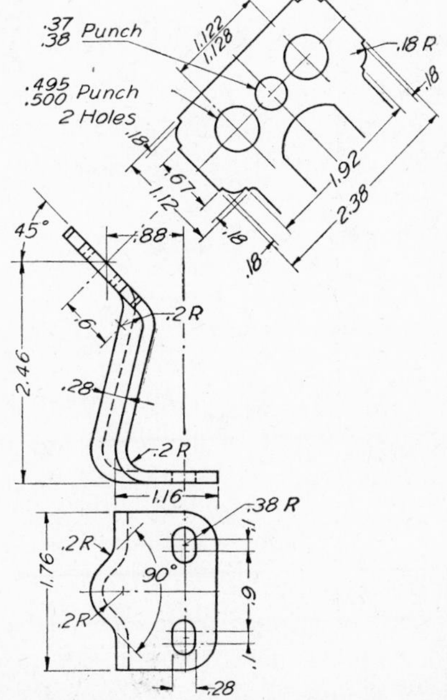

Fig. 342.—A Ford drawing.

All distances formerly designed and dimensioned with sufficient accuracy in common fractions are given to one place, as 3.5, 2.6. Where greater accuracy is required the second place is added but always in multiples of 2, as 3.56, 2.62, so as to be readable to the eye. With closer dimensions, measured with micrometers and for setting limits, it becomes only a matter of adding additional digits to an already existing decimal. The advantage in calculating, adding and checking, doing away with all conversion tables and lessening chances of error, is apparent. The transition from the old system to the new has been accomplished in the Ford plant "without confusion and with complete knowledge of what is taking place." Figure 342, illustrating the new system, is from a Ford drawing of a starting motor bracket.

It is suggested that one or two problems such as those of Figs. 444 to 450 be redesigned for decimal dimensioning under this system.

145. Dimensions for the Pattern Shop.—Some engineering offices prepare for all castings a set of "pattern drawings" for the exclusive use of the pattern shop, containing only the information needed by the pattern-maker. Figure 343 shows a pattern drawing of a cut gear

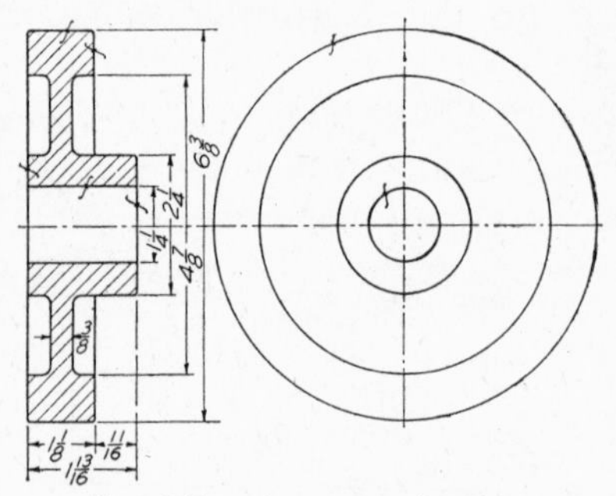

FIG. 343.—A pattern drawing.

blank. Where the weight of the rough casting is a factor, as in production work, the allowances for finish and draft are specified by the engineering department and included in the dimensions, in which case no finish marks are put on the drawing.

146. Dimensions for the Forge Shop.—Separate "forging drawings" are usually made when a piece is to be machined from a forging. These drawings are to scale (preferably full size) and show the completed forging in the stage ready for the machine shop, with all the dimensions needed by the forge shop. No dimensions for finish are given, but the outlines of the finished piece are shown in light dash-lines within the contour, as in Fig. 344.

147. Dimensions for the Machine Shop.—When separate drawings are made for the pattern shop or forge shop the machine shop drawing contains only the dimensions for machining the piece, as in

Fig. 345. The separate drawing system prevents congestion of the dimensions and makes the drawings easier to work from thereby. On the other hand, the single system has the advantage of having all the information about the piece on one sheet. Paragraphs 137 to 143 refer to machine shop dimensioning.

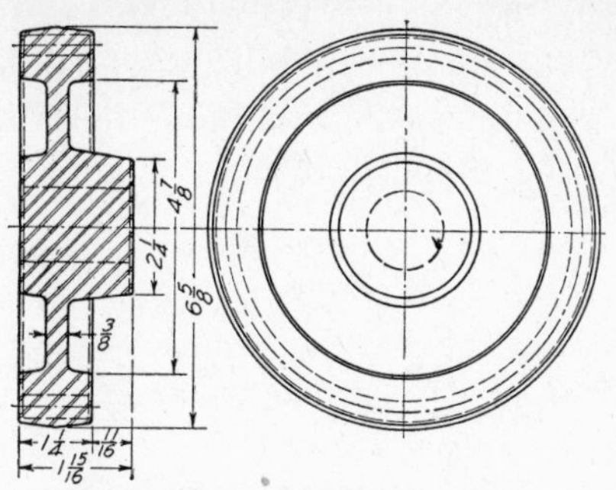

Fig. 344.—A forging drawing.

148. Dimensions for the Assembly Shop.—This information, placed on the assembly drawing, identifies and locates the various parts so that the machine can be built from it. Sometimes a separate sheet called an erection drawing is made.

149. Dimensions for the Purchaser.—Before the delivery of a machine the purchaser needs some dimensional information, such as

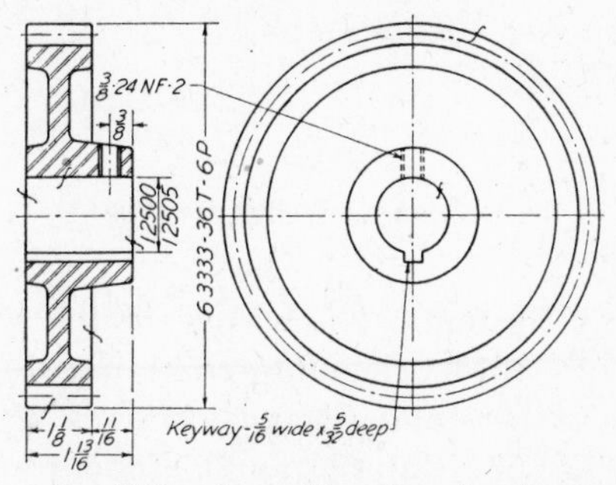

Fig. 345.—A machine shop drawing.

the method of mounting, size of foundation and location of bolts; the floor space and clear height required with all moving parts in maximum positions; the required locations of source of power, r.p.m. of driving pulleys, gears or motor, location of any piping or wiring, etc. These dimensions are given on a foundation plan or on an outline assembly drawing prepared for the customer's use. Sometimes the drawing of a templet to be built by the purchaser for setting foundation bolts is sent.

150. Dimensioning Pictorial Drawings.—When isometric or other pictorial forms are used as working drawings the size description is often more difficult than the shape description. With the principles in this chapter as a basis, the general rule to follow is to have all the extension lines and dimension lines parallel to the axes and make the figures appear to lie in the plane of the face containing the part dimensioned. To do this the figures should be pictorial drawings of *vertical* figures. Leaders and dimensions in note form will be necessary oftener than on orthographic drawings. Figure 346 illustrates the system.

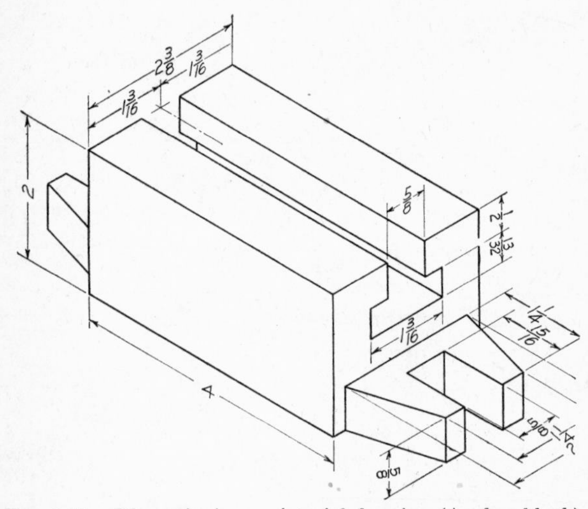

Fig. 346.—Dimensioning a pictorial drawing (Anchor block).

151. The Metric System.—Knowledge of the metric system will be of advantage as it will be encountered on drawings from countries where this system is the standard and in increasing instances in the United States. The first international standard of a mechanical device is that of ball bearings, which have been standardized in the metric system, except for sizes of balls.

Drawings in the metric system are not made to half size or quarter size. The first regular scale smaller than full size is one-fifth size, then one-tenth size. Sometimes the scale of 1 to 2½ is used. The unit of measurement on drawings is the millimeter (mm.) and the figures are all understood to be millimeters, without any indicating mark. Figure 347 is an example of metric dimensioning. A table of metric equivalents is given on page 444.

152. Notes and Specifications.—Some necessary information cannot be drawn and hence must be added in the form of notes. This would include the number required of each piece, the kind of material, kind of finish, number and kind of bolts and screws and any other specifications as to construction or use. A note may be a single word on a leader pointing to the surface, or it may be a sentence lettered near the part to which it refers. Notes should read horizontally on the sheet. General notes referring to the entire machine or to all drawings on one sheet are collected and lettered in one place.

Do not be afraid of putting notes on drawings. Supplement the graphic language by the English language whenever added information can be conveyed, but be careful to word it so clearly that the meaning cannot possibly be misunderstood.

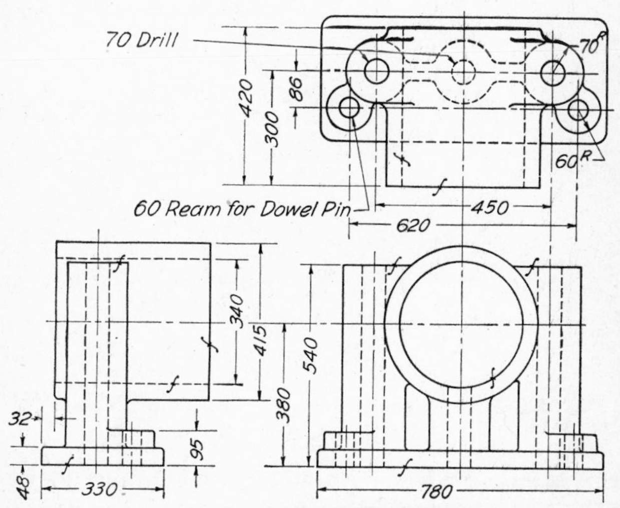

Fig. 347.—A metric drawing (front cam shaft bearing, Hispano-Suiza aero-engine).

If a note as to the shape of a piece will save making a view without sacrificing clearness, use it. In detailing right- and left-hand pieces, if different patterns are required both should be drawn; if one pattern can be used (as should be if possible) but machined right and left, both should be drawn; if identical but assembled right and left, one only is drawn and the number required noted. Standard bolts and screws, taper pins, washers, keys and nuts are not detailed when specified by note or in the bill of materials.

An approved form of wording for notes occurring more or less frequently on drawings is given in Fig. 348.

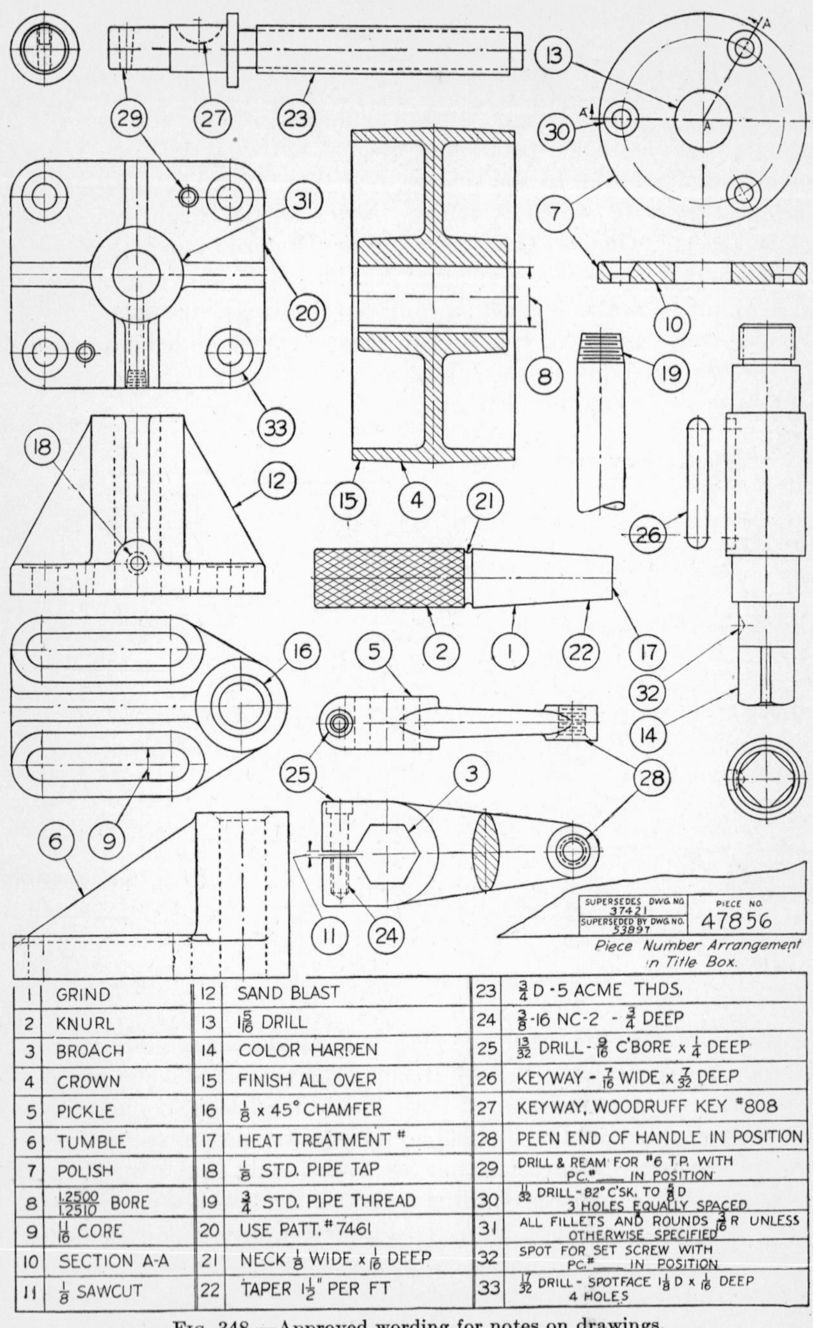

1	GRIND	12	SAND BLAST	23	$\frac{3}{4}$ D - 5 ACME THDS.
2	KNURL	13	$1\frac{5}{16}$ DRILL	24	$\frac{3}{8}$-16 NC-2 - $\frac{3}{4}$ DEEP
3	BROACH	14	COLOR HARDEN	25	$\frac{13}{32}$ DRILL - $\frac{9}{16}$ C'BORE x $\frac{1}{4}$ DEEP
4	CROWN	15	FINISH ALL OVER	26	KEYWAY - $\frac{7}{16}$ WIDE x $\frac{7}{32}$ DEEP
5	PICKLE	16	$\frac{1}{8}$ x 45° CHAMFER	27	KEYWAY, WOODRUFF KEY #808
6	TUMBLE	17	HEAT TREATMENT #____	28	PEEN END OF HANDLE IN POSITION
7	POLISH	18	$\frac{1}{8}$ STD. PIPE TAP	29	DRILL & REAM FOR #6 T.P. WITH PC.#____ IN POSITION
8	$\frac{1.2500}{1.2510}$ BORE	19	$\frac{3}{4}$ STD. PIPE THREAD	30	$\frac{11}{32}$ DRILL - 82° C'SK. TO $\frac{5}{8}$ D 3 HOLES EQUALLY SPACED
9	$\frac{11}{16}$ CORE	20	USE PATT. #7461	31	ALL FILLETS AND ROUNDS $\frac{3}{16}$ R UNLESS OTHERWISE SPECIFIED
10	SECTION A-A	21	NECK $\frac{1}{8}$ WIDE x $\frac{1}{16}$ DEEP	32	SPOT FOR SET SCREW WITH PC.#____ IN POSITION
11	$\frac{1}{8}$ SAWCUT	22	TAPER $1\frac{1}{2}$" PER FT	33	$\frac{17}{32}$ DRILL - SPOTFACE $1\frac{1}{8}$ D x $\frac{1}{16}$ DEEP 4 HOLES

Fig. 348.—Approved wording for notes on drawings.

PROBLEMS

153. The problems following are given as preliminary studies in dimensioning, on which to apply the principles of this chapter. Every working drawing is, of course, a dimensioning problem.

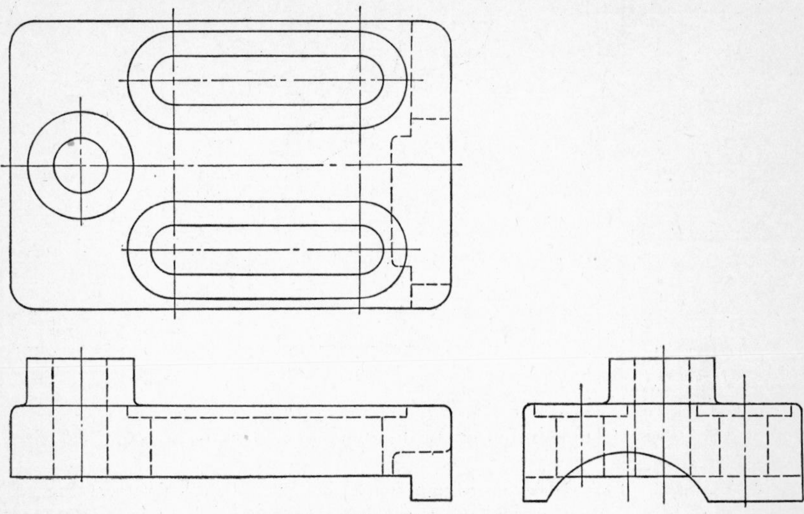

FIG. 349.—Pivot block.

Group I. Pieces to Be Drawn and Dimensioned.

The illustrations are either half or quarter size. Draw them full size by scaling or transferring with dividers, and add all dimensions necessary for the construction. Assume and mark finished surfaces.

1. Fig. 349. Pivot block, used to provide adjustment for a clamping cam. Cast iron, slots cored.

2. Fig. 350. Base clamp, for lathe tailstock. Cast iron, slot and hole cored.

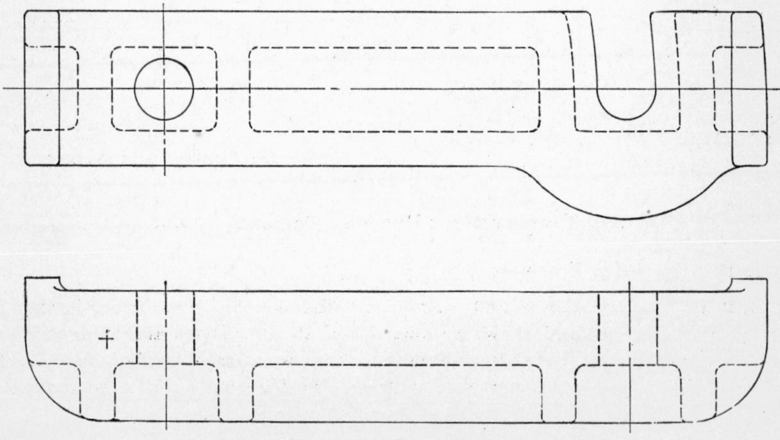

FIG. 350.—Base clamp.

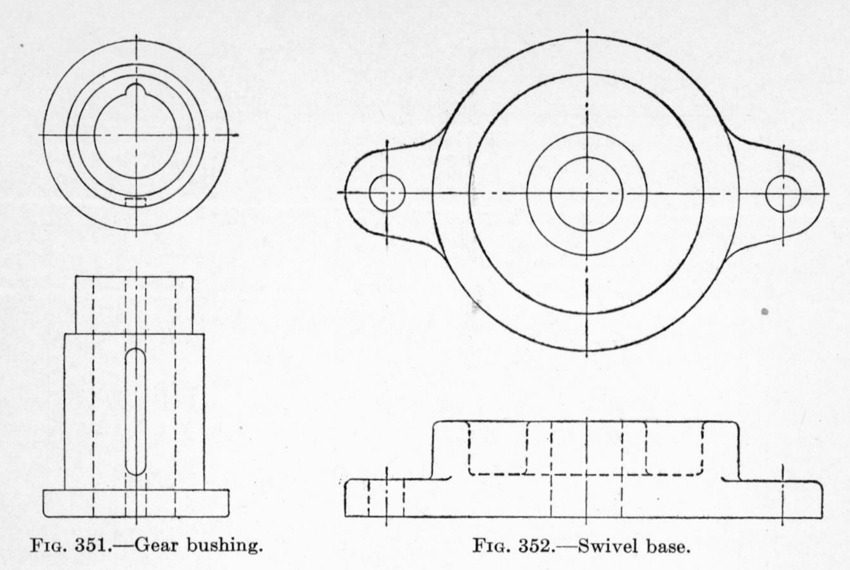

Fig. 351.—Gear bushing.

Fig. 352.—Swivel base.

3. Fig. 351. Compound gear bushing, used in feed gearing. Cast iron, finished all over.

4. Fig. 352. Swivel base, for angular adjustment. Bakelite die-casting.

5. Fig. 353. Chain guard, for hoist. Cast iron. Lower holes chamfered for peened guard pins.

6. Fig. 354. End plate for fractional horsepower motor. Cast iron.

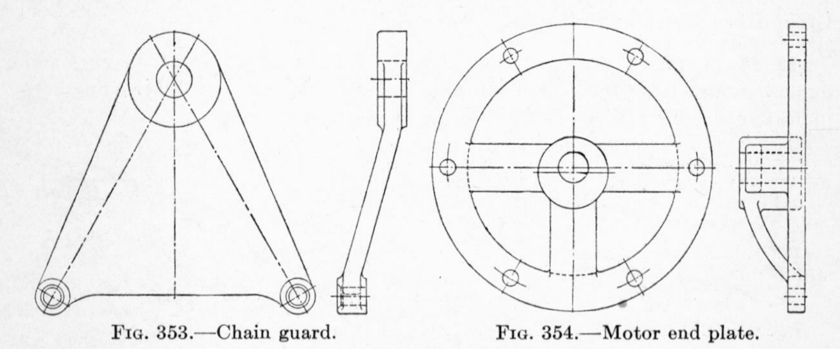

Fig. 353.—Chain guard.

Fig. 354.—Motor end plate.

7. Fig. 355. Filter press plate. Duriron. All holes cored.

Group II. Sketching Problems.

8, 9, 10, 11. Figs. 356 to 359. From pictorial sketches given make freehand orthographic sketches and show the location of all dimensions according to the rules for dimensioning, by adding dimension lines with arrow-heads. Instead of dimension figures use the letter *S* to indicate size dimensions and *L* to indicate location dimensions.

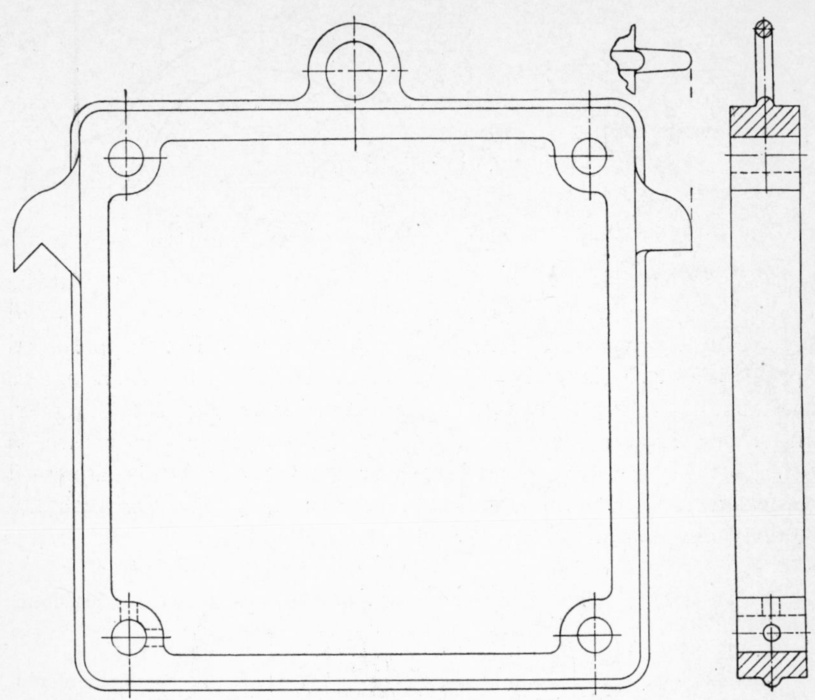

FIG. 355.—Filter press plate.

Group III. Sketching Problems.

12, 13, 14, 15. Figs. 356 to 359. Make freehand orthographic sketches and dimension-line completely. Fill in the blank dimensions with consecutive numbers indicating the order in which the drawing would be dimensioned.

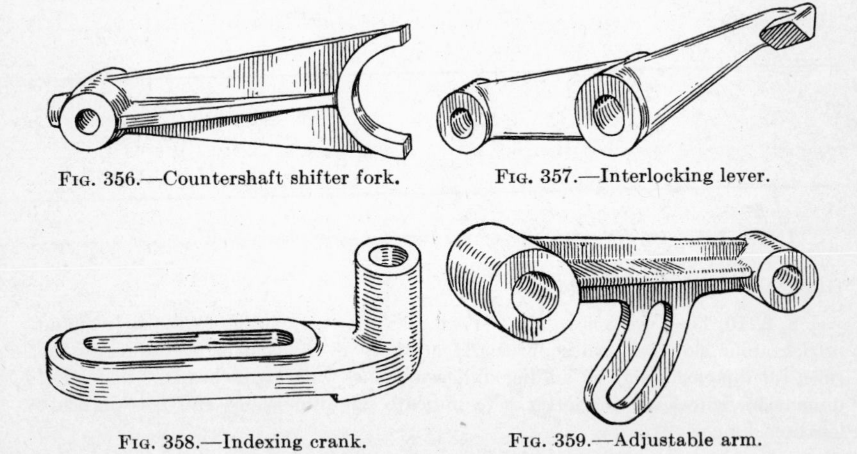

FIG. 356.—Countershaft shifter fork.

FIG. 357.—Interlocking lever.

FIG. 358.—Indexing crank.

FIG. 359.—Adjustable arm.

CHAPTER X

BOLTS, SCREWS, KEYS, RIVETS AND PIPE

154. The previous chapters of this book have been devoted to the theory or grammar of the language of drawing, and the problems and illustrations have been largely separate pieces. In the practical application of the language in making working drawings there occurs the necessity of representing the methods of fastening parts together, either with permanent fastenings, as rivets, or with removable ones, as bolts, screws and keys. The engineer must know the fundamental forms of these fastening parts and be thoroughly familiar with the conventional method of representation.

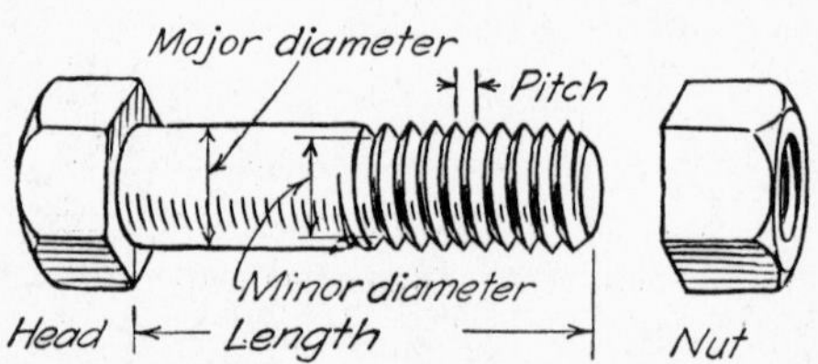

Fig. 360.—Standard hexagonal head bolt and nut.

The one occurring most frequently is, of course, the bolt, which is illustrated in pictorial form in Fig. 360. It will be noted that the nominal length of a bolt is its length under the head, and the diameter is the size of the shaft on which the threads are cut. The curve of the thread is a helix.

155. The Helix.—A helix is a space curve generated by a point moving uniformly along a straight line while the line revolves uniformly about another line as an axis. If the moving line is parallel to the axis it will generate a cylinder, and the word "helix" alone always means a cylindrical helix. If the moving line intersects the axis (at an angle less than 90°) it will generate a cone, and the curve made by the point moving on it will be a "conical helix." When the angle becomes 90° the helix degenerates into a spiral.

The distance parallel to the axis which the point advances in one revolution is called the *lead*.

156. To Draw a Helix.—Fig. 361. Draw the two views of the cylinder and measure the lead on the outer element. Divide this lead into a number of equal parts (say 12) and the circle into the same number, numbering the divisions from the same starting point. When the generating point has moved one-twelfth of the distance around the cylinder it has also advanced one-twelfth of the lead, when halfway around the cylinder it will have advanced one-half the lead. Thus points on the curve may be found by projecting the elements, whose ends are represented by the divisions of the circle, to intersect lines drawn across through the corresponding divisions of the lead. If the cylinder be developed the helix will appear on it as a straight line inclined to the base at an angle, called the "helix angle," whose tangent is $L/\pi d$. The conical helix is drawn similarly, the lead being measured along the axis.

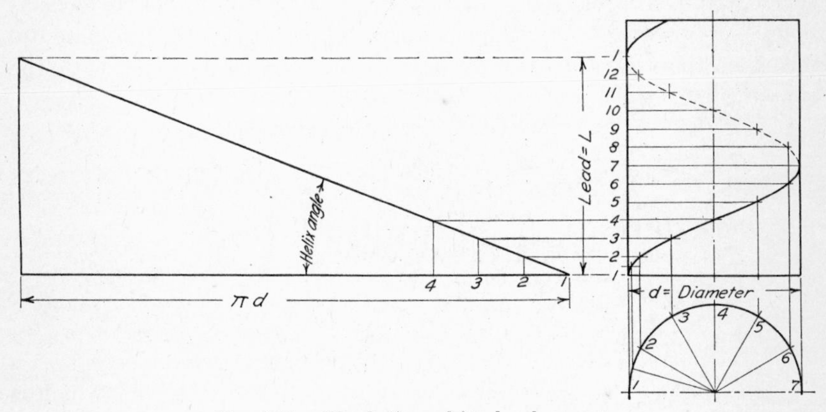

FIG. 361.—The helix and its development.

157. Forms of Threads.—Screws are used for fastenings, for adjustment and for transmitting power or motion. For these different purposes several different forms of threads are in use, Fig. 362. For fastenings the *American Standard* V-thread, with its crest and root flattened, is used in this country. The American Standard is discussed in detail in a following paragraph.

The *sharp* V at 60° is still used to some extent although it has little to recommend it except its increased holding power for set screws. The British Standard is the Whitworth thread cut at 55°, with tops and bottoms rounded one-sixth of the depth of the triangle, as shown in the figure. The *British Association Standard* at 47½° is used on very small screws. The French and International Standards have the same form as the American Standard but are dimensioned in the metric system.

For transmitting power or motion these V-shapes are not desirable, as part of the thrust tends to burst the nut. The *square* thread avoids this as it transmits all the forces parallel to the axis of the screw. It can have, evidently, only half the number of threads in the same space as a V-thread of the same pitch and thus in shear is only half as strong. A modification used very generally is the *Acme* or 29° thread. It is stronger, much more easily cut, and permits the use of a disengaging or split nut, which cannot be used on a square thread. The Brown and Sharpe *worm thread* for transmitting power to a worm

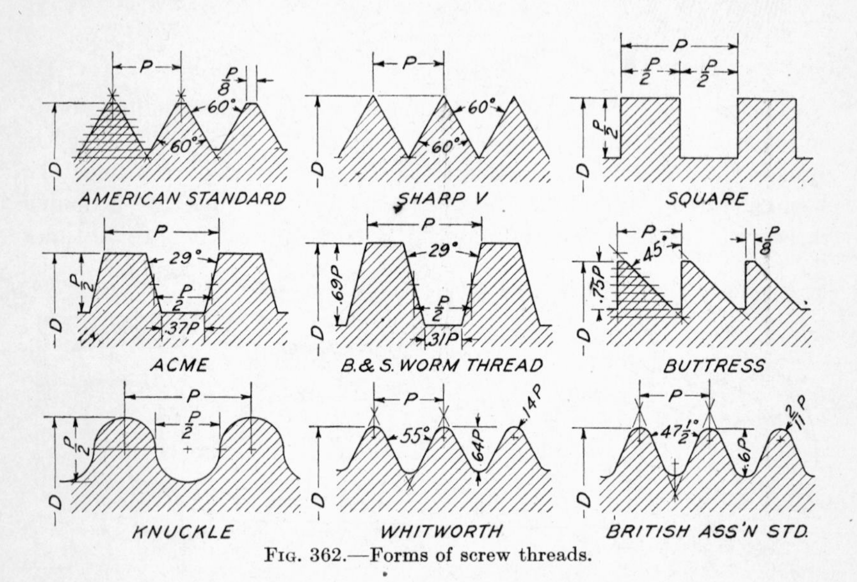

Fig. 362.—Forms of screw threads.

wheel resembles the Acme thread but has a longer tooth. The *buttress* thread for transmitting power in one direction has the advantage of the square thread and the strength of the V-thread. It is sometimes called the breech-lock thread as it is used to take the recoil in guns. The *knuckle* thread is used for rough work and can be cast in a mold. It may be seen in shallower form in sheet metal rolled threads as on an ordinary incandescent lamp.

158. Threads are always understood to be single and right-hand unless otherwise specified. A single thread has one thread of whatever section cut on the cylinder. When it is desired to give a more rapid advance without using a coarser thread, two or more threads are cut side by side, giving double, triple, etc., threads, as illustrated in Fig. 363.

A *right-hand* thread advances into engagement when turned clockwise. A *left-hand* thread advances counterclockwise. It can be distinguished from a right-hand thread by the direction of the slant. It is always marked plainly "L.H." on a drawing.

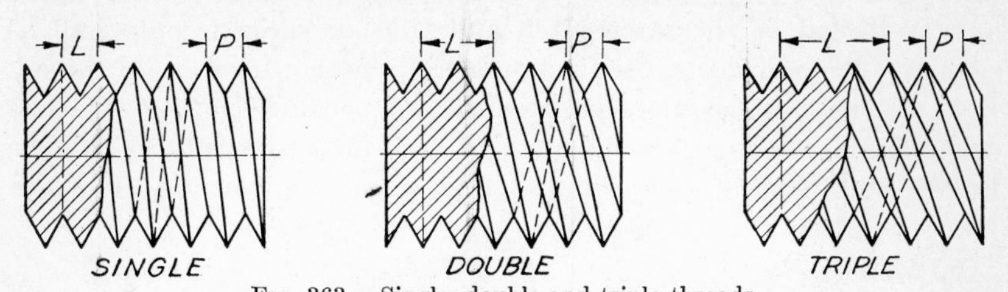

FIG. 363.—Single, double and triple threads.

The *pitch* of a thread is the distance between corresponding points on consecutive threads measured parallel to the axes. The *lead* has already been defined as the distance advanced in one revolution. In a single thread, therefore, the pitch and lead are equal, in a double thread the lead is twice the pitch, in a triple thread it is three times the pitch.

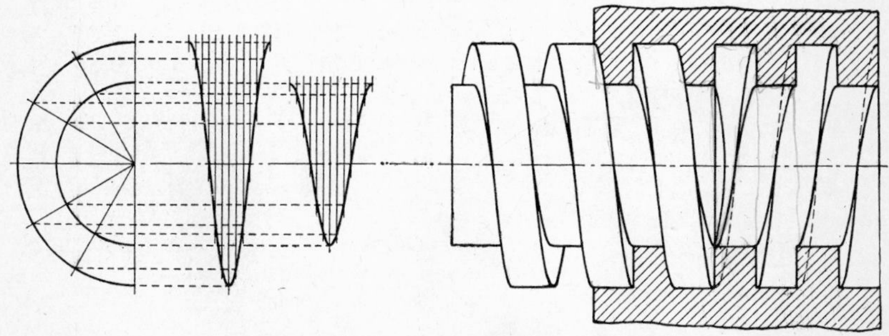

FIG. 364.—Square thread, external and internal.

159. To draw a screw thread we must know the shape of the thread, the diameter of the shaft on which it is cut, the number of threads per inch, and whether single or multiple and right- or left-hand. For true representation the thread shapes can be drawn with the lines of their crests and roots shown as helices having the same pitch but different diameters, as illustrated in Fig. 364. If many threads are to be drawn in this way a templet may be made by laying out the projections of the helices on a piece of cardboard or thin wood and cutting out with a sharp knife.

This drawing of the actual curves of a screw is a laborious proceeding and is rarely done, and then only on screws of large diameter. In ordinary practice the labor is altogether unnecessary, so the helix is conventionalized into a straight line. A square-thread screw would thus be drawn as shown in stages in Fig. 365 (illustrating a double thread), which, while not so realistic or pleasing as Fig. 364, requires very much less time.

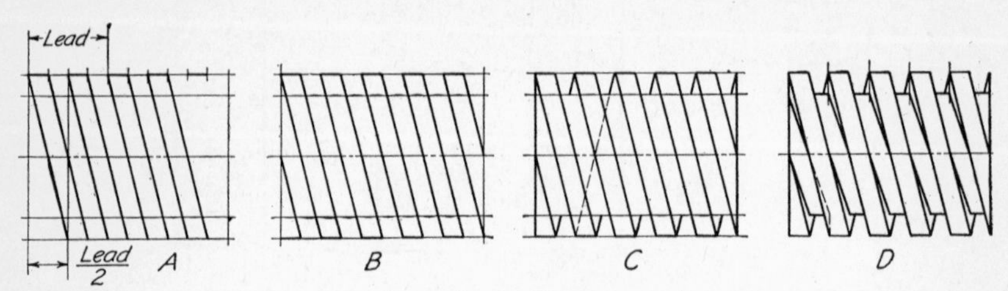

Fig. 365.—Stages in drawing square threads.

A V-thread would be drawn in the stages shown in Fig. 366, spacing the pitch on the lower line only, and should be inked in the same order. The flats of crest and root are not drawn.

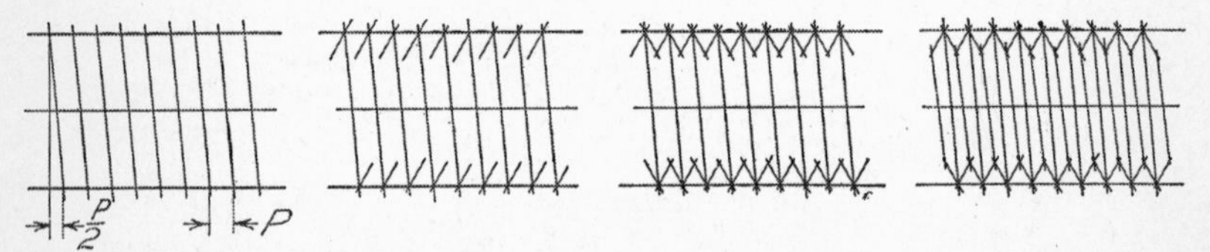

Fig. 366.—Stages in drawing V-threads.

160. Conventional Threads.—Since threads occur so frequently in machine drawing a conventional symbol is used for them and the thread profiles are not drawn except on large diameters. The American Standards Association gives two forms of thread symbols, "regular" and "simplified."

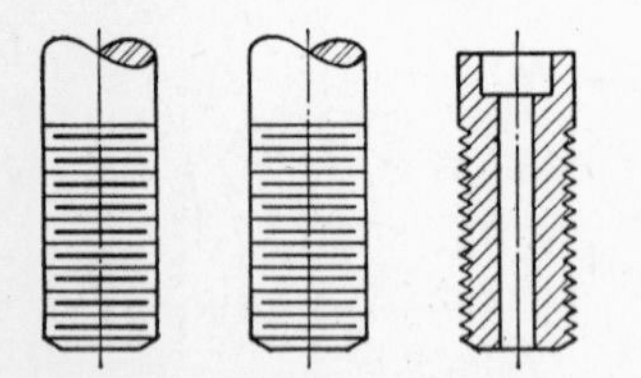

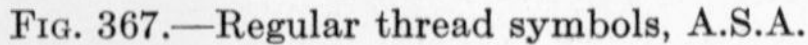

Fig. 367.—Regular thread symbols, A.S.A.

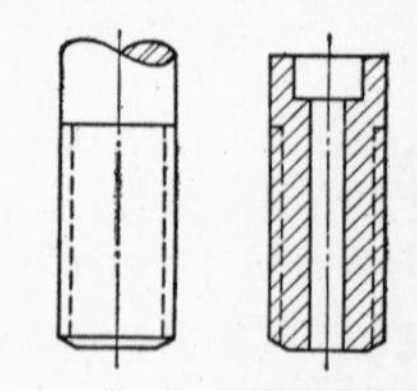

Fig. 368.—Simplified thread symbols, A.S.A.

In the regular thread symbols, Fig. 367, the threads are represented by alternate long and short cross-lines at *right angles* to the axis, representing the crests and roots of the threads, the crests drawn with lines and the roots with lines the weight of the outline (in rapid

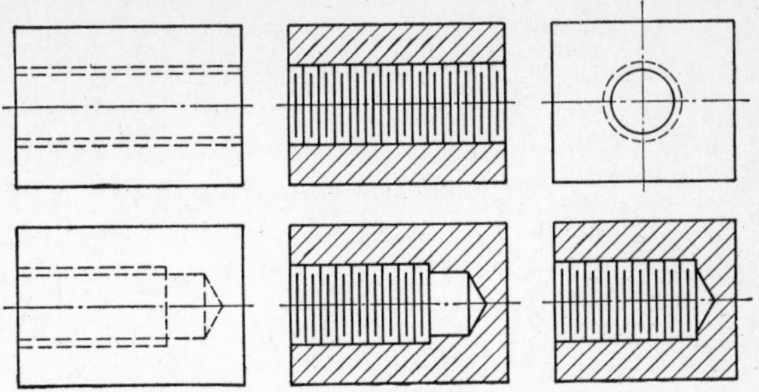

FIG. 369.—Regular internal thread symbols, A.S.A.

practice they may be made of equal weight). They are spaced by eye to look well and need not scale to the actual pitch.

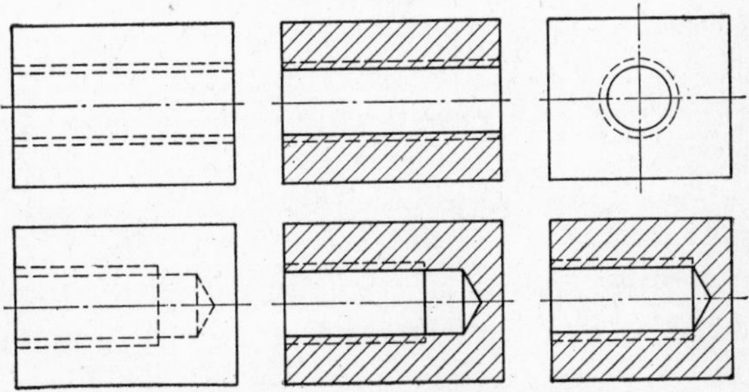

FIG. 370.—Simplified internal thread symbols, A.S.A.

The simplified thread symbols, Fig. 368, may be adopted when it is desirable to simplify drafting work. The depth of the thread is

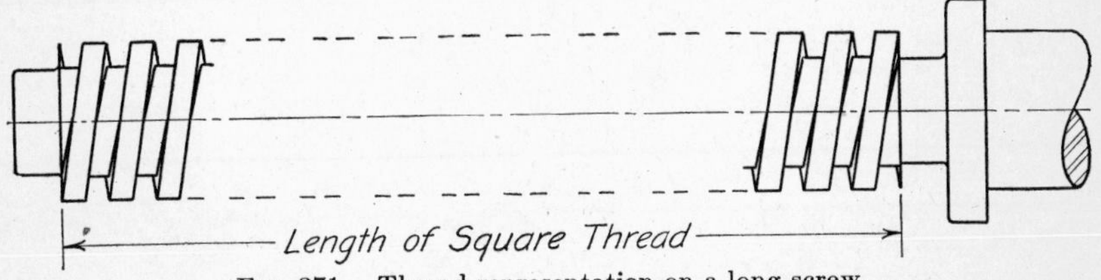

FIG. 371.—Thread representation on a long screw.

indicated by light lines consisting of short dashes parallel to the axis.

The regular symbols for internal threads in section and elevation are shown in Fig. 369 and the same in simplified symbols in Fig. 370.

When the tap drill does not go through, the depth of drill should preferably be given, and the drill point or approximate shape of the bottom of the hole (drawn at 60° with the axis) should always be shown.

It is not necessary to draw the threads on the whole length of a long screw. They may be started at each end as in Fig. 371.

When two pieces screwed together are shown in section the thread shapes should be drawn, as in Fig. 372.

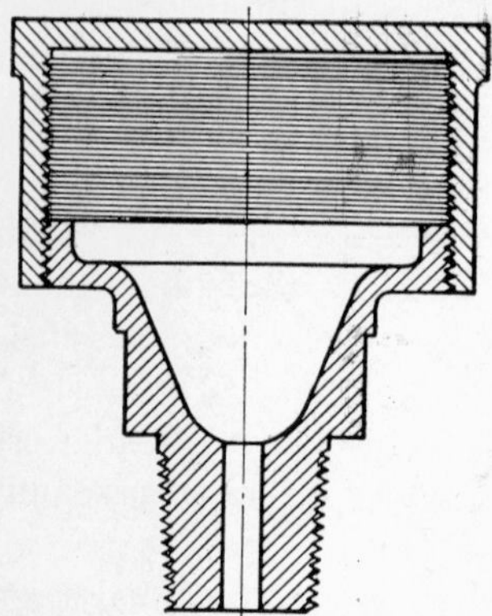

Fig. 372.—Threads in section.

161. American (National) Screw Threads.—The form of the American Standard is a 60° V-shape with the crest flattened to a width equal to one-eighth of the pitch and the root filled in a like amount. This form was previously known as the "United States Standard" or "Sellers' Profile."

The American Standard covers five series of screw threads, all of the same thread form but differing in the relation of pitch to diameter. These are the Coarse Thread Series, the Fine Thread Series, and three special series, the 8-pitch-, the 12-pitch- and the 16-pitch-thread Series.

The Coarse Thread Series is the former United States Standard supplemented by 12 numbered sizes below ¼ inch from the A.S.M.E. Standards. It is the series recommended for general use. See table, page 445, Appendix.

The Fine Thread Series is the former Regular Series of the Society of Automotive Engineers, with 13 numbered sizes below ¼ inch from the A.S.M.E. Standards. It is used where special conditions require a fine thread. See table, page 445.

The 8-pitch-thread Series.—Eight threads per inch. Sizes 1″ to 6″.

"Bolts for high-pressure pipe flanges, cylinder-head studs, and similar fastenings against pressure require that an initial tension be set up in the fastening by elastic deformation of the fastening and the component held together so that the joint will not open up when the steam or other pressure is applied. To secure a proper initial tension it is not practicable that the pitch should increase with the diameter of the thread as the torque required to assemble the fastening would be excessive. Accordingly, for such purposes the 8-pitch thread has come into general use for all classes of engineering work." [See table, page 445.]

The 12-pitch-thread Series.—Twelve threads per inch. Sizes ½″ to 6″.

Sizes of 12-pitch threads from ½ to 1¾ inches are used in boiler practice. This requires that worn stud holes be retapped with the next larger size. Twelve-pitch threads are also widely used in machine construction for thin nuts on shafts and sleeves. See table, page 445.

The 16-*pitch-thread Series.*—Sixteen threads per inch. Sizes ¾″ to 4″.

This is a uniform pitch series used primarily on threaded adjusting collars and bearing retaining nuts. See table, page 445.

162. Classification of Fits.—One of the important features of the work of the Committee on Standardization and Unification of Screw Threads (A.S.A. B1a 1934) is in the standardizing of classes of fits between bolt and nut. Four classes are provided, with detailed tables of dimensions and tolerances for manufacture to meet these classifications. These are:

Class 1 Fit.—This is "recommended only for screw thread work where clearance between mating parts is essential for rapid assembly and where shake or play is not objectionable."

Class 2 Fit.—This "represents a high quality of commercial screw thread product and is recommended for the great bulk of interchangeable screw thread work."

Class 3 Fit.—This "represents an exceptionally high quality of commercially threaded product and is recommended only in cases where the high cost of precision tools and continual checking is warranted."

Class 4 Fit.—This requires "selective assembly," there being an actual interference between a maximum screw and a minimum hole. It is "frankly experimental and it is still an open question whether or not it can be produced commercially."

163. Identification Symbols.—For specifying American (National) Standard threads on drawings, in correspondence, specifications, stock lists, etc., the diameter (or screw number) and number of threads per inch are given first, then the initial letters of the series, NC (National Coarse), NF (National Fine) or N (National Form but special pitch), followed by the class of fit. If left-hand thread the letters L.H. follow the number of threads.

Examples:

1″–8 NC–2
1″–14 L.H. NF–3
2″–8 N8–2
2″–12 N12–2
2″–16 N16–3

164. American Standard Bolts and Nuts.—The former "United States Standard" for the sizes of bolt heads and nuts is now replaced by the "American Standard Wrench Head Bolts and Nuts and Wrench Openings," first approved in 1927 and revised in 1933. Commercial manufacturers of bolts and screws are making their products to conform to the new Standard.

The Standard includes three series, as follows:

Regular Series Bolt Heads and Nuts.—Regular bolt heads and nuts are for general use. The dimensions and the resulting strengths of these bolt heads and nuts are based on the theoretical analysis of the stresses and on results of numerous tests. Slight deviations from the theoretical dimensions have been made in order to reduce the number of wrench openings and to conform to certain manufacturing processes. The dimensions listed in the tables are in accord with the tendencies of recent years toward the more economical use of material consistent with an ample margin of safety.

Heavy Series Bolt Heads and Nuts.—Heavy bolt heads and nuts are for use where greater bearing surface is necessary, that is, where a large clearance between the bolt and hole or a greater wrench bearing surface is considered essential.

Light Series Nuts.—Light nuts are for use where extreme saving in weight and material is desired.

165. Classes of Finish.—The American Standards Association specifies three classes of bolt heads and nuts in both the regular and the heavy series. These are (1) unfinished, (2) semi-finished, (3) finished.

Unfinished heads are not machined on any surface.

Semi-finished heads are machined under head only, either plain or washer-faced.

Finished heads are machined on all surfaces, with washer face on bearing surface, whose diameter is equal to the width across flats and thickness is one sixty-fourth of an inch.

Unfinished nuts are threaded but not machined on any other surface. Semi-finished nuts are threaded and machined on bearing surface only, either plain, with chamfered corners, or washer-faced. Finished nuts are threaded and machined on all surfaces, with washer face on bearing surface, whose diameter is equal to the width across flats and thickness is one sixty-fourth of an inch.

Unfinished and semi-finished are made both square and hexagonal, finished heads and nuts are hexagonal only.

166. Proportion of Bolt Heads and Nuts—Regular Series.—The regular series is for all ordinary uses and is always understood unless otherwise specified.

For **unfinished** hexagonal and square heads the width across flats is $1\frac{1}{2}D$ (three sizes, $\frac{5}{16}$, $\frac{7}{16}$, and $\frac{9}{16}$ are adjusted to avoid sixty-fourths), and the height of the head $\frac{2}{3}D$ (adjusted to fractions), Figs. 373 and 375.

Unfinished nuts over $\frac{5}{8}''$ are $1\frac{1}{2}D$ across flats and $\frac{7}{8}D$ thick.

Semi-finished heads and nuts are the same size across flats as the unfinished class, but the height of heads and thickness of nuts are a fraction less, owing to finishing the bearing surface.

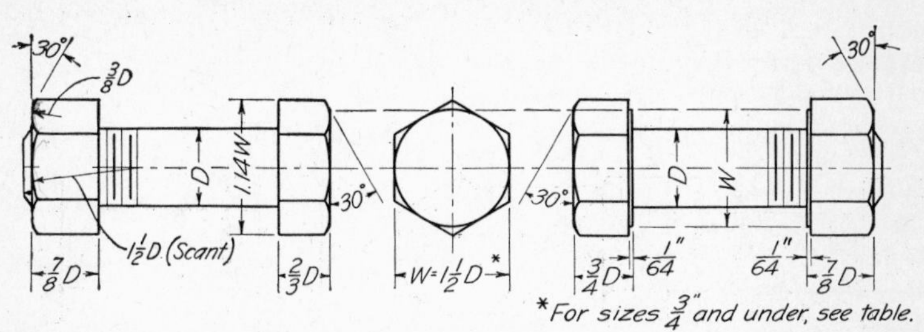

Fig. 373.—Am. St'd unfinished regular hex. head bolt.

Fig. 374.—Am. St'd finished regular hex. head bolt.

Finished heads and nuts over $\frac{5}{8}$ are the same across flats as the other classes, but the height of head is greater. The thickness of nut is the same as the unfinished, Fig. 374.

All these dimensions are given in the tables on pages 446 and 447 in the Appendix.

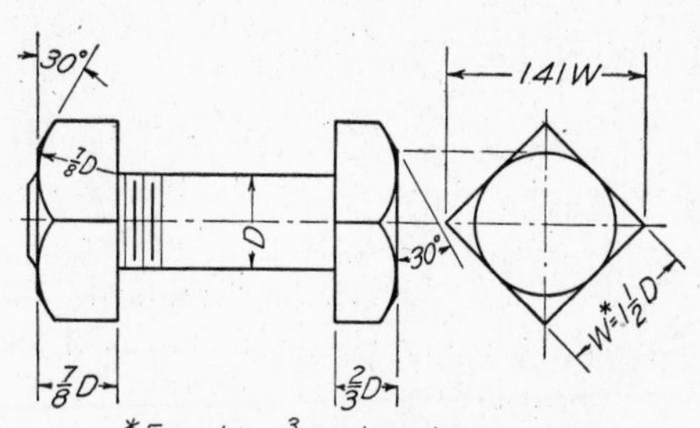

Fig. 375.—Am. St'd unfinished regular square head bolt.

Tops of heads and nuts are flat and chamfered. The angle of chamfer on hexagons is 30° and on squares 25°, but both are drawn at 30°. The diameter of top circle is the width across flats.

Bolt ends are flat and chamfered 35°, drawn 30°, the chamfer extending to the bottom of the thread.

167. Proportions of Heavy Bolt Heads and Nuts.—The heavy series is for use where greater bearing surface is desired. The width across flats for unfinished and semi-finished square and hexagonal, and finished hexagonal, heads and nuts is $1\frac{1}{2}D + \frac{1}{8}$, adjusted to sixteenths. Unfinished heads are $\frac{3}{4}D + \frac{1}{16}$ in height, Fig. 376. The thickness of unfinished nuts equals D. Semi-finished heads and nuts are a trifle thinner (See table, page 446). Finished heads are $D - \frac{1}{16}$ high and finished nuts D thick.

168. American Standard light nuts and light castle nuts are standardized in semi-finished hexagon form, for $\frac{1}{4}$ to $1\frac{1}{2}$ inch bolts. See tables, page 448, Appendix. They are usually made with fine threads.

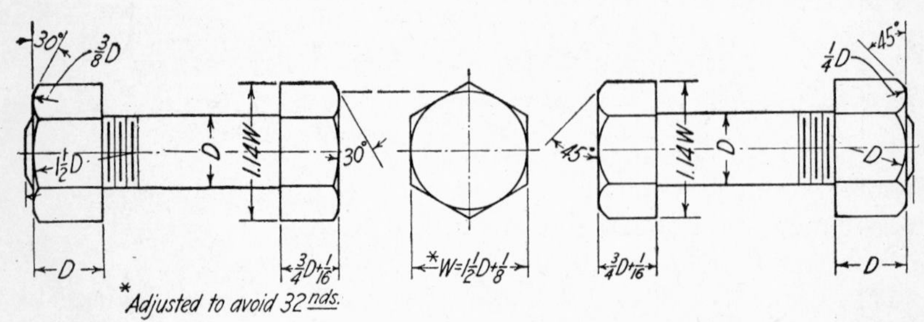

FIG. 376.—Am. St'd unfinished heavy hex. head bolt.

FIG. 377.—Old U. S. St'd hex. head bolt.

169. United States Standard Bolts and Nuts.—Before the adoption of the American Standard the United States Standard was in general use, and in some places it has not yet been superseded by the regular series of the American Standard. The proportions of the United States Standard are $W = 1\frac{1}{2}D + \frac{1}{8}''$; height of head $W/2$; thickness of nut, D, Fig. 377. Thus, it will be noted, the United States Standard is virtually the same as the heavy series of the American Standard, except that the angle of chamfer on the hexagon is 45° instead of 30° as in the American Standard. The "Unfinished Heavy" table on page 447 may therefore be used as a table for the old United States Standard

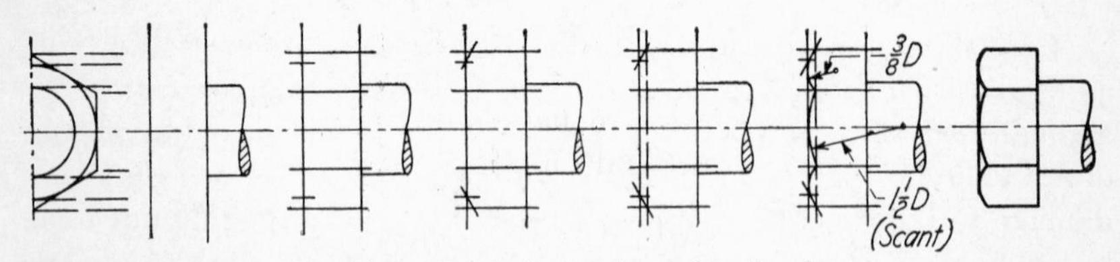

FIG. 378.—Stages in drawing a hex. head.

170. To Draw a Bolt Head and Nut.—Bolt heads and nuts are always shown on a drawing "across corners" on all views showing the faces unless there is some special reason for drawing them across flats. Figure 378 shows the stages of drawing a hex. head. First lay off the thickness of the head, or nut, then draw one-half the end view and project to the required view. The radii of the chamfer curves, $1\frac{1}{2}D$ (scant) and $\frac{3}{8}D$, are circle-arc approximations to the actual curves, which are hyperbolas.

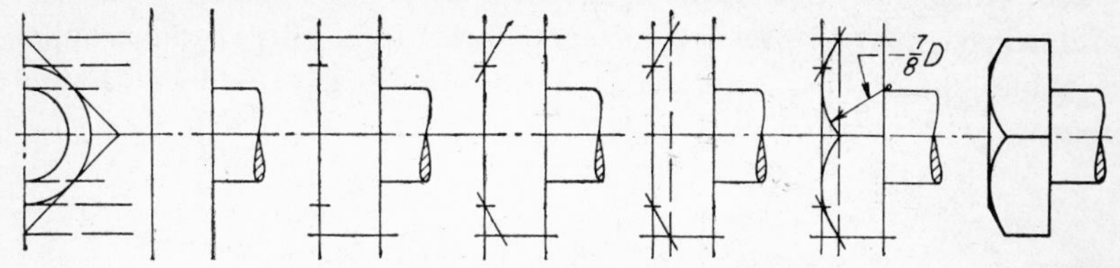

Fig. 379.—Stages in drawing a square head.

Figure 379 is a progressive drawing of a square head across corners. Figures 380 and 381 show the method of drawing hex. and square heads across flats. The standard length of thread on bolts is $1\frac{1}{2}D + \frac{1}{4}''$ for both coarse and fine threads.

171. Locknuts.—Fig. 382. Many different locking devices to prevent nuts from working loose under vibration are used in machine design. The commonest is the jam nut A. American Standard jam nuts have the same dimensions as corresponding full nuts except the thickness. This for both regular and heavy, unfinished and finished, is for sizes $\frac{1}{4}''$ to $\frac{7}{16}''$ $(\frac{1}{2}D + \frac{1}{32})$; $\frac{1}{2}''$ to $1\frac{1}{8}''$ $(\frac{1}{2}D + \frac{1}{16}'')$; $1\frac{1}{4}''$ to $2\frac{1}{4}''$ $(\frac{1}{2}D + \frac{1}{8}'')$ and $2\frac{1}{2}''$ to $4''$ $(\frac{1}{2}D + \frac{1}{4}'')$.

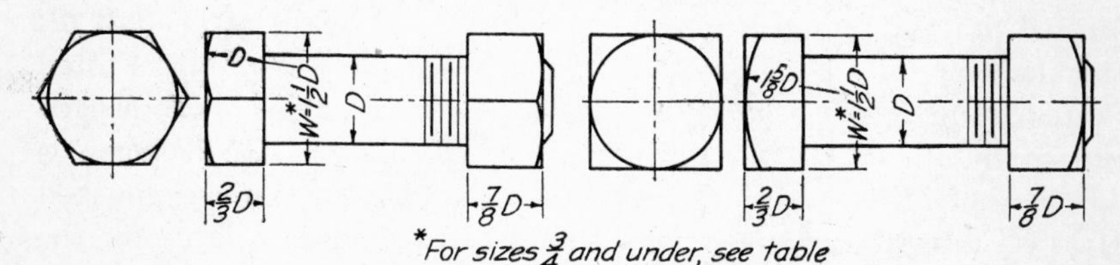

Fig. 380.—Hex. head across flats. Fig. 381.—Square head across flats.

Castellated nuts as used in automotive work are shown at I, and as used with fine and extra-fine threads on light tubular sections in aeronautical work, at J. At B is shown a round nut locked by means of a set screw. A brass plug is placed under the set screw to prevent damage to the thread. This is a common type of adjusting nut used in machine tool practice. At C is a locknut in which the threads are deformed after cutting. Spring washers are common devices. In addition to the plain form D there are numerous patented variations, as E and F. G is typical of a number of lock washers which are bent after the nut is in place. Spring cotters are used as at H or with castellated nuts. K and L are self-explanatory.

172. Dardelet Screw Thread.—The Dardelet self-locking thread is a special thread requiring no auxiliary locking devices to hold the nut under vibration. Its profile is quite similar to the Acme thread

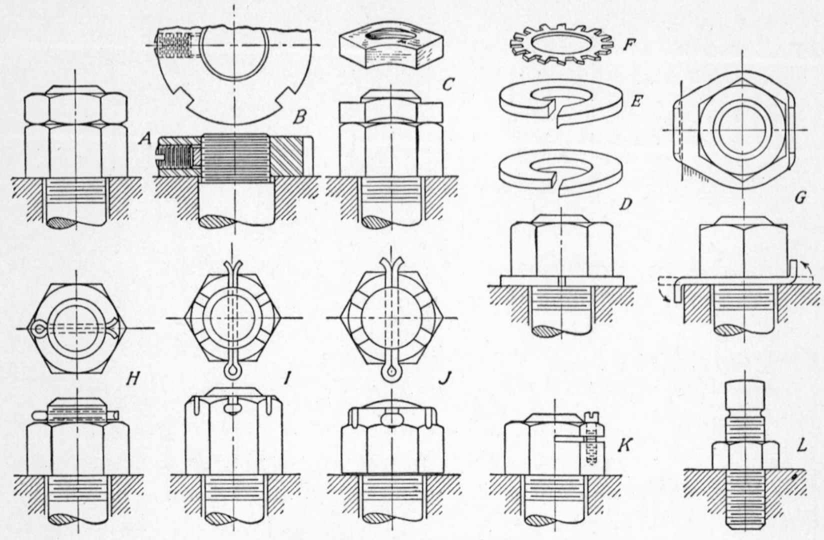

Fig. 382.—Locking devices.

but the roots of the external thread and the crests of the internal thread are tapered about 6° to the axis. The nut screws on very easily until its bearing surface comes to rest, then the wrench torque forces the two tapered surfaces into binding contact. Figure 383 shows the

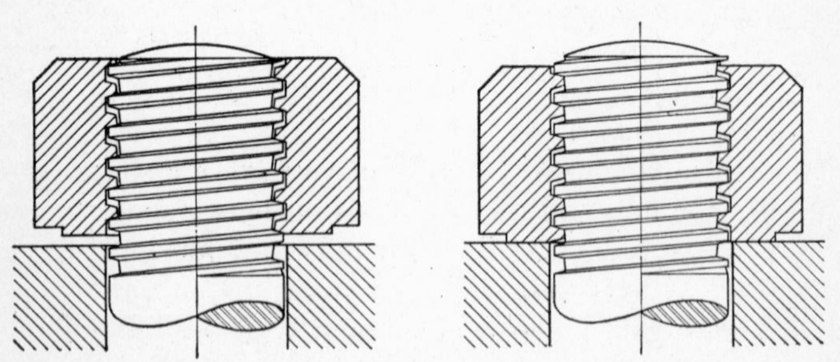
Fig. 383.—Dardelet thread, unlocked and locked.

nut in unlocked and locked positions. In drawing Dardelet bolts and nuts the heads have the same proportions as the American Standard Regular Series. The nuts are the same except in thickness. For drawing purposes this thickness may be made $1\frac{1}{8}D$.

173. Studs.—Fig. 384. The stud or stud bolt, threaded on both ends, is used when through bolts are not suitable, for parts which must be removed frequently, such as cylinder heads, chest covers, etc. One end is screwed permanently into a tapped hole, and the projecting

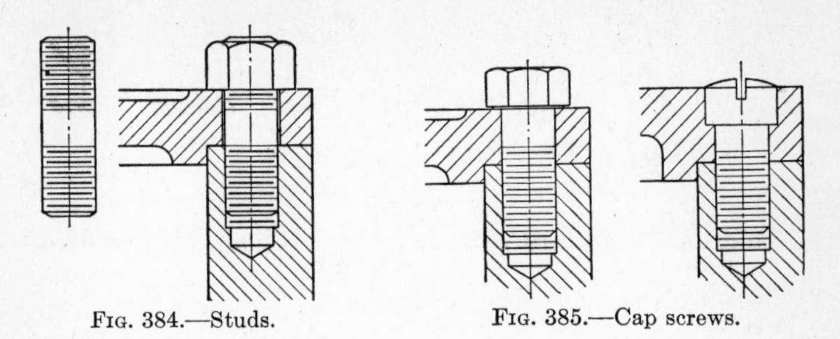

Fig. 384.—Studs. Fig. 385.—Cap screws.

studs guide the removable piece to position.

174. Cap screws, Fig. 385, differ from bolts in that they are used for fastening two pieces together by passing through a clear hole in one and screwing into a tapped hole in the other. Tables of sizes of American Standard hex. head and various forms of slotted head cap screws are given in the Appendix, page 449.

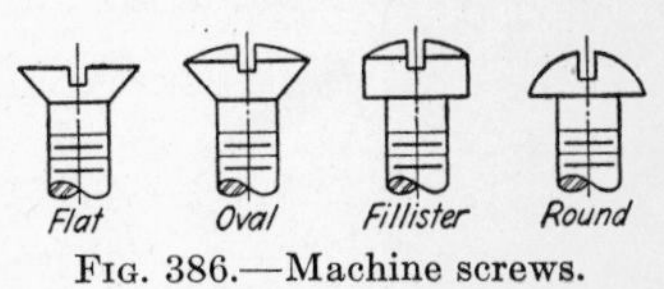

Fig. 386.—Machine screws.

175. Machine screws, Fig. 386, are used as fasteners in small work, particularly sheet metal. The American Standard dimensions for various heads and sizes are given in the Appendix, page 449.

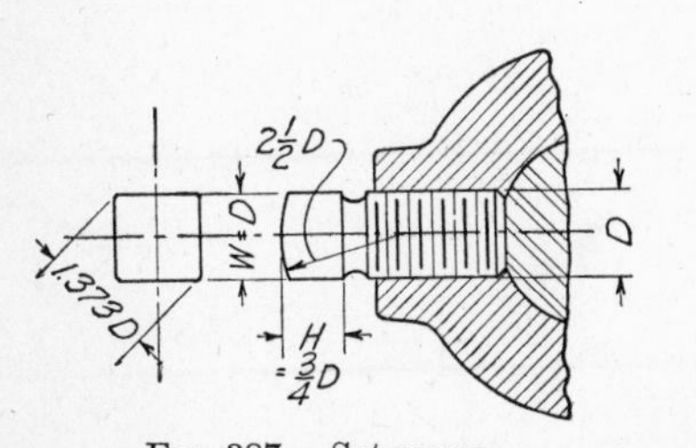

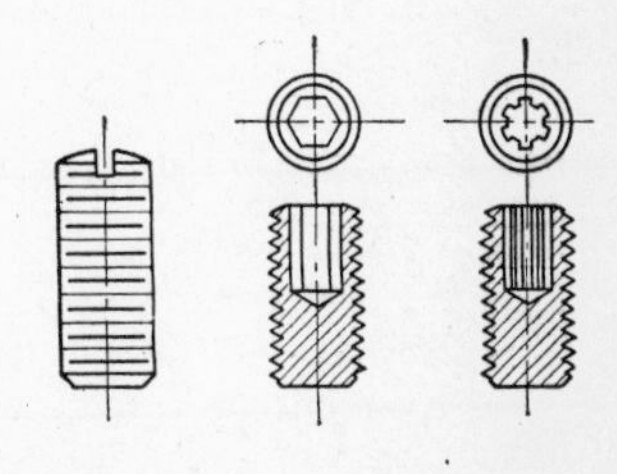

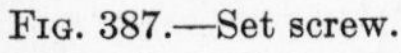

Fig. 387.—Set screw. Fig. 388.—Headless set screws.

176. Set screws, made of hardened steel, are used for holding two parts in relative position, being screwed through one part and having the point set against the other. The American Standard square head set screw is shown in Fig. 387. Headless set screws, Fig. 388, are made to comply with the safety code of factory inspection laws, which are very strict regarding the use of projecting screws on moving parts. Figure 389 shows various set screw points for different pur-

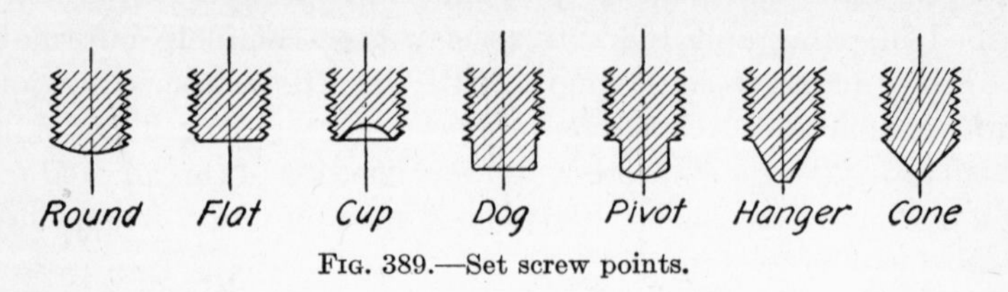

FIG. 389.—Set screw points.

poses. American Standard set screw dimensions are given on page 448, Appendix.

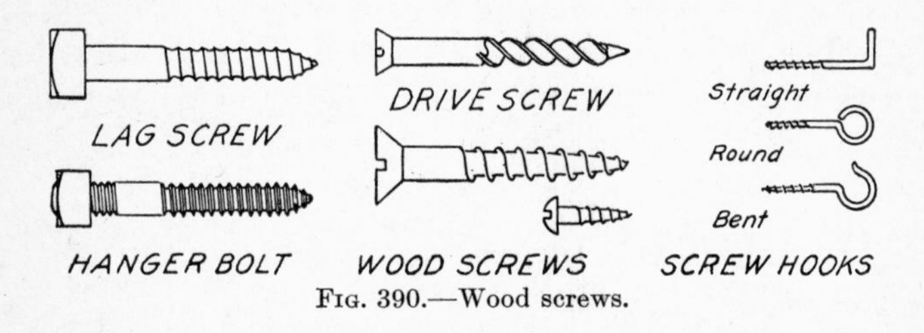

FIG. 390.—Wood screws.

177. Wood screws have the threads proportioned to the relative holding strengths of wood and metal. They are drawn as shown in Fig. 390.

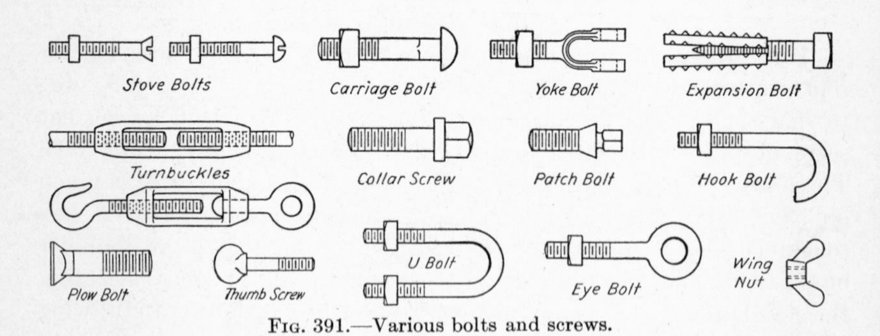

FIG. 391.—Various bolts and screws.

178. Other Forms.—Figure 391 illustrates the method of representing various other bolts and screws. Some of these have been standardized by the American Standard Association (see publications, page 438).

179. Dimensioning and Specifying Bolts and Screws.—*Bolts,* if standard head, are dimensioned as in Fig. 392 by giving the diameter and length under the head to the point, and specifying the thread as described in paragraph 163. If special, give complete information. *Studs,* give diameter and length, with length and specification of thread on each end. *Cap screws,* give diameter, length under head (over-all for countersunk heads), and specification of thread. *Machine screws,* give number, length, under head for round and fillister heads, over-all for countersunk heads, and specification of thread. *Set screws,* give diameter, thread specification and length under head to extreme point. For headless set screws give over-all length. For various safety types give name and manufacturer's number. *Wood screws,* give number, length, style of head and finish. *Lag screws,* give diameter, length under head and kind of head. *Screw hooks* and *screw eyes,* diameter and length over-all. *Boiler patch bolts,* for cup head, length under head; for bevel head, length from largest diameter of bevel.

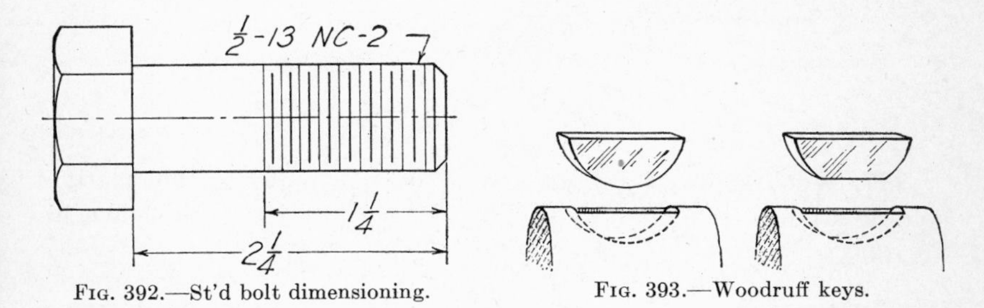

Fig. 392.—St'd bolt dimensioning.

Fig. 393.—Woodruff keys.

180. Keys.—In machine drawing there is frequent occasion for representing keyed fastenings as used in securing wheels, cranks, etc., to shafts. One of the commonest forms is the Woodruff key, a flat segmental disc with either round or flat bottom, as shown in Fig. 393. These are specified by number, and a table of standard sizes is given on page 457. A good basic rule for proportioning a Woodruff key to a given shaft is to have the width of the key one-fourth the diameter of the shaft and its radius equal to the radius of the shaft, selecting the standard key that comes nearest to these proportions. In drawing Woodruff keys care should be taken to place the center for the arc above the top of the key to a distance equal to one-half the thickness of the saw used in splitting the blank. This amount is given in Column *E* in the table on page 457.

181. Square and flat keys, both plain and tapered, have a variety of applications. Figure 394 shows at *A* a square key and at *B* a gib head taper key. Square and flat stock keys and taper stock keys have been standardized by the American Standards Association and a table of sizes for use with various diameters of shafts is given on page 456. At *C* is a "Pratt and Whitney" key with round ends. See

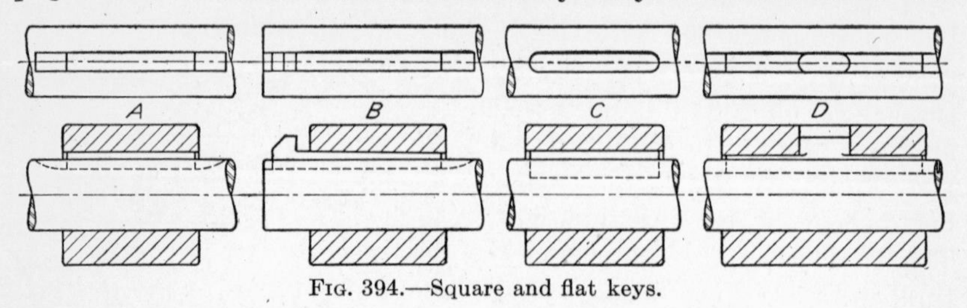

FIG. 394.—Square and flat keys.

table on page 458. A *feather* is a straight key which allows a piece to slide lengthwise on a shaft while preventing rotation on the shaft. A sliding feather sometimes has a gib on each end and sometimes is made with one or more projections as at *D*. With these the keyway must, of course, extend to one end of the shaft.

FIG. 395.—Keys for light duty.

Figure 395 shows three keys for light duty, the saddle key, the flat key and the pin or Nordberg key which is used at the end of a shaft, as, for example, in fastening a handwheel. A tapered pin is driven into a tapered hole machined into shaft and hub together as deep as the length of the hub.

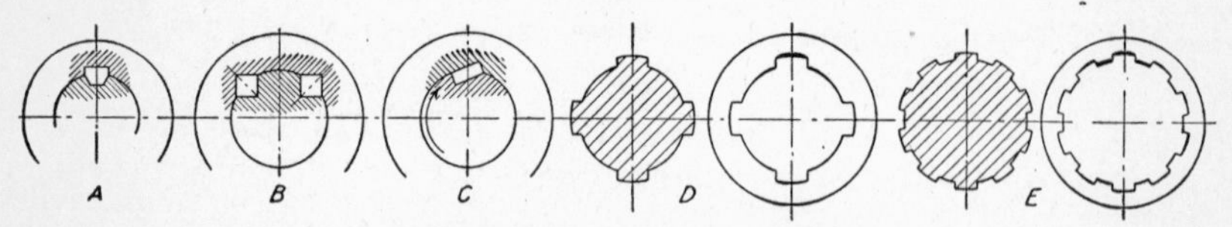

FIG. 396.—Keys for heavy duty.

Figure 396 shows some forms of heavy-duty keys. *A* is the Barth key, an improvement on the flat spline, *B* the Kennedy key, *C* the Lewis key for driving in one direction and *D* and *E* two forms of splined shaft, widely used instead of keyed shafts.

182. Rivets.—Rivets are used for making permanent fastenings, generally between pieces of sheet or rolled metal. They are round bars of steel or wrought iron with a head formed on one end and are put in place red-hot so that a head may be formed on the other end by pressing or hammering. Rivet holes are punched, punched and reamed, or drilled, 1/16″ larger than the diameter of the rivet, and the shank of the rivet is made just long enough to give sufficient metal to fill the hole completely and make the head.

It is not within our scope to consider the design of riveted joints, but we are concerned with the methods of representation. The two general uses of rivets are in structural steel construction and in boiler and tank work. In the former only two kinds of heads are needed, button heads and countersunk heads. The standard symbols used in structural work are given on page 361.

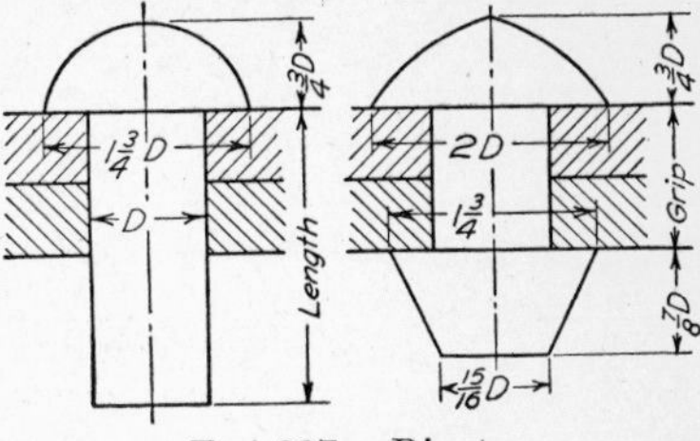

Fig. 397.—Rivets.

For boiler and tank work, pressure against the head as well as shear must be considered and the heads shown in Fig. 397 are used.

Plates are connected by either lap joints or butt joints. Single and double riveted lap joints are illustrated in Fig. 398 and double straps in Fig. 399.

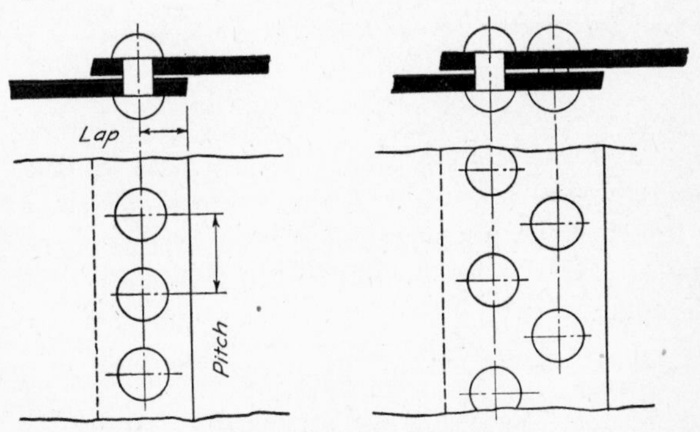

Fig. 398.—Lap joints.

The American Standard proportions for the heads of small rivets are shown in Fig. 400.

Fig. 399.—Butt joints.

183. Helical Springs.—Figure 401 shows the method of drawing the true projection of a helical spring with round section, by constructing the helix of the center line of the section, drawing on it a number of circles of the diameter of the wire and drawing an envelope curve tangent to the circles. This surface is known geometrically as a serpentine. On working drawings springs are drawn with straight

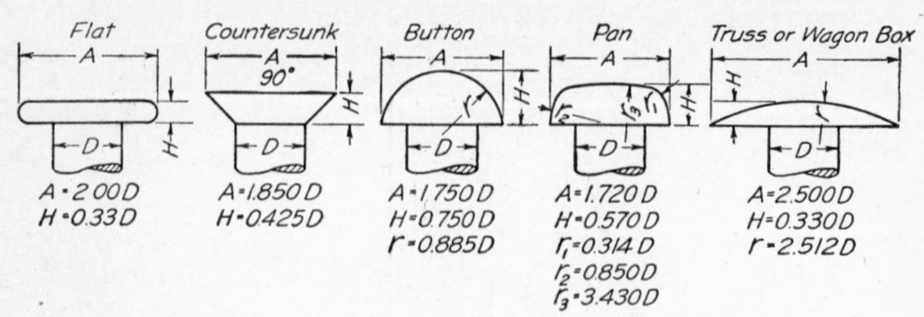

FIG. 400.—American Standard small rivet heads.

lines, and when in small size with single line representation. Compression springs are drawn to their free length. Figure 402 shows several conventional springs. The top view of the conical spring may be drawn as a four-center or two-center involute. *A* is a tension spring, illustrating the use of "ditto lines." *B* and *C* are single line conventions. Helical springs should have their line of action coincide with the axis; hence compression springs have their ends "closed and ground" as shown on *D*, *E* and *F*. By this is meant that the last coil has its lead gradually reduced to zero, touching the previous coil at the end of the last turn. Then the end is ground flat, giving approximately 50 to 80 per cent bearing area, upon which the spring can stand unsupported with its axis vertical.

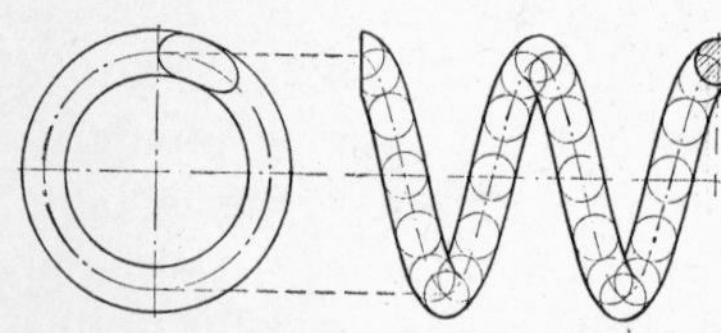

FIG. 401.—Spring, true projection.

184. Pipe.—A familiarity with pipe and pipe fittings is necessary not only for making piping drawings but because pipe is often used as a material of construction. Standard pipe of steel or wrought iron is designated by its nominal inside diameter, which differs somewhat from the actual inside diameter (early pipe manufacturers made the metal in the smaller sizes much too thick and in correcting this took the excess from the inside to avoid changing the sizes of fittings). For pressures heavier than 125 pounds "extra" and "double extra" heavy pipe having the same outside diameter as standard weight pipe of the same nominal size, the added thickness being on the inside, is used. Thus the outside diameter of all 1″ pipe is 1.315″, the inside diameter of standard 1″ pipe 1.05″, of 1″ extra strong 0.951″ and of XX 0.587″.

Pipe over twelve inches in diameter is designated as O.D. (outside diameter) pipe and is specified by its outside diameter and thickness of metal.

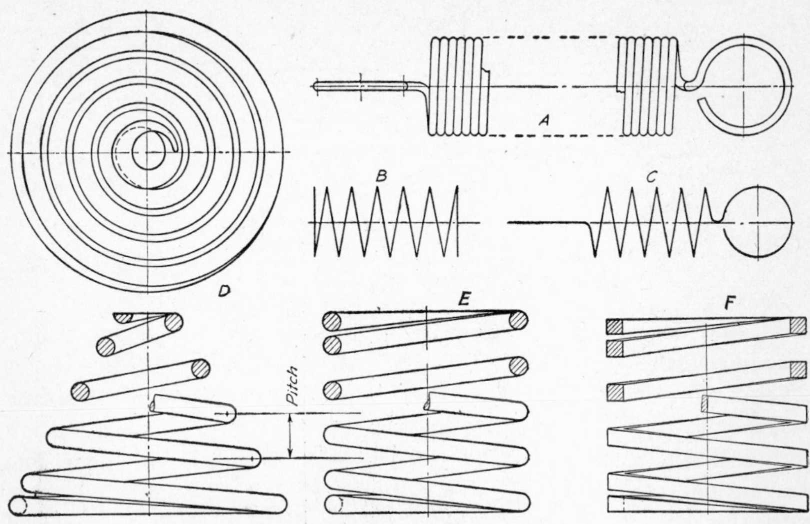

Fig. 402.—Springs, conventional.

Brass and copper tubing is made in outside diameters of ⅛″ to 10″. The small sizes are very flexible and are often used for oil piping in pressure oiling systems. For hot water piping brass pipe is best. Lead pipe and lead lined pipe are used in chemical work. Cast iron pipe is used for water and gas in underground mains, and for drains in buildings.

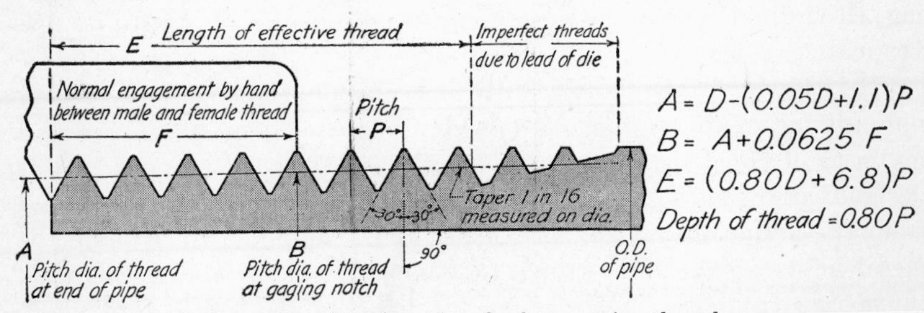

Fig. 403.—American Standard taper pipe thread.

Pipe is usually threaded on the ends for the purpose of screwing into fittings and making connections. The American Standard pipe thread (originated in 1882 as the "Briggs Standard") is illustrated in Fig. 403. The threads are cut on a taper of $\frac{1}{16}$″ per inch so that the distance the pipe enters a fitting is fixed and a tight joint insured.

185. Pipe threads are represented by the same conventional symbols as bolt threads. The taper is so slight that it will not show unless exaggerated. It need not be drawn unless it is desired to call attention to it as in Fig. 404. In plan view as at C the dotted circle should be the actual outside diameter of the pipe specified. See table, page 451, Appendix. The length of effective thread is $E = (0.80D + 6.8)P$.

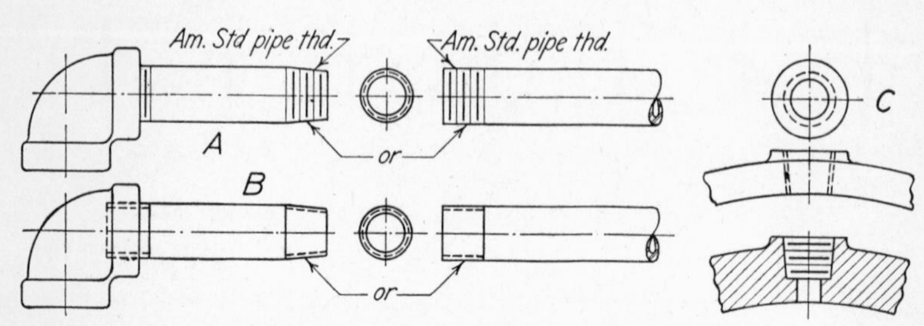

Fig. 404.—Conventional pipe threads.

186. Pipe Fittings.—Pipe fittings are the parts used in connecting and "making up" pipe. They are usually either cast iron or malleable iron, except couplings, which are wrought or malleable iron, and are designated by the nominal size of the pipe with which they are used. Some of the more commonly used fittings are shown in Fig. 405.

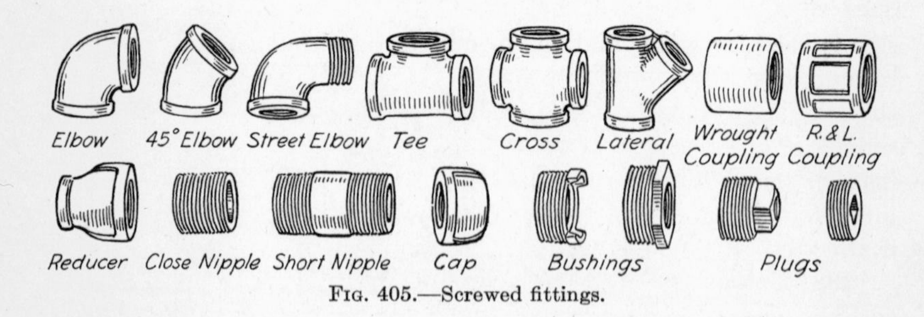

Fig. 405.—Screwed fittings.

Straight sections of pipe come in 12- to 20-feet lengths and are connected by couplings, short cylinders threaded on the inside. A right-hand *coupling* has right-hand threads at both ends. To close a system, although a union is preferable, a *right-and-left coupling* is sometimes used. It is readily distinguished by the ribs on the outside, four up to one inch and six on sizes larger than one inch. Pipes are also connected by screwing them into cast iron flanges and bolting the flanges together. It is recommended that flanged fittings be used on all systems over four inches unless the pressures are very low.

Nipples are short pieces of pipe threaded on both ends. If the threaded portions meet it is a *close nipple*. If there is a short unthreaded portion it is a *short nipple*. Long and extra long nipples range in length up to 12 inches.

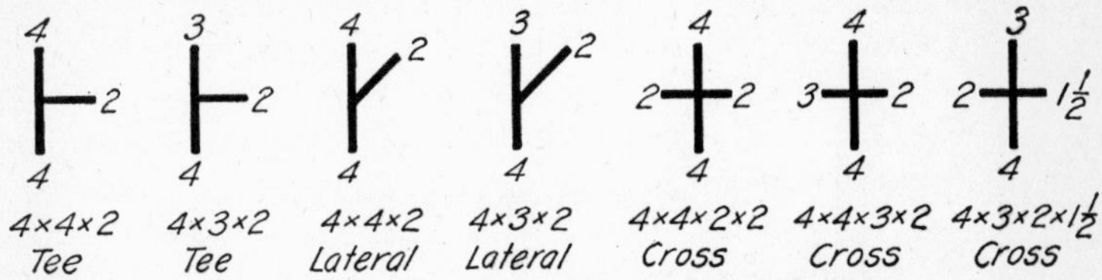

4×4×2 Tee | 4×3×2 Tee | 4×4×2 Lateral | 4×3×2 Lateral | 4×4×2×2 Cross | 4×4×3×2 Cross | 4×3×2×1½ Cross

Fig. 406.—Order of specifying reducing fittings.

A *cap* is used to close the end of a pipe. A *plug* is used to close an opening in a fitting. A *bushing* is used to reduce the size of an opening.

Formerly each manufacturer had his own sizes of elbows, tees and other fittings, but now the American Standards Association has standardized both screwed and flanged fittings, to the great advantage of all pipe users. Tables giving some of the standards will be found on pages 451 and 452.

187. Specifying Fittings.—Fittings are specified by the name, nominal pipe size and the material. When they connect more than one size of pipe the size of the largest run opening is given first, followed by the size at the opposite end of the run. The diagrams of Fig. 406 show the order of specifying reducing fittings. The word "male" must follow the size of the opening if an external thread is wanted.

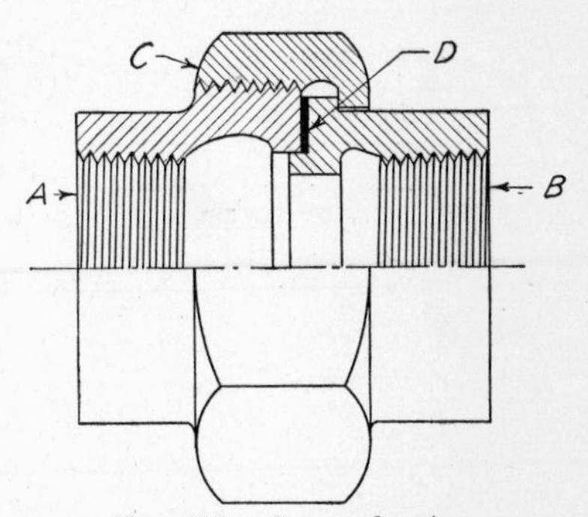

Fig. 407.—Screwed union.

188. Unions are used to close systems and to connect pipes that are to be taken down occasionally. A screwed union, Fig. 407, is composed of three pieces, two of which, *A* and *B*, are screwed firmly on the ends of the pipes to be connected. The third piece *C* draws them together, the gasket *D* forming a tight joint. They are also made with ground joints or with special metallic joints instead of gaskets. Flange unions, in a variety of forms, are used for large sizes of pipe.

189. Valves.—Figure 408 shows a few types of valves used in piping. *A* is a gate valve, used for water and other liquids, as it

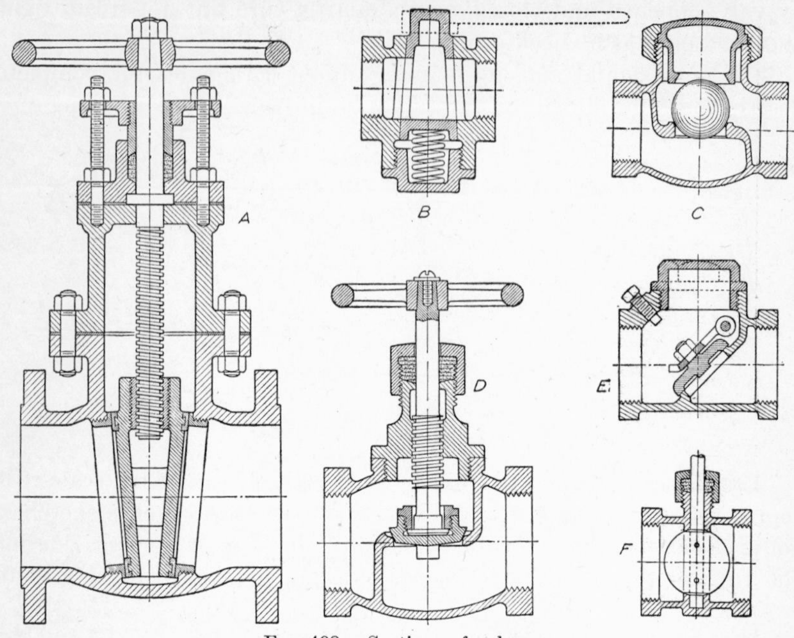

Fig. 408.—Sections of valves.

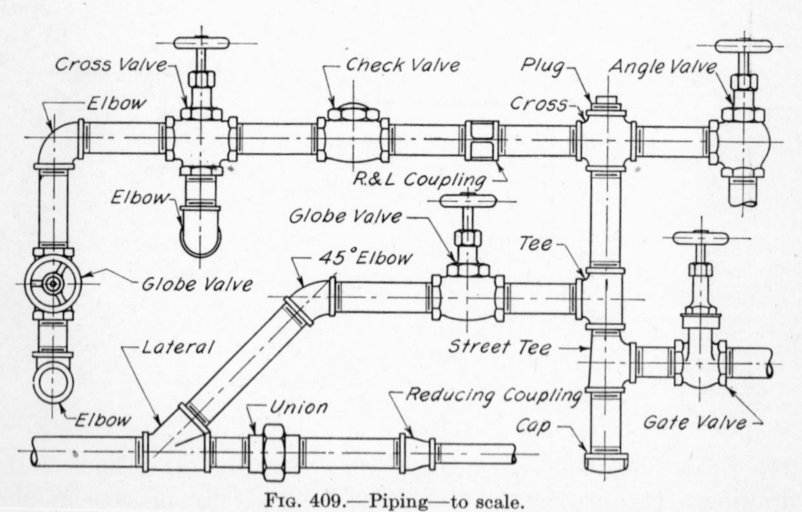

Fig. 409.—Piping—to scale.

allows a straight flow. *B* is a plug valve, opened and closed with a quarter turn; *C* a ball check and *E* a swing check valve permitting flow in one direction. For heavy liquids the ball check valve is preferred. D is a globe valve, used for throttling as in a steam valve; F is a butterfly valve, opened and closed with a quarter turn but not steam tight and used only as a check or damper.

Students should consult manufacturers' catalogues for complete descriptions and dimensions of valves and fittings.

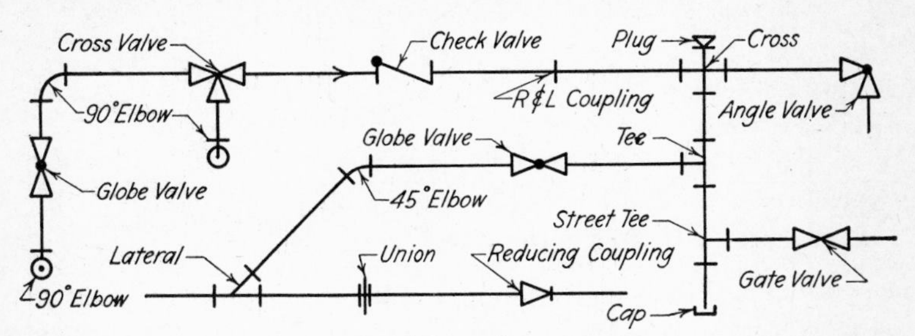

Fig. 410.—Piping—diagrammatic.

190. Piping Drawings.—When piping is drawn to large scale it is represented as in Fig. 409. When drawn to small scale or in sketches, conventional symbols are used for the fittings, with a single line for the runs of pipe, no matter what the diameters may be, Fig. 410.

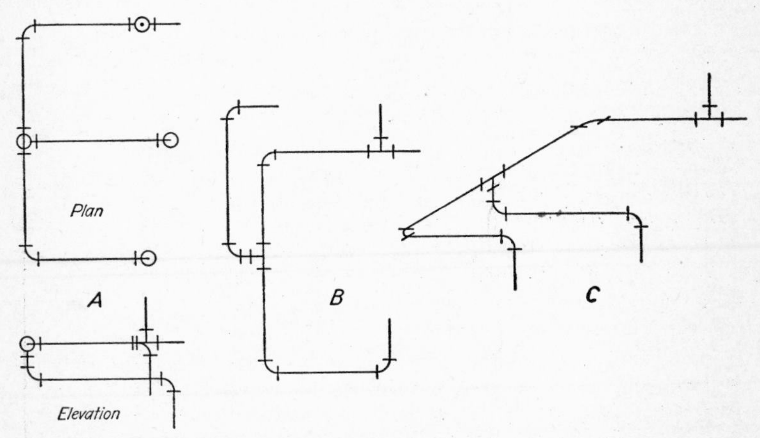

Fig. 411.—Piping in orthographic, developed and pictorial views.

The single line should be made heavier than the other lines of the drawing. The arrangement of views is generally in orthographic projection as in Fig. 411A. Sometimes, however, it is clearer to swing all the piping into one plane and make only one "developed view" as at B. Isometric and oblique drawings are very often used in piping diagrams, showing in one view the position of the piping, either alone or in connection with the orthographic or developed make-up drawings, as at *C*.

Dimensions should be given to the centers of piping, valves and fittings, in order to locate them. The allowances for make-up may be left to the pipe fitter. The sizes of pipe should be specified by a note telling its nominal diameter, never by a dimension line on the pipe itself.

Very complete notes are an important essential of all piping drawings and sketches.

A complete set of symbols for pipe fittings for flanged, screwed, ball-and-spigot, welded and soldered joints has been compiled by the American Standards Association.

PROBLEMS

Group I. Helices.

1. Draw three complete turns of a helix, diameter 3″, pitch 1¼″.

2. Draw three complete turns of a conical helix, top and front views, with 1½″ pitch, whose large diameter is 4″ and small diameter 1½″.

3. Draw four complete turns, two in section and two in full, of a helical spring made of ⅜″ square stock. Outside diameter 3½″, pitch 1½″.

4. Draw a helical spring 4″ long, made of ½″ round stock. Outside diameter 3″, pitch 1″.

Group II. Screw Threads.

5. Draw two views of a square thread screw and section of nut, separated, diameter 2½″, pitch ¾″, length of screw 3″. Nut American Standard hex. (except threads).

6. Same as Prob. 5 but for V-thread with ½″ pitch.

7. Draw in section the following forms of screw threads, 1″ pitch; American Standard; Acme; Whitworth; square.

8. Draw screws 2″ diameter and 3½″ long; single square thread, pitch ½″; single V-thread, pitch ¼; double V-thread, pitch ½; left-hand double square thread, pitch ½″.

Group III. Bolts.

9. Draw one view of an American Standard hex. head unfinished bolt and nut across corners. Diameter 1″, length 5″, length of thread 2¼″.

10. Same as Prob. 9 for a finished bolt and nut.

11. Same as Prob. 9 for a square head unfinished bolt and nut.

12. Same as Prob. 9 for a square head semi-finished bolt and nut.

13. Draw four ½″ × 1½″ cap screws, each with a different type of head. Name each.

14. Fig. 412. Draw the stuffing box and gland, showing the required fastenings. Dimension fastenings only. On C.L.'s *A* show ½″ hex. head cap screws (four required). On C.L.'s *B* show ½″ studs and Standard hex. nuts. Supply missing dimensions.

15. Fig. 413. Draw the bearing plate, showing the required fastenings. On C.L.'s *C* show $\frac{1}{2}''$ hex. bolts and nuts (four required). On C.L. *D* show $\frac{1}{2}''$ safety set screw. On C.L. *E* show $\frac{1}{2}''$ American Standard set screw. Set screws to have cone points. Supply missing dimensions.

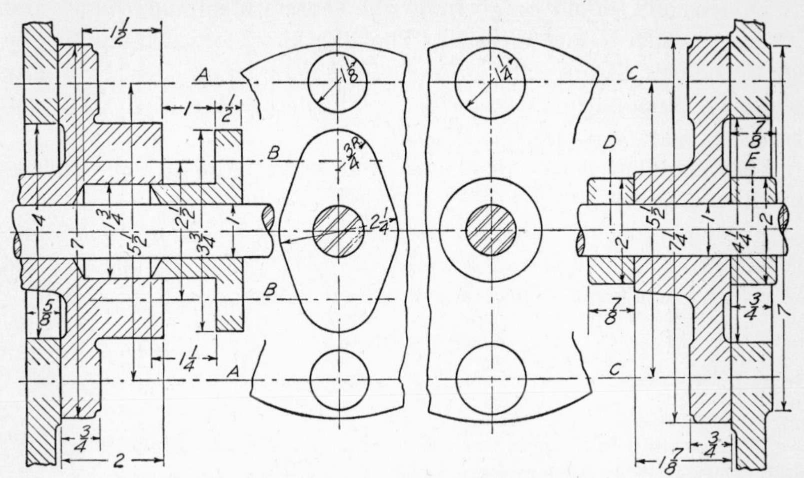

Fig. 412.—Stuffing box and gland.

Fig. 413.—Bearing plate.

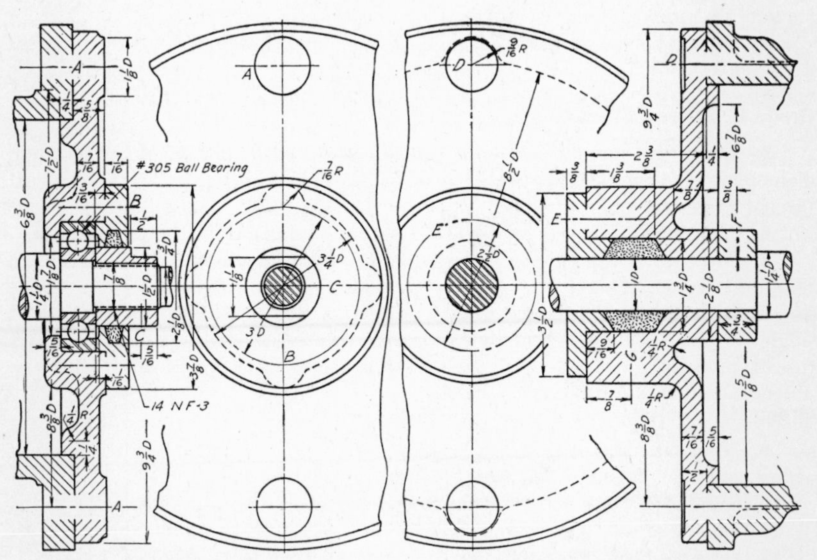

Fig. 414.—Ball bearing head.

Fig. 415.—Plain bearing head.

Problems 14 and 15 may be drawn together on an 11×17 sheet, or on separate sheets, showing full diameter of flanges.

16. Fig. 414. Draw the ball bearing head, showing the required fastenings. On C.L.'s *A* show $\frac{1}{2}'' \times 1\frac{3}{4}''$ finished hex. head bolts and nuts (six required), with heads to left and shown across flats. Note that this design prevents the heads from turning. On C.L.'s *B* show $\frac{5}{16}'' \times \frac{3}{4}''$ fillister head cap screws (four required). On C.L. *C* show a $\frac{3}{8}'' \times \frac{1}{2}''$ cone point safety set screw. Spot shaft with nut in position. Supply missing dimensions.

17. Fig. 415. Draw the plain bearing head, showing the required fastenings. On C.L.'s *D* show $\frac{1}{2}'' \times 2''$ studs and nuts (six required). Spot face $1''\ D \times \frac{1}{16}''$ deep. On C.L.'s *E* show $\frac{3}{8}'' \times 1''$ hex. head cap screws (four required). On C.L. *F* show a $\frac{7}{16}'' \times \frac{7}{8}''$ American Standard cone point set screw. On C.L. *G* show a $\frac{29}{64}''$ drilled hole plugged with a $\frac{1}{4}''$ pipe plug. This is for gun packing the gland. Supply missing dimensions.

Problems 16 and 17 may be drawn together on an $11'' \times 17''$ sheet, or on separate sheets, showing full diameter of flanges.

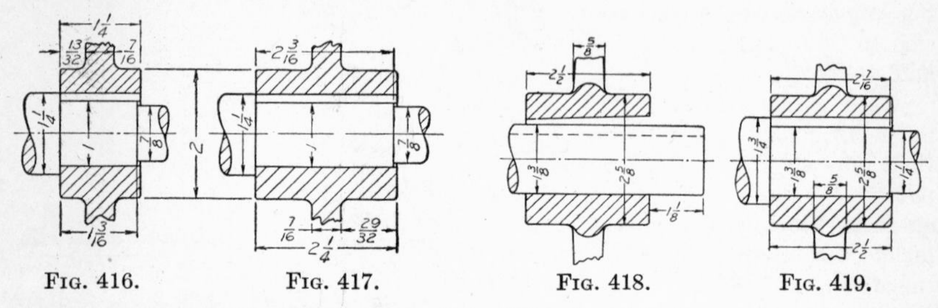

FIG. 416. FIG. 417. FIG. 418. FIG. 419.

Group IV. Keys and Rivets. Key sizes will be found in Appendix.

18. Fig. 416. Draw hub and shaft as shown, with a Woodruff key in position.

19. Fig. 417. Draw hub and shaft as shown, with a square key 2″ long, in position.

20. Fig. 418. Draw hub and shaft as shown, with a gib head key in position.

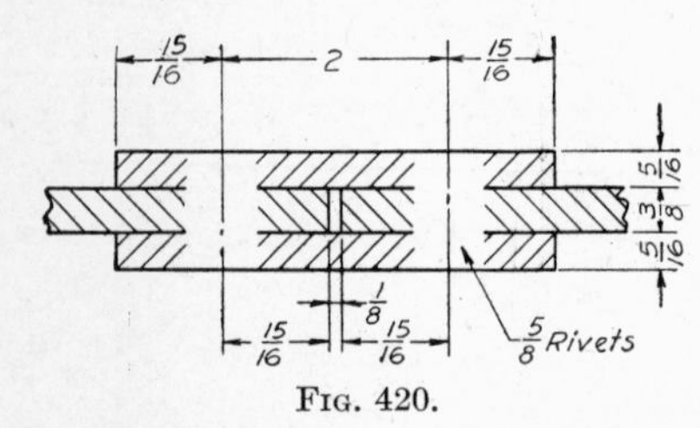

FIG. 420.

21. Fig. 419. Draw hub and shaft as shown, with a P. & W. (Pratt and Whitney) key in position.

22. Fig. 420. Draw top view and section of single riveted butt joint $10\frac{5}{8}''$ long. Pitch of rivets $1\frac{3}{4}''$. Fig. 397.

23. Fig. 421. Draw a column section made of $15'' \times 33.9$-lb. channels with cover plates, as shown, using $\frac{7}{8}''$ rivets (dimensions from American Institute of Steel Construction or other handbook).

Group V. Piping.

24. Pipe Fittings.—Make a complete developed layout of piping (full size), with necessary dimensions and specifications, showing the following: angle valve, globe valve, cross, 90° ell, 45° ell, Y, street tee, tee, screwed union, cap and plug. Place angle valve in one of the upper corners of the sheet. Add extra pipe and nipples but no extra fittings to close the system. Use $1\frac{1}{2}''$ pipe and fittings throughout.

25. Pipe Fittings.—In the upper left-hand corner of sheet draw a 2″ tee. Plug one outlet; in the second, place a $1\frac{1}{2}'' \times 2''$ bushing; in remaining outlet use a 2″ close nipple and on it screw a $1\frac{1}{2}'' \times 2''$ reducing coupling. Lay out remainder of sheet so as to include the following $1\frac{1}{2}''$ fittings: coupling, globe valve, R. & L. coupling, angle valve, 45° ell, 90° ell, 45° Y, cross, cap, three part union, flange union. Add extra pipe, nipples and fittings so the system will close at the reducing fitting first drawn.

26. Fig. 422. *A* is a storage tank for supplying the mixing tanks *B*, *C* and *D* and is located directly above them. The capacities of the mixers are in the ratios of 1, 2 and 3. Design (in one view) a piping system with sizes such that, neglecting frictional losses, the three tanks will fill in approximately the same time. So arrange the piping that any one of the tanks can be cut out or removed for repairs without disturbing the others. Use single line conventional representation. Dimension to center lines, and specify the name and size of fittings.

27. Fig. 422. Same as Prob. 26 except in the arrangement of the tanks. In plan the tanks *B*, *C* and *D* are placed at the points of an equilateral triangle whose sides are 12 feet long. The center of tank *A* is in line with *D* and *C* and 20 feet from *B*, the nearer one. Draw plan and developed elevation of the piping system, with single line representation. Dimension to center lines and specify fittings.

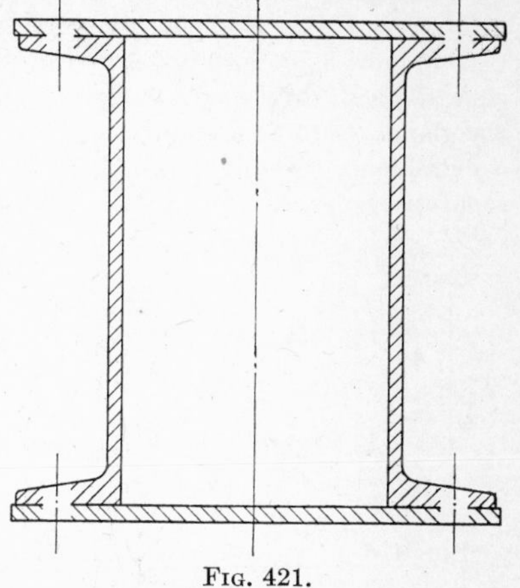

Fig. 421.

28. Figure 423 shows the arrangement of a set of mixing tanks. Make an isometric drawing of an overhead piping system to supply water to each tank. Water supply enters the building through a 2½″ main at point *A* 3 feet below floor level. Place all pipe 10 feet above floor level, except riser from water main

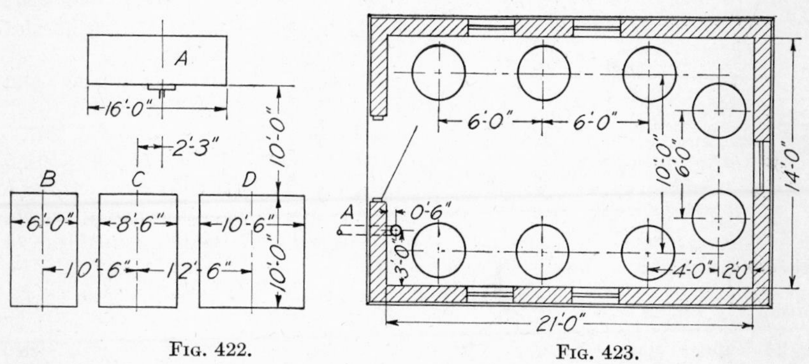

Fig. 422. Fig. 423.

and drops to tanks, which are to end with globe valves 5 feet above floor level. Arrange the system to use as little pipe and few fittings as possible. Neglecting frictional losses, sizes of pipe used should be such that they will deliver approximately an equal volume of water to each tank if all were being filled at the same time. The pipe size at the tank should not be less than ¾″. Dimension and specify all pipe and fittings.

29. Make a drawing of the system in Prob. 28. Show the layout in a developed view using double line conventional treatment. Dimension from center to center and specify all pipe and fittings.

30. Make a list of the pipe and fittings to be ordered for the system in Prob. 28. Arrange the list in a table, heading the columns as below:

Size	Pipe lengths	Valves		Fittings		Material	Remarks (make, kind of threads, etc.)
		Number	Kind	Number	Kind		

31. Make an oblique drawing of a system of piping to supply the tanks in Fig. 423. All piping except risers shall be in a trench 1 foot below floor level. Risers should not run higher than 6 feet above floor level. Other conditions as in Prob. 28.

32. Make a drawing of the system in Prob. 31. Show the layout in a developed view, using double line conventional treatment. Dimension from center to center and specify all pipe and fittings.

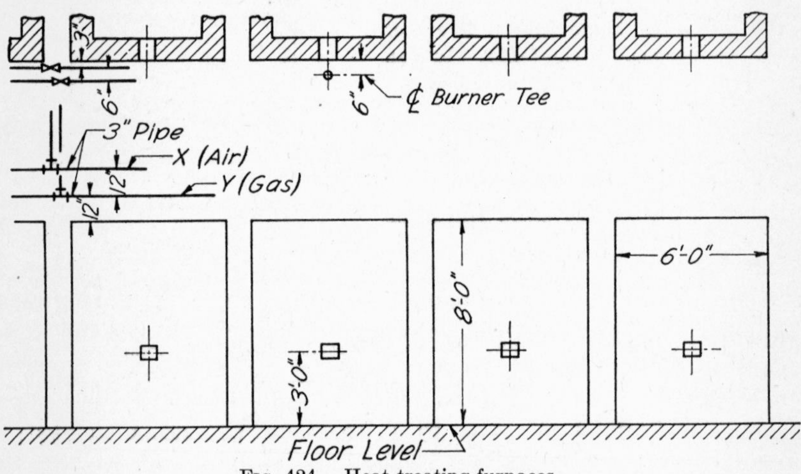

Fig. 424.—Heat treating furnaces.

33. Make a list of pipe and fittings to be ordered for the system in Prob. 32. Arrange the list in a table, heading the columns as in Prob. 30.

34. Figure 424 shows the outline of the right-hand half of a bank of eight heat treating furnaces. *X* and *Y* are the lead-ins from the compressed air and fuel mains. Draw the piping layout, using single line representation, to distribute the air and fuel to the furnaces. The pipe sizes should be reduced proportionately as the oven leads are taken off. Each tail pipe should be removable without disturbing the other leads or closing down the other furnaces. Dimension the piping layout and make a bill of material for the pipe and fittings.

Group VI. Sketching.

35. Make a sketch from memory of five methods of locking a nut.

36. Make a sketch from memory of eight kinds of screws.

37. Make a sketch from memory of five kinds of keys.

38. Make a sketch from memory of four kinds of rivet heads.

39. Make a sketch from memory of three kinds of valves.

40. Make a sketch from memory of eight different pipe fittings.

CHAPTER XI

WORKING DRAWINGS

191. Definition.—A working drawing is a drawing that gives all the information necessary for the complete manufacture or construction of the object represented.

It is a technical description of a machine or structure designed for a certain purpose and place and should convey all the facts regarding it so clearly and explicitly that no further instruction concerning either manufacture or erection would be required.

The drawing will thus include:

1. The full graphical representation of the shape and relationship of every part of the object (*shape description*).
2. The figured dimensions of all parts (*size description*).
3. Explanatory notes giving specifications in regard to materials, finish, heat treatment, etc.
4. A descriptive title.

Often, as in architectural and structural drawing, the notes of explanation and information concerning details of materials and workmanship are too extensive to be included on the drawings, so are made up separately in typed or printed form and called the "specifications." These are considered as virtually a part of the drawings, the information in them having equal weight and importance. Thus we have the term "drawings and specifications."

192. Choice of Views.—Although pictorial drawings are used to some extent in special cases, the basis of all working drawing is orthographic projection. Thus to represent an object completely, at least two views would be necessary, often more. The only general rule would be *make as many views as are necessary to describe the object clearly,* **and no more.** Instances may occur in which the third dimension is so well understood as to make one view sufficient, as, for example, in the drawing of a shaft or bolt. In other cases perhaps a half dozen views might be required to describe a piece completely.

With the object in a natural position select for the front view the face showing the largest dimension, preferably the obvious front of the object, then decide what other views are necessary. A vertical cylindrical piece, for example, would require only front and top views; a horizontal cylindrical piece a front and a side view only. Determine which side view to use, or whether both are needed. The one with the fewest hidden lines would be preferred. See whether an auxiliary view or a note will save one or more other views, and whether a section will be better than an exterior view. One statement may be made with the force of a rule: *If anything in clearness may be gained by the violation of any one of the strict principles of projection, violate it.*

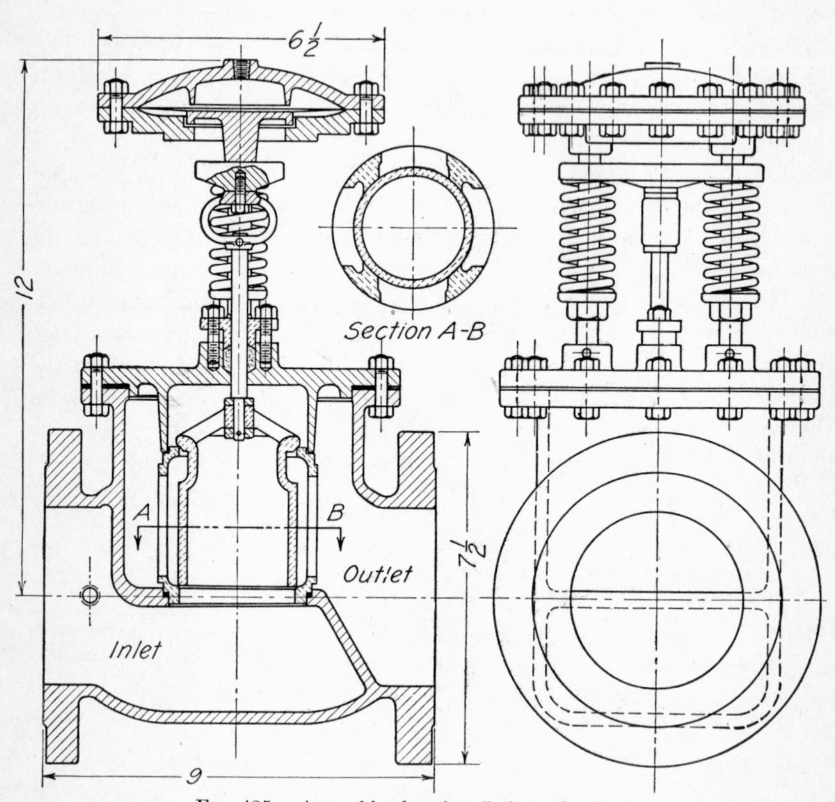

Fig. 425.—Assembly drawing (balanced valve).

Paragraphs 115 to 120, Chapter VIII, give a number of examples of conventions which are in violation of theoretical representation but made in the interest of clearness. The draftsman must remember that his responsibility is to the reader of the drawing and that he has no license to save himself any time or trouble at the expense of making the drawing less plain or easy to read. The time saved once by the draftsman may be lost to the company a hundredfold in the shop, where the drawing is used repeatedly.

193. Classes of Working Drawings.—Working drawings may be divided into two general classes, assembly drawings and detail drawings.

194. Assembly Drawings.—Fig. 425. An assembly drawing is, as its name implies, a drawing of the machine or structure put together, showing the relative positions of the different parts. The term "construction drawing" is sometimes used. Its views may be either exterior or sectional.

Under the term "assembly drawings" would be included preliminary design drawings and layouts, piping plans, unit assembly drawings and final complete drawings used for assembling or erecting the machine or structure.

The *design drawing* is the preliminary layout, full size if possible, on which the scheming, inventing and designing are worked out accurately, after freehand sketches and calculations have determined the general ideas. From it the detail drawings of each piece are made.

The *assembly drawing* is in some cases made by tracing from the finished design drawing. Oftener it is drawn from the design drawing, perhaps to smaller scale to fit a standard sheet, and working from the dimensions of the detail drawings. This makes a valuable check on the correctness of the detail drawings and should be done before the details are sent out as finished.

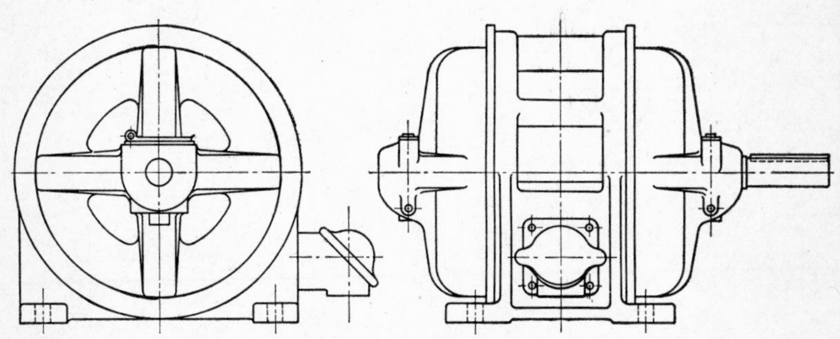

Fig. 426.—Outline assembly drawing (motor).

The assembly drawing may give the over-all dimensions and the distances from center to center or from part to part of the different pieces, indicating their location and relation, so that the machine can be erected by reference to it. It should not be overloaded with detail, particularly invisible detail. Unnecessary hidden lines should not be used on any drawing.

Assembly drawings often have reference letters or numbers on the different parts. These "piece numbers" are sometimes enclosed in circles with a leader pointing to the piece and are used in connection with the details and bill of material. See Fig. 515.

Diagram drawing is a term applied to the foregoing class of assembly drawings, as well as to those made to show piping, wiring, heating, etc.

An outline assembly drawing is used to give a general idea of a machine or structure and contains only the principal dimensions. When it is made for catalogue or other illustrative purposes, dimensions are often omitted, Fig. 426. Shade lines are occasionally used on this class of drawings, and sometimes line shading. See Chapter XXII.

An assembly working drawing, showing fully the construction of each piece as well as the relative positions, may be made for a simple machine.

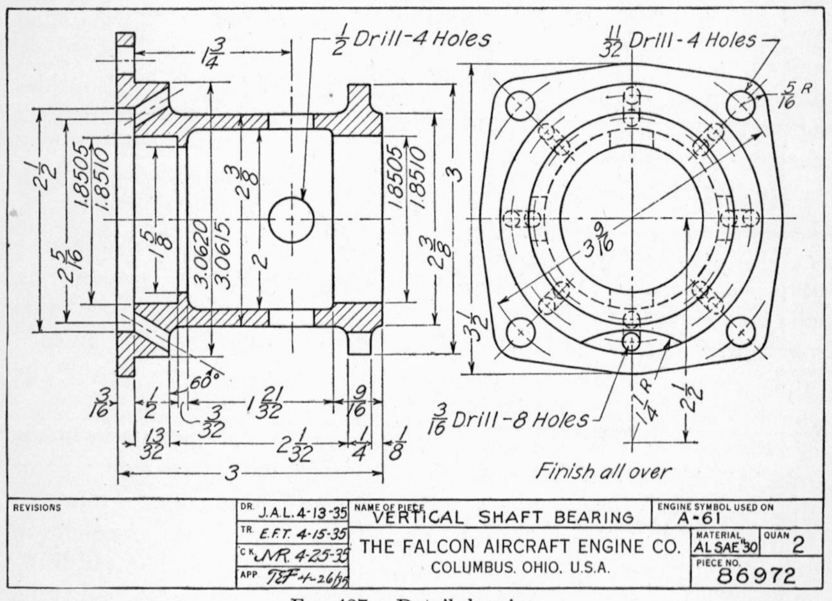

Fig. 427.—Detail drawing.

A unit assembly drawing, or sub-assembly, is a drawing of a related group of parts, used instead of, or together with, separate details of each part, in more complicated machinery. Thus there would be a unit assembly of such parts as rear axle and differential gear train; of transmission gear box; of lathe head-stock, etc.

A tabular drawing is a drawing, either assembly or detail, on which the dimensions are given with reference letters and an accompanying table lists the corresponding dimensions for a series of sizes of the machine or part, thus making one drawing serve for the range covered. See Fig. 456. It is not recommended for quantity production.

195. Detail Drawings.—A detail drawing is the drawing of a separate piece, giving a complete and exact description of its form, dimensions and construction. A successful detail drawing will tell the workman *simply* and *directly* the shape, size, material, and finish of each part, what shop operations are necessary, what limits of accuracy must be observed, and how many of each are wanted. Figure 427 is a detail drawing of a small piece, illustrating the use of decimal dimensions.

The *grouping* of the details is entirely dependent upon the requirements of the shop system. In a very simple machine and if only one or two are to be built (as, for example, in jig and tool work), all the details may perhaps be grouped on a single sheet. The detailed pieces should be in the same position as on the assembly and, to facilitate reading, placed as nearly as possible in natural relationship. Often parts of the same material or character are grouped together, as forgings on one sheet, special bolts and screws on another.

In large production the accepted and best system is to have each piece, no matter how small, on a separate sheet.

196. Set of Drawings.—A complete *set* of working drawings, therefore, consists of detail sheets and assembly sheets, the former giving all necessary information for the manufacture of each individual piece, while the latter shows the construction assembled as a finished unit or machine. The set may also include special drawings for the purchaser, such as foundation plans or oiling diagrams.

197. Style.—There is a *style* in drawing, just as there is in literature, which in one way indicates itself by the ease of reading. Some drawings "stand out," while others which may contain all the information are difficult to decipher. Although dealing with "mechanical thought," there is a place for some artistic sense in mechanical drawing. The number, selection and disposition of views, the omission of anything unnecessary, ambiguous or misleading, the size and placing of dimensions and lettering, and the contrast of lines are all elements concerned in the *style*.

198. Making a Working Drawing—Order of Penciling.—After the scheming, inventing and calculating have been done, the order of procedure would be:

First, lay off a sheet to standard size, with the excess paper to the right, as a convenient space for making sketches and calculations, and block out the space for the title. *Or* lay off the standard size very lightly, and, after the drawing is finished, shift the border to balance the sheet.

Second, decide what scale is to be used, choosing one large enough to show all dimensions without crowding, and plan the arrangement of the sheet by making a little preliminary freehand sketch, estimating the space each view will occupy, and placing the views to the best advantage for preserving if possible a balance in the appearance of the sheet.

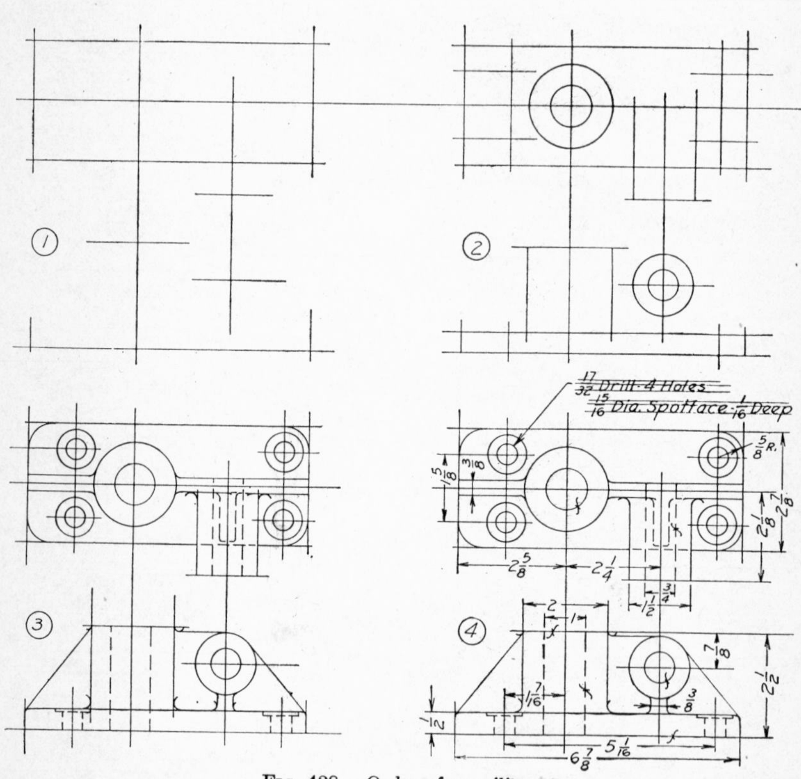

FIG. 428.—Order of penciling.

Third, draw the center lines for each view and on these "block in" the views by laying off the principal dimensions and outlines, using **light, sharp, accurate** pencil lines. Center lines are drawn for the axes of symmetry of all symmetrical views or parts of views. Thus every cylindrical part would have a center line through its axis. Every circle would have two center lines intersecting at its center.

Fourth, finish the projections, putting in minor details, such as fillets, rounded corners, etc., last. The different views should be carried on together, projecting a characteristic shape as shown on one view to the other views, not finishing one view before starting another.

Fifth, draw all necessary dimension lines, then put in the dimensions.

Sixth, draw guide lines for notes, then letter them.

Seventh, lay out the title.

Eighth, check the drawing carefully.

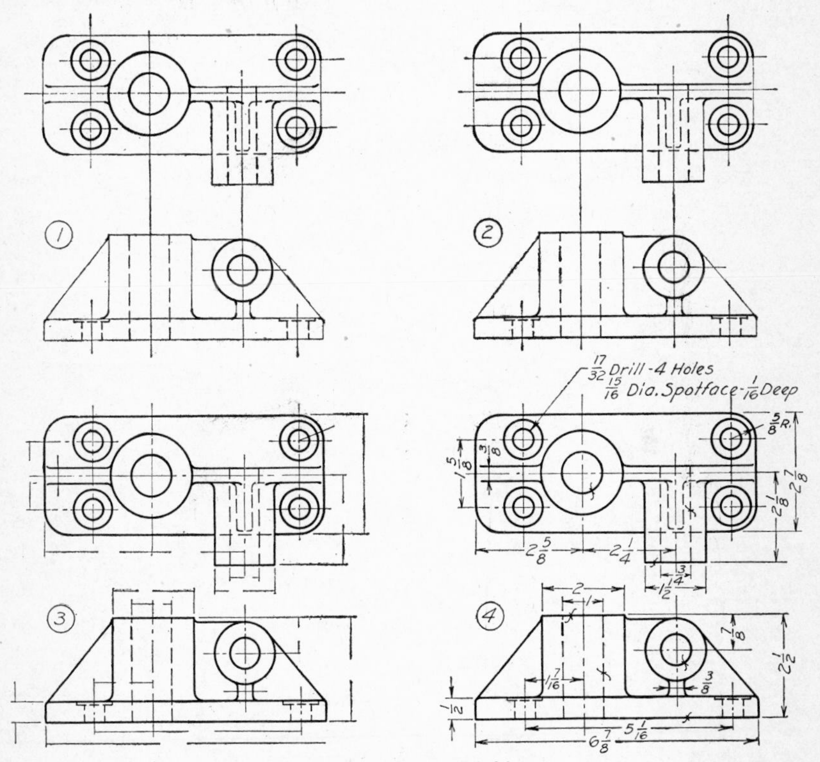

FIG. 429.—Order of inking.

As an aid in tracing, either in pencil or in ink, the finished outline or parts of it may if necessary be brightened by running over a second time with the pencil. The overrunning lines of the constructive stage should not be erased before tracing or inking. These extensions are often convenient in showing the stopping points. All unnecessary erasing should be avoided as it abrades the surface of the paper so that it catches dirt more readily.

As an aid in stopping tangent arcs in inking it is desirable to mark the tangent point on the pencil drawing by a short piece of the normal at the point of tangency. Figure 428 illustrates the stages of penciling.

199. Tracing.—Working drawings almost always go to the shop in the form of blue prints or black-line prints, printed from tracings made in ink on tracing cloth, or in pencil on tracing paper, or drawn directly on pencil cloth or translucent bond paper. The beginner should read carefully pages 403 and 404 before starting a tracing on cloth, noticing that the cloth is to be tacked down smoothly with the dull side up, prepared by chalking and the selvage torn off. Also that no view should be left overnight with only part of its lines traced.

200. Order of Inking.—*First,* ink all solid circles, beginning with the smallest, then circle arcs.

Second, ink dotted circles and arcs in the same order.

Third, ink any irregular curved lines.

Fourth, ink straight full lines in the order: horizontal, vertical, inclined.

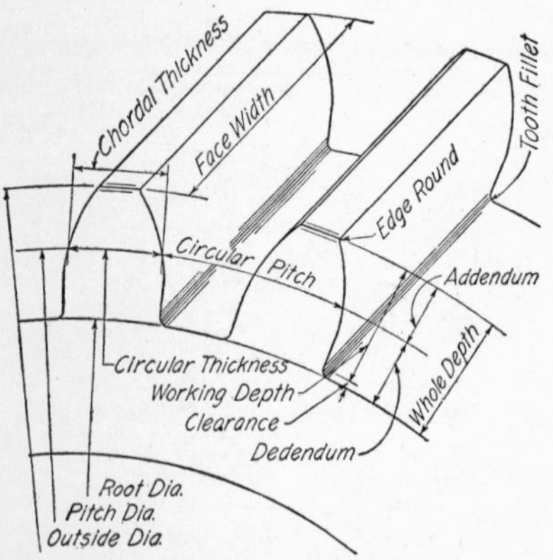

Fifth, ink straight dotted lines in the same order.

Sixth, ink center lines.

Seventh, ink extension and dimension lines.

Eighth, ink arrow heads and dimensions.

Ninth, section-line all cut surfaces.

Tenth, letter notes and titles. (On tracings draw pencil guide lines first.)

Eleventh, ink the border.

Fig. 430.—Nomenclature.

Twelfth, check the inked drawing.

Figure 429 shows the stages of inking.

201. Gears.—The theory of gearing belongs to the study of Mechanism, but the representation and specification of gears are of such common occurrence that the proportions and nomenclature should be familiar to the young engineer.

Briefly, gears are a substitute for rolling cylinders and cones, designed to insure positive motion. There are numerous kinds of gears, of which the most common forms are *spur gears* for transmitting motion from one shaft to another parallel shaft, and *bevel gears* for two shafts whose axes intersect, usually at right angles. When one of a pair of gears is much smaller than the other it is called a pinion.

Some of the terms in the American Standard nomenclature of gearing are given in Fig. 430. In the calculation of gears the following standardized terms and abbreviations are used.

N = number of teeth = $DP \times PD$

DP = diametral pitch = number of teeth in the gear for each inch of pitch diameter = N/PD

PD = diameter of pitch circle = N/DP

CP = circular pitch = the distance on the circumference of the pitch circle between corresponding points of adjacent teeth = $\pi PD/N = \pi/DP$

CTh = circular thickness = the thickness of the tooth on the pitch circle = $CP/2$

CT = chordal thickness = length of the chord subtended by the circular thickness arc = $PD \sin 90/N$

A = addendum = radial distance between the pitch circle and the top of the teeth = $\dfrac{\text{constant}}{DP} \left(= \text{for standard involute teeth } \dfrac{1}{DP}\right)$

D = dedendum = radial distance between the pitch circle and the bottom of the tooth space = $\dfrac{\text{constant}}{DP} \left(= \text{for standard involute teeth } \dfrac{1.157}{DP}\right)$

C = clearance = radial distance between the top of a tooth and the bottom of the mating tooth space = $\dfrac{\text{constant}}{DP} \left(= \text{for standard involute teeth } \dfrac{1.157}{DP}\right)$

WD = whole depth = radial distance between outside circle and root circle = $A + D$

WDe = working depth = greatest depth to which a tooth of one gear extends into the tooth space of a mating gear = $2A$

OD = outside diameter = the diameter of the greatest circle which contains the tops of the teeth = $2A + PD$

RD = root diameter = the diameter of the root circle = $PD - 2D$

FW = face width = width of pitch surface

ER = edge round = radius of the circumferential edge of a gear tooth (to break the corner)

TFi = tooth fillet = curved line joining the tooth flank and the bottom of the tooth space

The necessary information concerning a gear may be found by counting the number of teeth and measuring the outside diameter.

Example.—Given N and OD to find DP

$$\frac{N}{DP} + \frac{2}{DP} = OD$$

Then

$$DP = \frac{N+2}{OD}$$

In a similar way any required dimensions may be found by the solution of an equation.

In the working drawings of gears and toothed wheels the teeth are not all drawn. For cast gears the pitch circle, outside circle and root circles are drawn, and the full-sized outline of one tooth. For cut gears the blank is drawn and a note added concerning the number of teeth and pitch.

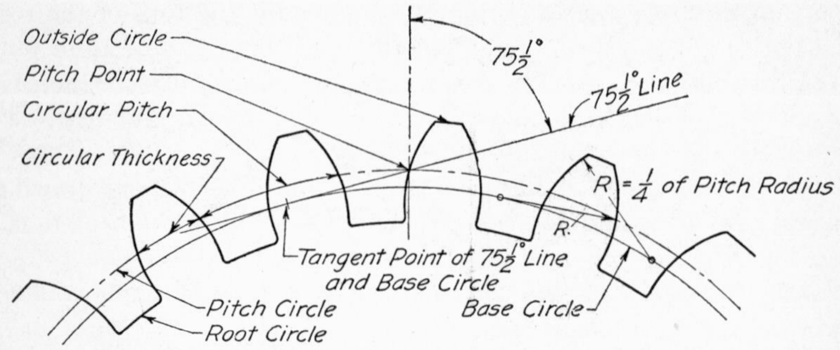

Fig. 431.—To draw involute spur gear, approximate method.

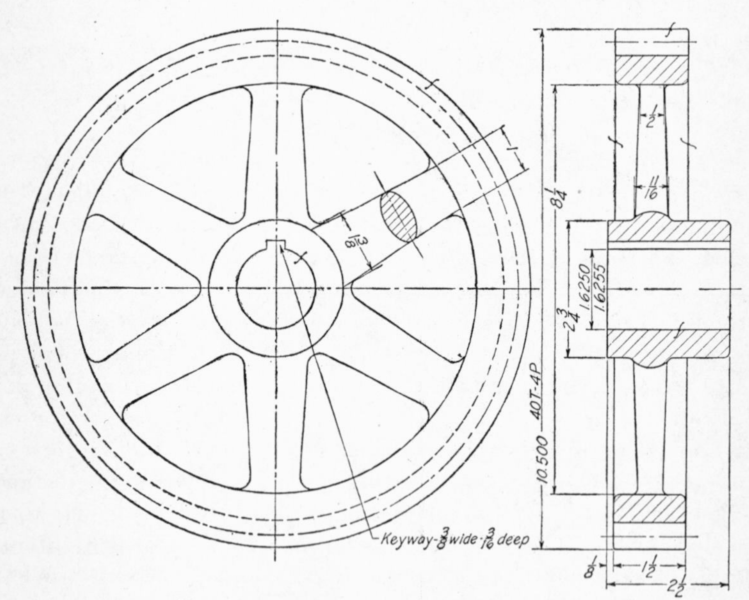

Fig. 432.—Working drawing of spur gear.

202. To Draw a Spur Gear.—Fig. 431. To draw the teeth of a standard involute tooth spur gear by an approximate circle-arc method, lay off the pitch circle, root circle and outside circle. Start with the pitch point and divide the pitch circle into distances equal to the circular thickness. Through the pitch point draw a line at 75½° with the center line (for convenience the draftsman uses 75°). Draw the base circle tangent to the 75° line. With compasses set to a radius equal to one-fourth the radius of the pitch circle describe arcs through the division points on the pitch circle, keeping the needle point on the base circle. Brighten the arcs for the tops of the teeth and bottom of the spaces, and add the tooth fillets. For 16 or fewer teeth the radius value of one-fourth the pitch radius must be increased to suit in order to avoid the appearance of excessive undercut. For stub teeth the 75½° line is changed to 70°.

This method of drawing gear teeth is useful on display drawings. On working drawings the teeth are not drawn but are indicated as in Fig. 432.

203. To Draw a Rack.—Fig. 433. To draw the teeth of a standard involute rack by an approximate method, draw the pitch line and lay off the addendum and dedendum distances. Divide the pitch line into spaces equal to the circular thickness. Through these points of division draw the tooth faces at 14½° (15° is used by draftsmen). Draw tops and bottoms and add the tooth fillets. For stub teeth use 20° instead of 14½°.

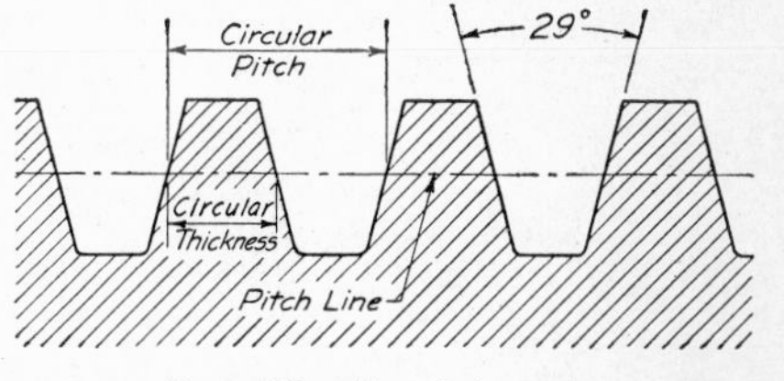

Fig. 433.—Involute rack.

204. To Draw a Bevel Gear.—Fig. 434. To draw the teeth of an involute tooth bevel gear by an approximate method (the Tredgold method). Draw the center lines, intersecting at O. Across the center lines lay off the pitch diameters (N)/(DP) and project them parallel to the center lines until the projectors intersect at the pitch point P. From the pitch point draw the pitch circle diameters for each gear and from their extremities the "pitch cones" to the vertex or "cone center" O. Lay off the addendum and dedendum distances for each gear on lines through the pitch points perpendicular to the cone elements. Extend one of these normals for each gear to intersect the axis, as at B and C, making the "back cones." With B as center swing arcs 1, 2 and 3 for the top, pitch line and bottom of a developed tooth. On a radial center line AB draw a tooth, by the method of Fig. 431. Start the plan view of the gear by projecting points 1, 2 and 3 across to its vertical center line and drawing circles through the points. Lay off the radial center lines for each tooth. With dividers take the circular thickness distances from A and transfer them to each tooth center line. This will give three points on each

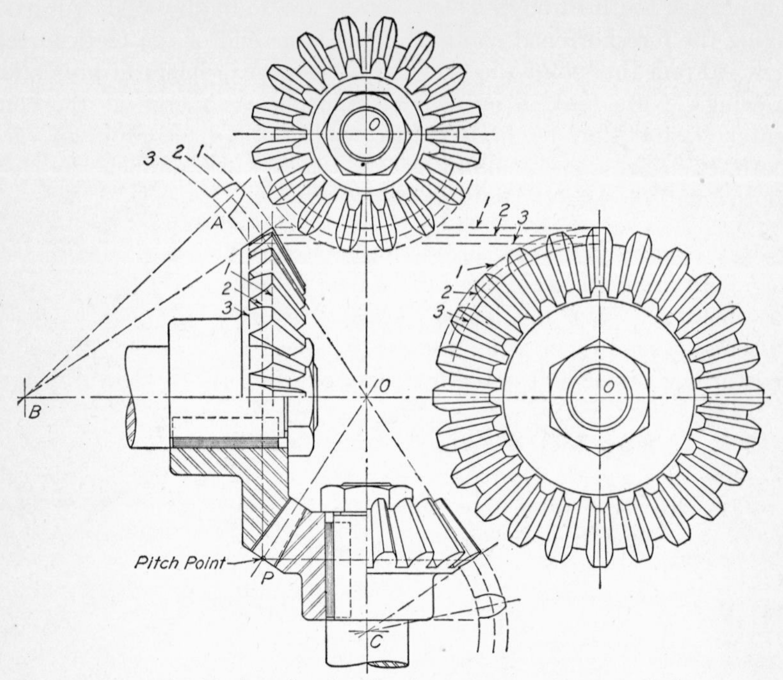

FIG. 434.—To draw involute bevel gears, approximate method.

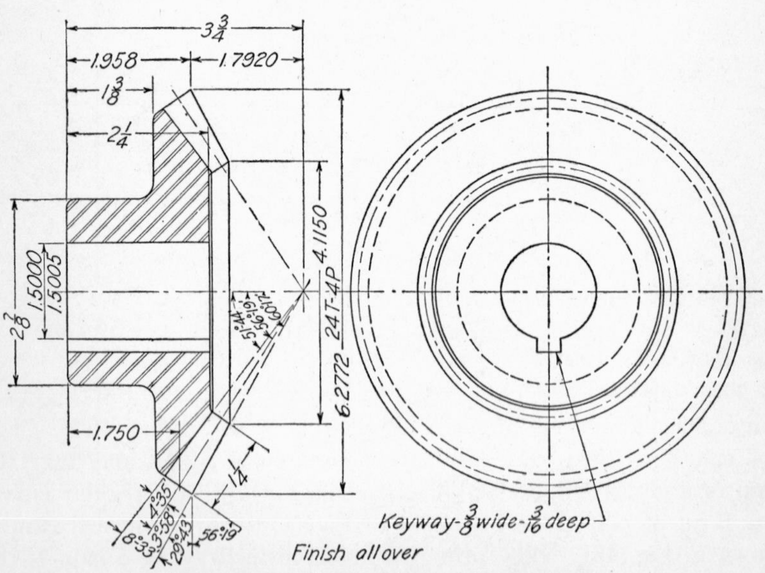

FIG. 435.—Working drawing of bevel gear.

side of each tooth through which a circle arc, found by trial, will pass, giving the foreshortened contour of the large end of the teeth in this view. From this point the drawing becomes a problem in projection drawing. Note that in every view the lines converge at the cone center O, and that by finding three points on the contour of each tooth, circle arcs can be found by trial which will be sufficiently close approximations to give the desired effect.

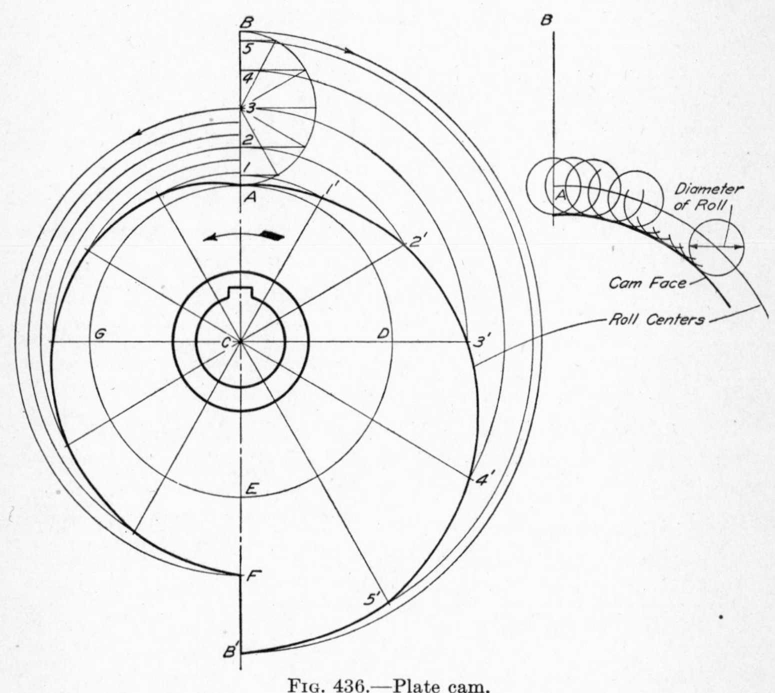

Fig. 436.—Plate cam.

This method is used for finished display drawings. For working drawings bevel gears are drawn without tooth outlines, as shown in Fig. 435.

205. Cams.—A cam is a machine element used to obtain an irregular or special motion not easily obtained by other means. The shape of a cam is derived from the motion required of it and may take the form of a circle, ellipse, involute, etc., or may be an irregular curve. One form of plate cam is shown in Fig. 436. A cylindrical cam is shown in Fig. 437. The principle involved in drawing a cam is the same in all cases.

Let it be required to move a machine part up and down with a specified motion. The part moved may be a roller, in which case the center of the roller is considered as a moving point. A plate attached to a revolving shaft may be given such a shape that it will cause the roller to rise and allow it to fall in a predetermined manner.

To find the cam outline, Fig. 436. Given point *C* the center of the shaft, point *A* the lowest position and point *B* the highest position of the center of the roller. It is required to raise the follower with harmonic motion during one-half revolution of the uniformly revolving shaft, allow it to drop one-half way down instantly and then drop the remaining distance with uniform motion.

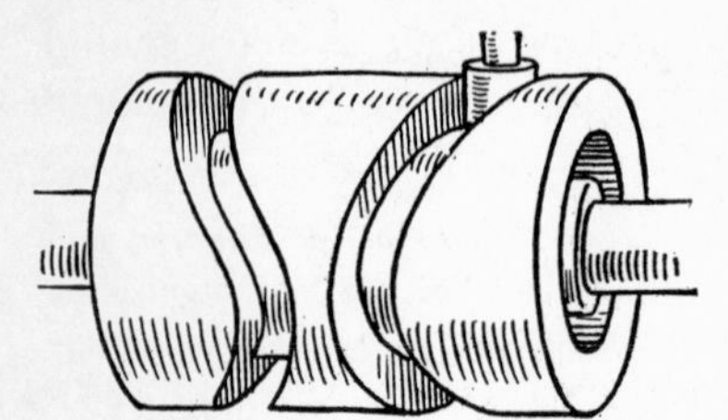

Fig. 437.—Cylindrical cam.

Divide the rise into parts proportional to harmonic motion. Divide the semi-circle *ADE* into as many equal parts as there are spaces in the rise, and draw radial lines. With *C* as center and radius *C*1 draw an arc intersecting the first radial line as 1′. In the same way locate points 2′, 3′, etc., and draw a smooth curve through them. If the cam is revolved in the direction of the arrow, it will raise the follower with the desired motion.

Draw *B′F* equal to one-half *AB*. Divide *A*3 into six equal parts and *EGA* into six equal parts. Then for equal angles the follower must fall equal distances. Circle arcs drawn as indicated will locate the required points on the cam outline.

This outline is for the center of the roller, allowance for which may be made by drawing the roller in its successive positions and then drawing a tangent curve as shown in the auxiliary figure.

206. Checking.—Before being sent to the shop a working drawing is carefully checked for errors and omissions. A first check of the pencil drawing is made by the chief designer, who knows the price at which the machine is to be made and checks the design and its mechanism for soundness and economy, sees if existing patterns for any parts can be used, checks for adequate lubrication, for correct representation and other points in the list following.

When the drawing is finished it is gone over by an experienced checker, who in signing his name to it becomes responsible for any inaccuracy. This is the final "proof reading" and cannot be done by the one who has made the drawing nearly so well as by another person. In small offices all the work is checked by the chief draftsman, and draftsmen sometimes check each other's work; in large drafting rooms one or more checkers who devote all their time to this kind of work are employed. All notes, computations and checking layouts should be preserved for future reference.

Students may gain experience in this work by being assigned to check other students' work.

To be effective, checking must be done in an absolutely systematic way and with thorough concentration.

207. To check a drawing, each of the following items[1] should be gone through separately, allowing nothing to distract the attention from it. As each dimension or feature is verified a check mark should be placed on or above it, and corrections indicated with soft or colored pencil.

1. Put yourself in the position of those who are to read the drawing and find out if it is easy to read and tells a straight story. Always do this before checking any individual features; in other words, before you have had time to become accustomed to the contents.

2. See that each piece is correctly designed and illustrated, and that all necessary views are shown, but none that is not necessary.

3. Check all the dimensions by scaling, and, where advisable, by calculation also. Preserve the calculations.

4. See that dimensions for the shop are given as required by the shop, and that the shop is not left to do any adding or subtracting in order to get a needed dimension.

5. Check for tolerances. See that they are neither too "fine" nor too "coarse" for the particular conditions of the machine, so as neither to increase unnecessarily the cost of production nor, on the other hand, to impair accuracy of operation or duplication.

6. Go over each piece and see that finishes are properly specified.

7. See that every specification of material is correct and that all necessary ones are given.

8. Look out for "interferences." This means check each detail with the parts that will be adjacent to it in the assembled machine and see that proper clearances have been allowed.

9. When checking for clearances in connection with a mechanical movement, lay out the movement to scale, figure the principal angles of motion and see that proper clearances are maintained in all positions, drawing small mechanism to double size or larger.

10. See that all the small details, screws, bolts, pins, keys, rivets, etc., are standard and that, where possible, stock sizes have been used.

11. Check every feature of the title or record strip, and bill of material.

12. Review the drawing in its entirety, adding such explanatory notes as will increase its efficiency.

208. The Bill of Material.—A bill of material is a tabulated statement placed on a separate sheet, as is always done in quantity

[1] Adapted from Follows' *Dictionary of Mechanical Drawing.*

production, or on the drawing, as illustrated in Fig. 510, which gives the piece number, drawing size, name, quantity, material size, stock size of raw material and sometimes the weight of each piece. A final column is usually left for remarks.

The blank ruling for a bill of material should not be crowded. Lines should never be spaced closer than one-fourth inch. Five-sixteenths or three-eighths is better, with the height of the lettering not more than half the space and centered between lines. Instead of being lettered, bills of material are frequently typed on forms printed on thin paper and blue printed. Doubling the impression by carbon paper on the back increases the opacity of the typing and a clearer blue print will result.

209. Title.—The title of a working drawing is usually boxed in the lower right-hand corner, the size of the space varying with the size of the drawing. For 11″ × 17″ sheets the space reserved may be about three inches long; for 17″ × 22″ sheets four or four and a half, and for 22″ × 34″ sheets five or five and a half inches.

Contents of Title.—In general the title of a machine drawing should contain:

1. Name of machine.
2. General name of parts (or simply "details").
3. Name of purchaser, if special machine.
4. Manufacturer (company or firm name and address).
5. Date (usually date of completion of tracing).
6. Scale or scales; required on assembly drawings, sometimes omitted from fully dimensioned detail drawings.
7. Drafting room record: names or initials of draftsman, tracer, checker, approval of chief draftsman, or other authority, each with date; and space for record of changes and revisions.
8. Numbers of drawing and of the order if special design. The filing number (which in detail drawings should be the same as the piece number) is often repeated in the upper left-hand corner upside down for convenience in case the drawing should be reversed in the drawer.

Form of Title.—Every drafting room has its own standard form for titles. In large offices the blank form is often printed in type on the tracing paper or cloth. Figures 438 and 439 are characteristic examples.

A form of title which is used to some extent is the *record strip*, a strip marked off entirely across the lower part of the sheet, containing the information required in the title, and space for the record of orders, revisions, changes, etc., which should be noted, with date, as they occur. Figure 440 illustrates one form.

It is sometimes desired to keep the records of orders and other private information on the tracing but not have them appear on the

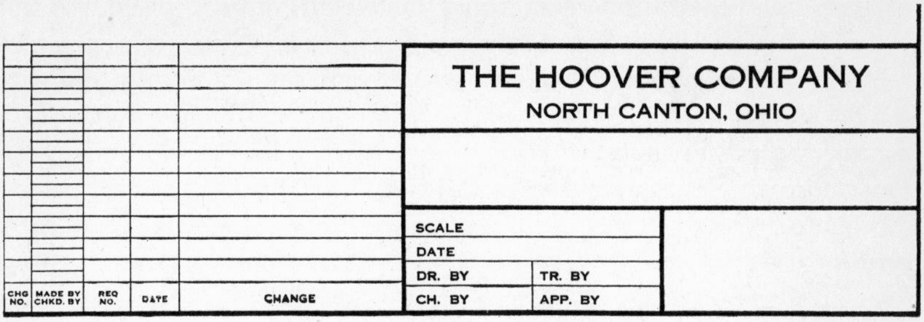

THE HOOVER COMPANY
NORTH CANTON, OHIO
SCALE
DATE
DR. BY | TR. BY
CH. BY | APP. BY
CHG NO. | MADE BY CHKD. BY | REQ NO. | DATE | CHANGE

FIG. 438.—A printed title form.

print. In such cases a record strip is put outside the border and trimmed off the print before sending it out.

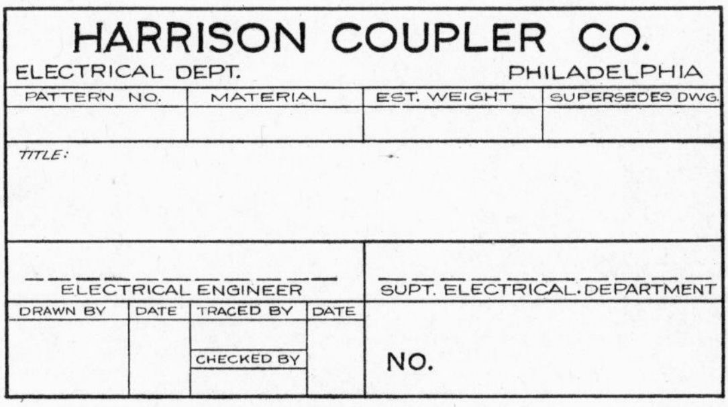

HARRISON COUPLER CO.
ELECTRICAL DEPT. PHILADELPHIA
PATTERN NO. | MATERIAL | EST. WEIGHT | SUPERSEDES DWG.
TITLE:
ELECTRICAL ENGINEER | SUPT. ELECTRICAL DEPARTMENT
DRAWN BY | DATE | TRACED BY | DATE
CHECKED BY
NO.

FIG. 439.—A printed title form.

To Draw a Title.—The title should be lettered freehand in single-stroke capitals either vertical or inclined, but not both styles in the same title. Write out the contents on a separate piece of paper, then refer back to page 45 where full instructions have been given.

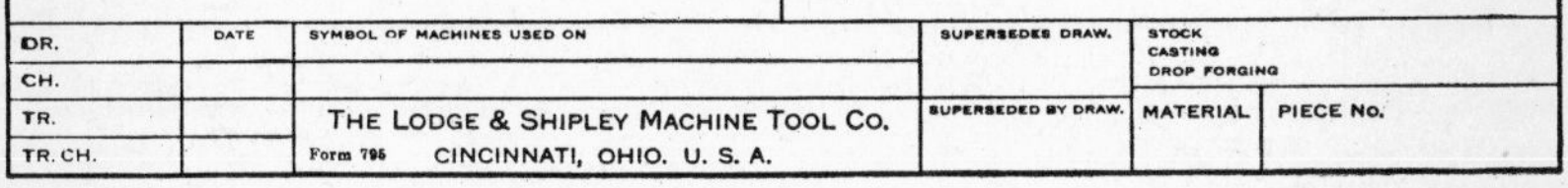

UNIT | NAME OF PIECE
DR. | DATE | SYMBOL OF MACHINES USED ON | SUPERSEDES DRAW. | STOCK CASTING DROP FORGING
CH.
TR. | THE LODGE & SHIPLEY MACHINE TOOL CO. | SUPERSEDED BY DRAW. | MATERIAL | PIECE NO.
TR. CH. | Form 795 CINCINNATI, OHIO. U. S. A.

FIG. 440.—A narrow strip title.

210. Commercial Practice.—In commercial drafting *accuracy* and *speed* are the two requirements. The drafting room is an expensive department and time is an important element. The draftsman must therefore have a ready knowledge not only of the principles of drawing but of the conventional methods and abbreviations, and any device or system that will save time without sacrificing clearness is desirable.

The usual criticism of the student by the employer is his lack of appreciation of the necessity of *speed*.

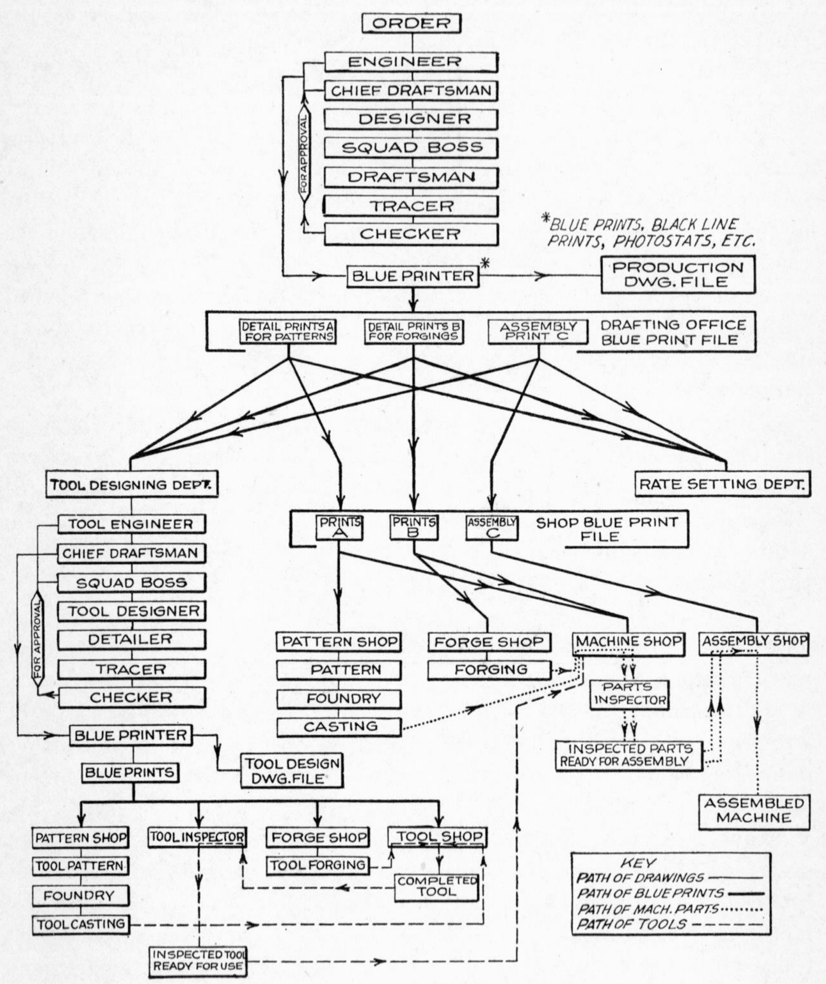

FIG. 441.—Development and distribution of drawings.

211. The Drawings and the Shop.—The relation of drawings and prints to the operations of production is illustrated in the graphical chart, Fig. 441, which shows in diagrammatic form the different steps in the development of the drawings, and their distribution and use in connection with the shop operations, from the time the order is received until the finished machine is delivered to the shipping room.

The following outline description of the various shop operations indicated on the chart should be supplemented by first-hand study. The young draftsman, whenever opportunity permits, should follow operations through the shops, get acquainted with shop men and enlarge his knowledge by reading and discussion.

On leaving the printer the original drawings are filed and the sets of prints delivered to the print files to be distributed as indicated.

Pattern Shop.—Details for all castings are sent to the pattern-maker, who makes a pattern for each in wood. From this, if a large quantity of castings is required, a metal pattern, often in "white metal," is made. The pattern-maker provides for the shrinkage of the casting by making the pattern oversize, using a "shrink rule" for his measurements, and allows extra metal for machining the finished surfaces. He also provides the "draft" or slight taper (not shown on the drawings) so that the pattern will come out of the sand. See paragraph 145.

The pattern-maker's first interest in studying the drawing is to see how the pattern can be best made so as to be molded most economically and efficiently, and whether a "solid," "two-part" or "three-part" pattern is necessary in order to withdraw it from the sand. He also makes the "core-boxes" for the sand cores that form the hollow parts of the piece.

Foundry.—The patterns and core-boxes are sent to the foundry and the castings made. Only in occasional instances does the foundry-man call for assistance from the drawing.

Forge Shop.—Detail prints for the pieces specified to be made of wrought metal or forged steel are sent to the forge shop and either hand forged or "drop forged," with allowance of metal for finish. See paragraph 146.

Tool Designing Department.—Larger concerns maintain a tool designing department whose function is to design the jigs, fixtures, tools and special machine tools necessary for the economical manufacture of the finished parts; and in some lines, as bearings and machine tools, this service is extended to their customers. This department has much the same organization as the engineering department proper, of which it is a part. Prints of the proposed product are sent to this department, where the drawings for the required tools are prepared, usually printed from pencil drawings on bond paper. From these drawings the tools are made, as shown in the chart, either in the tool shop or, as in some organizations, outside.

Machine Shop.—The rough castings and forgings come to the machine shop to be finished according to the drawing specifications. The special tools, jigs and fixtures made for the machine parts by the tool designing department are held in the tool room ready for the machine shop. Flat surfaces will be machined on a milling machine, planer or shaper; parts with round section on a lathe; slots, keyways, etc., on a shaper, or a milling machine, which is used for a variety of work. Holes are drilled, reamed, counterbored on a drill press; holes bored on a boring machine or lathe. In quantity production many special machine tools and automatic machines are in use. For exact work, grinding machines with wheels of abrasive material are used, and grinders are coming into greatly increased use for operations formerly made with cutting tools.

Inspection Department.—Careful inspection is an important feature of modern production. Good practice requires inspection after each operation. The term "preventive inspection" is used as meaning the inspection of the first piece of each set-up before the operator is allowed to proceed.

Assembly Shop.—After inspection all the finished parts are assembled or put together with the aid of the assembly drawings.

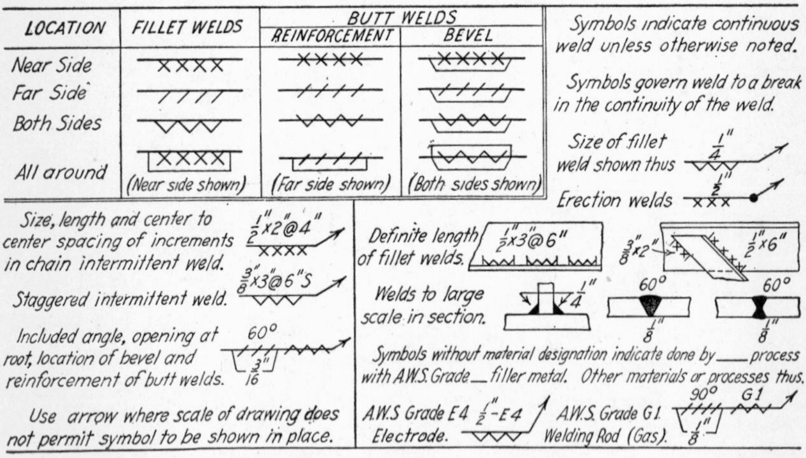

Fig. 442.—Symbols for arc welding.

212. Arc Welding.—A new process of manufacturing machine parts which have heretofore been made as castings is gaining rapid acceptance in many fields. It consists of building up these parts, such as machinery bases, pedestals, columns, etc., from standard steel shapes and plates, joining them by arc welding or oxyacetylene welding.

Since steel is six times as strong in tension as cast iron and two and one-half times as stiff, it is apparent that by using steel it is possible to secure greater strength and rigidity with less weight of metal. Designing for welded steel construction requires ingenuity but is in reality simpler than designing complicated cast parts. The strength and weight of rolled steel shapes are standard and the computations for sizes of members are therefore greatly simplified.

As to the strength of the welded connections, it is possible to make a welded joint as strong as the members joined.

Drawings for welded steel construction are usually simpler than for riveted or cast construction. The revised symbols (1934) of the American Welding Society for all types of products and structures fabricated by fusion welding are given in Fig. 442. These have been adopted as standard by the U. S. Navy and the American Marine Standards Committee.

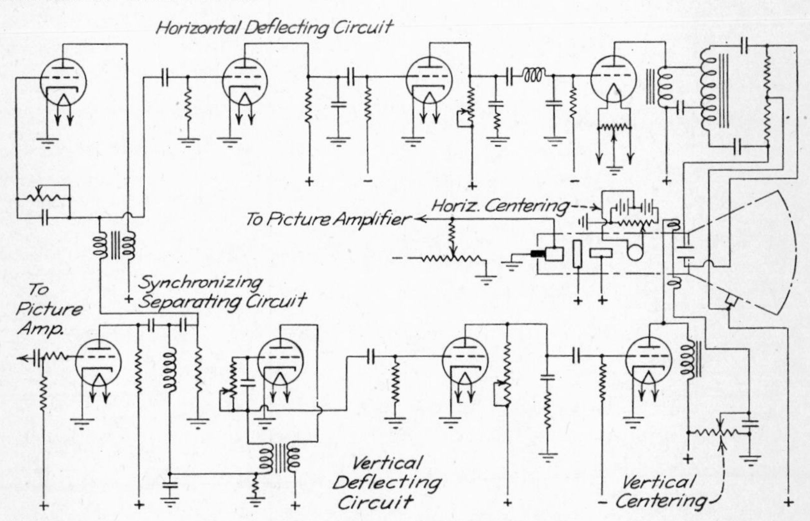

FIG. 443.—Schematic arrangement of a television kinescope deflecting circuit. (*Courtesy of Institute of Radio Engineers.*)

213. Chemical Drawing.—The study of drawing in preparation for chemical engineering involves all the basic principles considered in this and previous chapters. The chemical engineer should be informed on piping and on the various forms of equipment used in industrial chemistry such as mixing, grinding, filtering, drying and conveying machinery. Problems of special interest to chemical engineers are Group V in Chapter X, and in this chapter Probs. 12 and 79 to 86.

214. Electrical Drawing.—Electrical engineers need the same basic equipment in the language of drawing as do mechanical or other engineers. In its application in their profession it may be divided into two general classes, working drawings, as of electrical machinery, and diagrammatic or symbolic drawings, such as wiring diagrams, etc.

In electrical working drawings the principles and conventions of this chapter are all applicable. Figure 426 is an example, the outline assembly drawing of a motor. Figure 528 is an example of an erection working drawing.

Diagrammatic drawings, using conventional symbols for electrical connections and equipment, form an important class of electrical drawings. Electrical symbols, wiring symbols and radio symbols are given on page 460 and 461. An example of a diagrammatic drawing is shown in Fig. 443. A group of problems on electrical drawing, including electrical equipment, switchboards, motors, wiring and radio are included in Probs. 115 to 128.

215. Aeronautical Drawing.—Preparation for aeronautical drafting again requires a thorough grounding in fundamental principles, with attention to auxiliary projections and removed sections. Problems of interest are Figs. 310, 427, 493, and 502. Extreme accuracy is so essential that, for some work, honed plate glass is used for a drawing surface instead of paper.

PROBLEMS

216. The first part of any working drawing problem consists of the selection of views, the choice of suitable scales and the arrangement of the sheet. In class work a preliminary sketch layout should be submitted for approval before the drawing is commenced.

The problems following are designed to cover the points outlined in the text and their division into groups will suggest a selection of one or more made from each group in making up a course. They may be drawn on 11″ × 17″ or 17″ × 22″ sheets.

In dimensioning these problems the principles given in Chapter IX should be followed carefully. Before applying finish marks study the problem to determine which surfaces should be so marked. On parts which are to fit accurately, the class of fit is to be assumed or assigned and limit dimensions figured from the nominal sizes given, using the A.S.A. tables of allowances and tolerances in the Appendix, taking the illustration for the problem as the preliminary sketch from which an actual working drawing is to be made for the shop. Because of restricted space the illustrations are often crowded. Do not follow them as examples of good spacing or placing of dimensions.

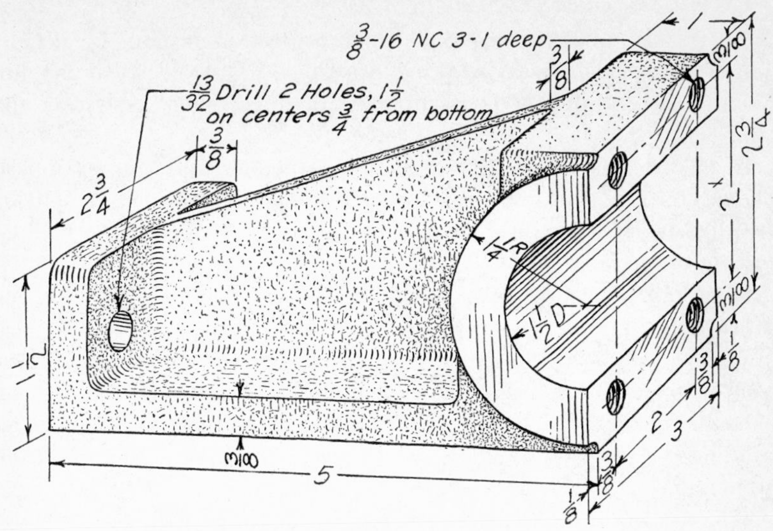

Fig. 444.—Support bearing.

Group I. Exterior Detail Drawings.

1. Fig. 444. Working drawing of support bearing. Three views, full size.

2. Fig. 445. Working drawing of centering yoke base. Three views, full size.

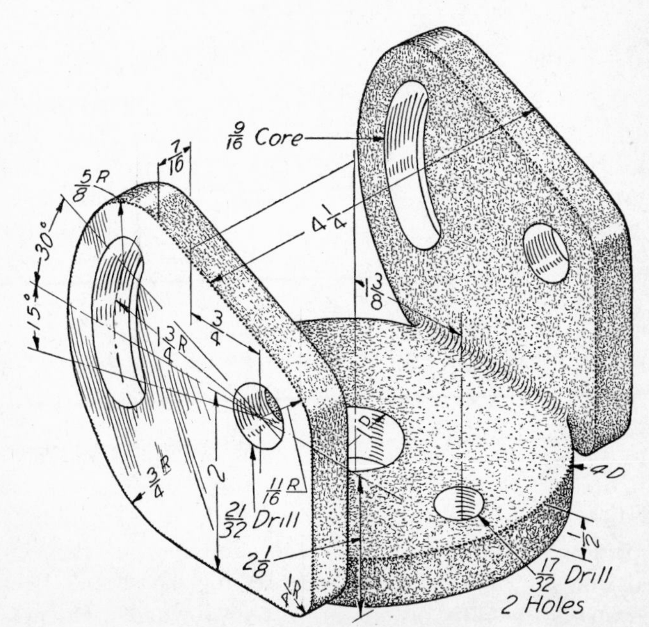

Fig. 445.—Centering yoke base.

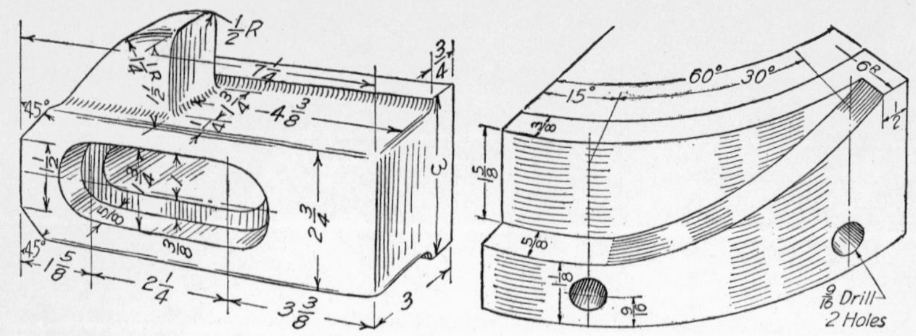

FIG. 446.—Steady rest jaw. FIG. 447.—Elevating cam.

3. Fig. 446. Working drawing of steady rest jaw. Full size.

4. Fig. 447. Top, front and right side views of elevating cam. The inclined surface may be found by taking eight ½″ consecutive chords on the 6″ radius arc, each having a rise of 13⁄64″.

5. Fig. 448. Working drawing of compound gear arm.

6. Fig. 449. Working drawing of fan bracket.

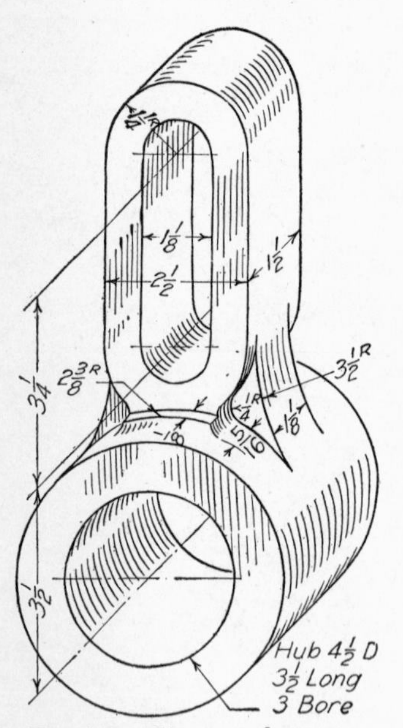

FIG. 448.—Compound gear arm.

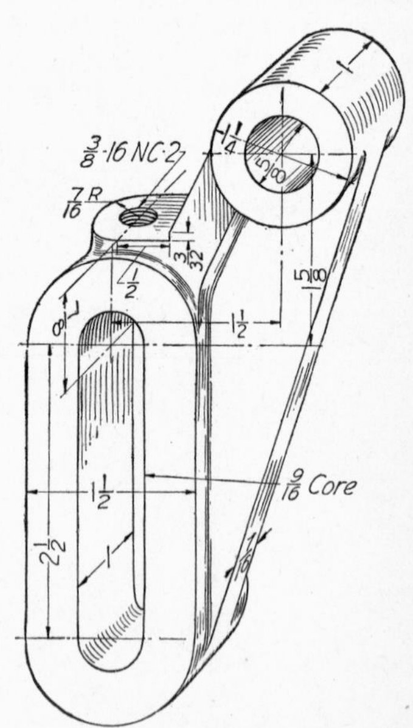

FIG. 449.—Fan bracket.

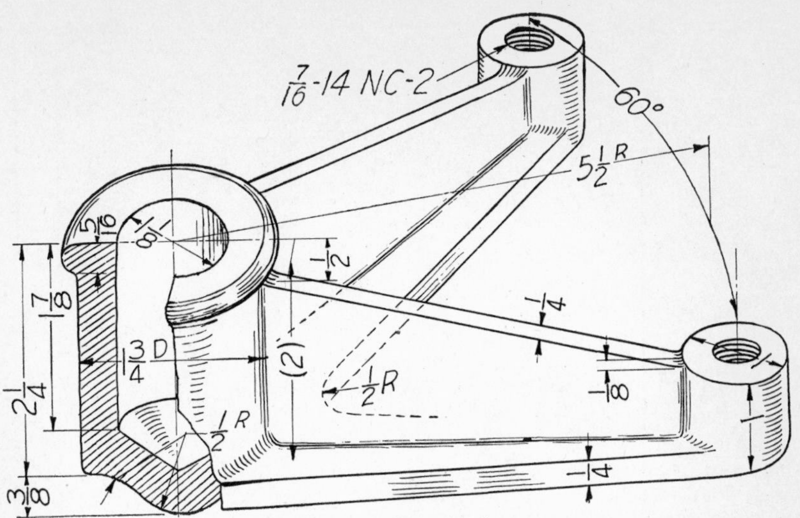

Fig. 450.—Adjustable base.

7. Fig. 450. Working drawing of adjustable base.
8. Fig. 451. Working drawing of friction shaft bearing.

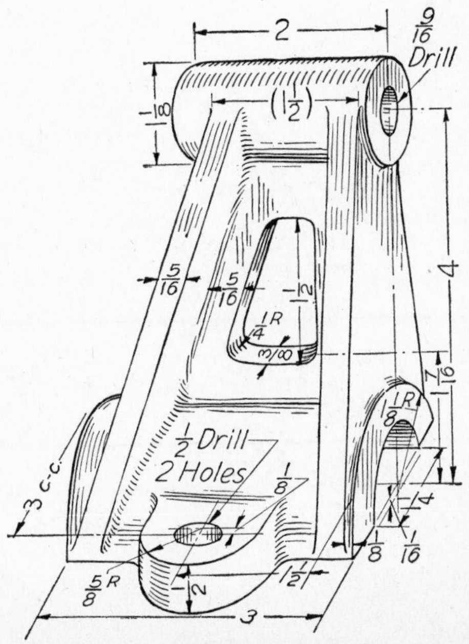

Fig. 451.—Friction shaft bearing.

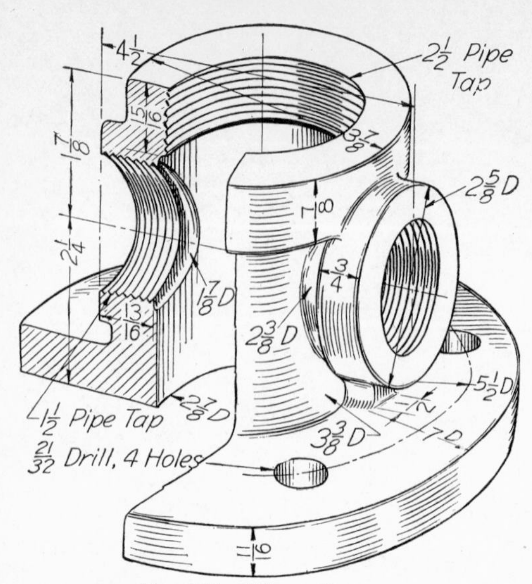

FIG. 452.—Blow-off cross.

Group II. Detail Drawings in Section.

9. Fig. 452. Working drawing of blow-off cross.
10. Fig. 453. Working drawing of face plate.

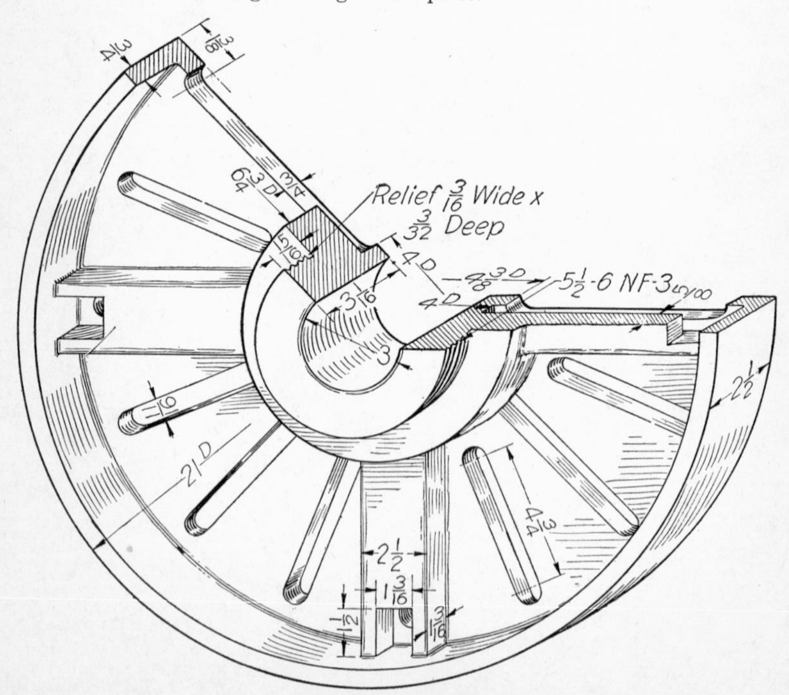

FIG. 453.—Face plate.

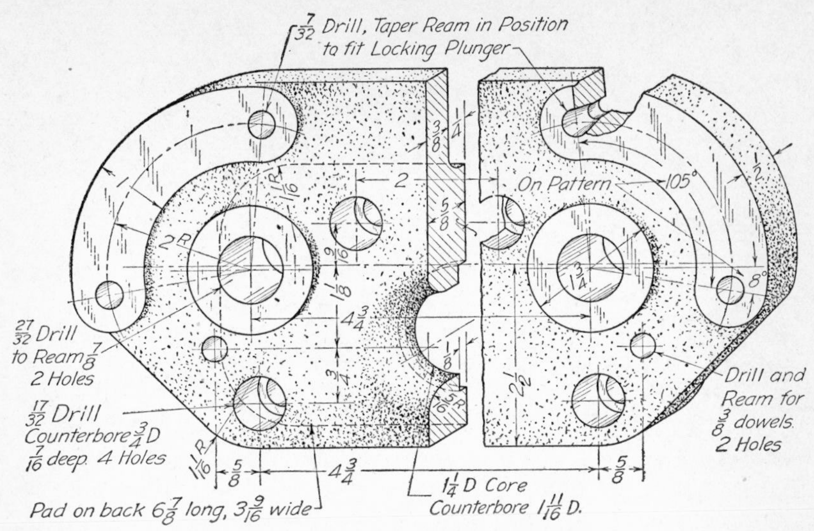

Fig. 454.—Gear shifter bracket.

11. Fig. 454. Working drawing of gear shifter bracket.

12. Fig. 455. Working drawing of cast iron pan or still for sulphuric acid works. Larger scale part-sections of inlet and outlet should be made, to avoid crowding dimensions on the complete views.

13. Fig. 456. Working drawing of flange coupling, assembled. Size to be assigned.

14. Fig. 457. Working drawing of pillow block assembled. Size to be assigned.

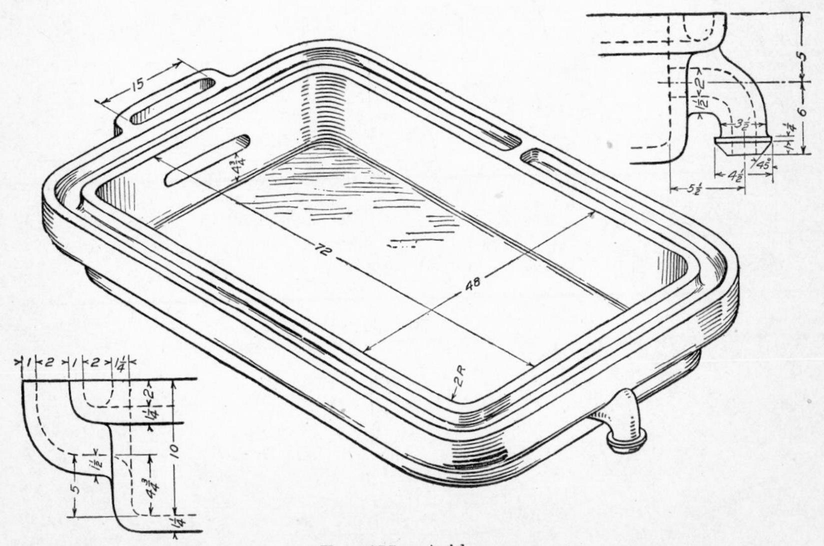

Fig. 455.—Acid pan.

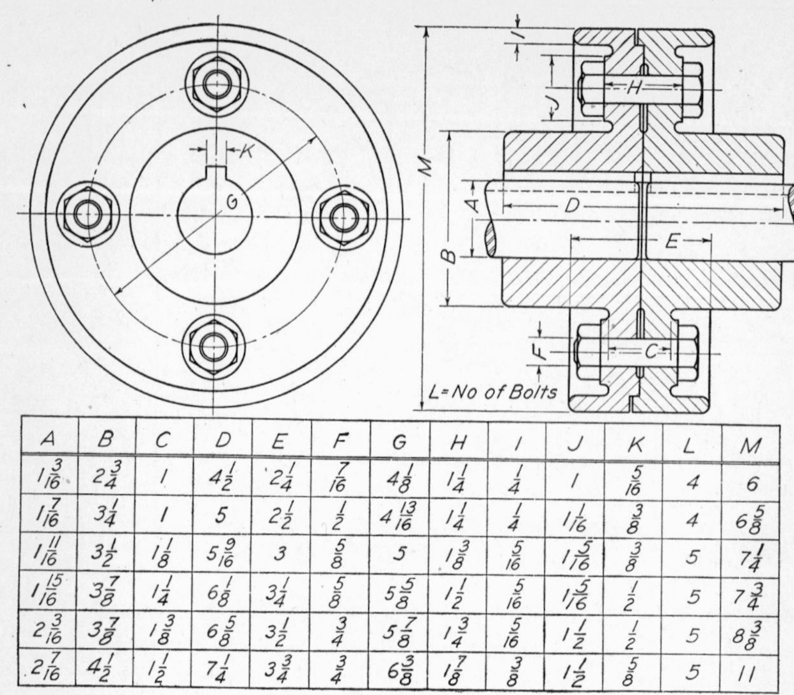

A	B	C	D	E	F	G	H	I	J	K	L	M
1 3/16	2 3/4	1	4 1/2	2 1/4	7/16	4 1/8	1 1/4	1/4	1	5/16	4	6
1 7/16	3 1/4	1	5	2 1/2	1/2	4 13/16	1 1/4	1/4	1 1/16	3/8	4	6 5/8
1 11/16	3 1/2	1 1/8	5 9/16	3	5/8	5	1 3/8	5/16	1 5/16	3/8	5	7 1/4
1 15/16	3 7/8	1 1/4	6 1/8	3 1/4	5/8	5 5/8	1 1/2	5/16	1 5/16	1/2	5	7 3/4
2 3/16	3 7/8	1 3/8	6 5/8	3 1/2	3/4	5 7/8	1 3/4	5/16	1 1/2	1/2	5	8 3/8
2 7/16	4 1/2	1 1/2	7 1/4	3 3/4	3/4	6 3/8	1 7/8	3/8	1 1/2	5/8	5	11

Fig. 456.—Flange coupling.

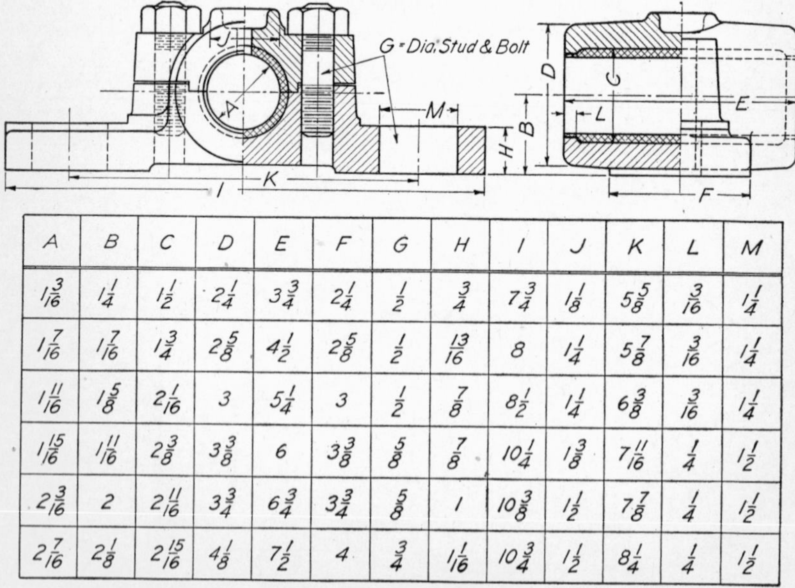

A	B	C	D	E	F	G	H	I	J	K	L	M
1 3/16	1 1/4	1 1/2	2 1/4	3 3/4	2 1/4	1/2	3/4	7 3/4	1 1/8	5 5/8	3/16	1 1/4
1 7/16	1 7/16	1 3/4	2 5/8	4 1/2	2 5/8	1/2	13/16	8	1 1/4	5 7/8	3/16	1 1/4
1 11/16	1 5/8	2 1/16	3	5 1/4	3	1/2	7/8	8 1/2	1 1/4	6 3/8	3/16	1 1/4
1 15/16	1 11/16	2 3/8	3 3/8	6	3 3/8	5/8	7/8	10 1/4	1 3/8	7 11/16	1/4	1 1/2
2 3/16	2	2 11/16	3 3/4	6 3/4	3 3/4	5/8	1	10 3/8	1 1/2	7 7/8	1/4	1 1/2
2 7/16	2 1/8	2 15/16	4 1/8	7 1/2	4	3/4	1 1/16	10 3/4	1 1/2	8 1/4	1/4	1 1/2

Fig. 457.—Pillow block.

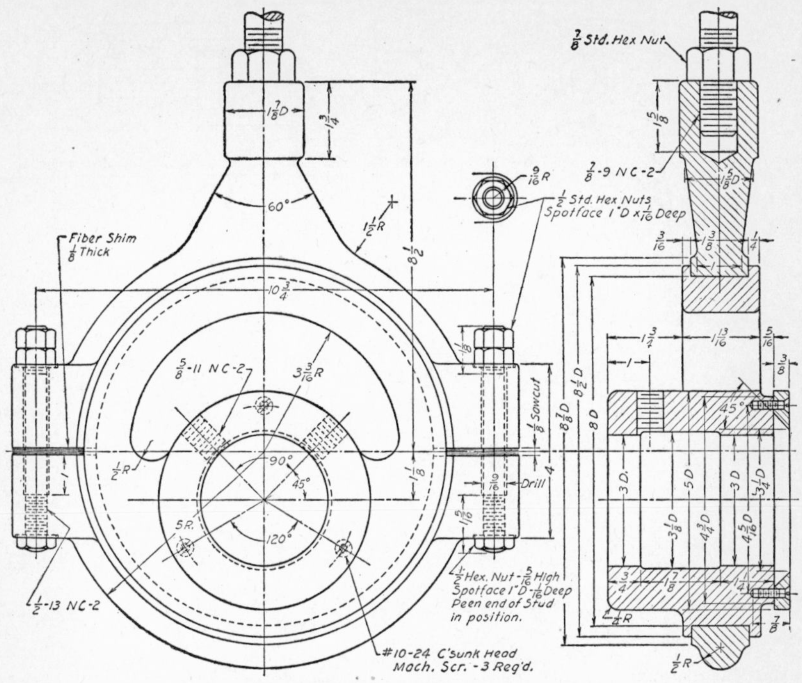

Fig. 458.—Eccentric and strap.

15. Fig. 458. Working drawing of eccentric and strap, assembled.

16. Fig. 459. Working drawing of pulley. Suggested sizes: (*A*) 10″ diam., 3″ face, 1″ bore; (*B*) 12 diam., 3¼″ face, 1⅛″ bore; (*C*) 14″ diam., 3½″ face, 1¼″ bore; (*D*) 16″ diam., 3¾″ face, 1⅜″ bore; (*E*) 18″ diam., 4″ face, 1½″ bore; (*F*) 20″ diam., 4½″ face, 1⅝″ bore; (*G*) 24″ diam., 5″ face, 1¾″ bore.

17. Fig. 460. Working drawing of flywheel. Calculate weight of rim.

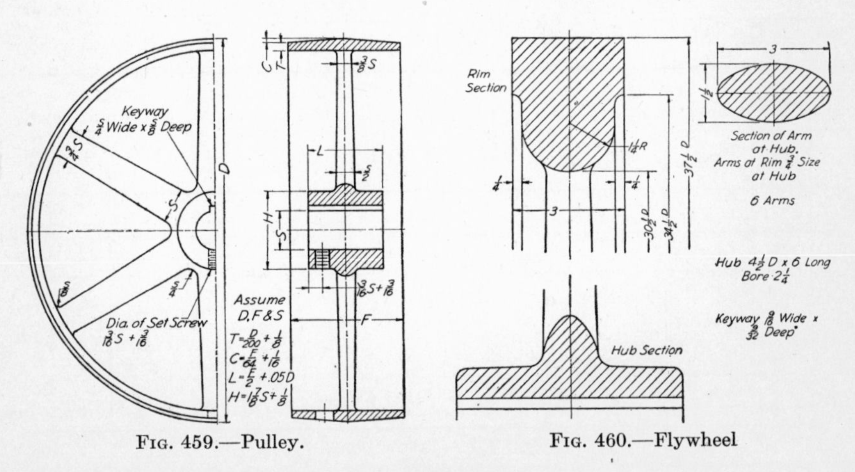

Fig. 459.—Pulley.

Fig. 460.—Flywheel

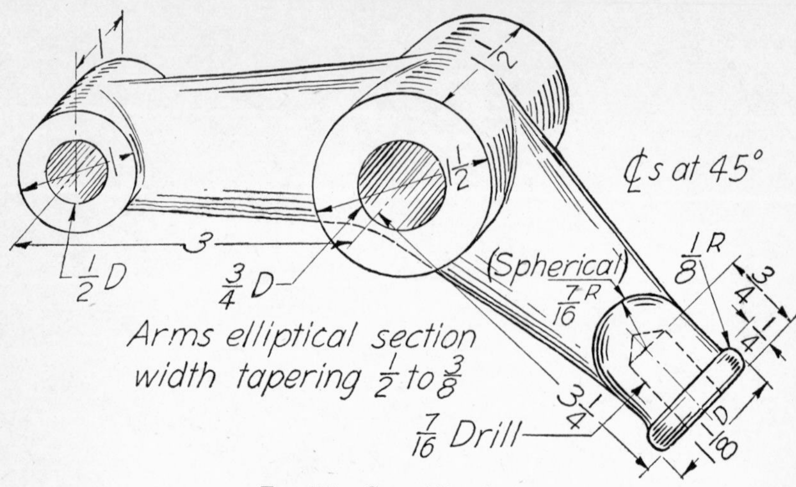

FIG. 461.—Gear shifter lever.

Group III. Auxiliary View Drawings. Determine best views and part views to use.

18. Fig. 461. Working drawing, with auxiliary view, of gear shifter lever.

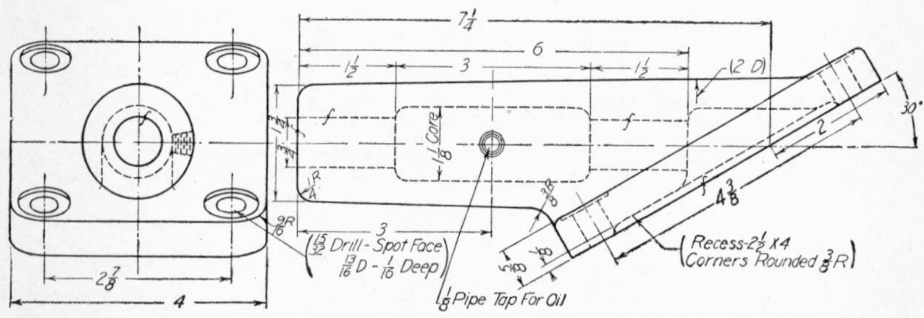

FIG. 462.—Angle bracket.

19. Fig. 462. Working drawing, with auxiliary view, of angle bracket.

20. Fig. 463. Working drawing, with auxiliary view, of rocker arm.

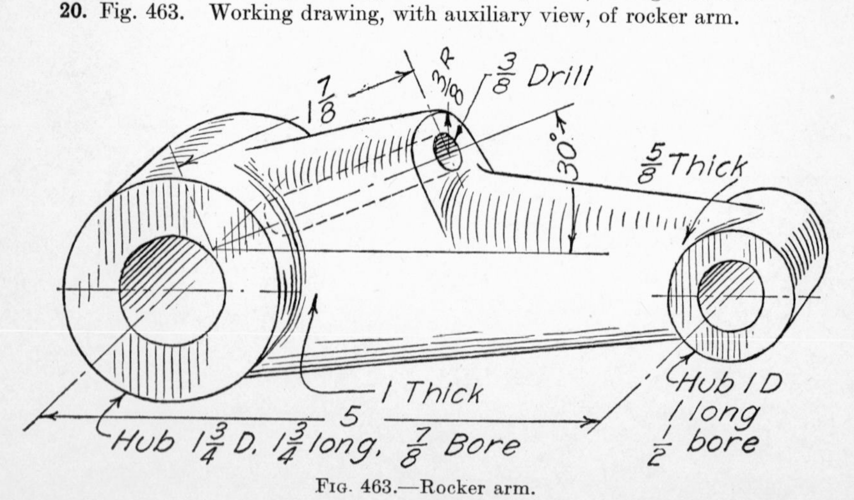

FIG. 463.—Rocker arm.

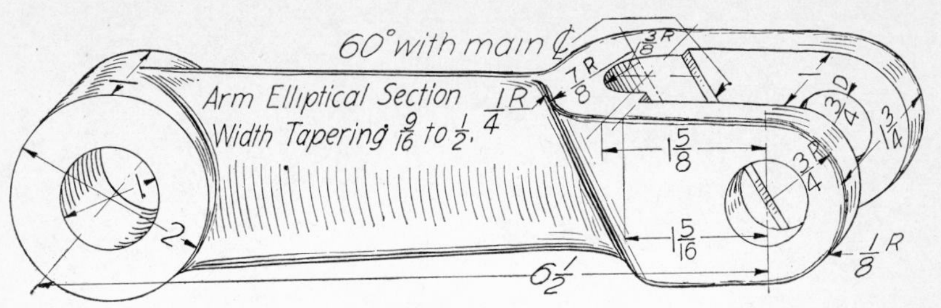

Fig. 464.—Pawl carrier.

21. Fig. 464. Working drawing, with auxiliary view, of pawl carrier.

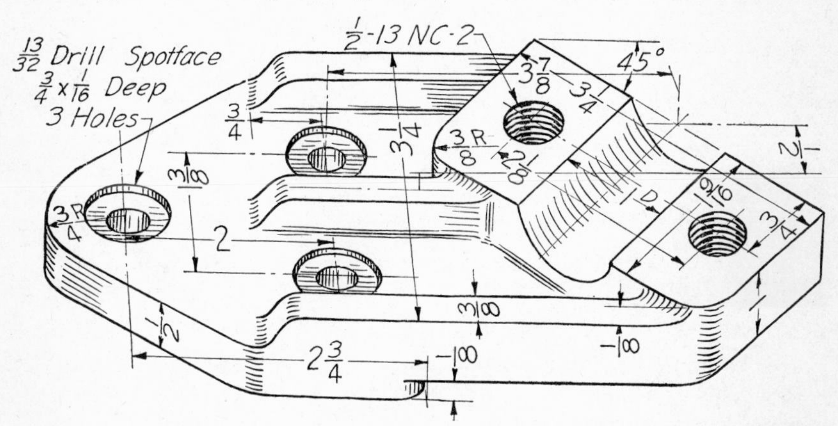

Fig. 465.—Hinge base.

22. Fig. 465. Working drawing, with auxiliary view, of hinge base. Ogee curve to suit.

23. Fig. 466. Working drawing, with auxiliary views, of slide base.

24. Fig. 467. Working drawing, with auxiliary view, of bevel gear housing and cover.

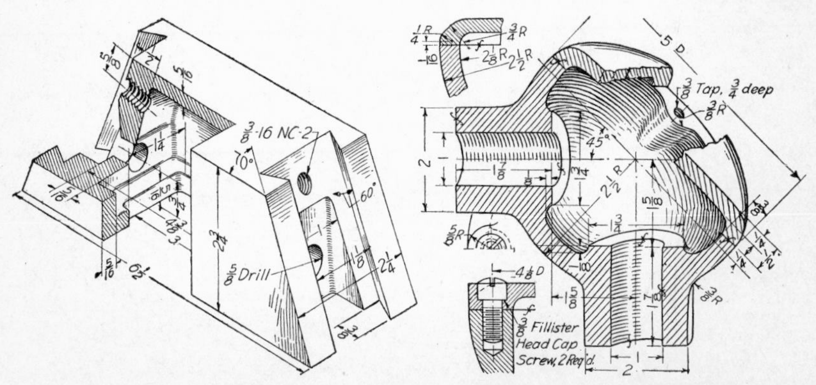

Fig. 466.—Slide base. Fig. 467.—Bevel gear housing.

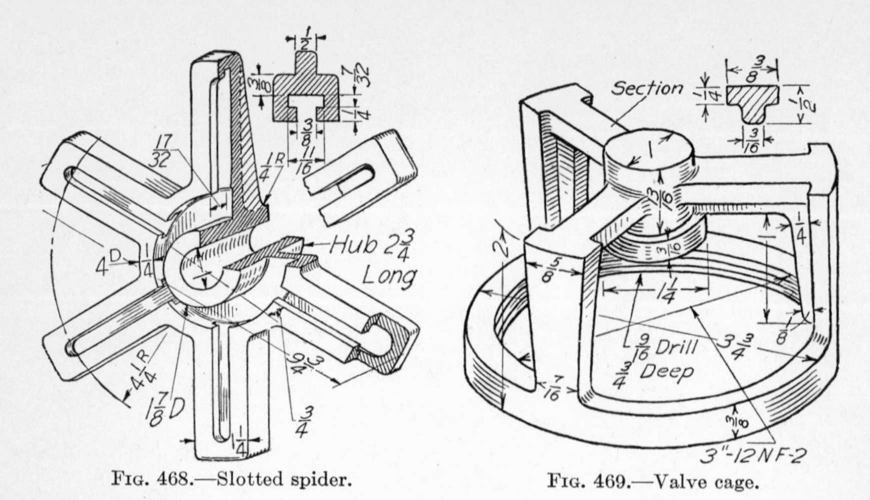

FIG. 468.—Slotted spider.

FIG. 469.—Valve cage.

25 to **30.** Working drawings, with auxiliary views, of Figs. 262 to 267.

Group IV. Double Auxiliaries.

31 to **34.** Working drawings, with auxiliary views, of Figs. 268, 270, 271, 272.

Group V. Special Representation.

This group illustrates the statements of paragraphs 109 to 121 concerning the violation of theory in the interest of clearness. Select views carefully.

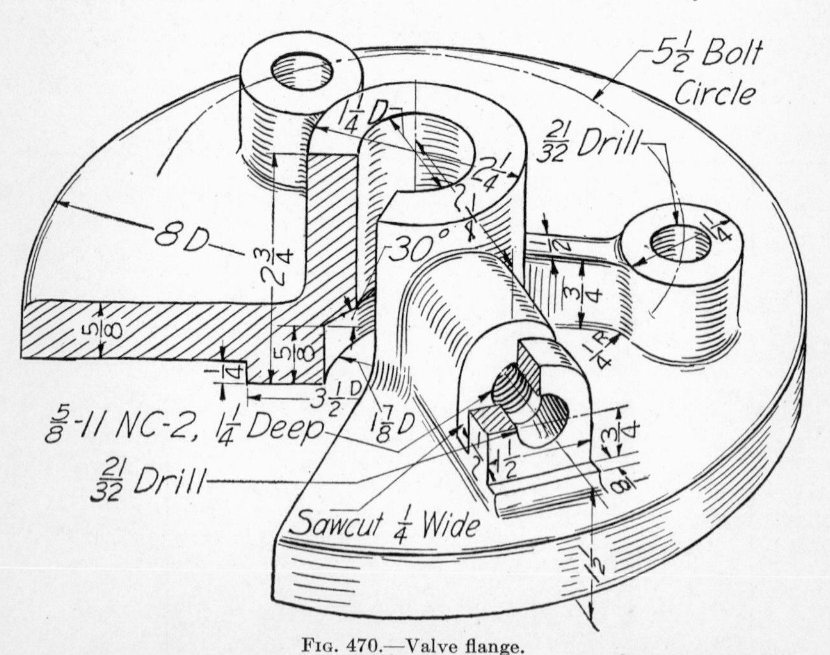

FIG. 470.—Valve flange.

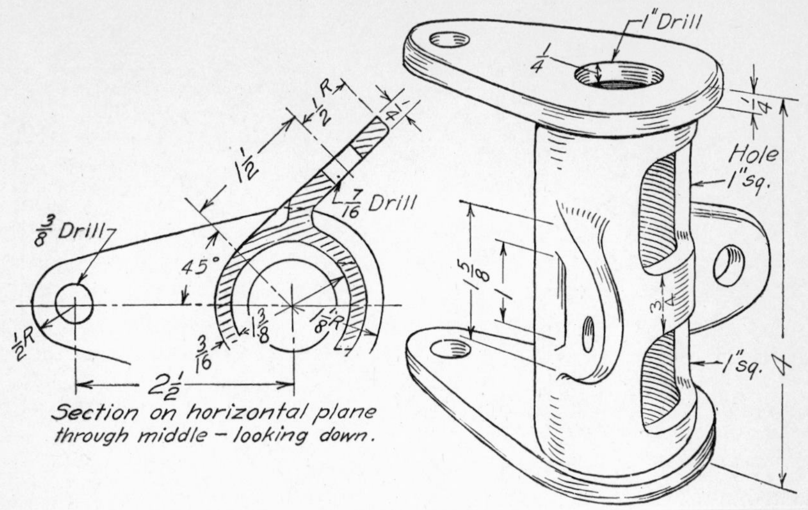

Fig. 471.—Stake socket.

35. Fig. 468. Working drawing of slotted spider.
36. Fig. 469. Working drawing of valve cage.
37. Fig. 470. Working drawing of valve flange.
38. Fig. 471. Working drawing of stake socket.
39. Fig. 472. Working drawing of draw-in chuck collet.
40. Fig. 473. Working drawing of split bushing.

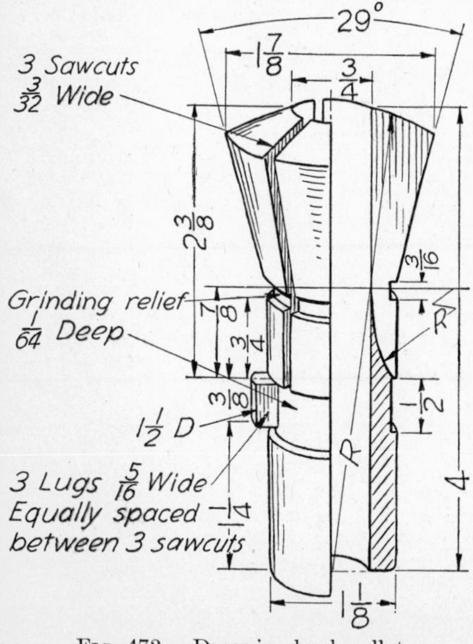

Fig. 472.—Draw-in chuck collet.

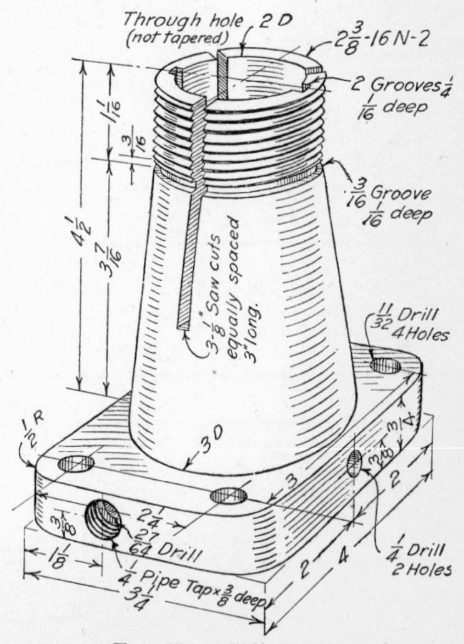

Fig. 473.—Split bushing.

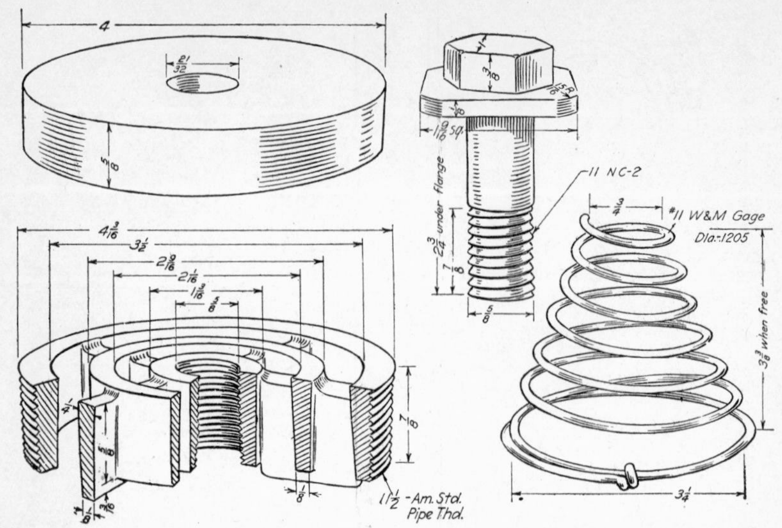

FIG. 474.—Pump valve details.

Group VI. Small Assembly Drawings from Details.

41. Fig. 474. Assembly drawing of pump valve. Valve seat, stem and spring are brass; disc is rubber.

42. Fig. 475. From detail sketches make assembly drawing of pop-off valve. All brass except spring.

43. From detail sketches make assembly drawing of leveling block, Fig. 529.

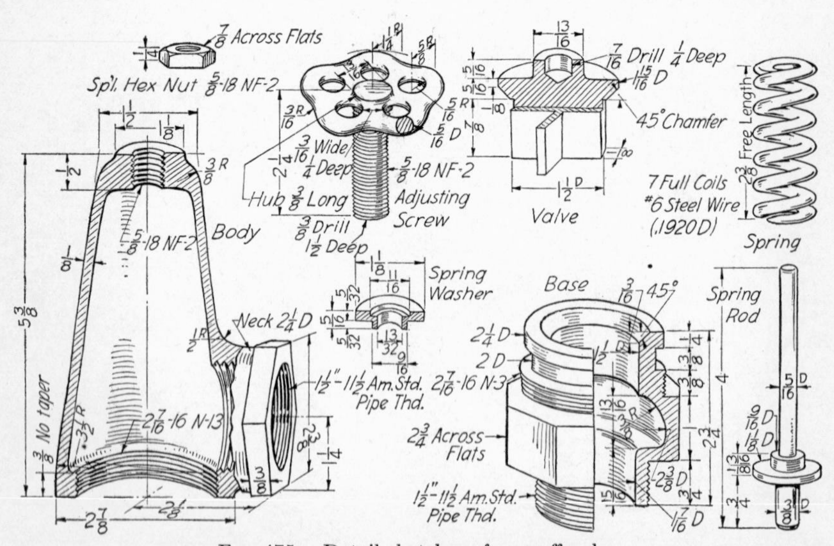

FIG. 475.—Detail sketches of pop-off valve.

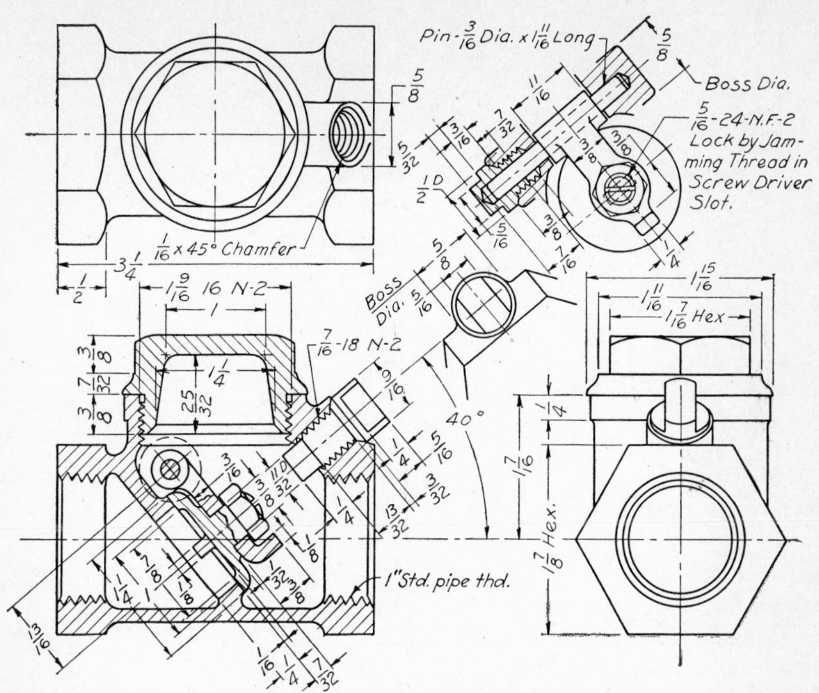

Fig. 476.—Horizontal check valve.

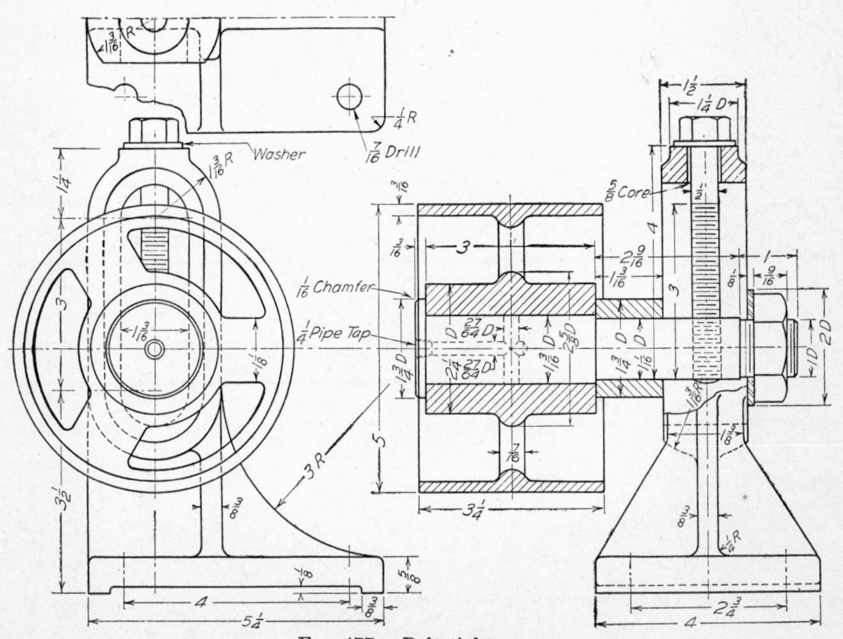

Fig. 477.—Belt tightener.

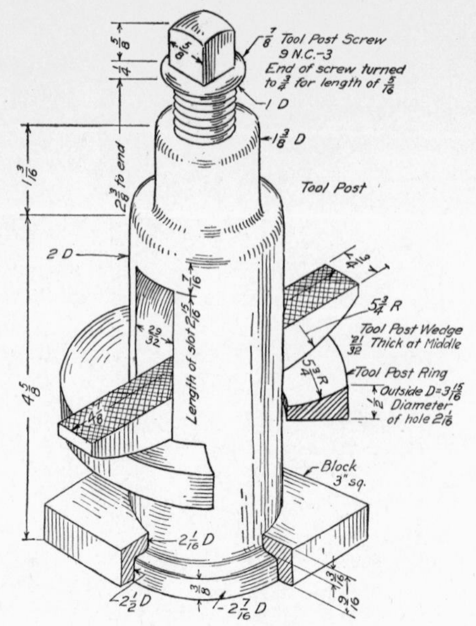

FIG. 478.—Tool post.

Group VII. Details from Assembly Drawings.

44. Fig. 476. Detail drawings of horizontal check valve. All brass.

45. Fig. 477. Detail drawings of belt tightener. Number the parts and make a bill of material.

46. Fig. 478. Detail drawings of tool post.

47. Fig. 479. Detail drawings of compensating nut. The purpose of this device is to take up the wear resulting from heavy duty imposed on a feed screw. To adjust the nut the cap screw at the left is loosened and the nut on the draw screw is tightened, the wedging action pushing the loose nut to the left until all lost motion is taken up.

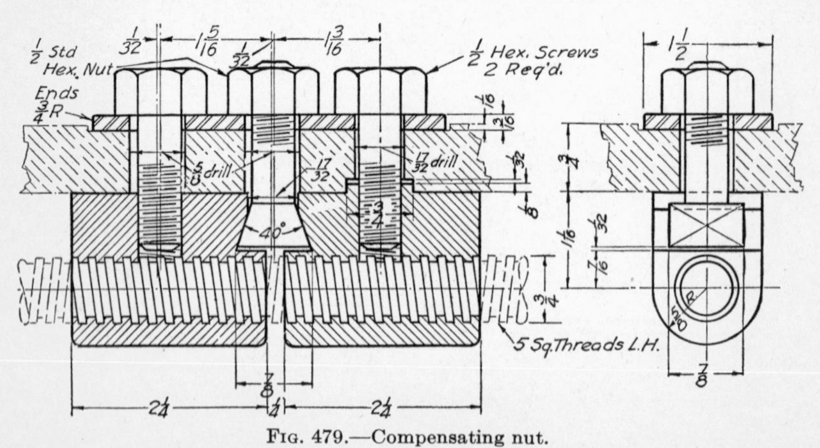

FIG. 479.—Compensating nut.

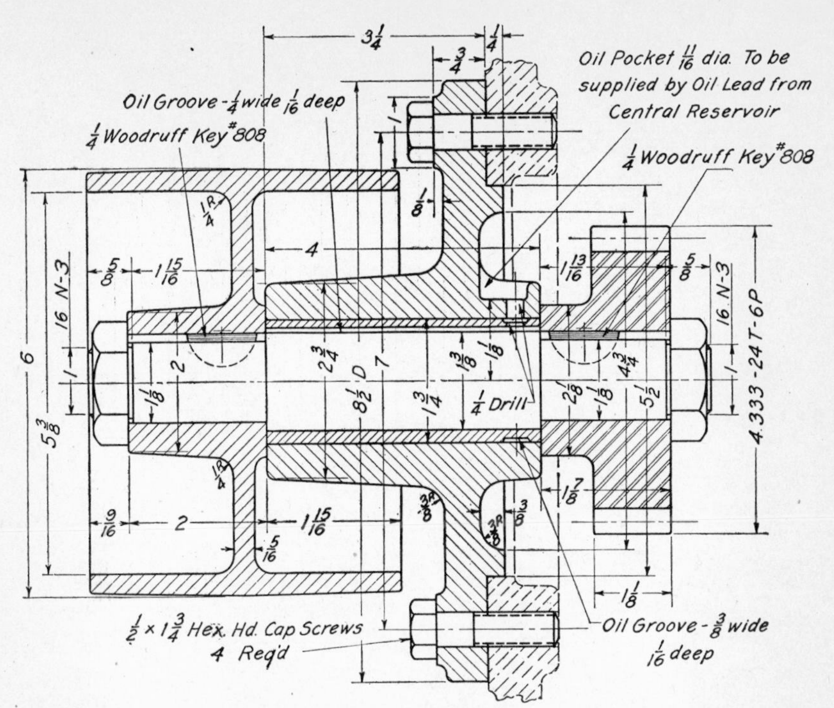

FIG. 480.—Belt drive.

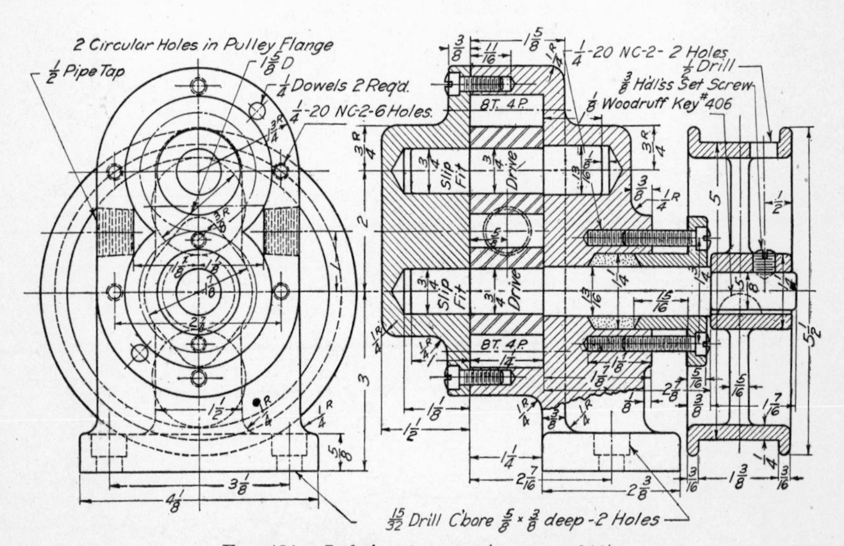

FIG. 481.—Lubricant pump (see page 219).

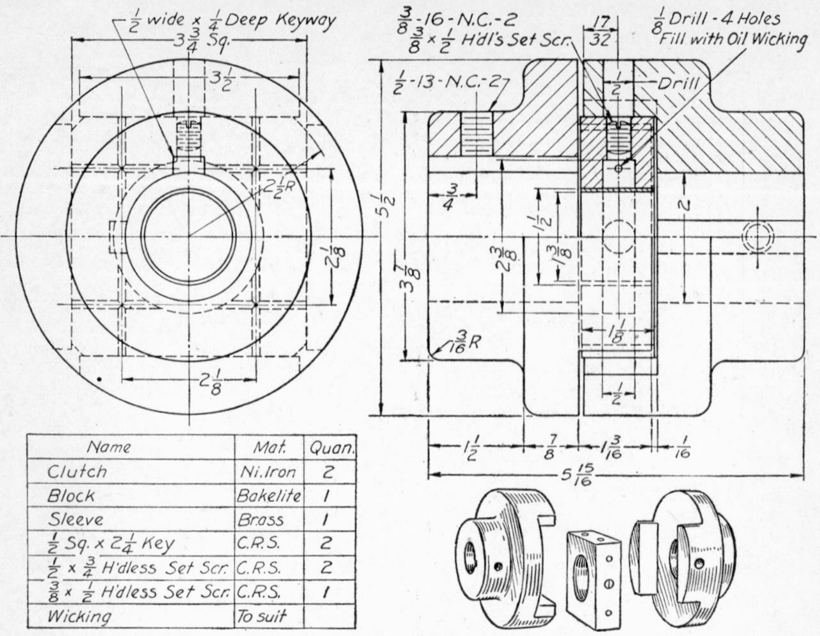

Name	Mat.	Quan.
Clutch	Ni. Iron	2
Block	Bakelite	1
Sleeve	Brass	1
1/2 Sq. x 2 1/4 Key	C.R.S.	2
1/2 x 3/4 H'dless Set Scr.	C.R.S.	2
3/8 x 1/2 H'dless Set Scr.	C.R.S.	1
Wicking	To suit	

FIG. 482.—James flexible coupling.

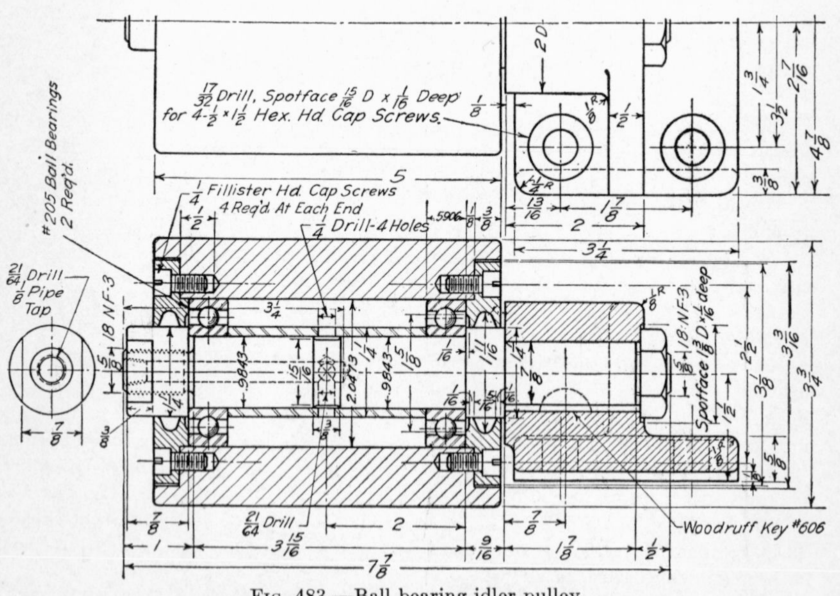

FIG. 483.—Ball bearing idler pulley.

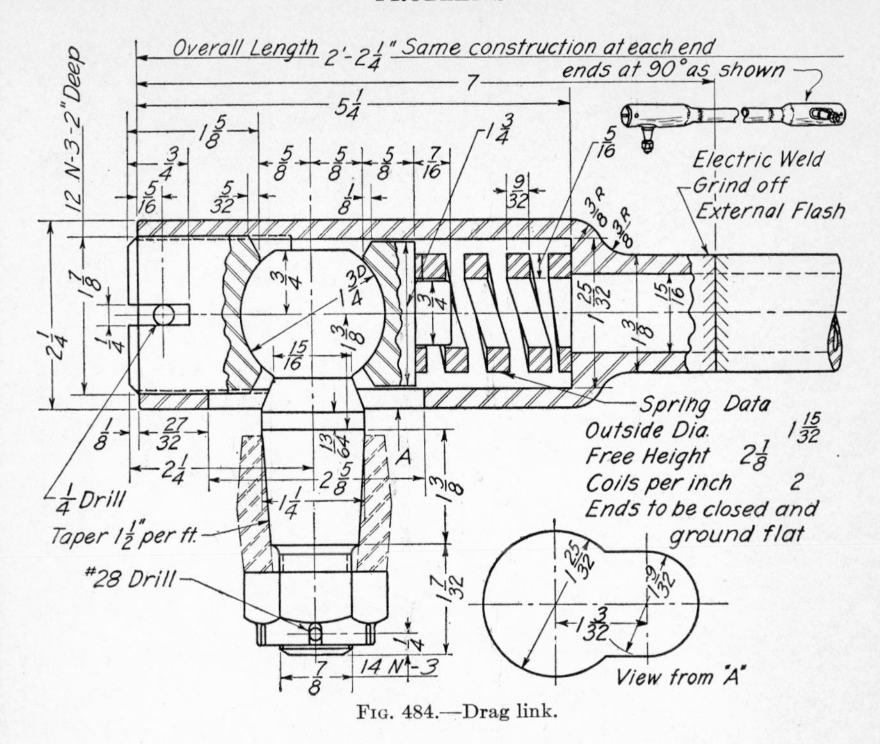

FIG. 484.—Drag link.

48. Fig. 480. Detail drawings of belt drive.

49. Fig. 481. Detail drawings of lubricant pump. Note that on the end view, shown with cover removed, the gears are represented conventionally.

50. Fig. 482. Detail drawings of the D. O. James flexible coupling. This is used for connecting the ends of two rotating shafts which are not in accurate alignment.

51. Fig. 483. Detail drawings of ball bearing idler pulley. Contour of web to be designed.

52. Fig. 484. Detail drawings of drag link. Specify as material for link, ball seat and plug, No. 1045; stud, 3335; spring, 1360, S.A.E. steels.

53. Fig. 485. Detail drawings of adjustable roller stand. Provide lock for the adjusting screw nut.

54. Fig. 486. Detail drawings for split nut. This well-known mechanism provides for engagement and disengagement of a nut on a screw while the screw is in motion. A 90° movement of the hand lever actuates the two pins in the half nuts by means of the milled slots in the cam, thus raising or lowering the half nuts.

55. Fig. 487. Detail drawings of conveyer roll. The dimensions of the roller bearings may be found in a Timken catalogue.

56. Fig. 488. Detail drawings and bill of material for swing saw frame head. The bearing sizes may be obtained from a ball bearing catalogue. For belt clearance make base elliptical, 5" × 4".

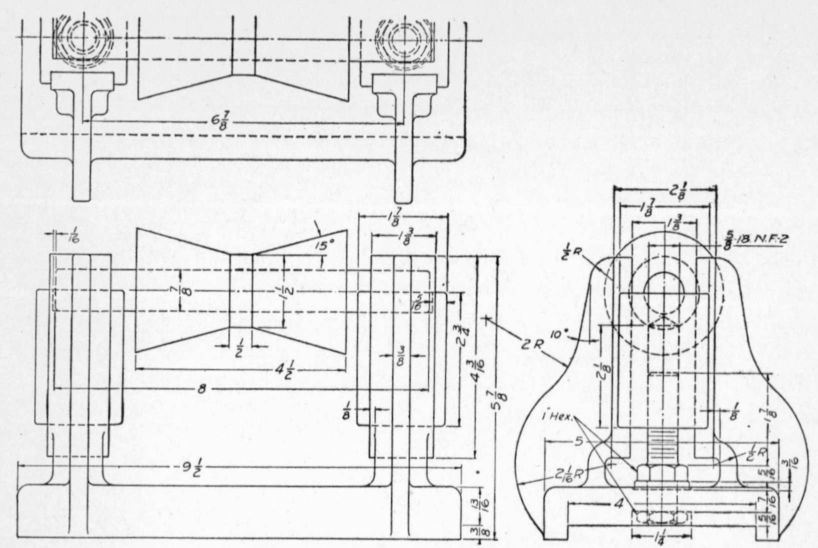

FIG. 485.—Adjustable roller stand (see page 219).

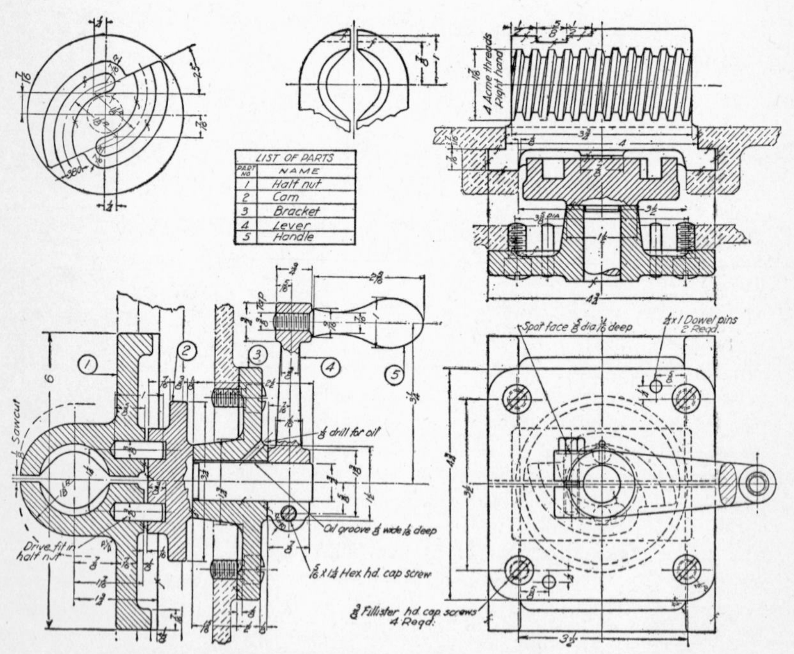

PART NO.	LIST OF PARTS NAME
1	Half nut
2	Cam
3	Bracket
4	Lever
5	Handle

FIG. 486.—Split nut (see page 219).

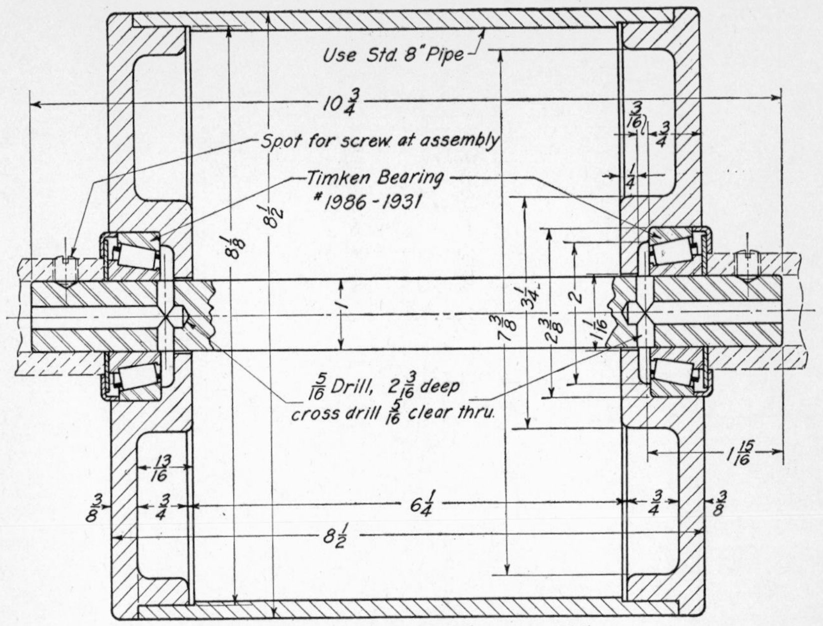

FIG. 487.—Conveyer roll (see page 219).

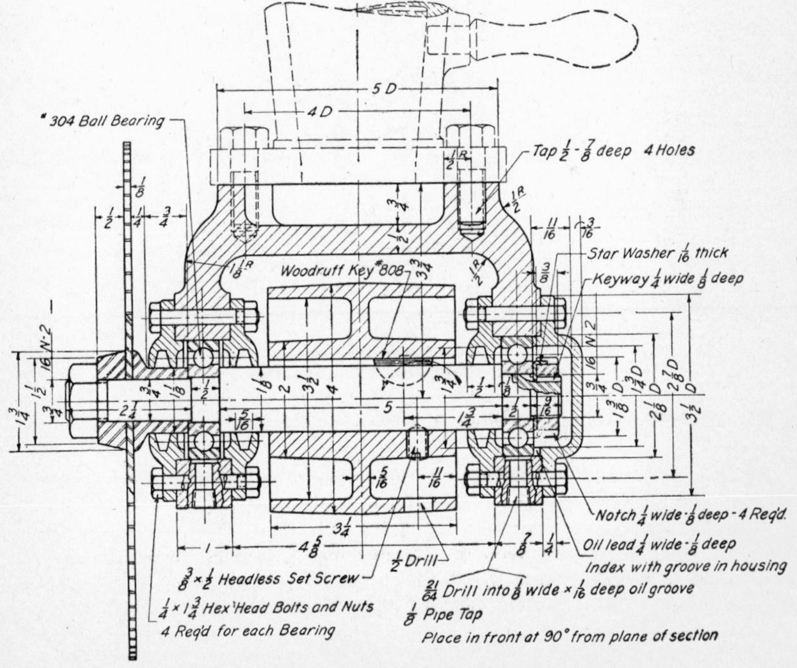

FIG. 488.—Swing saw frame head (see page 219).

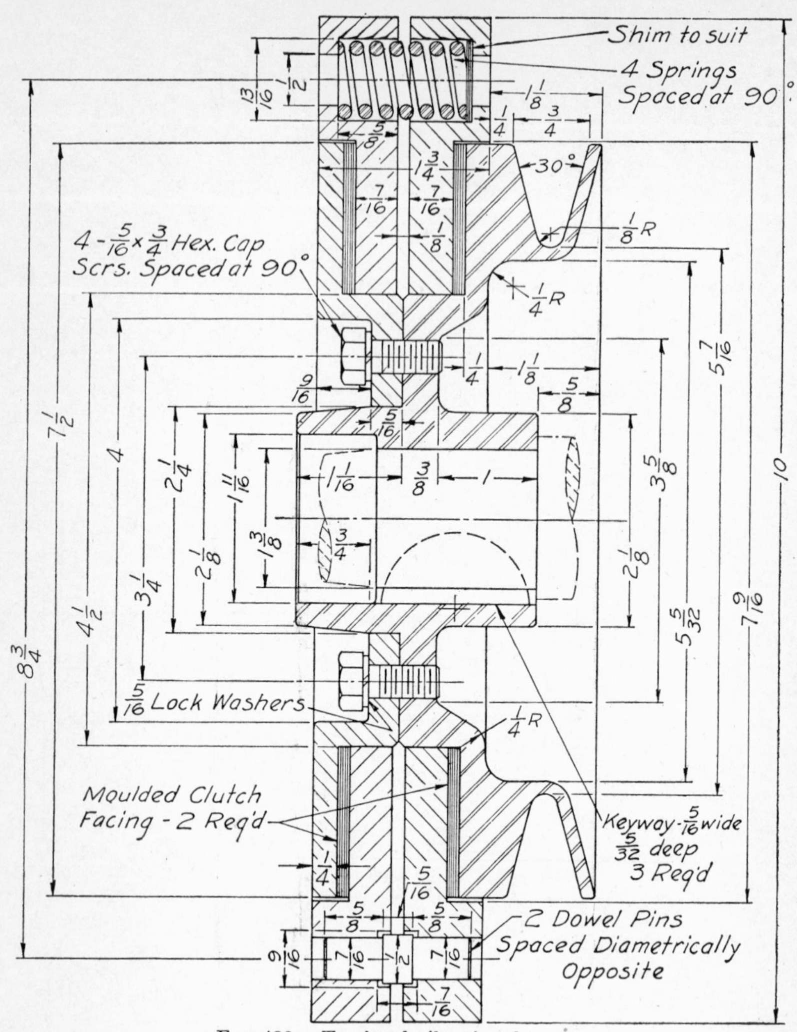

FIG. 489.—Torsional vibration damper.

57. Fig. 489. Detail drawings of torsional vibration damper for automobile crankshaft.

58. Fig. 490. Detail drawings and bill of material for single plate automobile clutch. The piece names are *A*, flywheel; *B*, transmission main drive gear bearing retainer; *C*, clutch pressure plate; *D*, driven plate; *E*, clutch case; *F*, pressure spring thimble; *G*, pressure lever; *H*, pressure pin; *J*, pressure lever fulcrum plate; *K*, pressure lever guide plate; *L*, pressure release bearing sleeve; *M*, pilot bearing packing plate; *N*, pilot bearing packing ring; *O*, clutch pilot bearing; *P*, pressure release bearing.

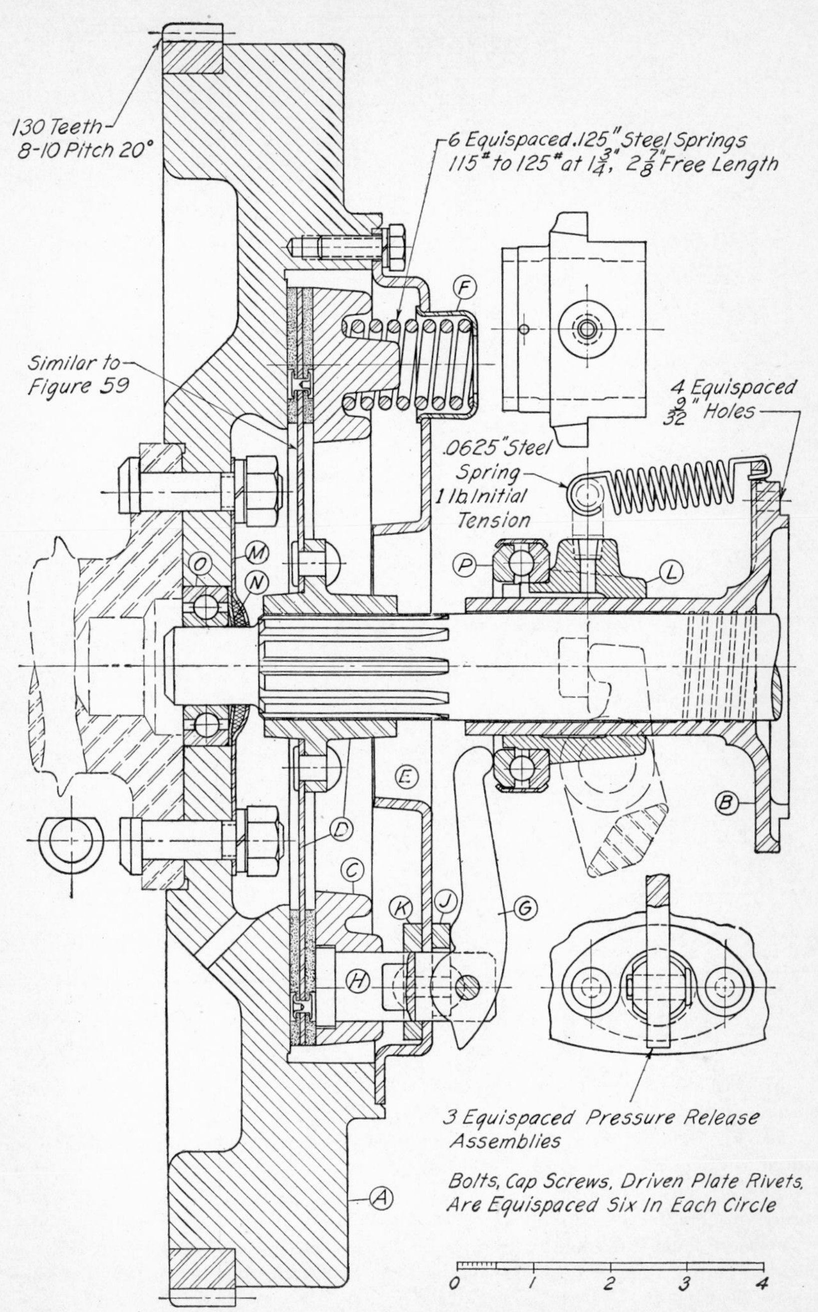

Fig. 490.—Dry disc single plate clutch.

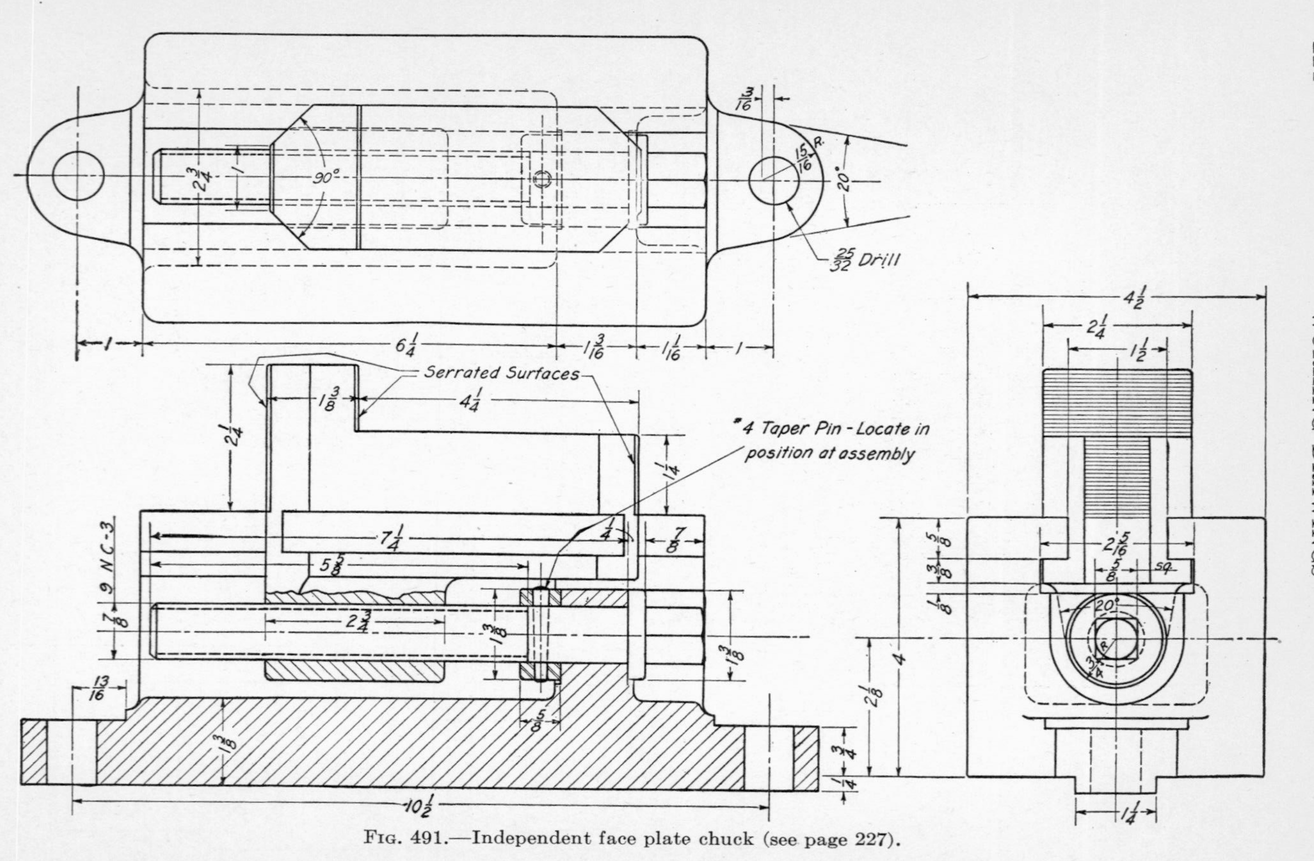

FIG. 491.—Independent face plate chuck (see page 227).

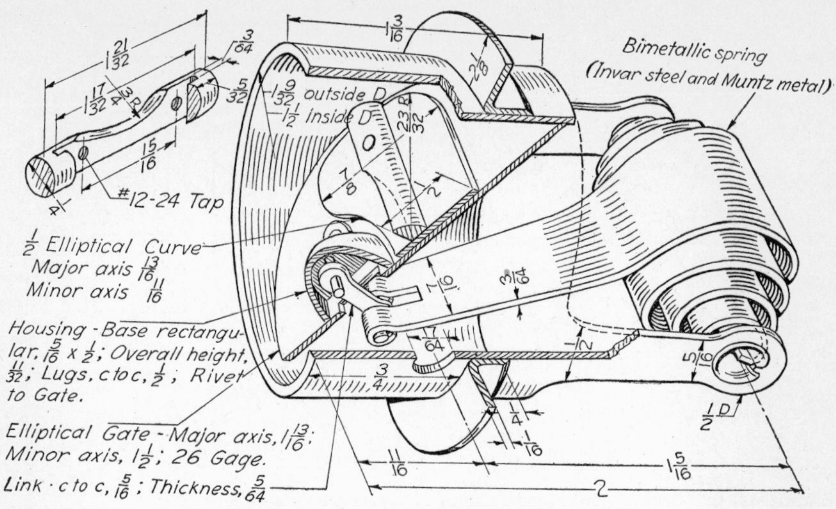

Fig. 492.—Automotive thermostat (see page 227). (*Courtesy of The Dole Valve Company.*)

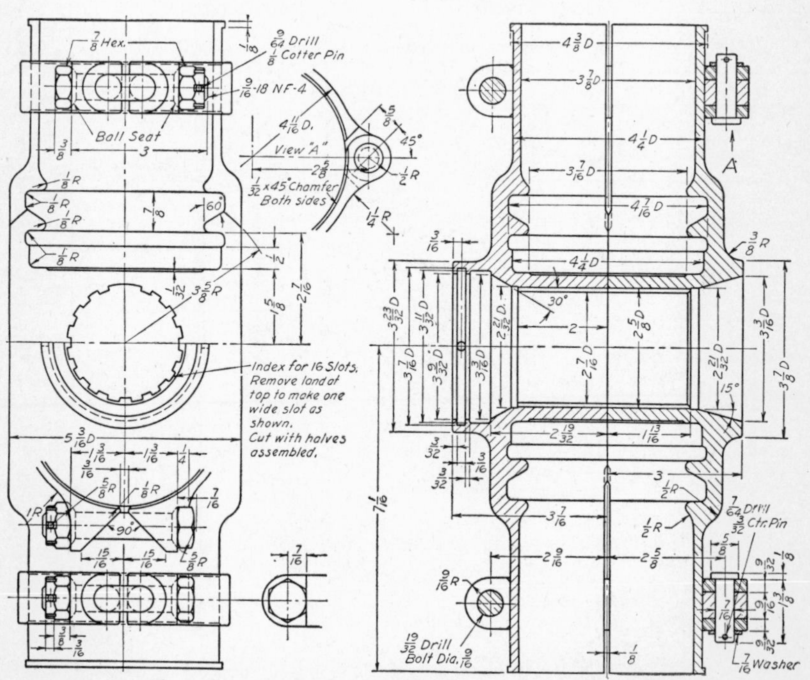

Fig. 493.—Propeller hub (see page 227).

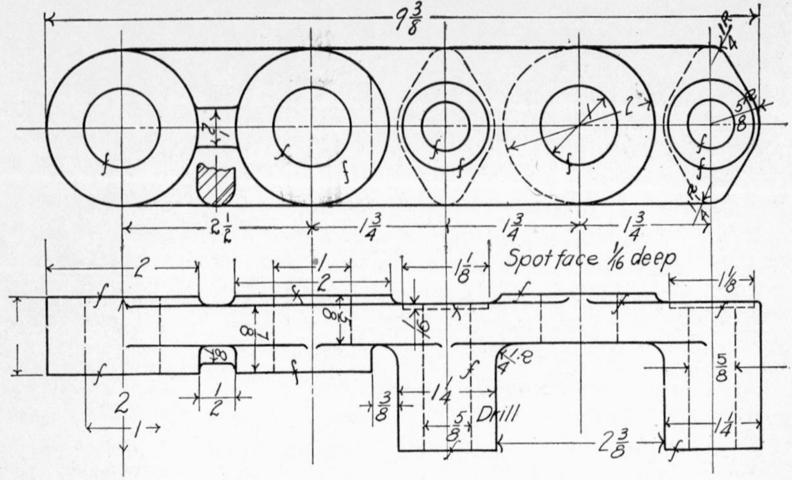

FIG. 494.—An **incorrect** drawing to be checked for errors (gear shifter bracket).

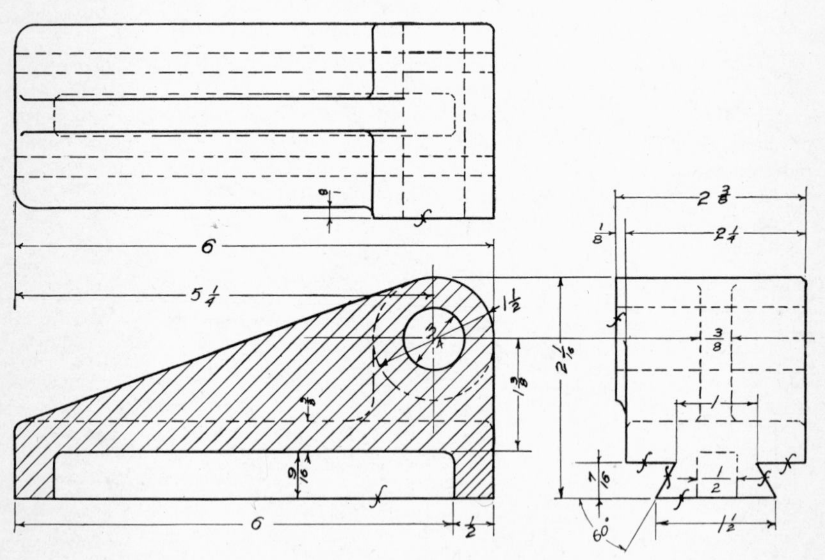

FIG. 495.—An **incorrect** drawing to be checked for errors (bar slide).

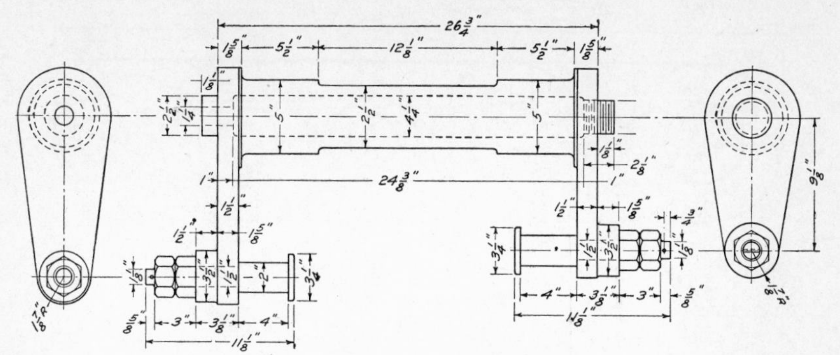

FIG. 496.—An **incorrect** drawing to be checked for errors (rocker arm).

59. Fig. 491. Detail drawings of independent face plate chuck.

60. Fig. 492. Detail drawings of automotive thermostat. Draw double size, in natural position, axis vertical, spring at bottom.

61. Fig. 493. Detail drawings of propeller hub, fixed pitch propeller, type. An illustration of the blade used with this hub will be found on page 116. To respect the wishes of the company, The Hamilton Standard Propeller Corporation, nominal dimensions only have been used instead of the manufacturing tolerances.

Group VIII. Checking Studies.—The drawings in this group are incorrect in technique, representation and dimensioning. Check for errors, following the system given in paragraph 207 and redraw in good form, redesigning to better proportions where advisable. Mark the faults in pencil on the figure before redrawing.

62. Fig. 494. Check for errors and redraw gear shifter bracket.

63. Fig. 495. Check and redraw the bar slide.

64. Fig. 496. Redraw rocker arm correcting all mistakes.

65. Fig. 497. Check errors and redraw driven cone.

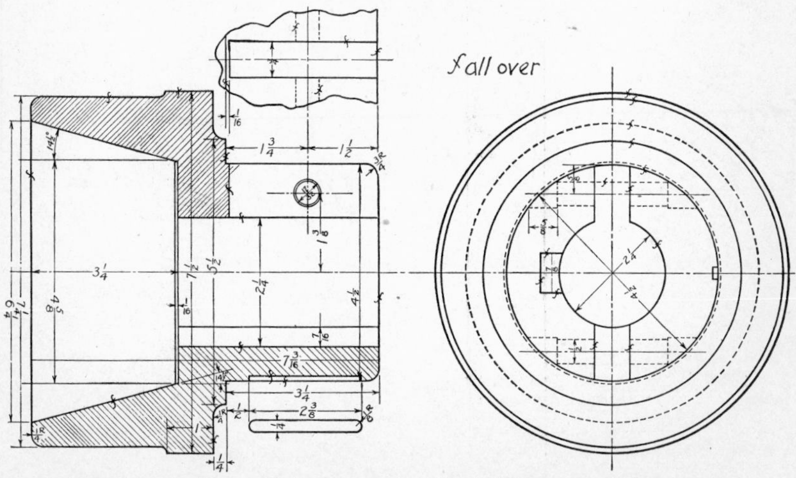

FIG. 497.—An **incorrect** drawing to be checked for errors (driven cone).

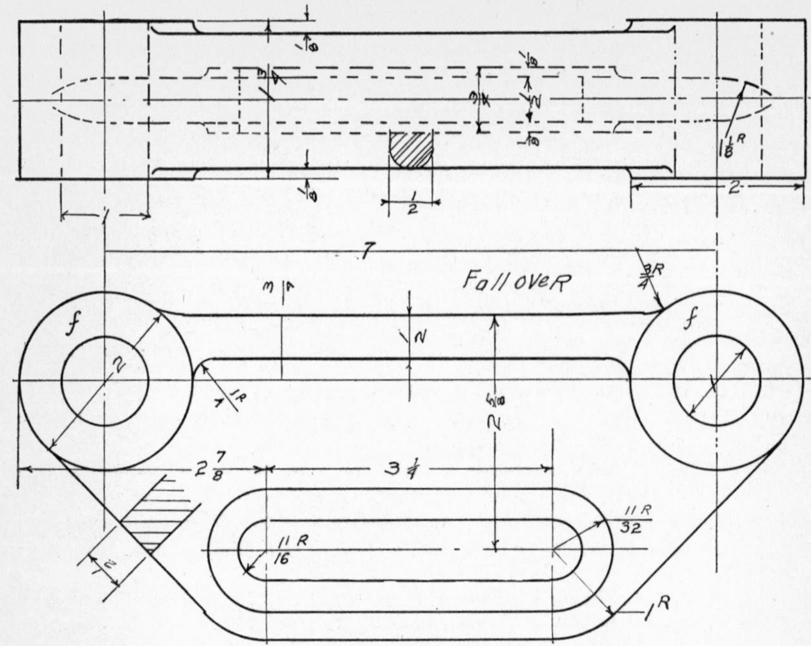

FIG. 498.—An **incorrect** drawing to be checked for errors (slotted slide).

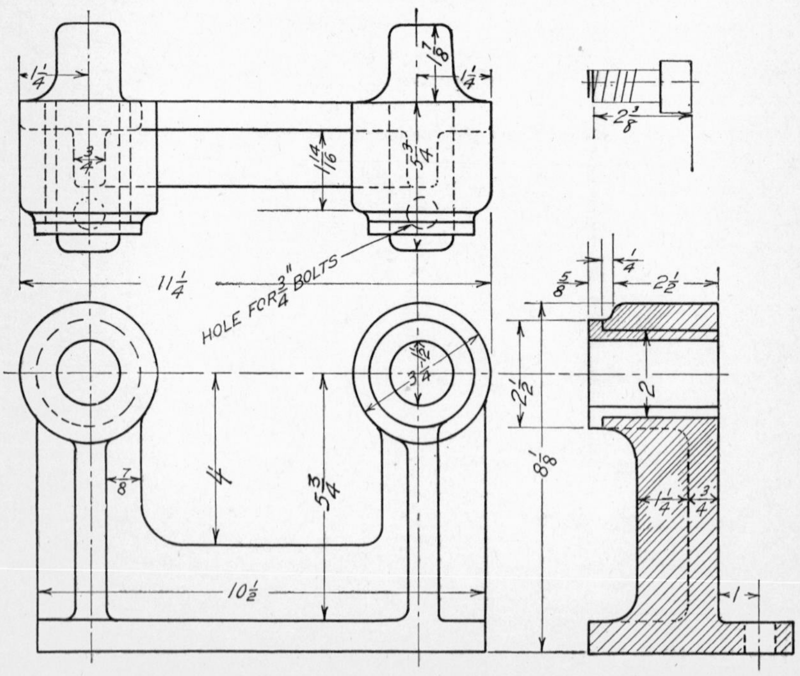

FIG. 499.—An **incorrect** drawing to be checked for errors and redesigned (bushed bearing support).

66. Fig. 498. Check for errors and redraw slotted slide.

67. Fig. 499. Check the bushed bearing support for errors, then redesign to better and more pleasing proportions.

Group IX. Assembly and Detail Drawings.

68. Fig. 500. Assembly drawing of Boyle union from details shown.

69. Fig. 501. Assembly drawing of expansion joint.

70. Fig. 502. Assembly drawing of piston, master rod and articulated rod (baby rod) for Wright Whirlwind engine (for J-6). In this problem nominal dimensions only have been used instead of the manufacturing limits of the maker, and numerous details of design such as locking devices, lubrication ducts, etc., have been intentionally omitted, to simplify it as a drawing problem, as well as to respect the wishes of the company in avoiding publication of detailed information on such a highly specialized product.

71. Fig. 503. Assembly drawing of drill press vise.

72. Fig. 504. Assembly drawing of bench grinder. Supply nuts, bolts, set screws, grease cups and grinding wheels.

73. Fig. 504. Redesign bench grinder for ball bearing installation.

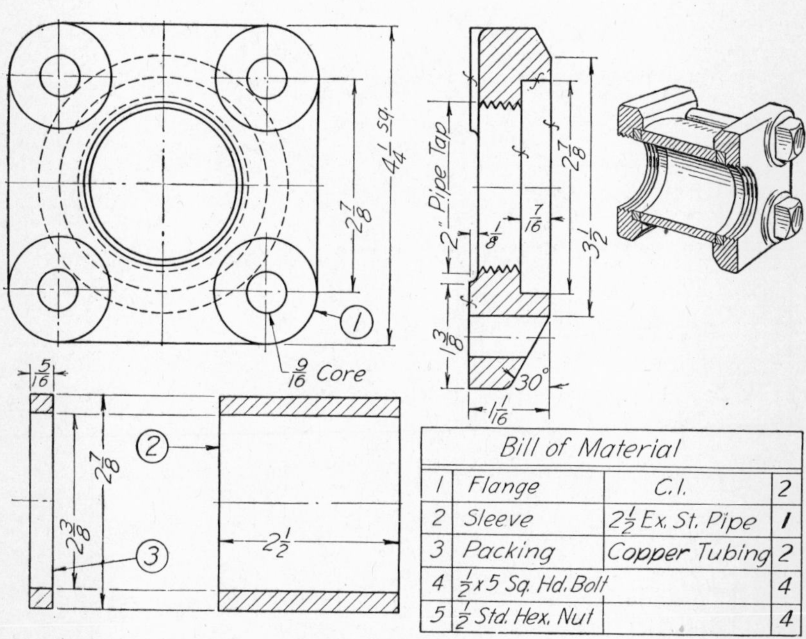

Fig. 500.—Boyle union.

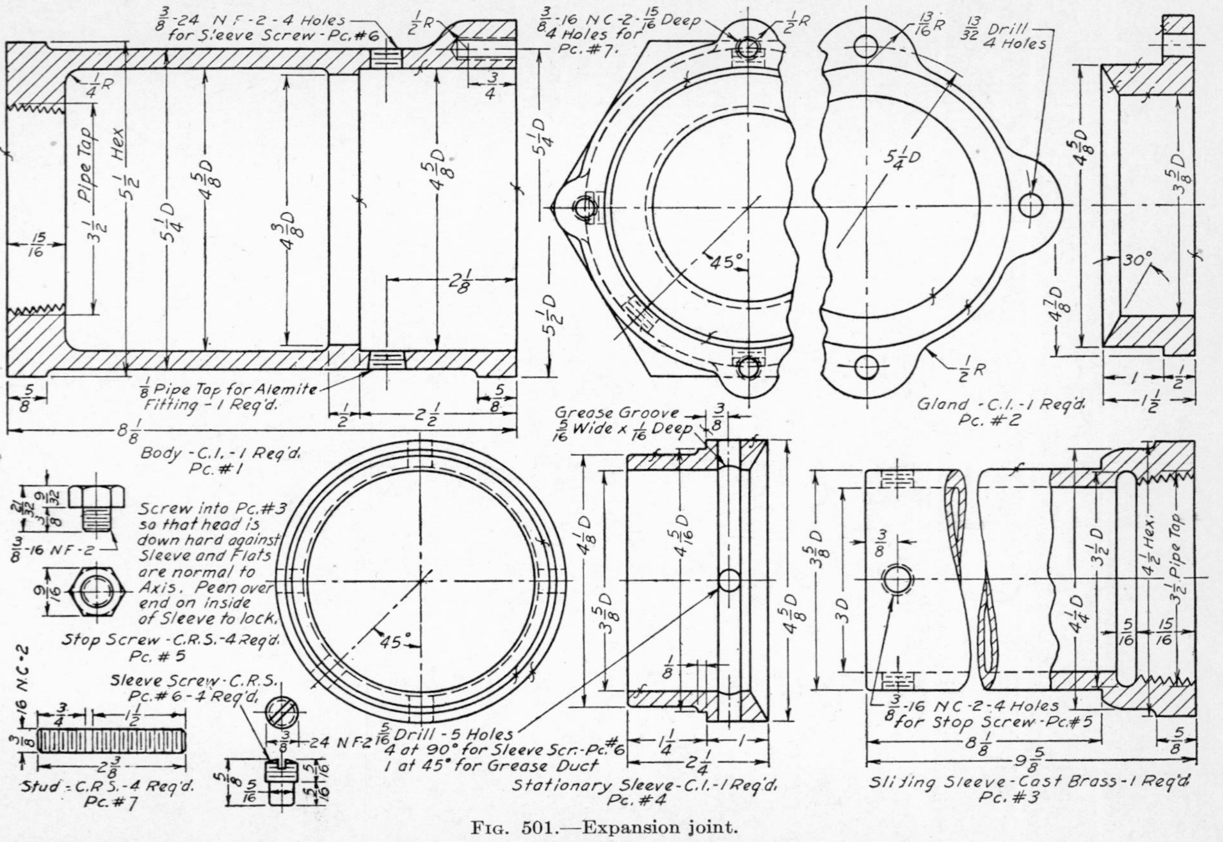

FIG. 501.—Expansion joint.

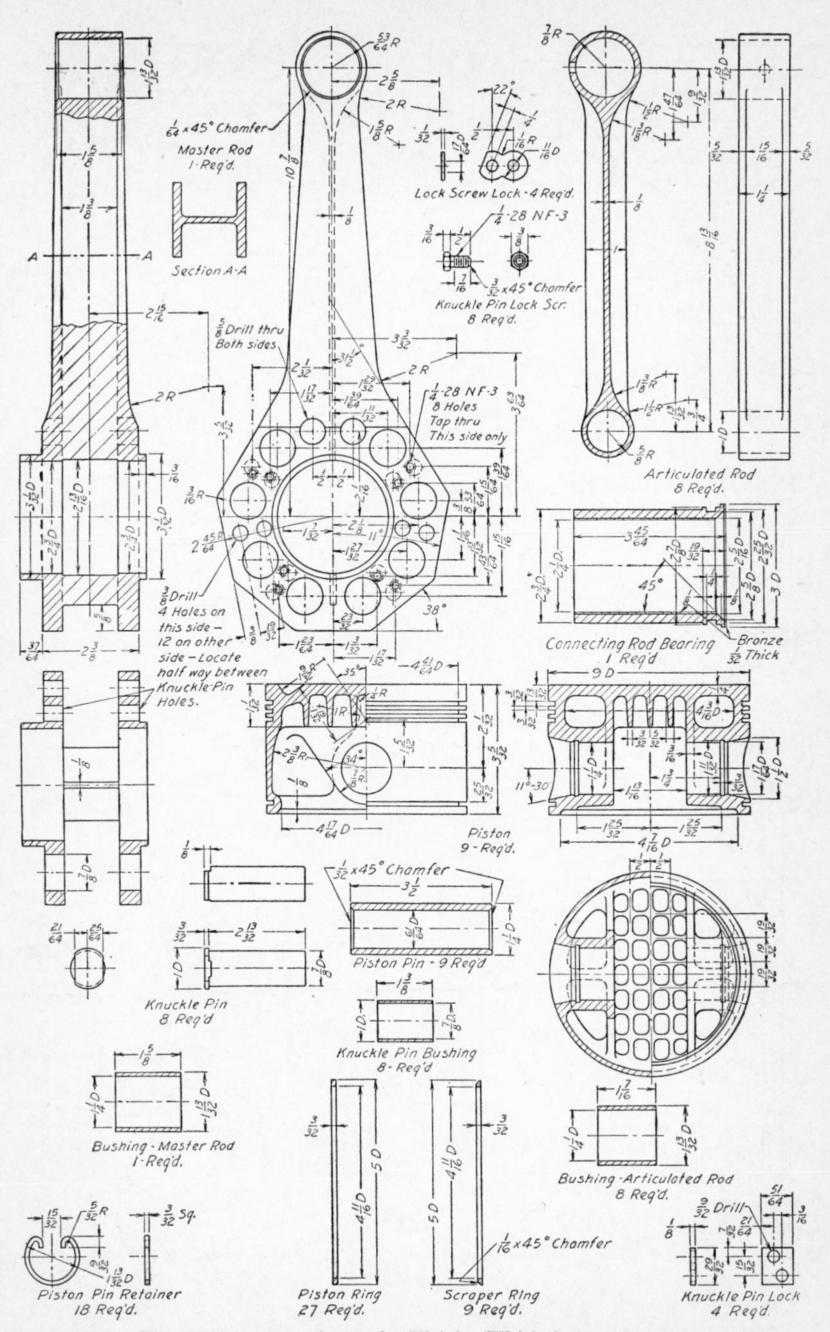

FIG. 502.—Piston and connecting rods, Wright Whirlwind engine (see page 229).

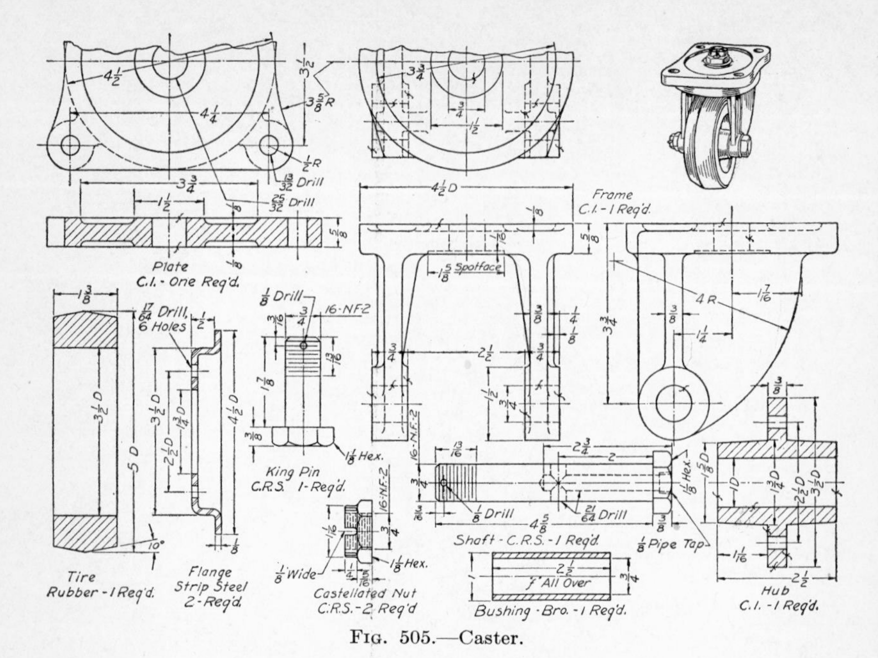

FIG. 505.—Caster.

74. Fig. 505. Assembly drawing, front view in section, of caster.

75. Fig. 505. Redesign caster for ball bearing installation.

76. Fig. 506. Assembly drawing of ball bearing live center, front view in section.

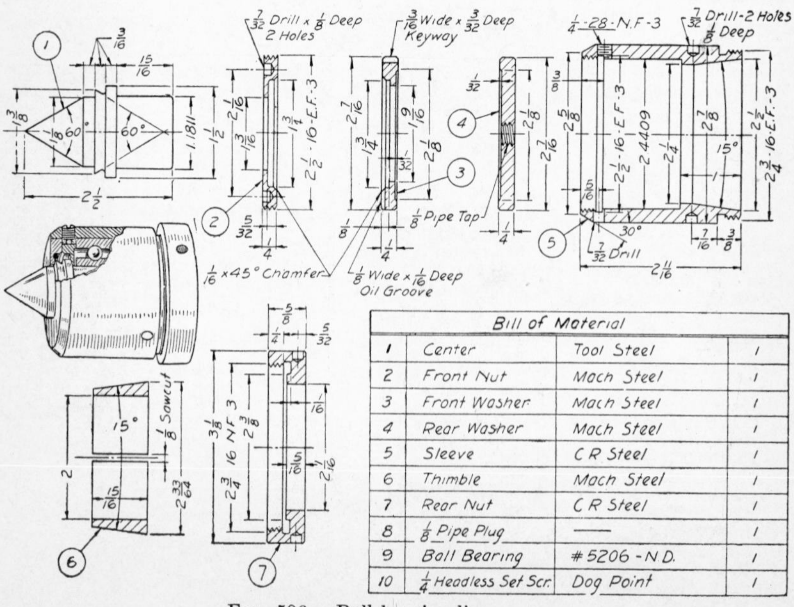

Bill of Material			
1	Center	Tool Steel	1
2	Front Nut	Mach Steel	1
3	Front Washer	Mach Steel	1
4	Rear Washer	Mach Steel	1
5	Sleeve	C R Steel	1
6	Thimble	Mach Steel	1
7	Rear Nut	C R Steel	1
8	1/8 Pipe Plug	——	1
9	Ball Bearing	#5206 - N.D.	1
10	1/4 Headless Set Scr.	Dog Point	1

FIG. 506.—Ball bearing live center.

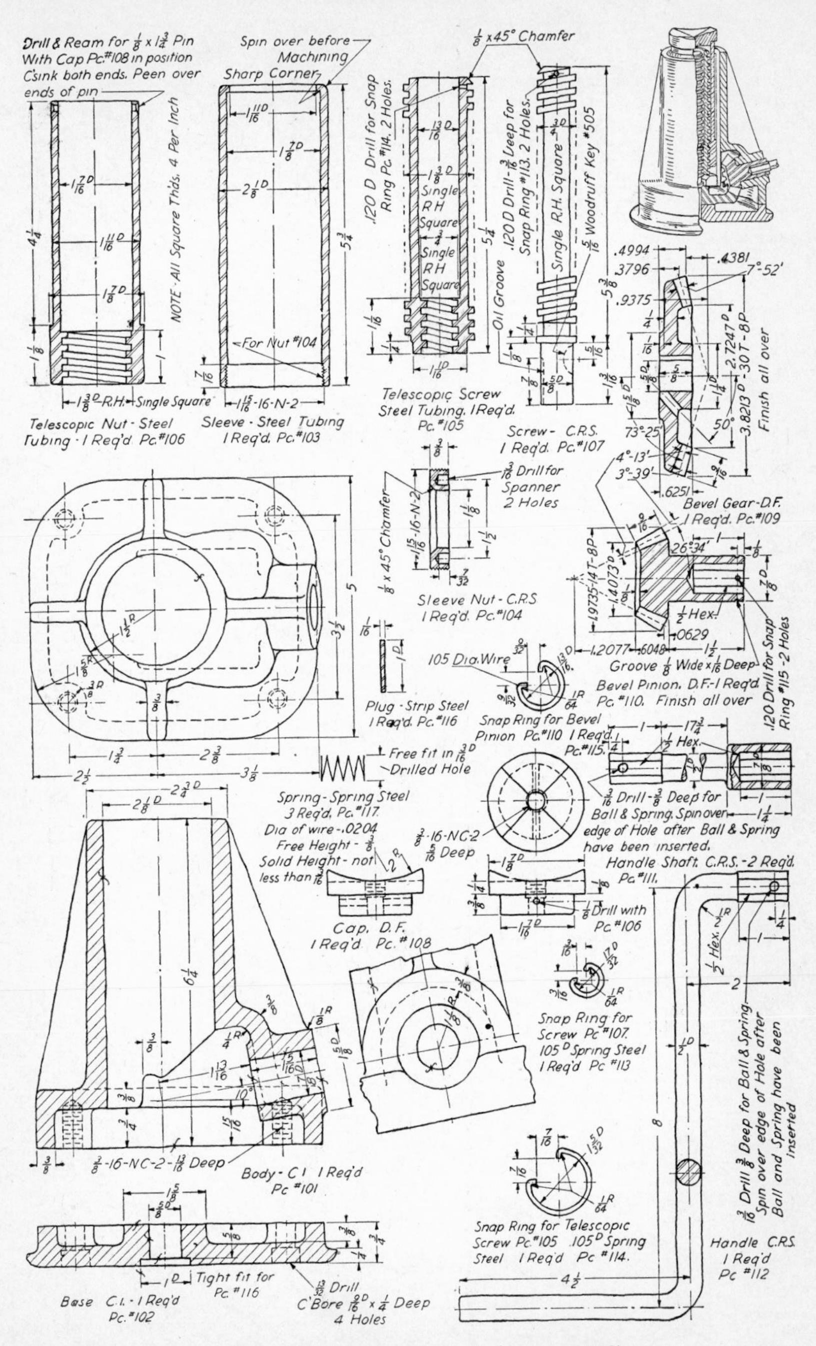

FIG. 507.—Telescopic screw jack (see page 238).

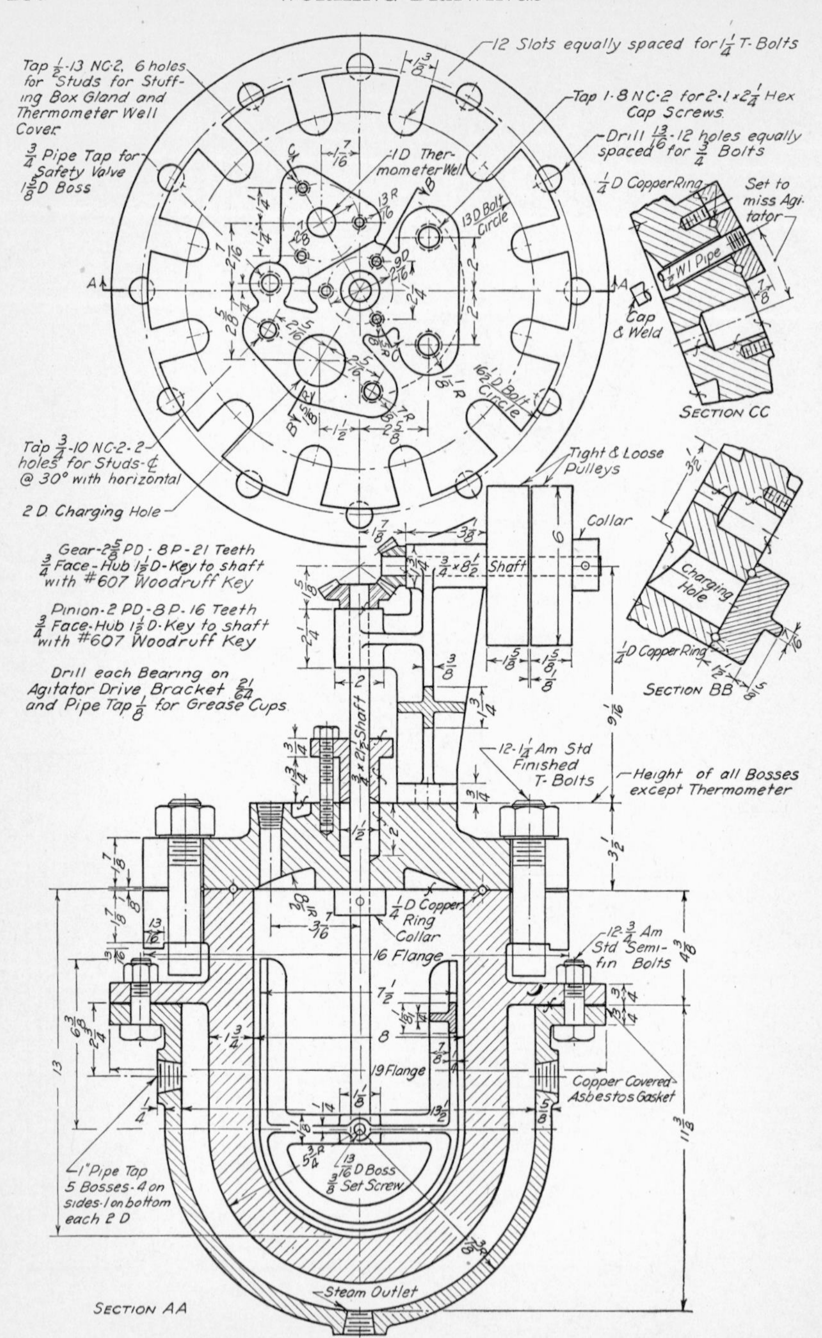

FIG. 508.—Steam-jacketed autoclave (see page 238).

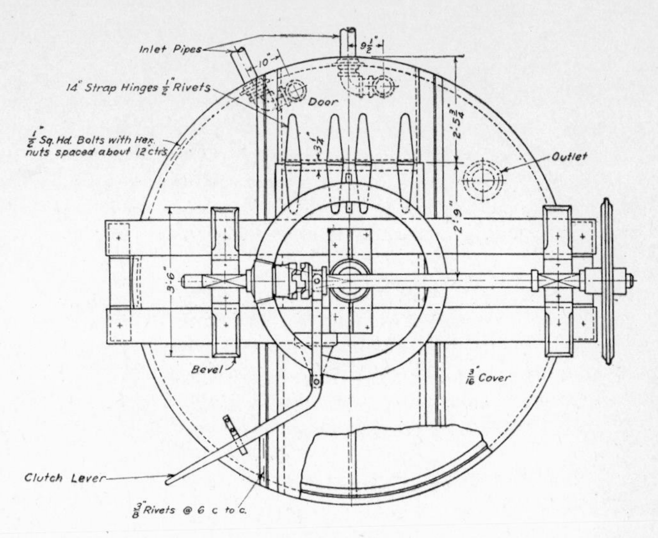

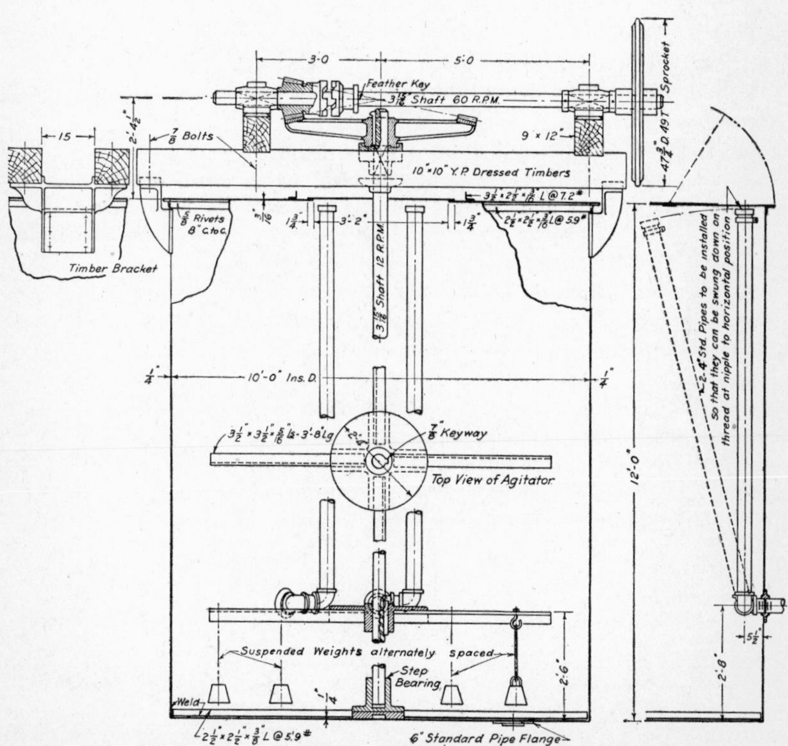

FIG. 509.—Alkali-mixing tank (see page 238).

77. Fig. 507. From detail sketches make assembly drawing of telescopic screw jack, front view in section.

78. Fig. 507. Redesign jack for ball bearing installation.

79. Fig. 508. Detail drawings for steam-jacketed laboratory autoclave. An autoclave is a piece of chemical apparatus used where chemical action under pressure is required. It may be built with a steam jacket as in Fig. 508, or without. Stirring devices may or may not be provided, depending on the use. The autoclave shown has a 2-gallon capacity and is designed for 800 pounds working pressure.

80. Design an autoclave of 10-gallon capacity. Provide an agitator to revolve at 125 r.p.m. driven from motor running at 1,200 r.p.m. Calculate size of pulley and bevel gears. Figure wall thickness for 900 pounds pressure. On steam jacket shell add three lugs for supporting legs. Provide openings in cover for safety valve, pressure gauge and thermometer well. Use T-bolts, calculating area and refer to handbook for corresponding bolt size. Make complete assembly drawing.

81. Make detail drawings of autoclave from Prob. 80, including design of supporting legs.

82. Fig. 509. Assembly drawing of alkali-mixing tank. Figure net capacity in gallons. Calculate size of bevel gears for speeds as indicated. Make a complete bill of material for fabricating tank. Sides and bottom are welded.

83. Fig. 509. Make detail drawings of the transmission machinery used in Prob. 82.

84. Fig. 509. Make detail drawing of the timber bracket.

85. Fig. 509. Make an assembly drawing of an alkali-mixing tank with diameter 14′-0″ inside and depth 10′-0″. Use one swing pipe instead of two. Joints to be riveted instead of welded. Laps on 1/4″ plates to be 2″. Laps on 3/16″ plates to be 1 3/4″.

86. Fig. 509. Make detail drawings of mixing tank of Prob. 85.

87. Fig. 510. Make detail drawings of Corliss engine dash-pot. This is the spring type as made by the Allis-Chalmers Manufacturing Company.

88. Fig. 511. From detail sketches make assembly and detail drawings of "Unipump" centrifugal pump, as made by the Weinman Pump Company, in which the pump casing is mounted directly on a driving motor, making a compact and efficient design. Cross-sections of the volute taken at intervals of 45° should be shown by removed sections, either successive or superimposed, and similar sections should be made through the impeller. At 3,425 r.p.m. this pump delivers 520 gallons per minute against a head of 160 feet.

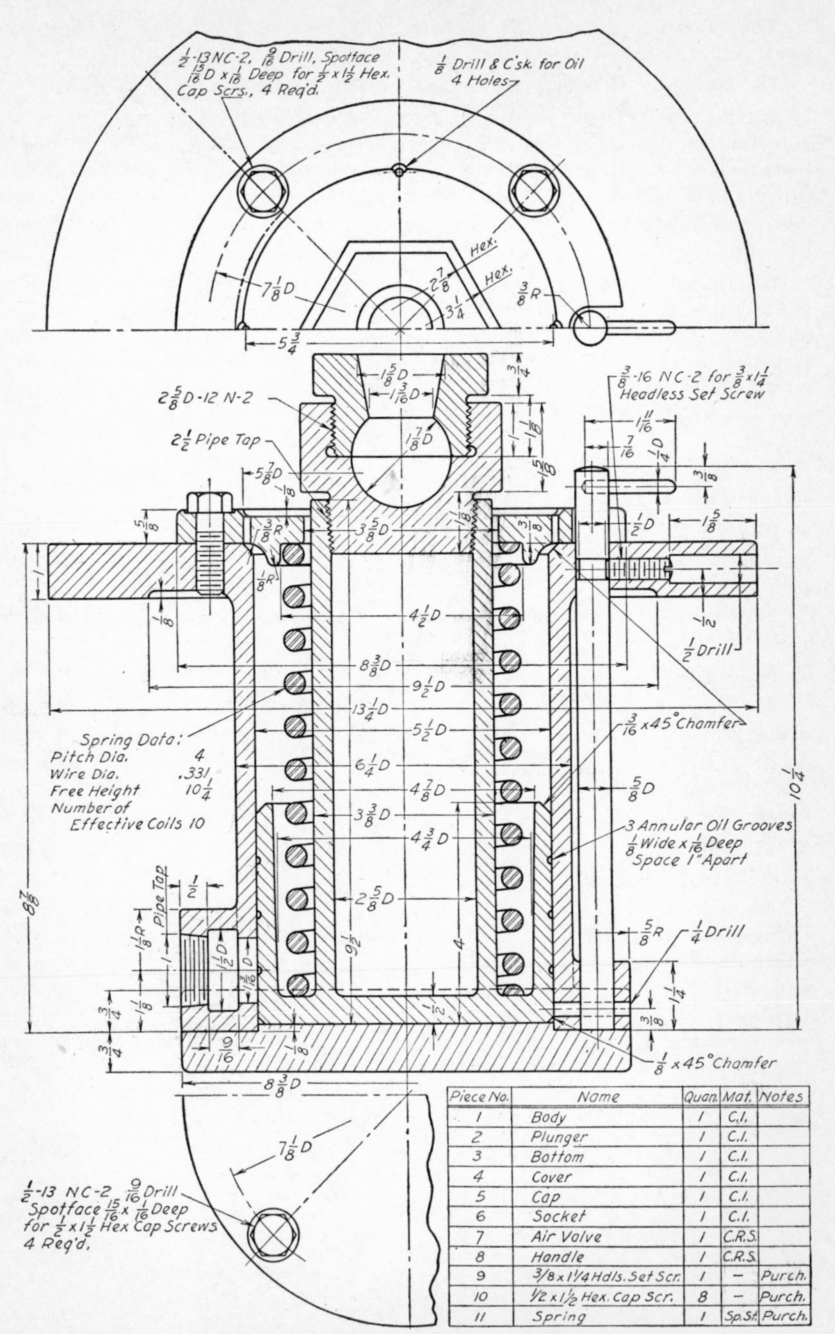

Piece No.	Name	Quan.	Mat.	Notes
1	Body	1	C.I.	
2	Plunger	1	C.I.	
3	Bottom	1	C.I.	
4	Cover	1	C.I.	
5	Cap	1	C.I.	
6	Socket	1	C.I.	
7	Air Valve	1	C.R.S.	
8	Handle	1	C.R.S.	
9	3/8 x 1 1/4 Hdls. Set Scr.	1	–	Purch.
10	1/2 x 1 1/2 Hex. Cap Scr.	8	–	Purch.
11	Spring	1	Sp.St.	Purch.

FIG. 510.—Corliss engine dash-pot.

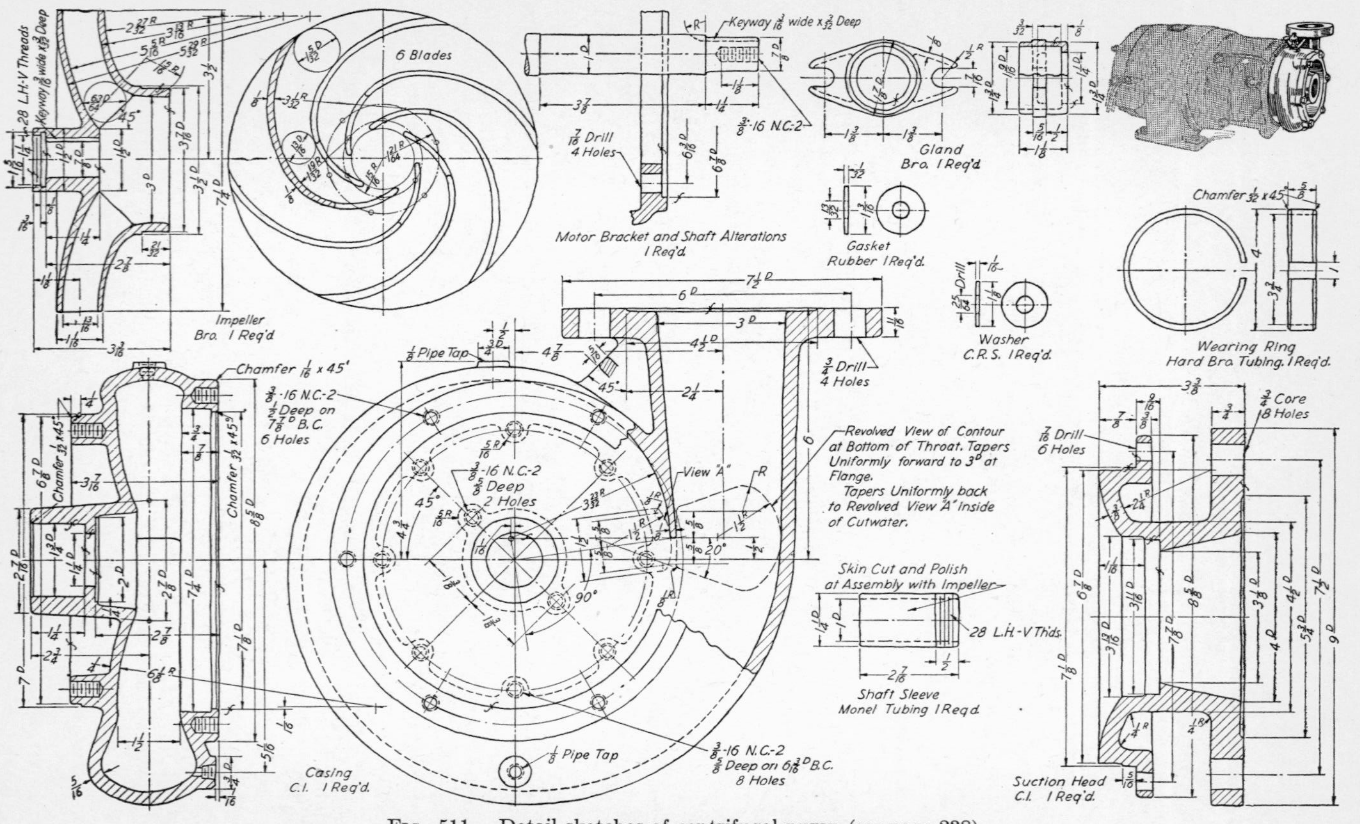

FIG. 511.—Detail sketches of centrifugal pump (see page 238).

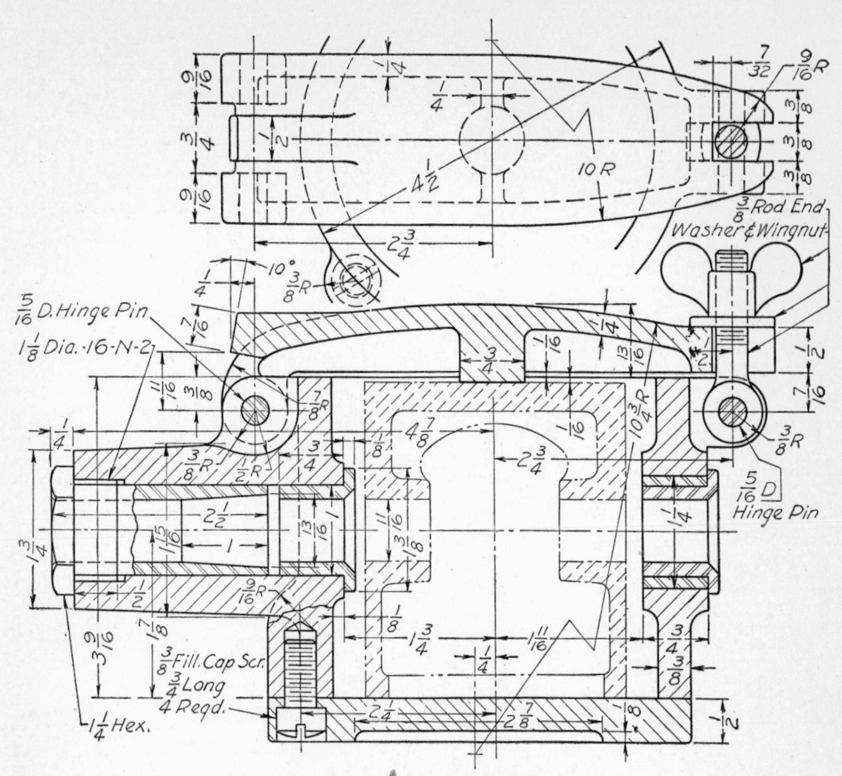

Fig. 512.—Piston drilling jig.

89. Fig. 512. Make complete detail drawings for piston drilling jig. The piston to be drilled is shown in phantom.

90. Fig. 513. The rectangular inset shows the detail sketch of a dumper clutch fork and a picture of the jig used in machining it. Sketches of the parts of the jig are given in the figure. Make complete detail drawings for the jig, with bill of material and title.

91. Fig. 513. Make complete assembly drawing, three views, of jig with clutch fork shown in phantom, giving "go-together" dimensions. If Prob. 90 is omitted, this assembly drawing should be fully dimensioned.

92. Fig. 514. From detail sketches make assembly drawing of motor base drilling jig, showing in phantom the piece to be machined (the motor base sketch shows the piece only in outline, omitting coring).

93. Fig. 514. Make detail drawings of motor base drilling jig. Note that complete working drawings will sometimes have more views than the sketches.

94. Fig. 514. Redesign motor base drilling jig, using screw and knob arrangement instead of hand lever and toggle, to operate the clamping levers.

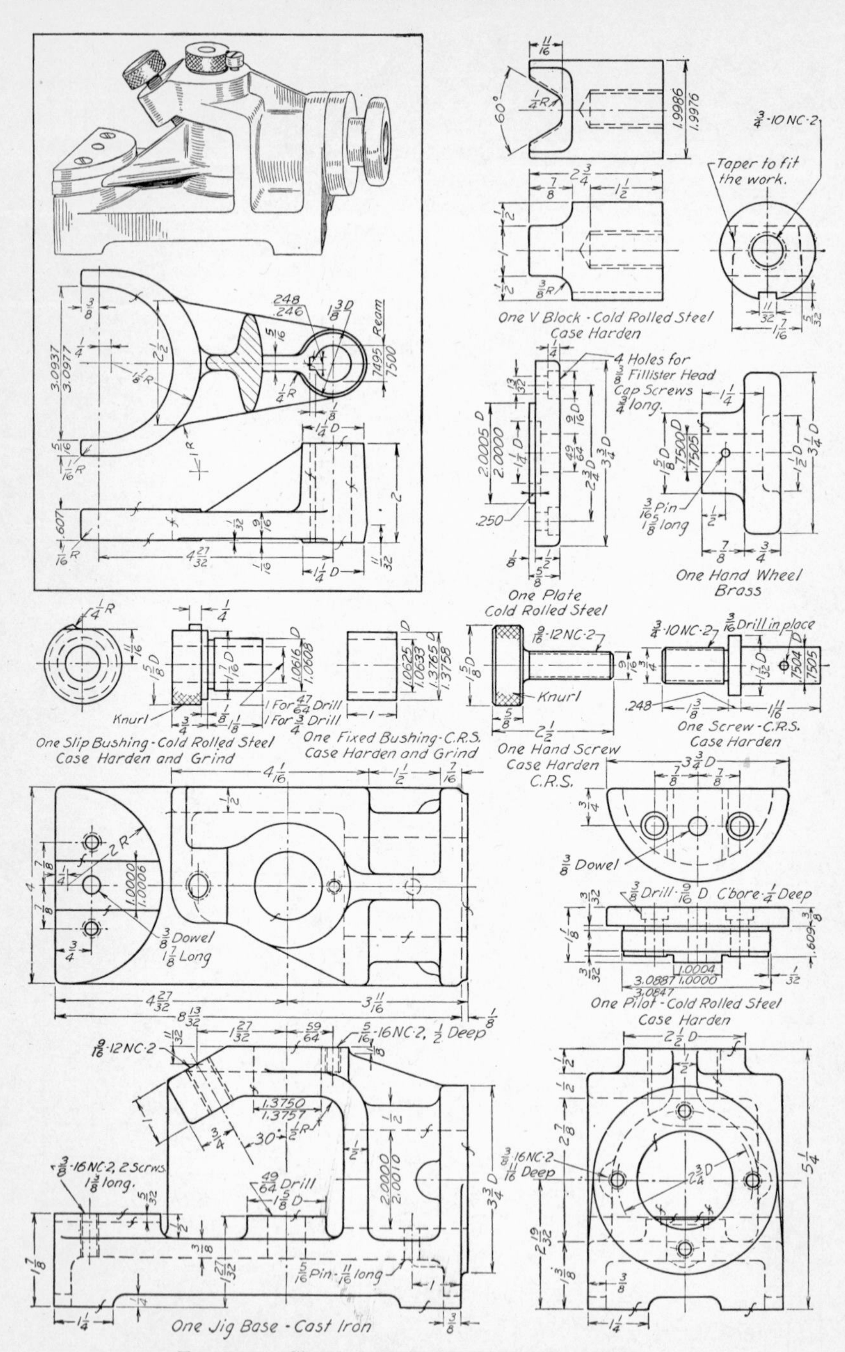

Fig. 513.—Clutch fork jig details (see page 241).

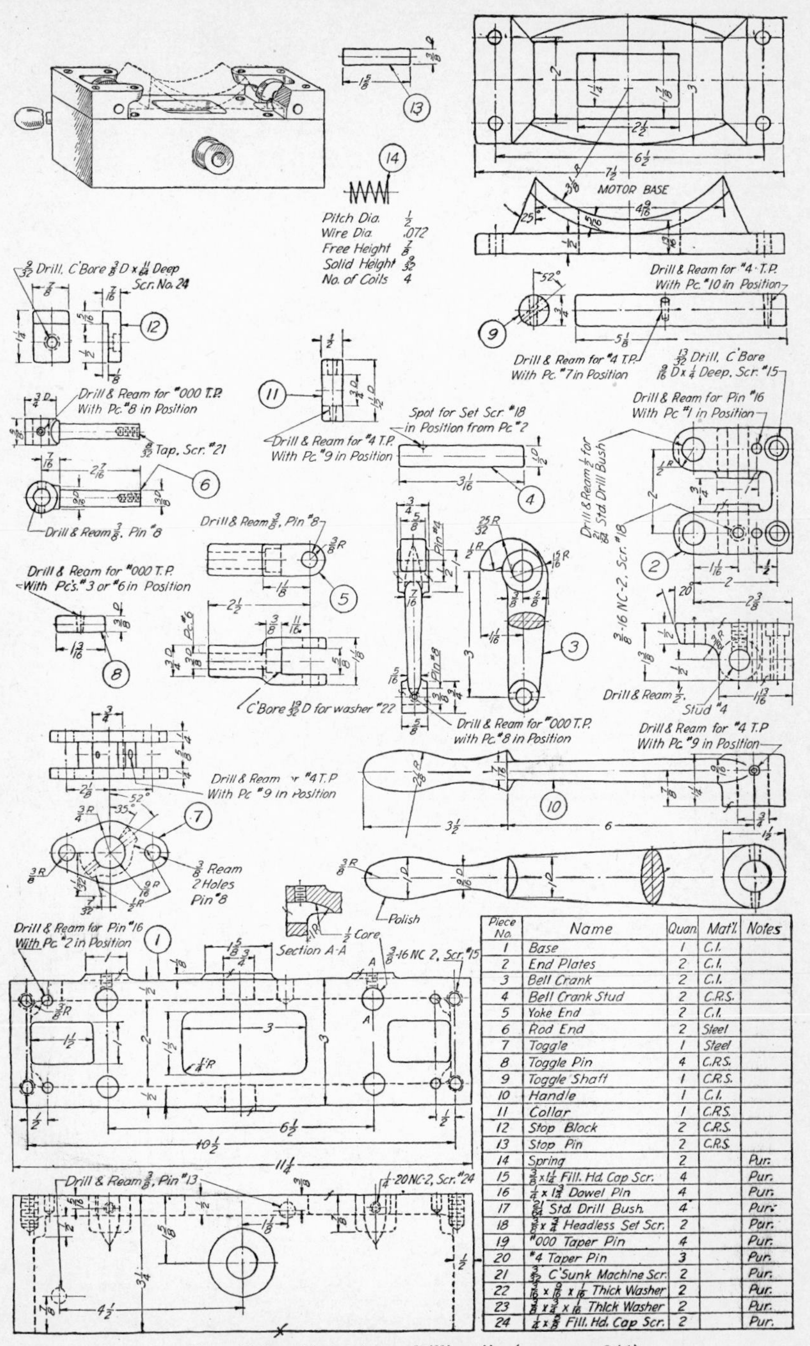

Piece No.	Name	Quan.	Mat'l.	Notes
1	Base	1	C.I.	
2	End Plates	2	C.I.	
3	Bell Crank	2	C.I.	
4	Bell Crank Stud	2	C.R.S.	
5	Yoke End	2	C.I.	
6	Rod End	2	Steel	
7	Toggle	1	Steel	
8	Toggle Pin	4	C.R.S.	
9	Toggle Shaft	1	C.R.S.	
10	Handle	1	C.I.	
11	Collar	1	C.R.S.	
12	Stop Block	2	C.R.S.	
13	Stop Pin	2	C.R.S.	
14	Spring	2		Pur.
15	3/8 x 1 1/2 Fill. Hd. Cap Scr.	4		Pur.
16	1/4 x 1 3/4 Dowel Pin	4		Pur.
17	21/64 Std. Drill Bush.	4		Pur.
18	3/8 x 3/4 Headless Set Scr.	2		Pur.
19	#000 Taper Pin	4		Pur.
20	#4 Taper Pin	3		Pur.
21	3/32 C'Sunk Machine Scr.	2		Pur.
22	9/16 x 9/16 x 1/16 Thick Washer	2		Pur.
23	3/8 x 3/4 x 1/16 Thick Washer	2		Pur.
24	1/4 x 5/8 Fill. Hd. Cap Scr.	2		Pur.

FIG. 514.—Motor base drilling jig (see page 241).

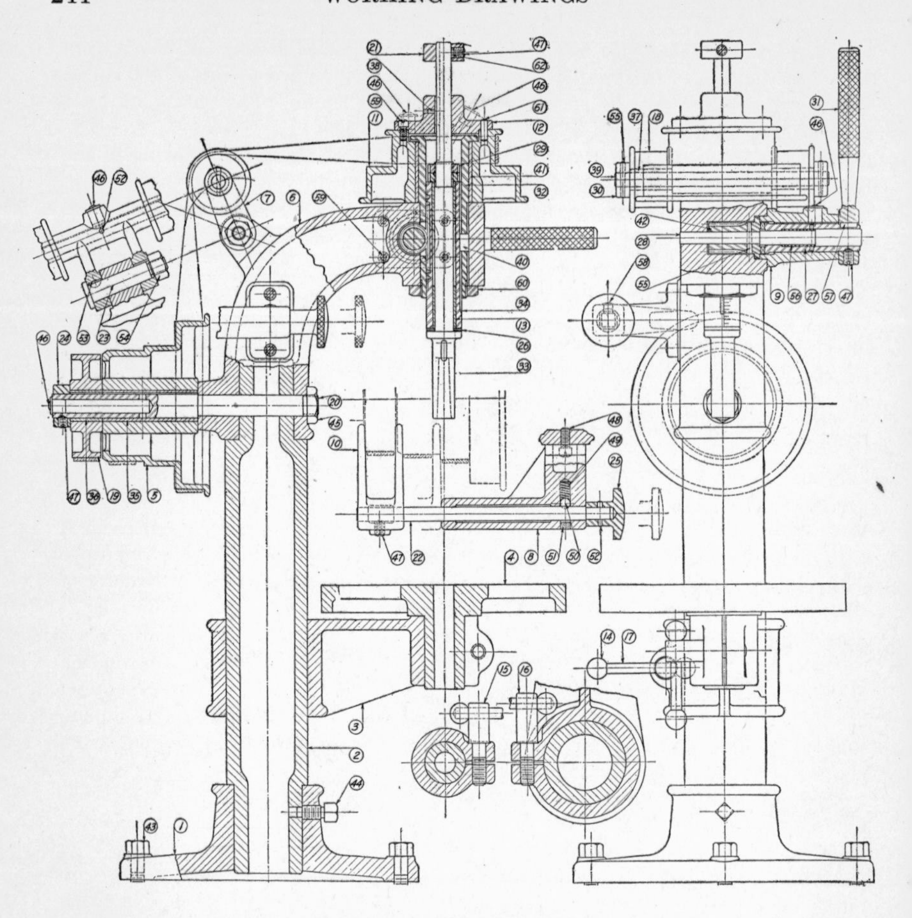

BILL OF MATERIAL												
								Purchased Finished				
Pce No	Name	Q	Mat.	Pce No.	Name	Q	Mat.	Pce No.	Name	Q	Used on Name	Pce No.
1	Base	1	C.I.	31	Hand Lever	1	Steel Forg.	43	1/2x2 Hex Cap Scrw.	4	Base	1
2	Column	1	C.I.	32	Spindle Cone Sleeve	1	M.S.	44	1/2x1 Dog Pt Set Scrw.	1	Base	1
3	Knee	1	C.I.	33	Spindle	1	45-55 Carbon St.	45	3/4 Hex Nut 3/8 Thick	1	Driving Cone Shft	20
4	Table	1	C.I.	34	Spindle Sleeve	1	M.S.	46	1/2 Ball & Sprg Oiler	1	Driving Cone Shft	20
5	Driving Cone	1	C.I.	35	Driving Cone Bush	1	Bro.	46	1/2 Ball & Sprg Oiler	1	Idler Pulley Frame	7
6	Head	1	C.I.	36	Loose Pulley Bush	1	Bro.	46	1/2 Ball & Sprg Oiler	1	Hand Lever Bracket	9
7	Idler Pulley Frame	1	C.I.	37	Idler Pulley Bush	2	Bro.	46	1/2 Ball & Sprg Oiler	2	Driving Flange	12
8	Belt Shifter Bracket	1	C.I.	38	Spindle Key	1	45-55 Carbon St.	47	3/8x1/2 Hdlss Set Scrw	1	Driving Shft Collar	24
9	Hand Lever Bracket	1	C.I.	39	Idler Pulley Shaft	1	C.R.S.	47	3/8x1/2 Hdlss Set Scrw	1	Belt Shifter	10
10	Belt Shifter	1	C.I.	40	Spindle Sleeve Key	1	C.R.S.	47	3/8x1/2 Hdlss Set Scrw	1	Hand Lever	31
11	Spindle Cone	1	C.I.	41	Spindle Cone Bush	1	Bro.	47	3/8x1/2 Hdlss Set Scrw	1	Spdle Stop Collar	21
12	Driving Flange	1	C.I.	42	Pinion	1	M.S.	48	5/16x3/4 Fill. Hd. Cap Scrw	2	Belt Shifter Bracket	8
13	Spindle Bushing	2	Bro.					49	Spring 11/32 OD 1" Long	1	Belt Shifter Bracket	8
14	Clamp Handle Ball	4	C.R.S.					50	3/8 Steel Ball	1	Belt Shifter Bracket	8
15	Table Clamp	1	C.R.S.					51	13/32x1/4 Cork Plug	1	Belt Shifter Bracket	8
16	Knee Clamp	1	C.R.S.					52	#2 Taper Pin 1" Long	1	Belt Shifter Knob	25
17	Clamp Handle	2	C.R.S.					52	#2 Taper Pin 1" Long	1	Idler Pulley Frame	7
18	Idler Pulley	2	C.I.					53	#404 Woodruff Key	1	Idler Pulley Frame Std	23
19	Loose Pulley	1	C.I.					54	1/2 Std Hex Nut	1	Idler Pulley Frame Std.	23
20	Driving Cone Shaft	1	C.R.S.					55	#2 Taper Pin 1 1/4" Long	2	Idler Pulley Shft Collar	30
21	Spindle Stop Collar	1	C.R.S.					55	#2 Taper Pin 1 1/4" Long	1	Pinion	42
22	Belt Shifter Rod	1	C.R.S.					56	Spring 13/32" OD 2" Long	1	Hand Lever Clutch	27
23	Idler Pulley Frame Stud	1	M.S.					57	#5 P&W. Key	1	Hand Lever Clutch	27
24	Driving Cone Shaft Collar	1	C.R.S.					58	5/16 Ball & Sprg Oiler	1	Belt Shifter Brkt	8
25	Belt Shifter Knob	1	C.R.S.					59	1/4x1/2 Fill Hd Cap Scrw	4	Hand Lever Brkt	9
26	Spindle Washer	1	Red Fiber					59	1/4x1/2 Fill Hd Cap Scrw	4	Driving Flange	12
27	Hand Lever Clutch	1	M.S.					60	1 3/4 Hex Nut 3/8 Thk 16 U.S.F. Thd	1	Spdle Cone Sleeve	32
28	Hand Lever Shaft	1	C.R.S.					61	1/4x3/4 Straight Pin	1	Driving Flange	12
29	Spindle Nut	2	C.R.S.					62	3/32x1/8 B'ss Plug	1	Spindle Stop Collar	21
30	Idler Pulley Shaft Collar	2	C.R.S.									

FIG. 515.—Assembly and bill of material of bench drill.

95. Figs. 515, 516, 517, 518. Make complete detail drawings of bench drill, with title and bill of material. The driving cone is designed to run at 400 r.p.m. with corresponding spindle speeds of 300 and 630 r.p.m. The curves on head (piece 6) should be obtained by the method of Fig. 155.

96. Figs. 515 to 518. From detail drawings make assembly drawing of the bench drill, with piece numbers, bill of material and title.

97. Figs. 515 to 518. Redesign bench drill for ball bearing installation in spindle and driving cones.

98. Figs. 515 to 518. Redesign bench drill as follows: spindle cone diameters, 5 7/16″ and 7 7/16″; driving cone diameters, 6 5/8″ and 8 9/16″. Note that this will change the position of the belt shifter bracket and the idler pulleys. Check for interference with the driving cone and knee.

99. Figs. 515 to 518. Redesign bench drill for a loose pulley sped of 350 r.p.m. and spindle speeds of 600 and 325.

Group X. Cams and Gears.

100. Make a drawing for a plate cam to satisfy the following conditions: On a vertical center line a point *A* is 7/8″ above a point *O*, and a point *B* is 1 3/4″ above *A*. With center at *O*, revolution clockwise, the follower starts at *A* and rises to *B* with uniform motion during 1/3 revolution, remains at rest 1/3 revolution, and drops with uniform motion the last 1/3 revolution, to the starting point. Diameter of shaft 3/4″; diameter of hub 1 1/4″; thickness of plate 1/2″; length of hub 1 1/4″; diameter of roller 1/2″.

101. A broken spur gear has been measured and the following information obtained: number of teeth, 33; outside diameter, 4 3/8″; width of face, 1″; diameter of shaft, 7/8″; length of hub, 1 1/4″. Make drawing of gear blank with all dimensions and information necessary for making a new gear. Dimensions not given above may be made to suit as the drawing is developed.

102. Make a drawing for a spur gear. The only information available is as follows: root diameter, 7.3372″; outside diameter, 8.200″; width of face, 1 7/8″; diameter of shaft, 1 3/8″; length of hub, 2″.

103. Fig. 519. Make complete detail drawings of reversing mechanism, with bill of material and title. The purpose of this device is to drive a shaft in either direction from a shaft at right angles to it which always revolves in the same direction. In the design shown, either shaft may be driver, the gear ratios being 3 to 2.

The two bevel pinions, pieces 6, are keyed to clutches, piece 4, which are bushed, piece 5, and run free on the splined shaft. These bevel pinions are always in mesh with the gear, piece 7, and, being on opposite sides of it, revolve on the splined shaft in opposite directions. The clutch, piece 3, is splined to its shaft and is free to shift axially into mesh with either of the two clutches, piece 4. This movement is controlled by the shifter arrangement, pieces 11, 12, 13, 14, 15 and 16. Three reamed tapered holes are provided in the pad on the top of the housing for the locking plunger, piece 15. This insures positive retention of the clutch in either neutral or driving positions.

104. Fig. 519. Make assembly drawing of reversing mechanism, with title and piece numbers.

105. Fig. 519. Redesign reversing mechanism for complete ball bearing installation.

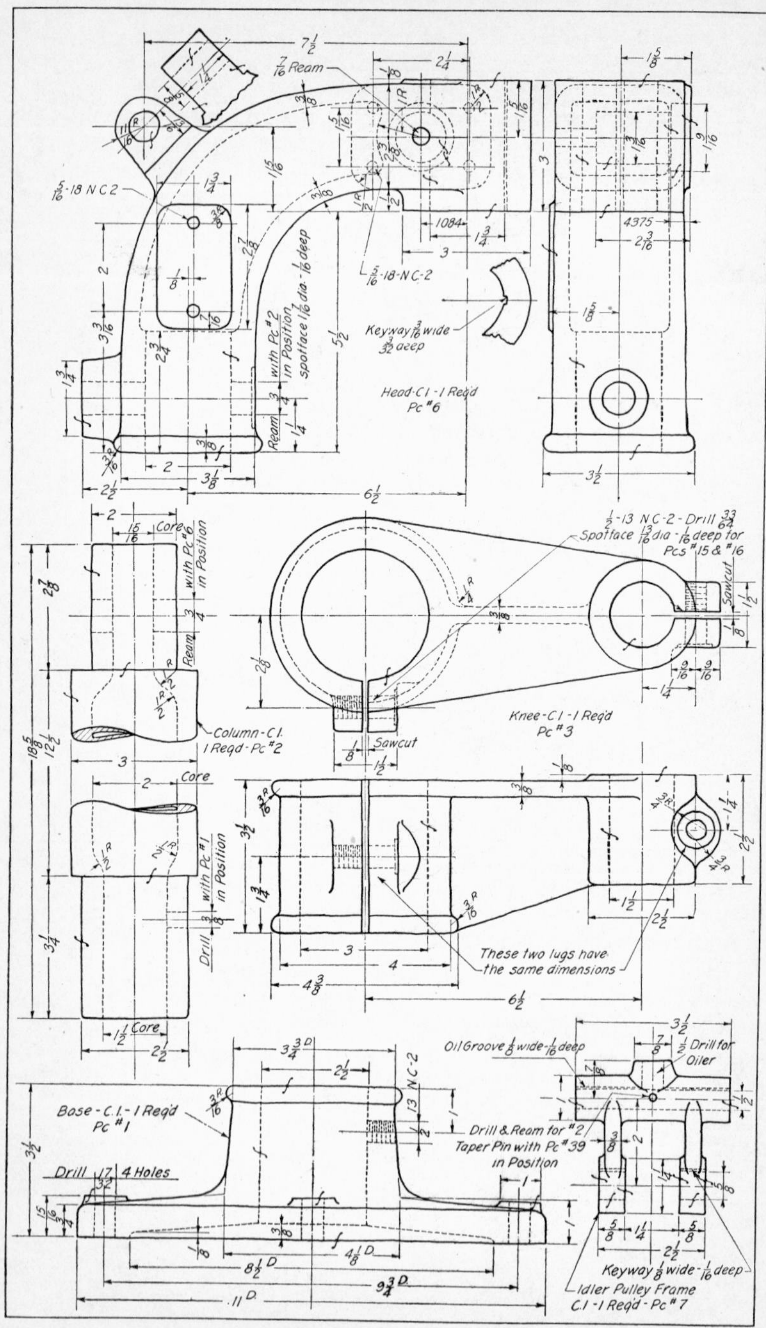

FIG. 516.—Bench drill details.

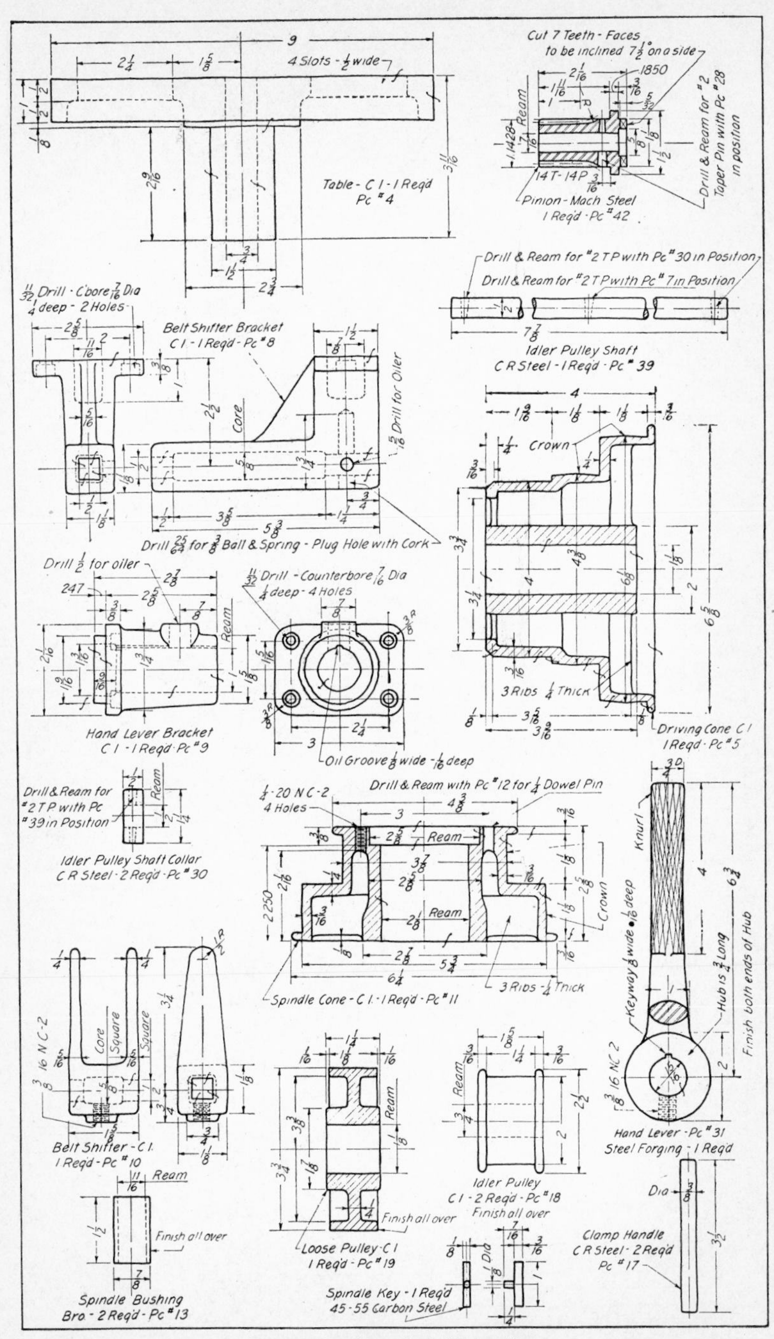

FIG. 517.—Bench drill details.

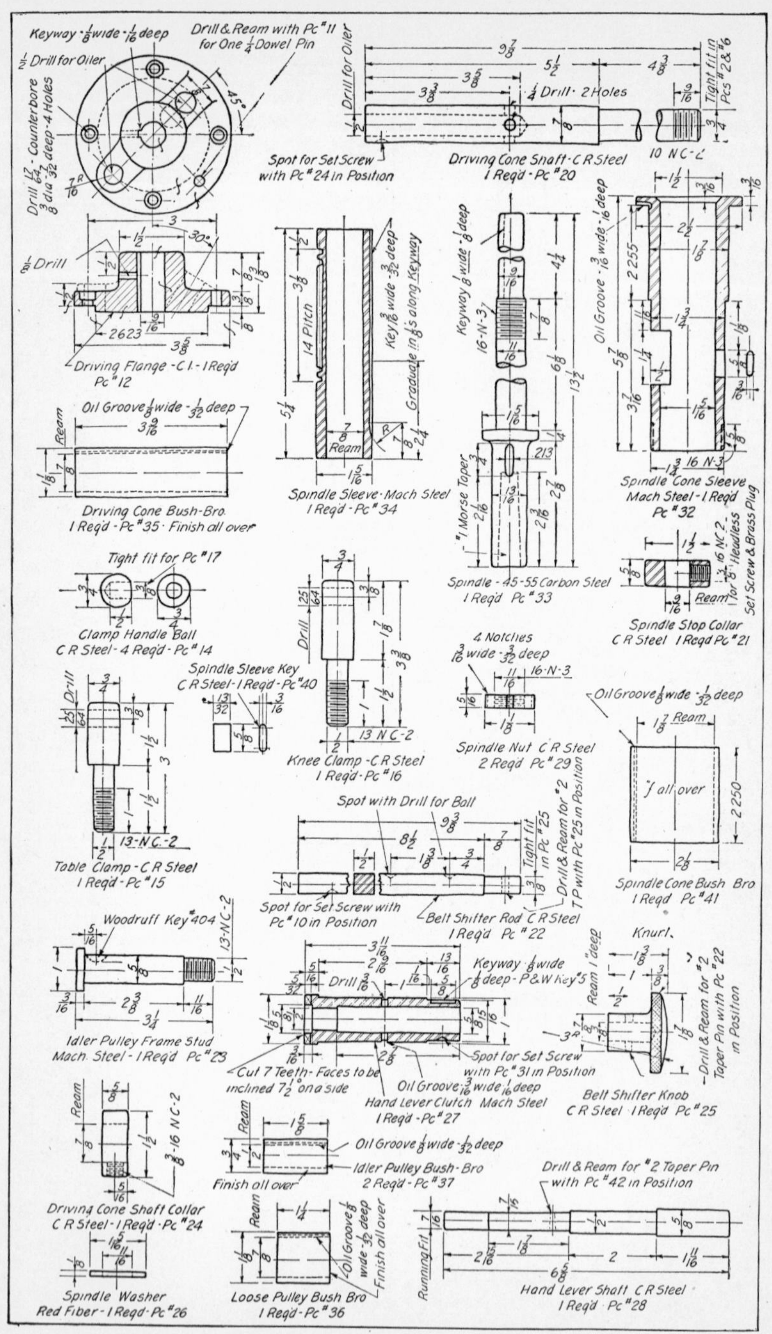

FIG. 518.—Bench drill details.

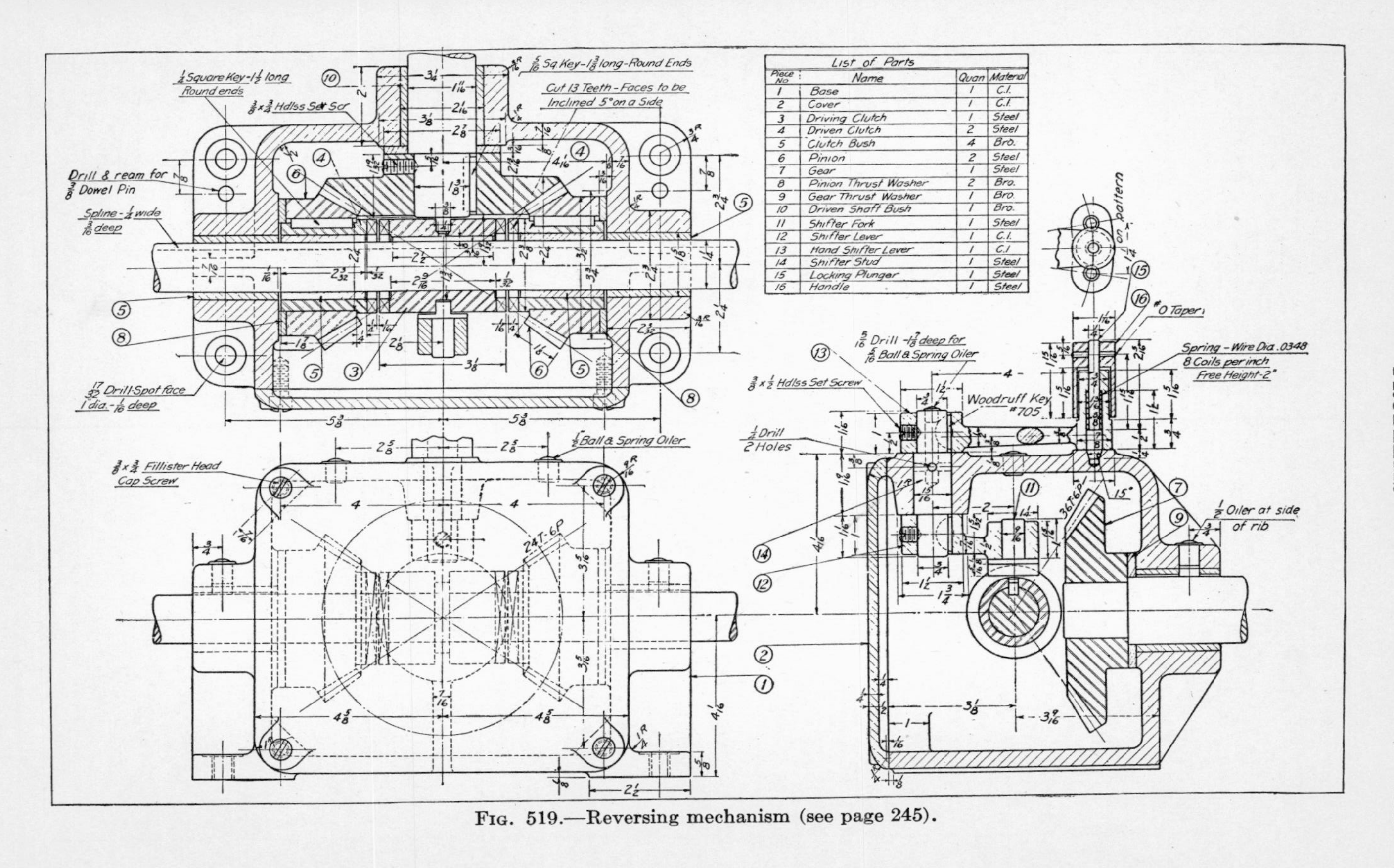

FIG. 519.—Reversing mechanism (see page 245).

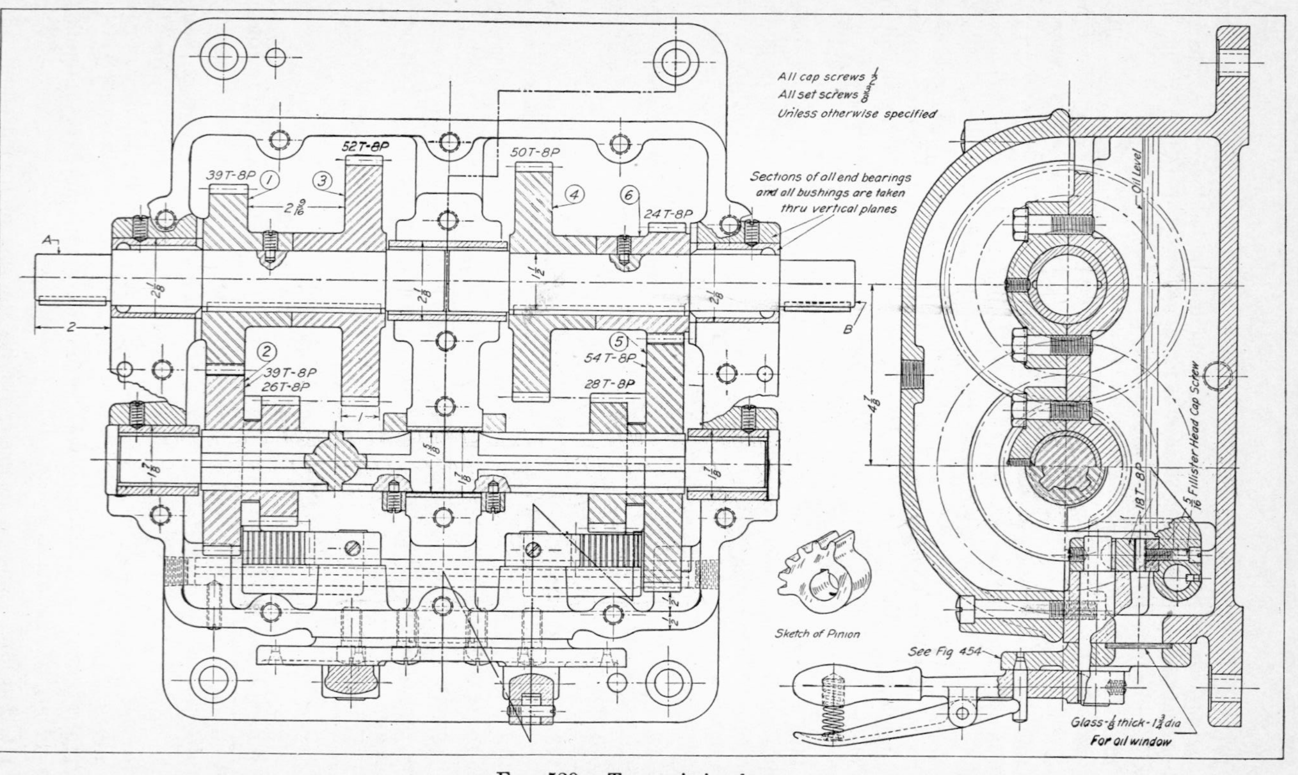

FIG. 520.—Transmission box.

106. Fig. 519. Redesign reversing mechanism, with gear ratio 7 to 4 instead of 3 to 2.

107. Fig. 519. Redesign reversing mechanism as follows: gear ratios 7 to 5 instead of 3 to 2; all thrust requirements to be met by ball bearing installation. Spline shaft diameters to be 1″ instead of 1¼″. Keyed shaft to be 1⅛″ instead of 1⅜″. Use one centralized oiling system for the whole mechanism.

108. Fig. 519. Redesign reversing mechanism for splash lubrication. Provision must be made for retaining the oil at cover joint and where shafts enter the box. Do not neglect to provide filling and draining plugs and an oil level gage.

109. Fig. 519. Redesign reversing mechanism as follows: Make pieces 3, 4 and 6 in one piece, and spline to shaft as in present design. This will dispense with two bushings, piece 5, and also the clutch teeth. This new piece is called a double bevel gear and should be made long enough to be shifted axially in and out of mesh with gear, piece 7. Be sure to provide a neutral position. This design requires the thrust of the bevel gears to be taken by the shifter fork, which should be redesigned to take this load. It is suggested that a double fork of bronze be used with a strengthened locking plunger.

110. Fig. 520. Four-speed machine tool transmission box. The power comes in on shaft A at a constant rate and leaves on shaft B at a rate depending on the positions of the sliding gears. Only the top view and end in section are given. The detail drawing of the gear shifter bracket is shown in Fig. 454. Make a complete assembly drawing showing the front, top and end views.

111. Fig. 520. Make complete working details with bill of material from the design of Prob. 110.

112. Fig. 520. Redesign Prob. 110 for ball bearing installation.

113. Fig. 520. Redesign Prob. 110 for speed ratios of 1 to 1, 1 to 1.228. 1 to 1.437 and 1 to 1.776, making pieces 1 and 6 duplicates. Shaft centers to remain as in Prob. 110. Note that in the required set of speeds the ratio between each successive speed is approximately a constant (1.2).

114. Fig. 520. Redesign Prob. 110 using gears ¾″ wide, shafts A and B to be 1⅜″ in diameter. Omit center bearing for jack shaft but leave its diameter unchanged.

Electrical Problems

The following problems include assembly, detail and diagrammatic drawings, a few of which will require the use of handbooks and catalogues of electrical equipment. A small amount of design work will enter into the solution of a few of the problems. Tables of electrical symbols will be found in the Appendix.

115. Fig. 521. Make a complete working drawing of the four-bolt bar terminal cap. Material, cast brass.

116. Fig. 522. Make a complete working drawing of the cross-arm cable terminal bracket. Material, galvanized malleable iron.

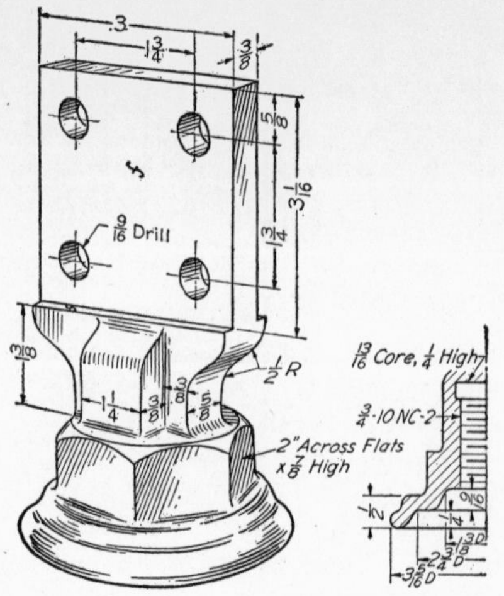

FIG. 521.—Terminal cap.

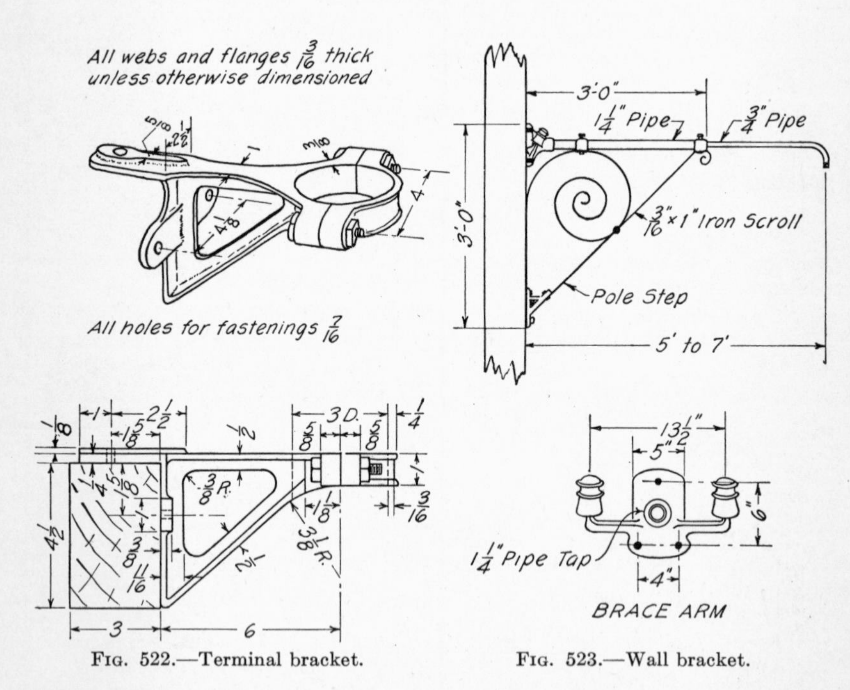

FIG. 522.—Terminal bracket.

FIG. 523.—Wall bracket.

117. Fig. 523. Make detail working drawings of the telescope wall bracket. A fixture for the bracket may be selected from a catalogue and shown with the other details.

118. Fig. 524. Make an assembly drawing of the immersion heater from the details, the drawing to have such dimensions and explanatory notes as would usually occur in a catalogue illustration.

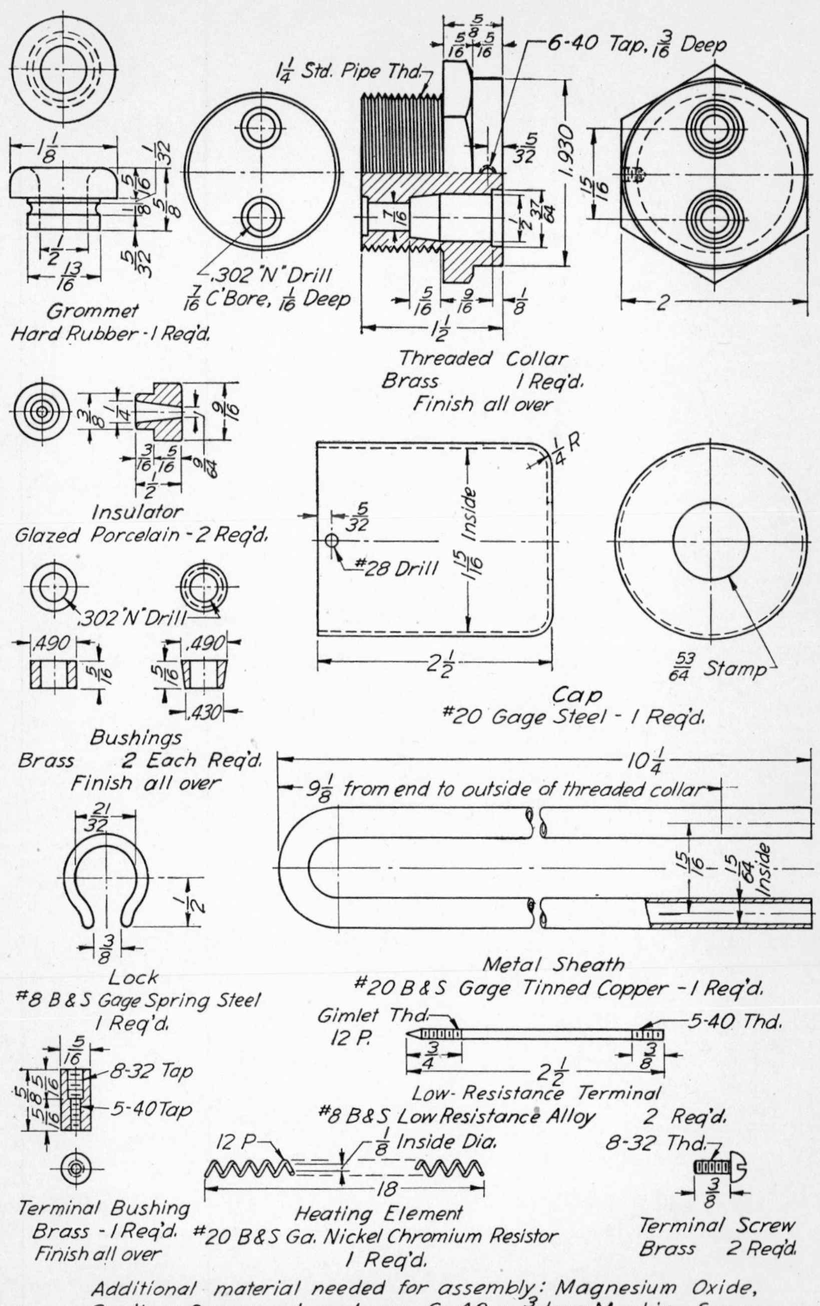

FIG. 524.—Details of immersion heater (see page 251).

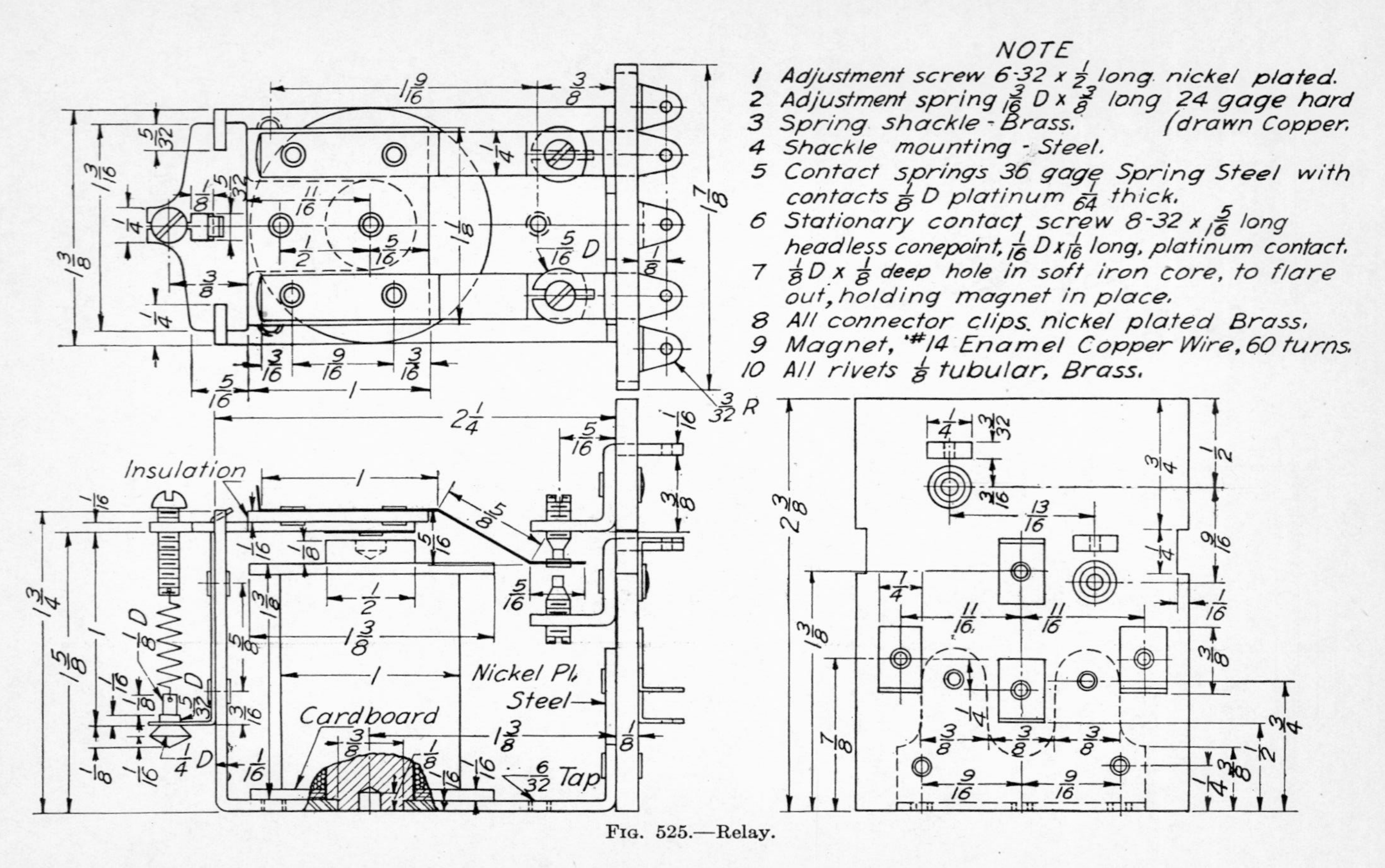

NOTE
1 Adjustment screw 6-32 x 1/2 long nickel plated.
2 Adjustment spring 3/16 D x 3/8 long 24 gage hard drawn Copper.
3 Spring shackle - Brass.
4 Shackle mounting - Steel.
5 Contact springs 36 gage Spring Steel with contacts 1/8 D platinum 1/64 thick.
6 Stationary contact screw 8-32 x 5/16 long headless conepoint, 1/16 D x 1/16 long, platinum contact.
7 1/8 D x 1/8 deep hole in soft iron core, to flare out, holding magnet in place.
8 All connector clips nickel plated Brass.
9 Magnet, #14 Enamel Copper Wire, 60 turns.
10 All rivets 1/8 tubular, Brass.
Insulation
Nickel Pl. Steel
Cardboard
6/32 Tap

Fig. 525.—Relay.

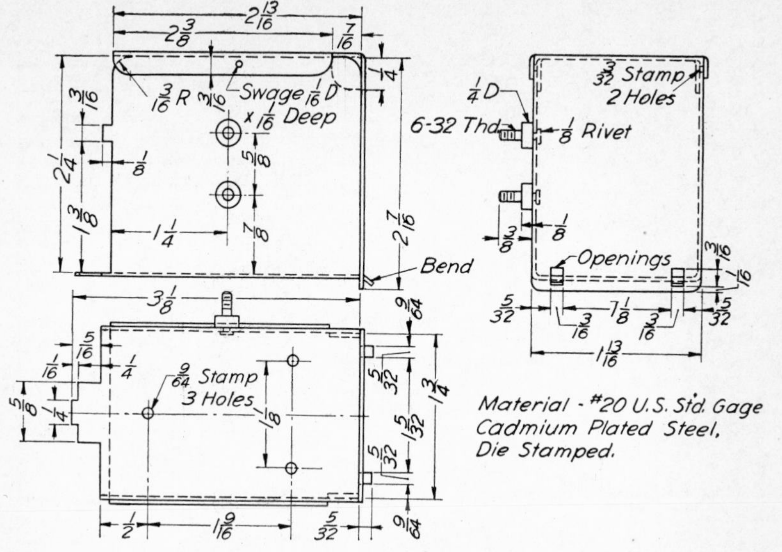

FIG. 526.—Case for relay.

119. Fig. 525. Make detail working drawings of all parts of the relay. All metal parts are die-stamped; hence developed views can be used to advantage in showing these parts.

120. Fig. 526. Make a developed working drawing of the relay case. Add on the sheet a bill of material for the complete relay and case, and a drawing of the panel to show connections needed.

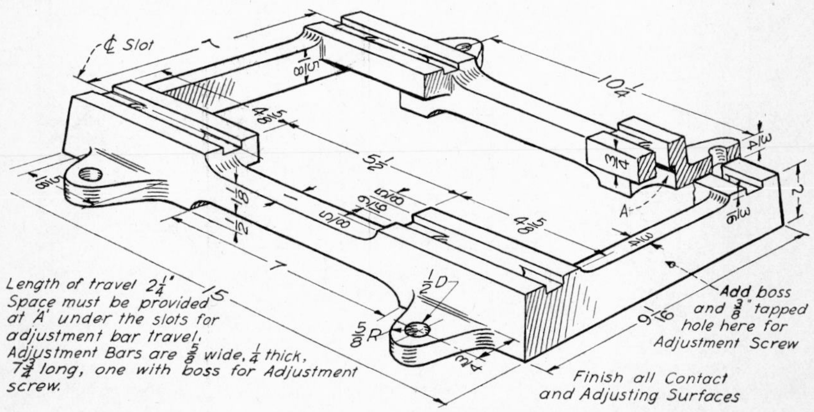

℄ Slot
A
1/2 D
5/8 R
Length of travel 2 1/4"
Space must be provided at 'A' under the slots for adjustment bar travel.
Adjustment Bars are 5/8 wide, 1/4 thick, 7 3/4 long, one with boss for Adjustment screw.
Add boss and 3/8" tapped hole here for Adjustment Screw
Finish all Contact and Adjusting Surfaces

FIG. 527.—Motor base.

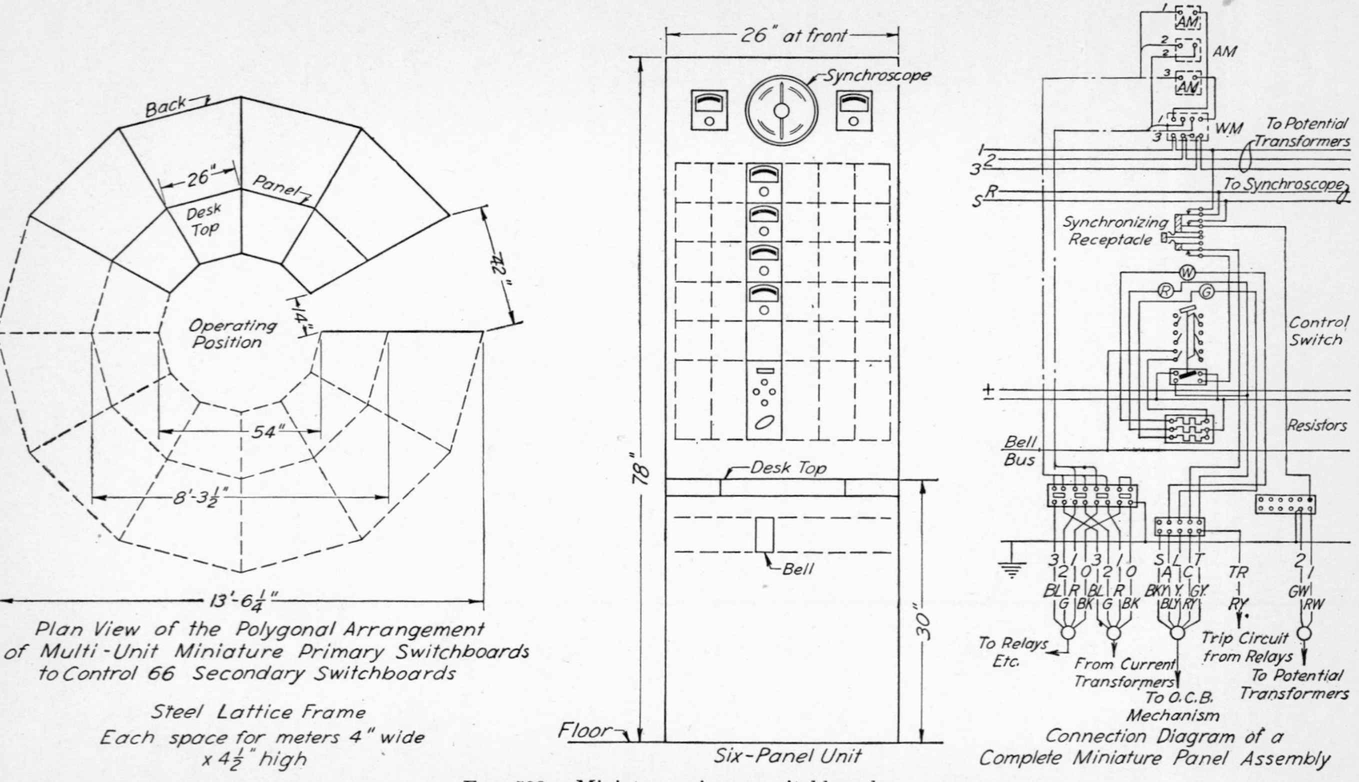

FIG. 528.—Miniature primary switchboard.

121. Fig. 527. Make a complete detail working drawing showing all parts of the motor base for a 3 horsepower motor. Include a $\frac{3}{8}''$ diameter machine screw for sliding adjustment, two adjustment bars (to be designed), hold-down bolts for motor and guide washers (to be designed) to prevent slewing.

122. Fig. 528. Miniature switchboard. A miniature switchboard is used to control the larger main switchboard and equipment in a power station or substation. Draw a floor plan of a substation using three miniature switchboards to control 18 main switchboards, each 24″ wide, 48″ deep, 90″ high, arranged in one unit. Show lighting, windows, doors and any other features necessary on the floor plan, making the floor space adequate for inspection of the rear of the main switchboards. Building to be of reinforced concrete and brick fireproof construction.

123. Figs. 688, 689, 690. Make outline plan drawings of the house, scale $\frac{1}{4}'' = 1\text{-}0''$. Add the wiring plans for each, using the standard wiring symbols. House to be supplied with single phase three wire 110-volt overhead service at rear.

124. Make a wiring diagram showing the proper meter connections for the foregoing problem.

125. Make a material list for roughing-in wiring for the house in the above problem. All wiring to be in BX cable with boxes and appliances which are used with it.

126. Make a material list of the fixtures, switches and receptacles for the foregoing problem.

127. Make a similar wiring diagram for one of the house plans of Figs. 705 to 709.

128. Select a popular radio hookup and make a complete wiring diagram of the circuit, using symbols shown in Fig. 806.

CHAPTER XII

TECHNICAL SKETCHING

217. Facility in making a freehand orthographic drawing is an essential part of the equipment of every engineer. So necessary is the training in freehand sketching it might almost be said that the preceding 11 chapters have all been in preparation for this one. Such routine men as tracers and detailers may get along with skill and speed in mechanical drawing, but the designer must be able to sketch his ideas with a sure hand and clear judgment. In all mechanical thinking in invention, all preliminary designing, all explanation and instructions to draftmen, freehand sketching is the mode of expression. It represents the mastery of the language, gained only after full proficiency in drawing with instruments, and is the mastery which the engineer, inventor, designer, chief draftsman, and contractor, with all of whom time is too valuable to spend in mechanical execution, must have. It is the chief engineer's method of design.

The use and value of sketching are not confined to the engineering staff. A service man, for example, out on a trouble-giving machine may have to make a sketch, or a salesman in his daily report may need to send back sketches, perhaps of a customer's product, or even of some point of advantage in a competitor's machine.

Training in sketching develops accuracy of observation. It may be necessary to go a long distance from the drawing room to get some preliminary information and the record thus obtained would be valueless if any detail were missing or obscure. Mistakes or omissions that would be discovered quickly in making an accurate scale drawing may easily be overlooked in a freehand sketch, and constant care must be observed to prevent their occurrence.

Sometimes, if a piece is to be made but once, a sketch is used as a working drawing and afterward filed.

218. Kinds of Technical Sketches.—Sketches may be divided into two general classes: first, those made before the structure is built, second, those made after the structure is built. In the first class are included the sketches made in connection with the designing of the structure and might be classified as (1) *scheming* or *idea sketches*, used in studying and developing the arrangement and proportion of parts. These are followed by (2) *computation sketches,* made in connection with the figured calculations for motion and strength; (3) *executive sketches,* made by the chief engineer, inventor, or consulting engineer, to give instructions for special arrangements or ideas which must be embodied in the design; (4) *design sketches,* used in working up the schemes and ideas into such form that the design drawing can be started; (5) *working sketches,* made as substitutes for working drawings.

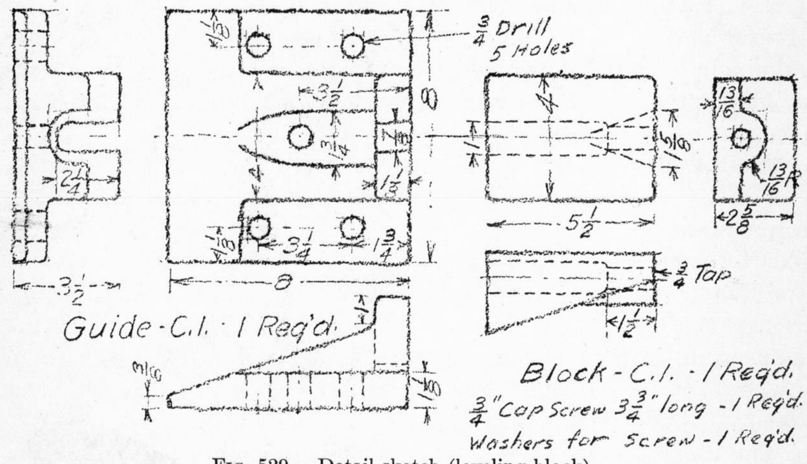

Fig. 529.—Detail sketch (leveling block).

The second class includes (1) *detail sketches,* made from existing parts, with complete notes and dimensions, from which duplicate parts may be made directly, or from which mechanical drawings may be made, Fig. 529; (2) *assembly sketches,* made from an assembled machine to show the relative positions of the various parts, with center and location dimensions, or sometimes for a simple machine, with complete dimensions and specifications; (3) *outline* or *diagrammatic sketches,* generally made for the purpose of location, sometimes to give the size and location of pulleys and shafting, piping or wiring for use in connection with setting up of machinery, sometimes to locate a single machine, giving the over-all dimensions, sizes and center distances for foundation bolts, and other necessary information.

219. Materials.—The only necessary materials for sketching are a pencil (F or H) sharpened to a long conical point, not too sharp, a pencil eraser, to be used sparingly, and paper, in notebook, pad or single sheet clipped on a board.

In making working sketches from objects a two-foot rule and calipers will be needed to obtain dimensions. Other machinists' tools may be required, such as a try square, surface gage, depth gage, thread gage and for accurate measurements a micrometer caliper. Sometimes a plumb line is of service. Much ingenuity is often required to get dimensions from an existing machine.

220. Technique.—The pencil should be held with freedom, not close to the point. Vertical lines are drawn downward with a finger movement in a series of overlapping strokes, with the hand somewhat

Fig. 530.—Sketching a vertical line.   Fig. 531.—Sketching a horizontal line.

in the position of Fig. 530. Horizontal lines are drawn with either a wrist or a forearm motion, shifting the hand to the position of Fig. 531. In drawing any straight line between two points keep the eyes on the point to which the line is to go rather than on the point of the pencil. Do not try to draw the whole length of a line in a single stroke. It may be an aid to draw a *very* light line first, then to sketch the finished line, correcting the direction of the light line without rubbing it out. Do not be disturbed by any nervous waviness. Accuracy of direction is more important than smoothness of line.

It is legitimate in technical sketching to draw long vertical or horizontal lines by using the little finger as a guide along the edge of pad or clip board.

Inclined lines running downward from right to left are drawn easily with the same movement as vertical lines, but those running downward from left to right are much harder (except for left-handed persons). They may be drawn by turning the paper and drawing as horizontal lines.

Circles may be drawn by marking the radius on each side of the center lines or, more accurately, by drawing two diagonals in addition to the center lines and marking points equidistant from the center on the eight radii. At these points draw short arcs perpendicular to the radii, then complete the circle, as shown in Fig. 532. Large circles can be done very smoothly after a little practice by using the finger as a pivot, holding the pencil stationary and rotating the paper. Another way of drawing a circle is to sketch it in its circumscribing square.

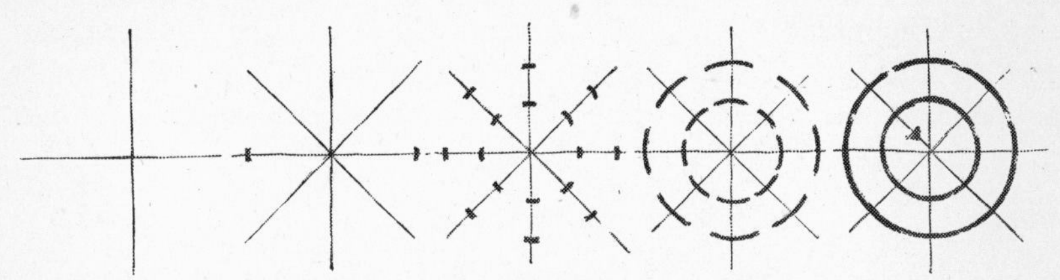

Fig. 532.—Method of sketching circles.

221. Practice.—The best preliminary training for this work is the drawing in the public schools, training the hand and eye to see and represent form and proportion. Those who have not had this preparation should practice drawing lines with the pencil, until the hand obeys the eye to a reasonable extent.

The best practice is obtained by sketching from castings, machine parts, or simple machines, and making working drawings from the sketches without further reference to the object. In class work a variation may be introduced by exchanging the sketches so that the working drawing is made by another student. This emphasizes the necessity of putting down all the information and not relying on memory to supply that missing; and working with the idea that the object is not to be seen after the sketch is made. A most valuable training in the observation of details is the sketching from memory of a piece previously studied. It is an excellent training in sureness of touch to make sketches directly in ink, perhaps with a fountain pen.

222. Making a Sketch.—In making an orthographic sketch the principles of projection and rules of practice for working drawings are to be remembered and applied. A systematic order should be followed for both idea sketches and sketches from objects, as follows:

1. Visualize the object.
2. Determine the views.
3. Determine the size.
4. Locate the center lines.
5. Block in the main outlines.
6. Complete the detail.
7. Add dimension lines and arrow heads.
8. Put on the dimensions.
9. Check the drawing.

Before a good graphical description of an object or idea can be developed it is essential that the mental image of it be definite and clear. The clearness of the sketch is a direct function of this mental picture. Hence the first step is to concentrate on visualization. This leads directly to the second step, determination of the necessary views and part views. These will probably not be just the same as would be made in a scale drawing. For example, a note in regard to thickness or shape of section will often be used to save a view, Fig. 533. More than one view of a piece circular in cross-section would thus not be necessary. In other cases additional part views and extra sections may be sketched rather than complicating the regular views with added lines which would confuse a sketch, although the same lines might be perfectly clear in a measured drawing. The third step is to proportion the sketch to the sheet. Have it large enough to show all detail clearly but allow plenty of room for dimensions, notes and memoranda. Small parts may be sketched larger than full size. Do not attempt to crowd all the views on a single sheet of paper. Use as many as may be required, but name each view and indicate the direction in which it is taken in reference to the other views.

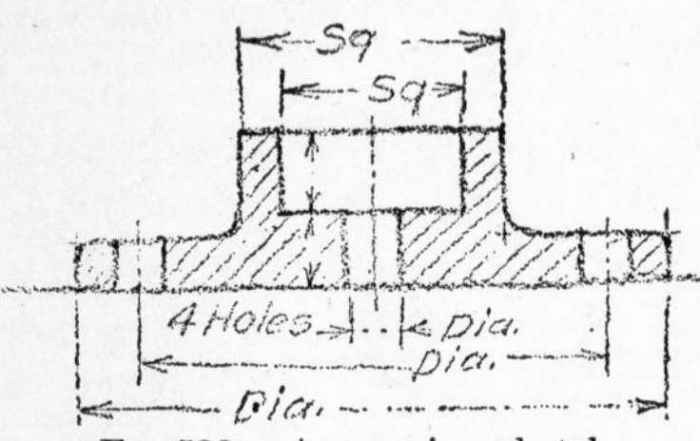

Fig 533.—A one-view sketch.

In beginning a sketch always start by locating the center lines or datum lines, and remember that the view showing the contour or characteristic shape should be drawn first. This is generally the view showing circles if there are any. Block in the main outlines, watching carefully the proportions of width to height, selecting one edge as a unit from which to estimate the proportionate lengths of the other edges. When the main outlines are satisfactory, add the details in correct proportion.

In drawing on plain paper, the location of the principal points, centers, etc., should be marked so the sketches will fit the sheet, and the whole sketch, with as many views, sections and auxiliary views as are necessary to describe the piece, drawn *without taking any measurements* but in as nearly correct proportion as the eye can determine.

A machine should, of course, be represented right side up, in its natural working position. If symmetrical about an axis, often one-half only need be sketched. If a whole view cannot be made on one page it may be put on two, each part being drawn up to a break line used as a datum line.

223. Dimension Lines.—After the sketching of a piece is entirely finished it should be gone over and dimension lines for all the dimensions needed for the construction added, drawing extension lines and arrow heads carefully and checking to see that none is omitted, but still *making no measurements.*

224. Measuring and Dimensioning.—Up to this stage the object has not been handled and the drawing has been kept clean. The measurements for the dimensions indicated on the drawing may now be added. The 2-foot rule or steel scale will serve for getting most of the dimensions. Never use the draftsman's scale for measuring castings; its edges will be marred and it will be soiled. The diameters of holes may be measured with inside calipers. It is often necessary to lay a straight-edge across the surface as in Fig. 534. In measuring

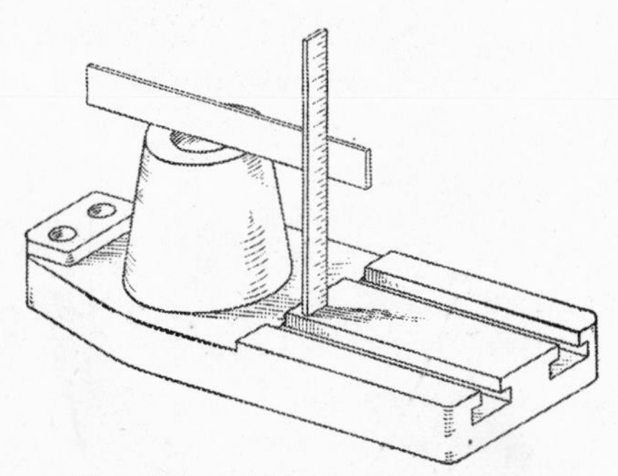

Fig. 534.—Taking a measurement.

the distance between centers of two holes of the same size, measure from edge to corresponding edge. Always measure from finished surfaces if possible. Judgment must be exercised in measuring rough castings so as not to record inequalities. Curves are measured by coordinates or offsets, as shown in Figs. 333 and 334. A curved outline may be recorded by laying a sheet of paper on it and making a "rubbing."

Add all remarks and notes that may seem to be of any value.

The title should be written or lettered on the sketch, and for class sketches the amount of time spent.

Always *date* every sketch. Valuable inventions have been lost through inability to prove priority, because the first sketches had not been dated. In commercial work the draftsman's notebook with sketches and calculations is preserved as a permanent record, and sketches should be made so as to stand the test of time and be legible after the details of their making have been forgotten.

The final step is to check the sketch. It is a curious fact that when a beginner omits a dimension it is usually a basic, vital one, as of the center height of the machine or the rise of the arch.

For gaining skill through practice, sketches should be made entirely freehand, although in commercial work an engineer often saves time by making large circles with the compasses, without measuring.

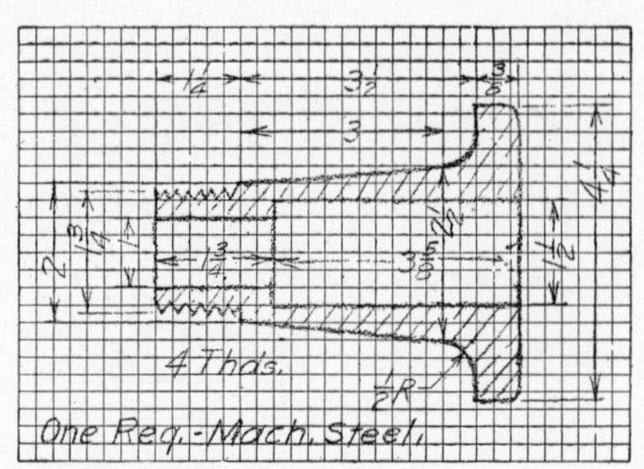

Fig. 535.—Sketch on coordinate paper.

225. Cross-section Paper.—Sketches are often made on coordinate paper ruled faintly in sixteenths, eighths or quarters of an inch, using it either simply as an aid in drawing straight lines and judging proportions, or by assigning suitable values to the unit spaces and drawing to approximate scale, Fig. 535. The latter use is more applicable to design sketches than to sketches from the object.

PROBLEMS

226. Sketching problems may be made in great variety from pictorial views and from castings or models. The following are suggested:

Group I. Preliminary Line Practice.

1. Draw Figs. 46 to 49 without measurement in squares of about six-inch sides.

Group II. Orthographic Sketches of Details.

2. Sketch the necessary orthographic views, without dimensions, of the pieces shown in Fig. 536.

3. Make orthographic sketches of selections from Figs. 204 to 233, adding the necessary dimensions according to the rules for dimensioning, paragraph 134.

4. From the assembly drawings, Figs. 476 to 493, select a single piece and make a detail sketch of it.

Group III. Memory Sketching.

5. Look at one of the pieces of Fig. 536 with concentration for 15 seconds. Close the book and make its three views.

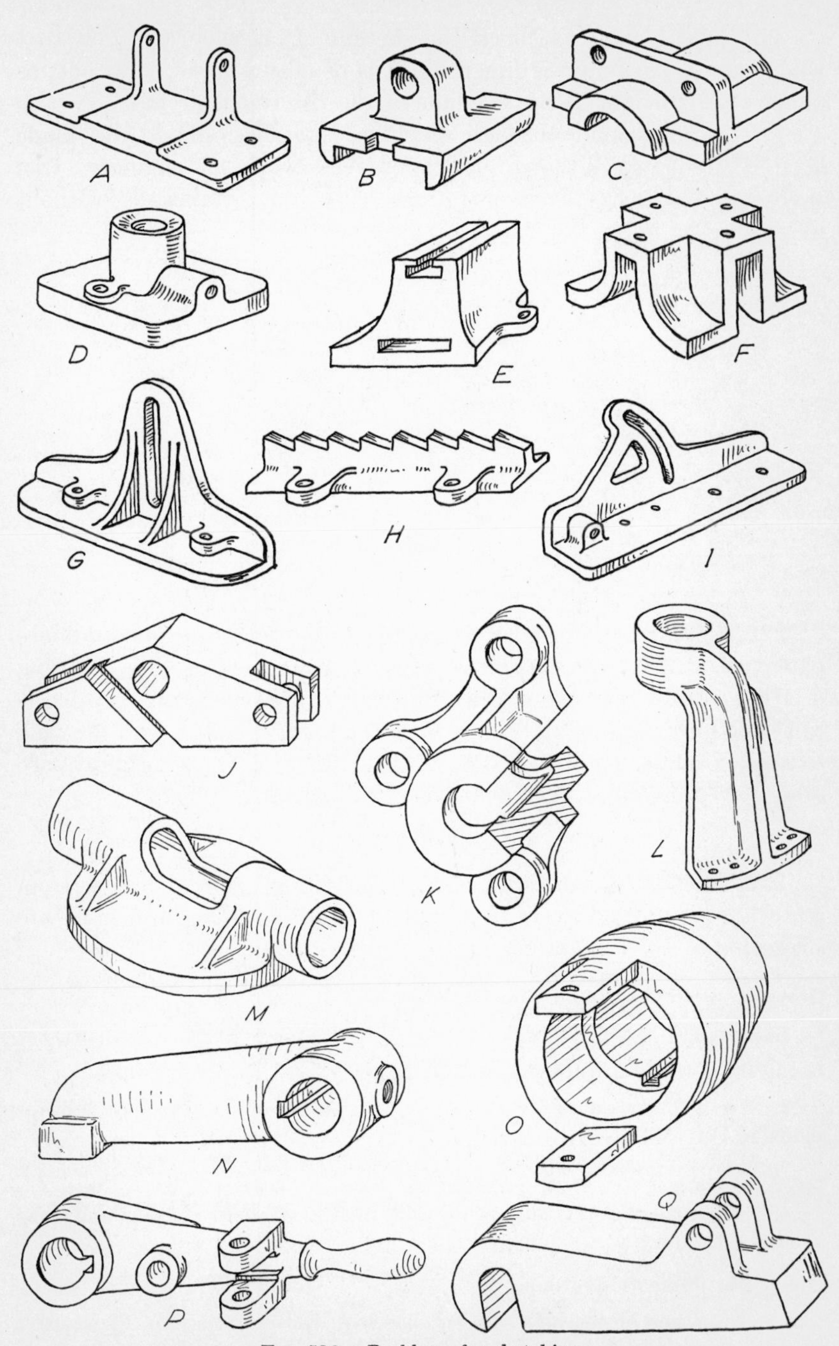

Fig. 536.—Problems for sketching.

CHAPTER XIII

DEVELOPED SURFACES AND INTERSECTIONS[1]

227. Surfaces.—A surface may be considered as generated by the motion of a line. Surfaces may thus be divided into two general classes: (1) those which can be generated by a moving straight line, (2) those which can be generated only by a moving curved line. The first are called *ruled surfaces;* the second, *double curved surfaces.* Any position of the moving line is called an *element.*

Ruled surfaces may be divided into (*a*) *planes,* (*b*) *single curved surfaces,* (*c*) *warped surfaces.*

A *plane* may be generated by a straight line moving so as to touch two other intersecting or parallel straight lines.

Single curved surfaces have their elements either parallel or intersecting. These are the cylinder and the cone; and a third surface, which we shall not consider, known as the convolute, in which the consecutive elements intersect two and two.

Warped surfaces have no two consecutive elements either parallel or intersecting. There is a great variety of warped surfaces. The surface of a screw thread and that of the pilot of a locomotive are two examples.

Double curved surfaces are generated by a curved line moving according to some law. The commonest forms are *surfaces of revolution* made by the revolution of a curve about an axis in the same plane, as the sphere, torus or ring, ellipsoid, paraboloid, hyperboloid, etc. Illustrations of various surfaces may be found in Fig. 163.

228. Development.—In some kinds of construction full-sized patterns of different faces or of the entire surface of an object are required; as, for example, in stone cutting, a templet or pattern giving the shape of an irregular face, or in sheet-metal work, a pattern to which a sheet may be cut that when rolled, folded or formed will make the object.

The operation of laying out the complete surface on one plane is called the *development* of the surface.

[1] The full theoretical discussion of surfaces, their classification, properties, intersections and development may be found in any good descriptive geometry.

Surfaces about which a thin sheet of flexible material (as paper or tin) could be wrapped smoothly are said to be developable; these would include figures made up of planes and single curved surfaces only. Warped and double curved surfaces are non-developable, and when patterns are required for their construction they can be made only by some method of approximation, which assisted by the ductility or pliability of the material will give the required form. Thus, while a ball cannot be wrapped smoothly, a two-piece pattern developed approximately and cut from leather may be stretched and sewed on in a smooth cover, or a flat disc of metal may be die-stamped, formed or spun to a hemispherical or other required shape.

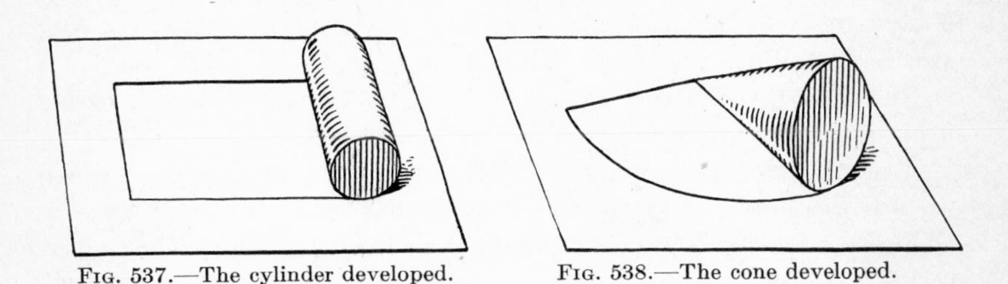

FIG. 537.—The cylinder developed. FIG. 538.—The cone developed.

We have learned the method of finding the true size of a plane surface by projecting it on an auxiliary plane. If the true size of all the faces of an object made of planes be found and joined in order, at their common edges, the result will be the developed surface. This may be done usually to the best advantage by finding the true lengths of the edges.

The development of a right cylinder would evidently be a rectangle whose width would be the altitude, and length the rectified circumference, Fig. 537; and the development of a right cone with circular base would be a sector with a radius equal to the slant height, and arc equal in length to the circumference of the base, Fig. 538.

As illustrated in Figs. 537 and 538, developments are drawn with the inside face up. Sheet-metal workers make their punch marks for folding on the inside surface.

In the laying out of real sheet-metal problems an allowance must be made for seams and lap, and in heavy sheets for the thickness and for the crowding of the metal; there is also the consideration of the commercial sizes of material, and of economy in cutting, in all of which some practical shop knowledge is necessary. This chapter will be confined to the principles alone.

In the development of any object its projections must first be made, drawing only such views or parts of views as are necessary to give the lengths of elements and true size of cut surfaces.

229. To Develop a Hexagonal Prism.—Fig. 539. Since the base is perpendicular to the axis it will roll out into the straight line *AB*. This line is called by sheet-metal workers the "stretchout." Lay off on *AB* the length of the perimeter of the base, and at points 1, 2, 3, etc., erect perpendiculars, called "measuring lines," representing the edges. Measure on each of these its length as given on the front view, and connect the points. For the development of the entire surface

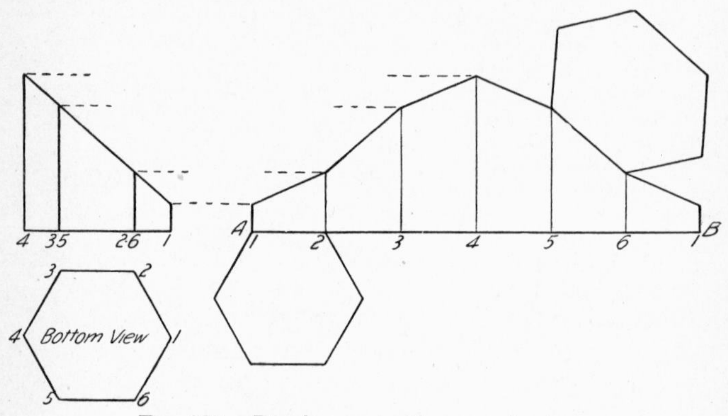

FIG. 539.—Development of hexagonal prism.

in one piece attach the true size of the upper face and the bottom in their proper relation on common lines, finding the true size of the upper face by an auxiliary view as described in paragraph 99. For economy of solder or rivets and time it is customary to make the seam on the shortest edge.

230. To Develop a Right Cylinder.—Fig. 540. In rolling the cylinder out on a tangent plane, the base, being perpendicular to the axis, will develop into a straight line. For convenience in drawing divide the base, here shown as a bottom view, into a number of equal parts, representing elements. Project these elements up to the front view. Draw the stretchout and measuring lines as before. Transfer the lengths of the elements in order, either by projection or with dividers, and join the points by a smooth curve, sketching it in very lightly freehand before fitting the French curve to it. This might be one-half of a two-piece elbow. Three-piece, four-piece, or five-piece elbows may be drawn similarly, as illustrated in Fig. 541. As the base is symmetrical, one-half only need be drawn. In these cases the intermediate pieces as B, C and D are developed on a stretchout line formed by laying off the perimeter of a section, called a "right section," obtained by a plane perpendicular to the elements. Taking

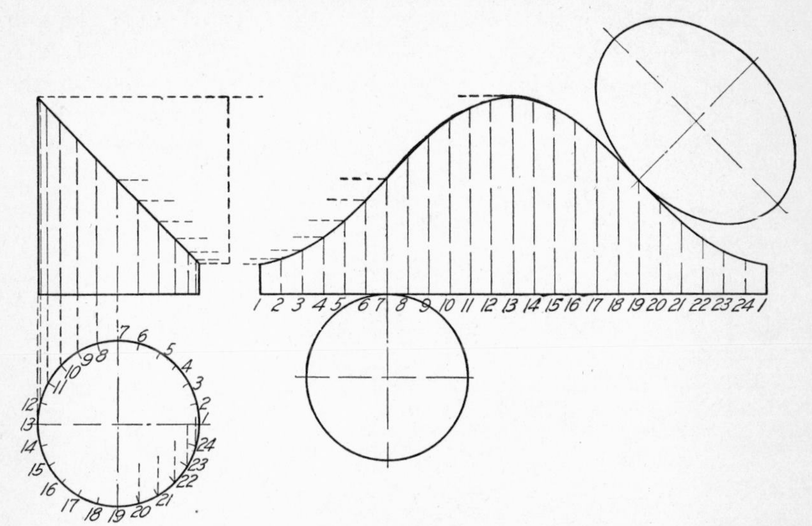

Fig. 540.—Development of right cylinder.

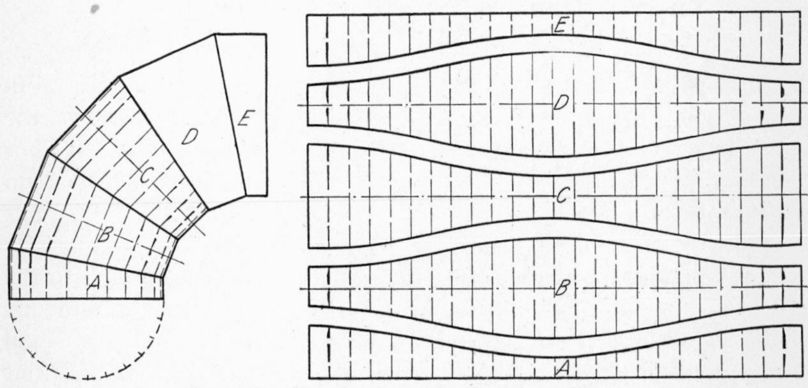

Fig. 541.—Development of a five-piece elbow.

this plane through the middle of the piece the stretchout line becomes the center line of the development.

Evidently any elbow could be cut from a single sheet without waste if the seams were made alternately on the long and short sides.

The octagonal dome, Fig. 542, illustrates an application of the development of cylinders. Each piece is a portion of a cylinder. The elements are parallel to the base of the dome and show in their true lengths in the top view. The true length of the stretchout line shows in the front view at O^vA^v. By considering O^hA^h as the edge of a right section the problem is identical with the preceding problem.

The true shape of a hip rafter is found by revolving it until it is parallel to the vertical plane, in the same manner as finding the true length of any line, taking a sufficient number of points on it to get a smooth curve.

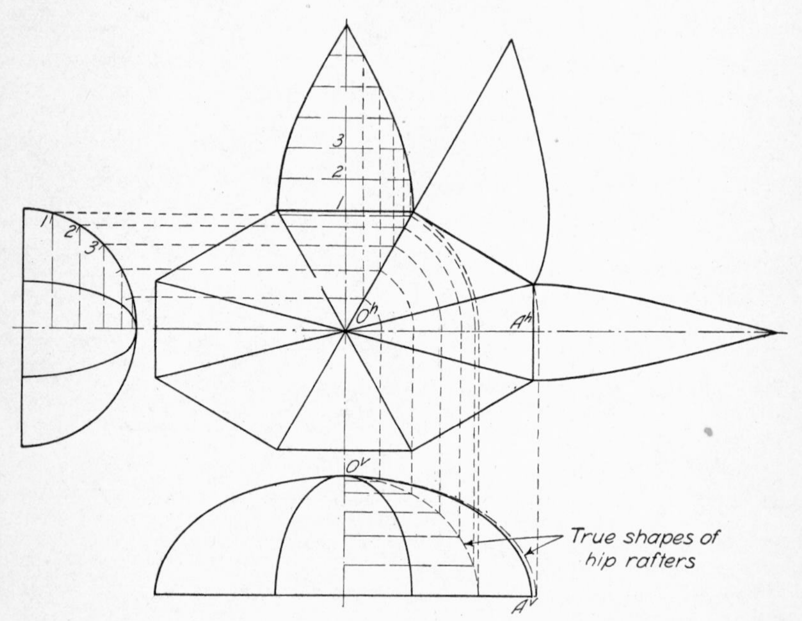

Fig. 542.—Development of octagonal dome.

231. To Develop a Hexagonal Pyramid.—Fig. 543. Since this is a right pyramid the edges are all of equal length. The edges OA and OD are parallel to the vertical plane and consequently show in their true length on the front view. With a center O_1 taken at any convenient place, and a radius O^vA^v, draw an arc. On it step off the perimeter of the base and connect these points successively with each other and with the vertex O_1.

The line of intersection of the cutting plane is developed by laying off the true length of the intercept of each edge on the corresponding line of development. The true length of these intercepts is found by revolving them about the axis of the pyramid until they coincide with O^vA^v as explained on page 93. The path of any point, as K^v, will be projected on the front view as a horizontal line. For the development of the entire surface of the truncated pyramid attach the base; also find the true size of the cut face and attach it on a common line.

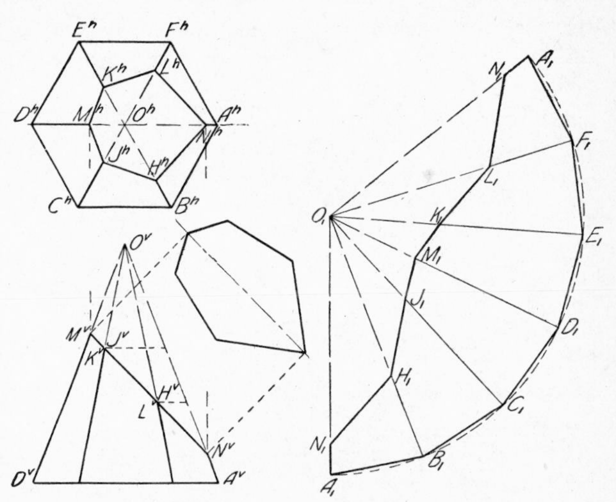

Fig. 543.—Development of hexagonal pyramid.

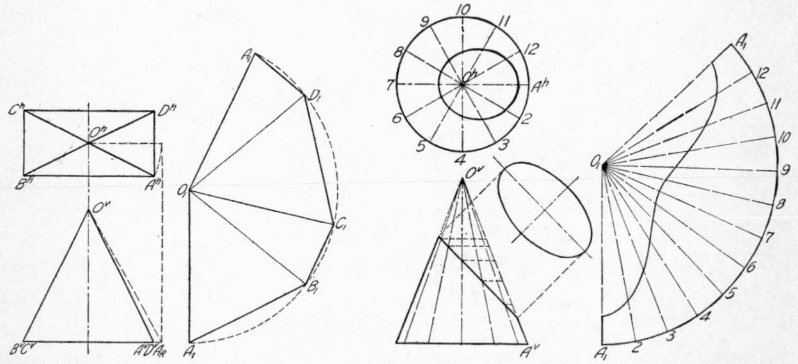

Fig. 544.—Development of rectangular pyramid.

Fig. 545.—Development of right cone.

The rectangular pyramid, Fig. 544, is developed in a similar way, but as the edge OA is not parallel to the plane of projection it must be revolved to O^vA_R to obtain its true length. See paragraph 102.

232. To Develop a Truncated Right Cone.—Fig. 545. Divide the top view of the base into a convenient number of equal parts, project these points on the front view and draw the elements through them. With a radius equal to the slant height of the cone, found from the contour element O^vA^v, which shows the true length of all the elements, draw an arc, and lay off on it the divisions of the base, obtained from the top view. Connect these points with O_1 giving the developed positions of the elements. Find the true length of each element from vertex to cutting plane by revolving it to coincide with the contour element O^vA^v, and mark the distance on the developed position. Draw a smooth curve through these points.

233. Triangulation.—Non-developable surfaces are developed approximately by assuming them to be made up of narrow sections of developable surfaces. The commonest and best method for approximate development is by triangulation, that is, assuming the surface to be made up of a large number of triangular strips, or plane triangles with very short bases. This is used for all warped surfaces and also for oblique cones, which, although single-curved surfaces and capable of true theoretical development, can be done much more easily and accurately by triangulation.

The principle is extremely simple. It consists merely in dividing the surface into triangles, finding the true lengths of the sides of each and, constructing them one at a time, joining these triangles on their common sides.

234. To Develop an Oblique Cone.—Fig. 546. An oblique cone differs from a right cone in that the elements are all of different lengths. The development of the right cone was practically made up of a number of equal triangles meeting at the vertex, whose sides were elements and bases the chords of short arcs of the base of the cone. In the oblique cone each triangle must be found separately.

Divide the base into a number of equal parts 1, 2, 3, etc., and through these points draw elements of the cone (as the plan is symmetrical about the axis O^hC^h one-half only need be constructed). If the seam is to be on the short side the line OC will be the center line of the development and may be drawn directly at O_1C_1 as its true length is given at O^vC^v. Find the true lengths of the elements O_1O_2, etc., by revolving them until parallel to V. This can be done by the usual method but may be done without confusing the drawing by constructing a "true length diagram," as shown. The true length of any element would be the hypotenuse of a right triangle whose altitude is the altitude of the cone and whose base is the length of the top view of the element. Thus, to make the diagram, draw the altitude

O_RD_R coinciding with or parallel to O^vD and on the base lay off the length of the top view of each element. O_R1_R will be the true length of the element $O1$.

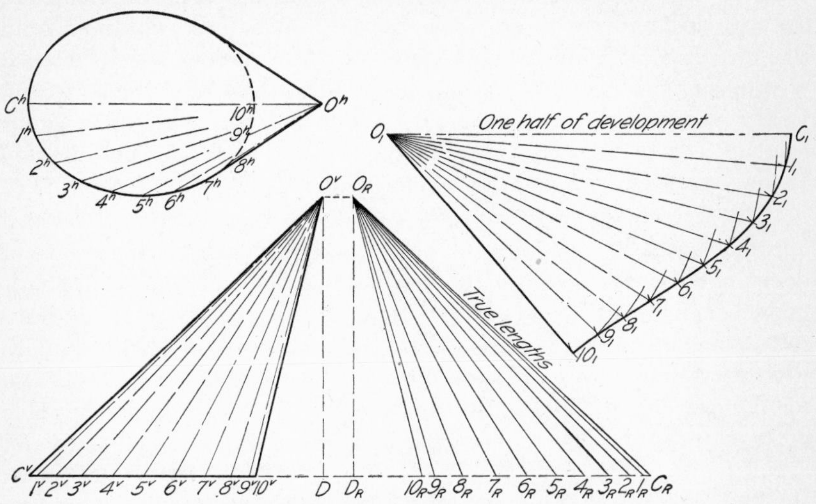

FIG. 546.—Development of oblique cone by triangulation.

With O_1 as center and radius O_R1_R draw an arc on each side of O_1C_1. With C_1 as center and radius C^h1^h intersect these arcs at 1_1; then O_11_1 will be the developed position of the element $O1$. With 1_1 as center and arc 1^h2^h intersect O_12_1 and continue the operation.

235. A conical connection between two parallel cylindrical pipes of different diameters is shown in Fig. 547 as an application of the development of an oblique cone. The contour elements are extended to find the apex of the cone and the true length of the elements found on a true length diagram. Notice that since the base is cut on a slant instead of being horizontal, as in Fig. 546, each element will have a different base line, projected across from the front view, on which to lay off the length of the top view. As each true length is found, project the upper end across from the front view. The base of the cone is foreshortened in the top view; hence its true size must be found, either by an auxiliary view or by revolution, in order to get the different lengths of the short sides of the triangles into which the surface was divided. In Fig. 547 this was done by revolving the base until horizontal, about an axis through A, when its true shape would be seen on the top view. With A_v as a center revolve each point on the front view of the base down to a horizontal line, C_v falling at C_R^v. Project these points up to meet horizontal lines drawn through corresponding points on the top view, thus obtaining points on the ellipse forming the true size of the base. The development is drawn by

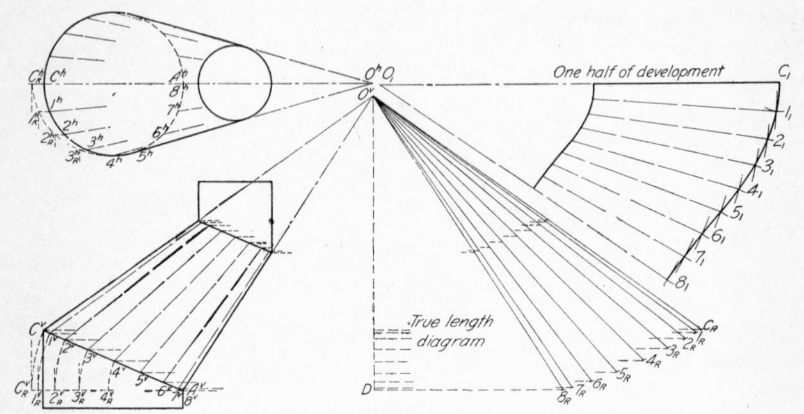

FIG. 547.—Development of a conical connection.

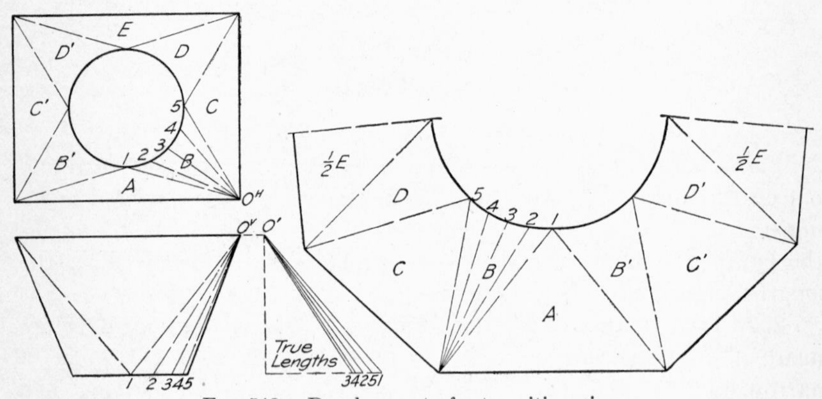

FIG. 548.—Development of a transition piece.

laying out each triangle in turn, from apex to base, starting on the center line O_1C_1, then measuring on each element the true length from base to upper end and drawing a smooth curve through the points.

236. Transition pieces are used to connect pipes or openings of different shapes of cross-section. Figure 548, for connecting a round pipe and a rectangular pipe on the same axis, is typical. These are always developed by triangulation. The piece shown in Fig. 548 is, evidently, made up of four isosceles triangles whose bases are the sides of the rectangle, and four parts of oblique cones. To develop it, make a true length diagram as in Fig. 546. The true length of $O1$ will give the sides of the triangle A. Attach cones B and B', then triangles C and C', and so on.

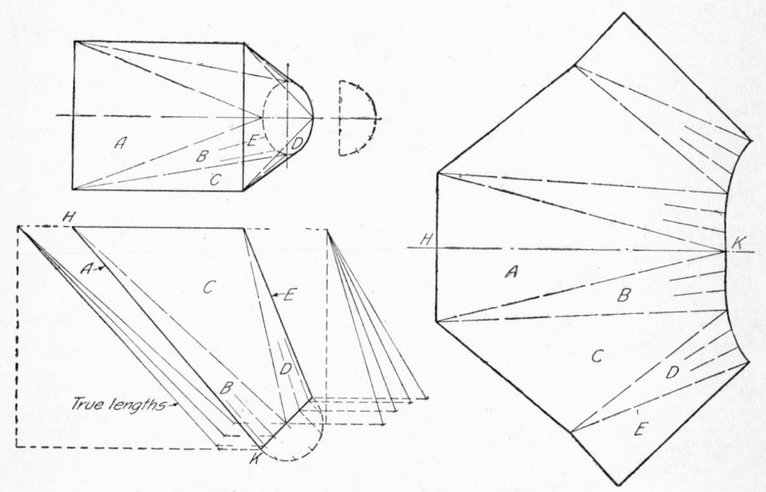

FIG. 549.—Development of a transition piece.

Figure 549 is another transition piece from rectangular to round not on the same axis. By using an auxiliary view of the round opening, the divisions for the bases of the oblique cones can be found (as the figure is symmetrical, one-half only need be divided). The true lengths of the elements are obtained as in Fig. 547.

237. Triangulation of Warped Surfaces.—The approximate development of a warped surface is made by dividing it into a number of narrow quadrilaterals between successive elements, then splitting each of these quadrilaterals into two triangles by a diagonal, which is assumed as a straight line, although theoretically it is a curve. Figure 550 shows a warped transition piece generated by a straight line moving from 1-1′ to 7-7′. Find the true size of one-half the elliptical base from its major and minor axes, divide it into a number of equal parts (say six) and project these to the top and front views. (Notice the variation from the method of paragraph 235.) Divide the top semicircle into the same number and connect the points, thus dividing the surface into six approximate quadrilaterals. Cut each into two triangles by a diagonal. On true length diagrams find the lengths of the elements and the diagonals, and draw the development by constructing the true sizes of the triangles in regular order.

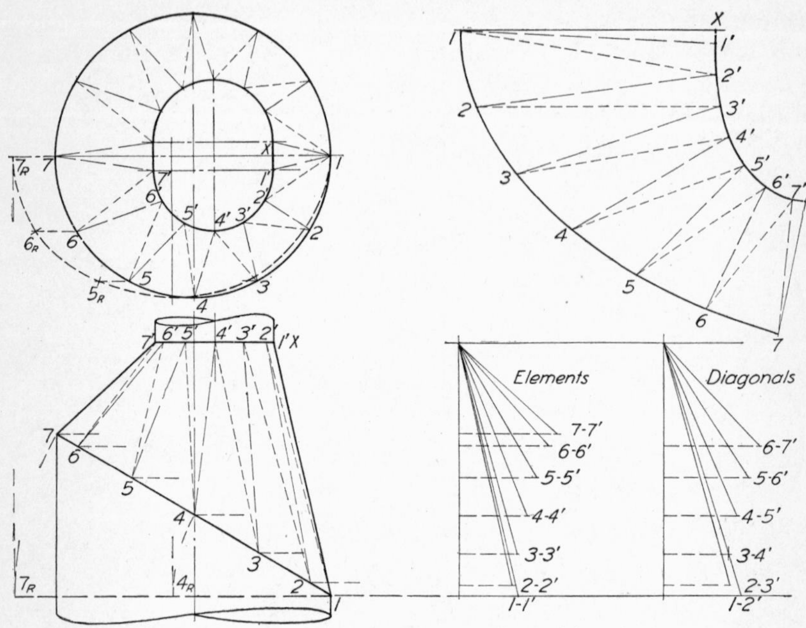

Fig. 550.—Development of a warped transition piece.

238. To Develop a Sphere.—The sphere may be taken as typical of double curved surfaces, which can only be developed approximately. It may be cut into a number of equal meridian sections, as in Fig. 551, and these considered to be sections of cylinders. One of these sections developed as the cylinder in Fig. 542 will give a pattern for the others.

Another method is to cut the sphere in horizontal sections, each of which may be taken as the frustum of a cone whose apex is at the intersection of the extended chords, Fig. 552.

239. The Intersection of Surfaces.—When two surfaces intersect, the line of intersection, which is a line common to both, may be thought of as a line in which all the elements of one surface pierce the other. Practically every line on a drawing is a line of intersection, generally the intersection of two planes, or a cylinder cut by a plane, giving a circle. The term "intersection of surfaces" refers, however, to the more complicated lines occurring when geometrical surfaces such as cylinders, cones, prisms, etc., intersect each other.

Two reasons make it necessary for the draftsman to be familiar with the methods of finding the intersections of surfaces: first, intersections are constantly occurring on working drawings and must be represented; second, in sheet-metal combinations the intersections must be found before the piece can be developed. In the first case it is necessary only to find a few critical points and "guess in" the curve; in the second case enough points must be determined to enable the development to be laid out accurately.

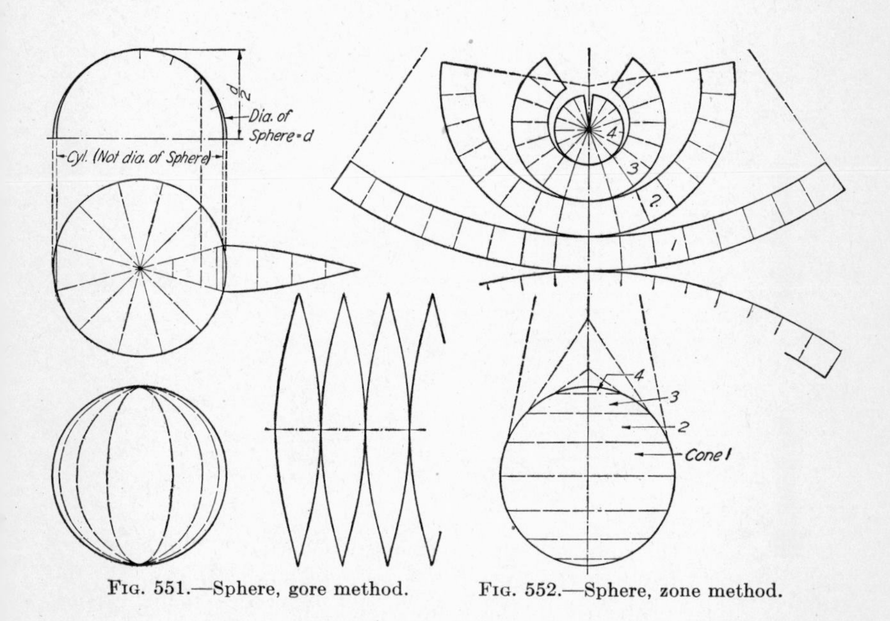

Fig. 551.—Sphere, gore method. Fig. 552.—Sphere, zone method.

Any practical problem resolves itself into some combination of the geometrical type forms. In general, the method of finding the line of intersection of any two surfaces is to pass a series of planes through them in such a way as to cut from each the simplest lines. The intersection of the lines cut from each surface by a plane will give one or more points on the line of intersection.

A study of the following typical examples will explain the method of working this class of problems.

240. To Find the Intersection of Two Prisms.—Fig. 553. Since the triangular prism would pass entirely through the square prism there are two closed "curves" of intersection. A plane *A-A* parallel to the vertical plane through the front edge of the triangular prism cuts two elements from the square prism. The front view shows where these elements cross the edge of the triangular prism, thus locating one point on each curve. The plane *C-C* will contain the other two edges of the triangular prism and will give two more points on each curve. As on the left side only one face of the square prism is penetrated, the curve would be a triangle, two sides of which are visible and one

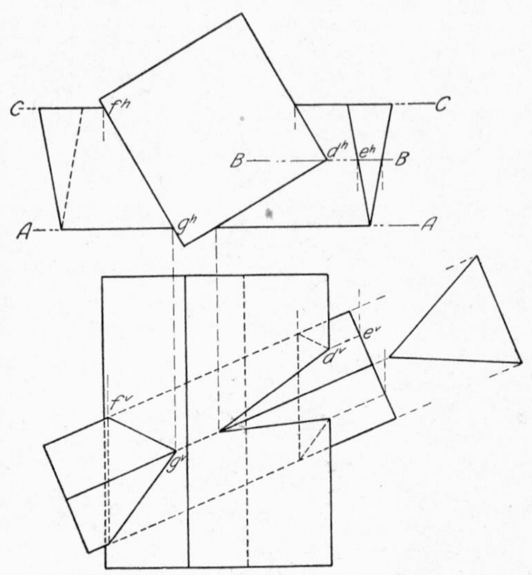

Fig. 553.—Intersection of two prisms.

invisible. On the right side two faces are penetrated. The plane *B-B* is thus passed through the corner, the two elements cut from the triangular prism projected to the front view, where they intersect the corner as shown.

241. To Find the Intersection of Two Cylinders.—Fig. 554. In the position shown, three views or part views are necessary. The planes *A*, *B*, *C*, *D*, parallel to *V* and shown in the same relative position on top and end views, cut elements from each cylinder, the intersections of which are points on the curve. The pictorial sketch shows a section on one of the planes. The development of the upper cylinder is evident from the figure.

When the axes of the cylinders do not intersect, as in Fig. 555, the same method is used, but care must be taken in the choice of cutting planes. Certain "critical planes" give the limits and turning points of the curve. Such planes should always be taken through the contour elements. In the position shown, the planes A and D give the width of the curve, the plane B the extreme length and the plane C the tangent or turning points on the contour element of the vertical cylinder. After the critical points are determined a sufficient number of other cutting planes are used to give an accurate curve.

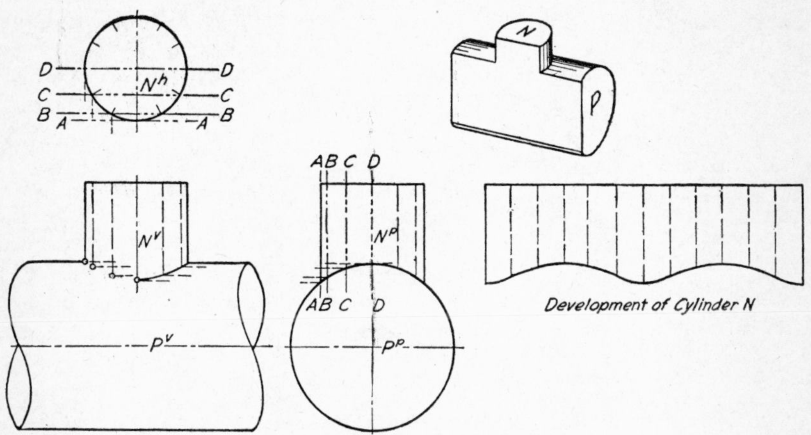

Fig. 554.—Intersection of two cylinders.

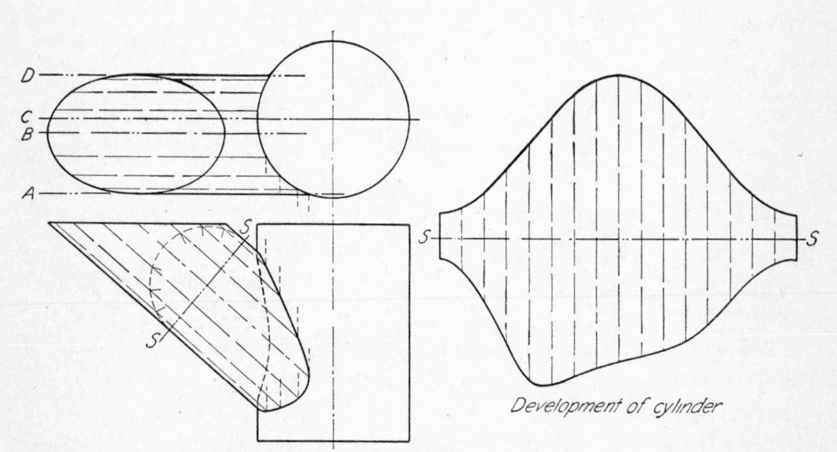

Fig. 555.—Intersection of two cylinders, axes not intersecting.

To develop the inclined cylinder, a right section at S-S is taken, whose stretchout would be a straight line. If the cutting planes are taken at random the elements would not be spaced uniformly. To simplify the development, other planes may be assumed, by dividing the turned section into equal parts, as shown.

242. To Find the Intersection of a Prism and a Cone.—Fig. 556. In this case the choice of cutting planes would be made as parallel to *H*. Thus each plane would cut a circle from the cone and a hexagon from the prism, whose intersections would give points on the curve. The curve would be limited between the plane *A* cutting a circle whose diameter is equal to the short diameter of the hexagon and the plane *C* cutting a circle equal to the long diameter. As the prism is made up of six vertical planes the entire line of intersection of cone and prism would consist of the ends of six hyperbolas, three of which are visible, one showing its true shape, as cut by the plane *D*, the two others foreshortened. This illustrates the true curve on a chamfered hexagonal bolt head or nut. In practice it is always drawn approximately with three circle arcs.

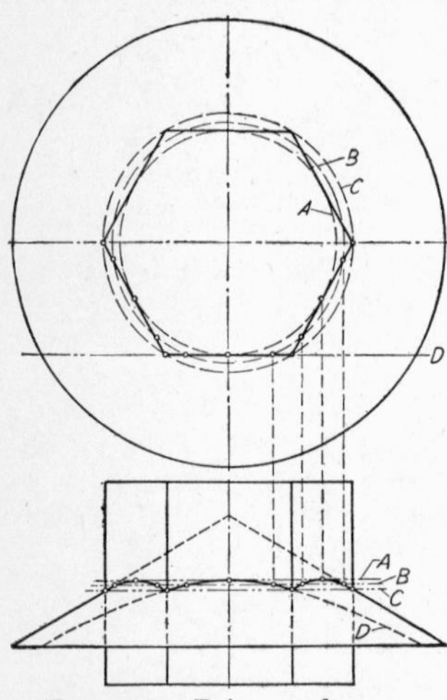

FIG. 556.—Prism and cone.

243. To Find the Intersection of a Cylinder and a Cone.—Fig. 557. Here the cutting planes may be taken so as to pass through the vertex of the cone and parallel to the elements of the cylinder, thus cutting elements from both cylinder and cone; or with a right cone they may be taken parallel to the base so as to cut circles from the cone. Both are illustrated in the figure. Some judgment is necessary in the selection of both the direction and number of the cutting planes. More points need to be found at the places of sudden curvature or changes of direction of the projections of the line of intersection.

244. To Find the Intersection of a Plane and a Surface of Revolution.—Fig. 558. Planes perpendicular to the axis of any surface of revolution (right sections) will cut circles. Thus the intersection of a surface of revolution and a plane is found by passing a series of planes perpendicular to the axis of revolution, cutting circles on the end view. The points at which these circles cut the "flat" are projected back as points on the curve.

PROBLEMS

245. Selections from the following problems may be constructed accurately in pencil without inking. Any practical problem can be resolved into some combination of the "type solids," and the exercises given illustrate the principles involved in the various combinations.

An added interest in developments may be found by working the problems on suitable paper, allowing for fastenings and lap, and cutting them out. It is recommended that at least one or two models be constructed in this way.

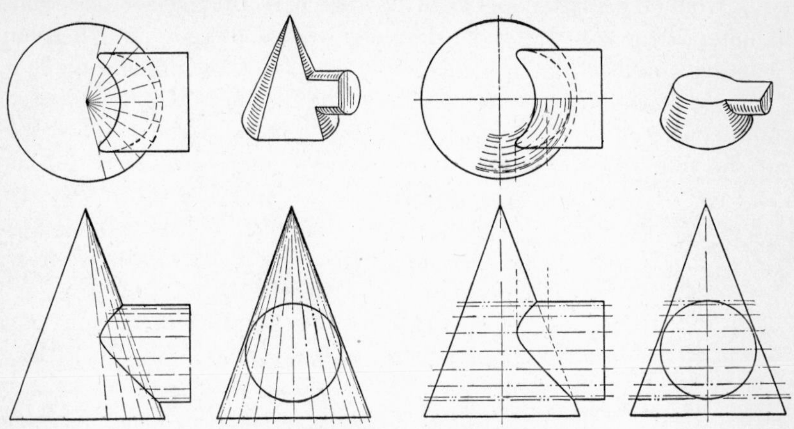

FIG. 557.—Intersections of cylinder and cone.

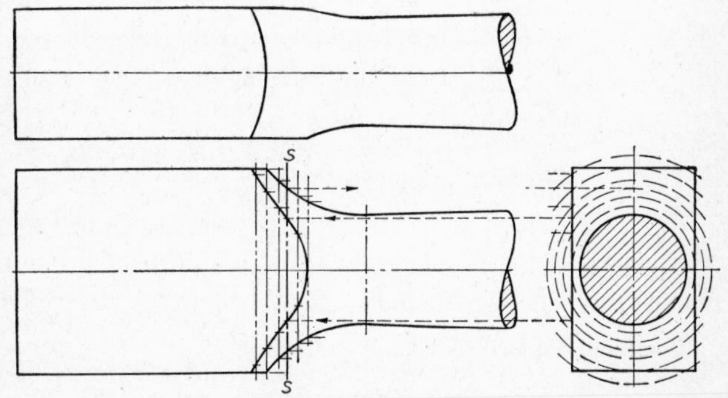

FIG. 558.—Intersection of a surface of revolution and a plane.

In the sheet-metal shops, development problems unless very complicated are usually laid out directly on the iron.

The following figures and their developments may be drawn on 8½″ × 11″ or 11″ × 17″ sheets. Assume them as made of thin metal with open ends unless otherwise specified:

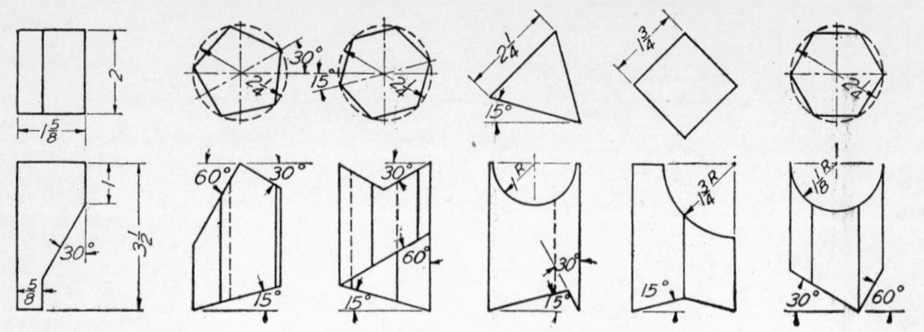

FIG. 559.—Prisms (Probs. 1 to 6).

Group I. Prisms.

1 to 6. Fig. 559. Develop lateral surfaces of the prisms.

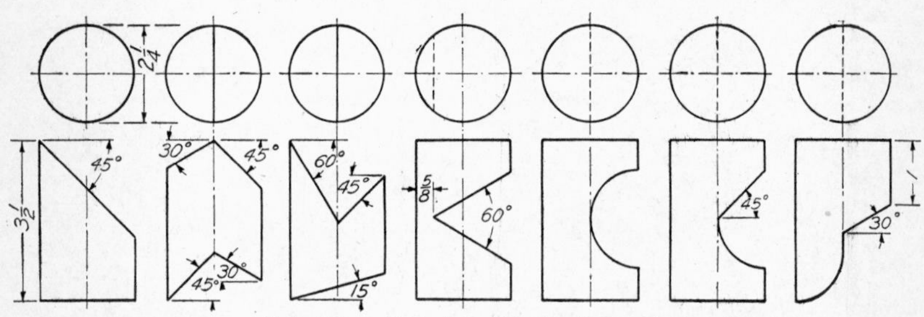

FIG. 560.—Cylinders (Probs. 7 to 13).

Group II. Cylinders.

7 to 13. Fig. 560. Develop lateral surfaces of the cylinders.

Group III. Combinations of Prisms and Cylinders.

14, 15, 16. Fig. 561. Develop lateral surfaces.

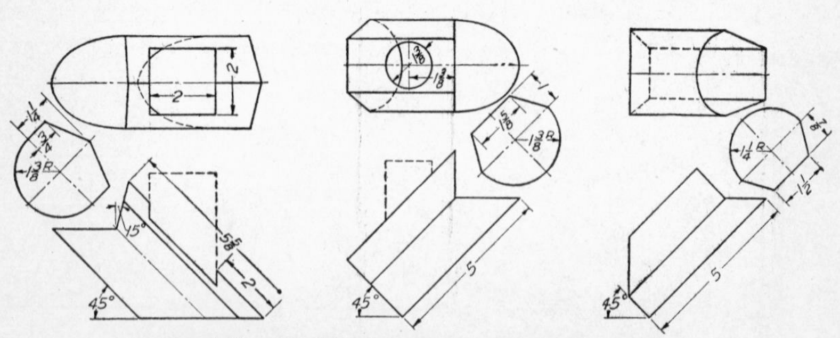

FIG. 561.—Combination surfaces (Probs. 14 to 16).

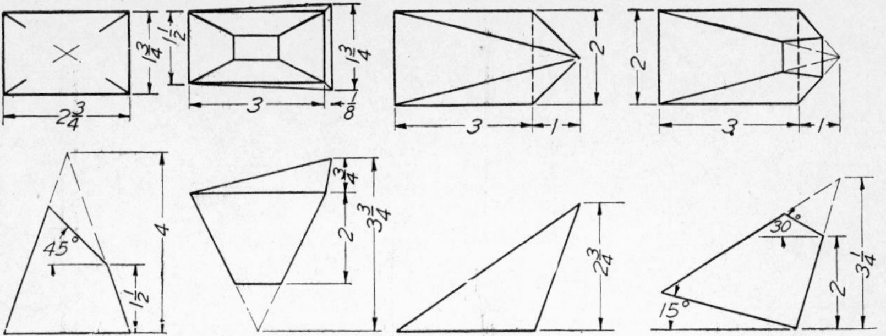

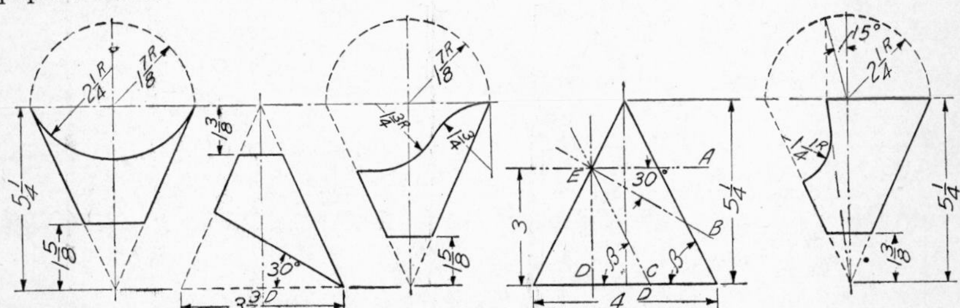

Fig. 562.—Pyramids (Probs. 17 to 20).

Group IV. Pyramids.

17, 18, 19, 20. Fig. 562. Develop lateral surfaces of the pyramids. Make paper models.

Fig. 563.—Cones (Probs. 21 to 25).

Group V. Cones.

21, 22, 23, 25. Fig. 563. Develop lateral surfaces and make paper models.

24. Develop surface of cone cut by one of the planes *A*, *B*, *C* or *D*. Show true size of cut surface (see Conic Sections, Fig. 140).

Group VI. Developments.

26, 27, 28, 29. Fig. 564. Develop lateral surfaces of the objects. Note that 27 is a *G.I.* gutter (on Probs. 28 and 29 one-half may be developed).

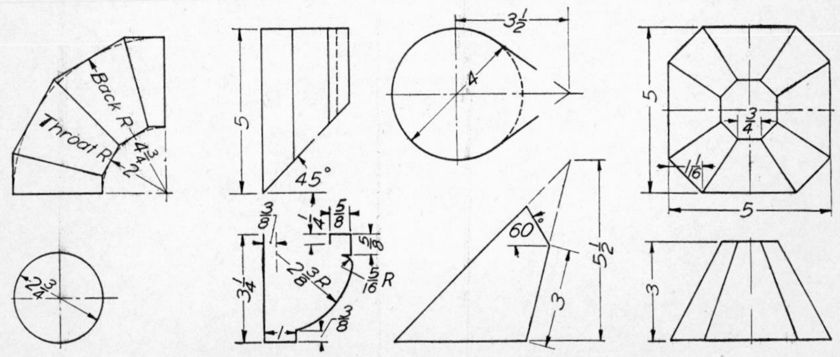

Fig. 564.—Various surfaces (Probs. 26 to 29).

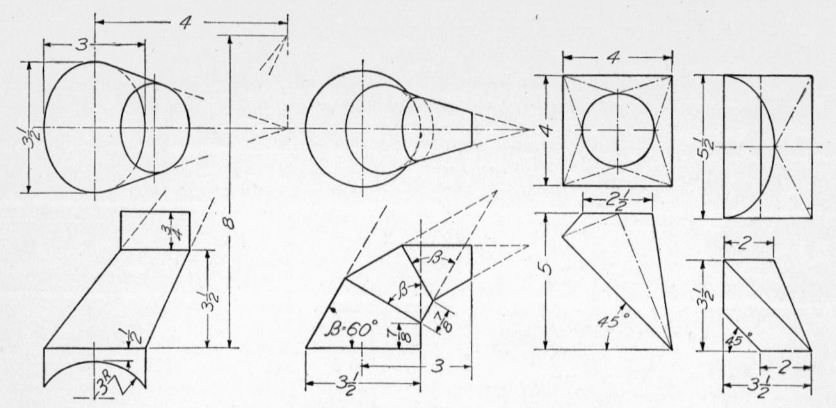

FIG. 565.—Transition pieces (Probs. 30 to 33).

Group VII. Cones and Transition Pieces.

30, 31, 32, 33. Fig. 565. Develop lateral surfaces of the objects (one-half).

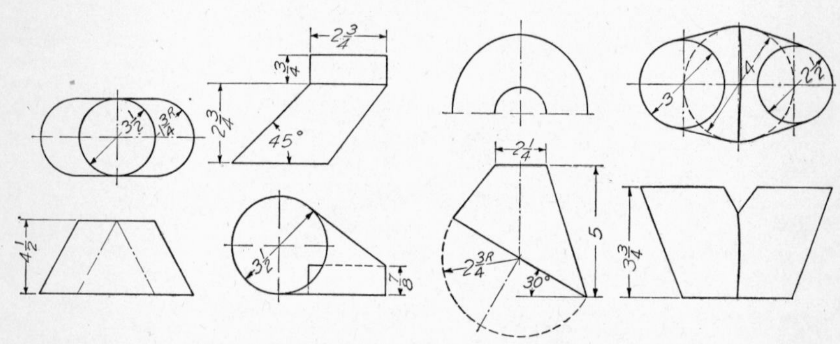

FIG. 566.—Transition pieces (Probs. 34 to 38).

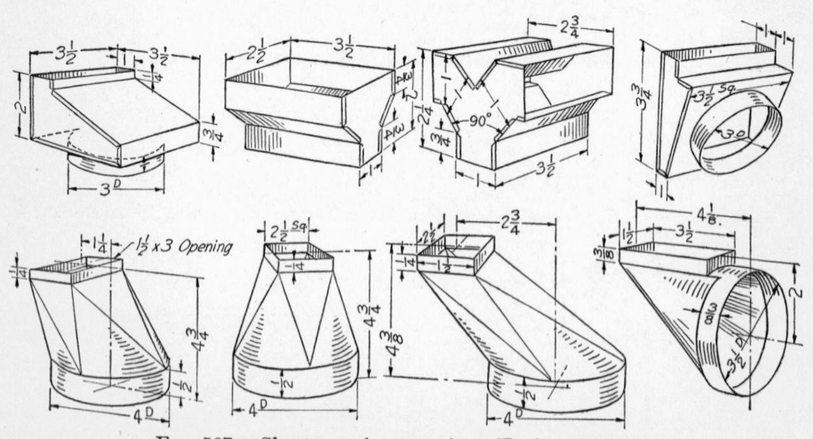

FIG. 567.—Sheet-metal connections (Probs. 39 to 46).

34, 35, 36, 37. Fig. 566. Develop lateral surfaces of the objects (one-half of Probs. 34, 36, 37).

38. Fig. 566. Develop surfaces of Y connection, first finding intersection of the two cones (one sheet for figure and one-half of one leg).

Group VIII. Furnace Pipe Fittings.

39 to 46. Fig. 567. Develop surfaces and make paper models.

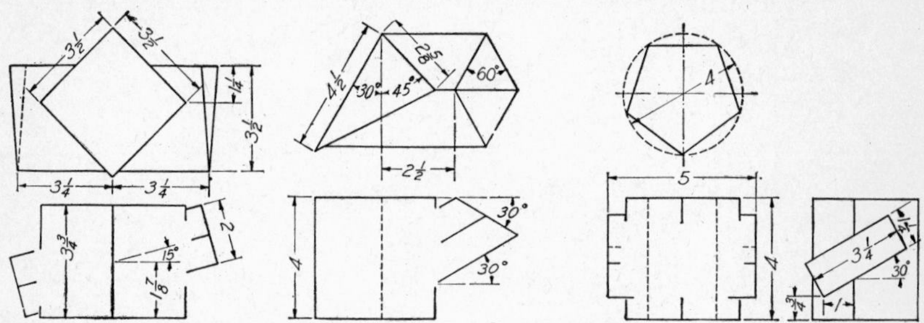

FIG. 568.—Intersections of prisms (Probs. 47 to 49).

Group IX. Intersections of Prisms.

47, 48, 49. Fig. 568. Find line of intersection, considering prisms as pipes opening into each other. Use particular care in indicating visible and invisible portions of line of intersection. On another sheet develop the surfaces.

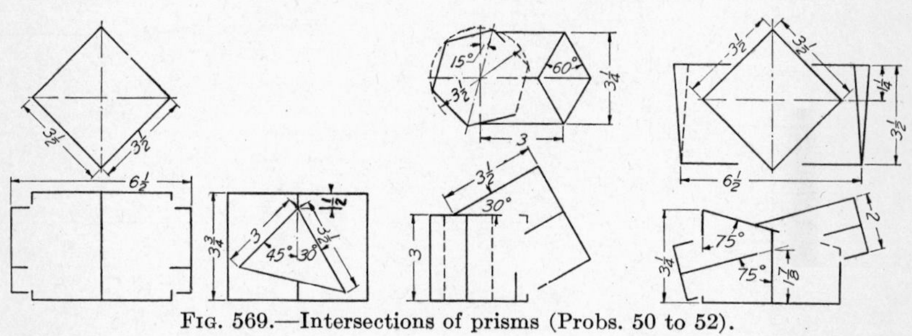

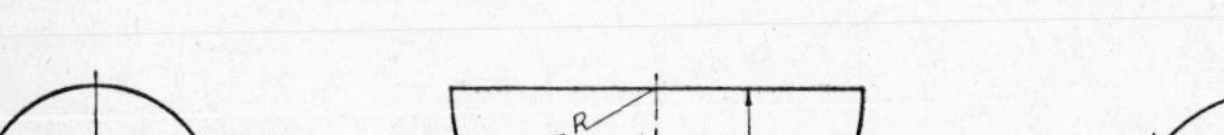

FIG. 569.—Intersections of prisms (Probs. 50 to 52).

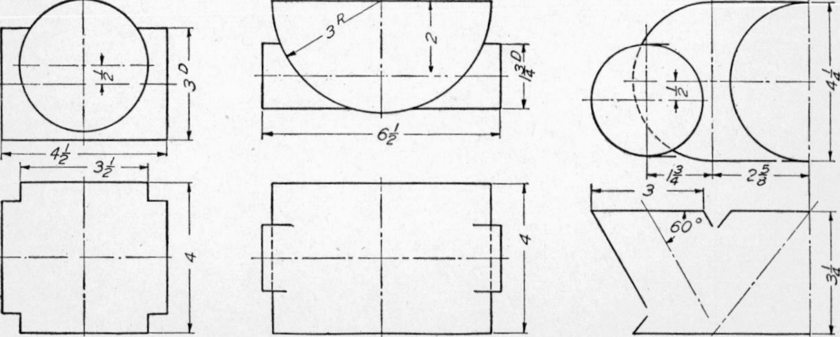

FIG. 570.—Intersections of cylinders (Probs. 53 to 55).

50, 51, 52. Fig. 569. Find line of intersection, indicating visible and invisible parts, and considering prisms as pipes opening into each other. Note that in Probs. 51 and 52 the vertical pipes must have heads, cut out to fit inclined pipe.

Group X. Intersections of Cylinders.

53, 54, 55. Fig. 570. Find line of intersection, indicating visible and invisible portions, and considering cylinders as pipes opening into each other. On another sheet develop the surfaces of each cylinder.

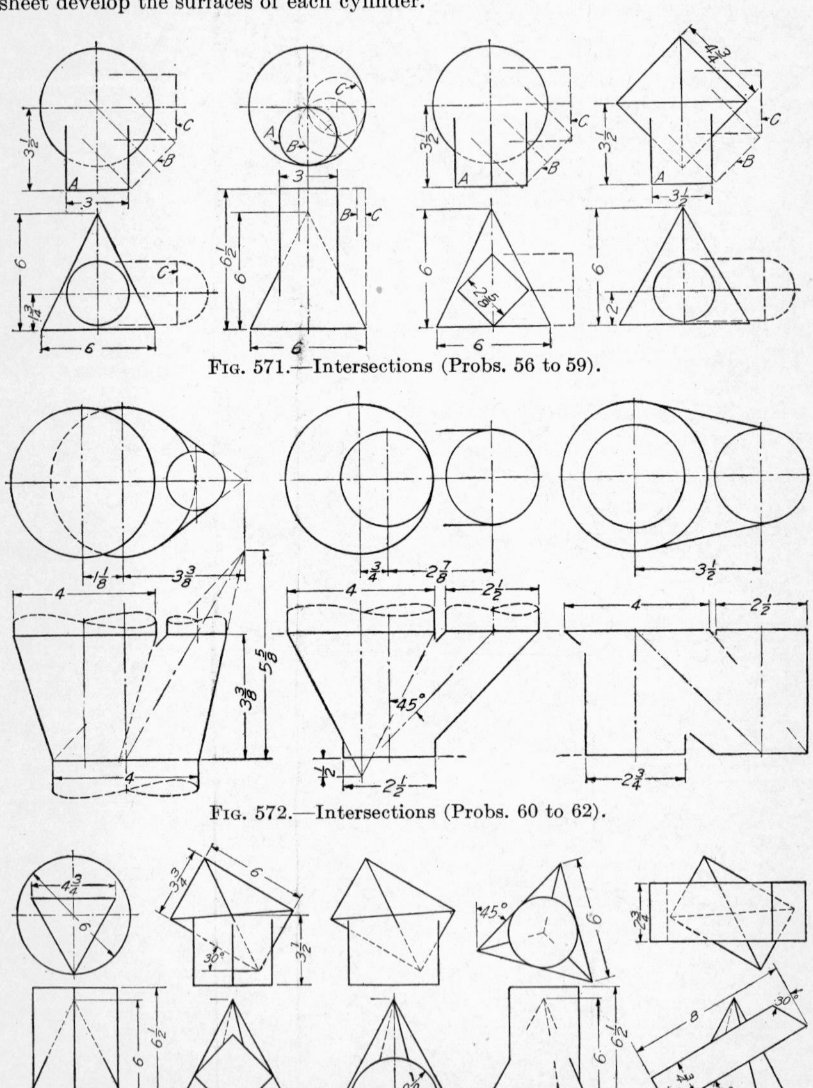

Fig. 571.—Intersections (Probs. 56 to 59).

Fig. 572.—Intersections (Probs. 60 to 62).

Fig. 573.—Intersections (Probs. 63 to 67).

Group XI. Intersections of Surfaces.

56, 57, 58, 59. Fig. 571. Find lines of intersection.

60, 61, 62. Fig. 572. Find lines of intersection and develop surfaces.

63, 64, 65, 66, 67. Fig. 573. Find lines of intersection and develop surfaces.

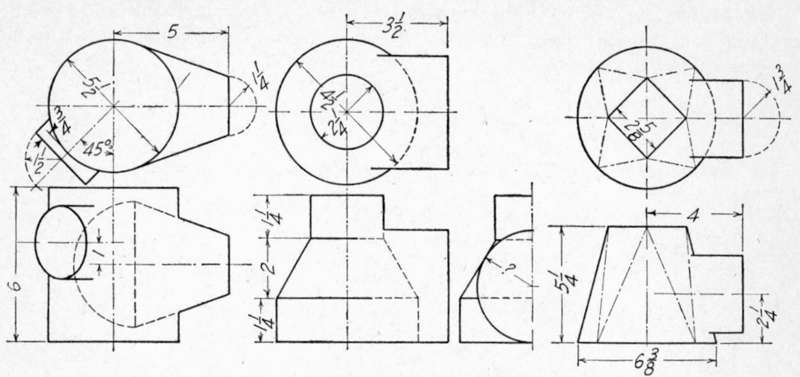

Fig. 574.—Intersections (Probs. 68 to 70).

68, 69, 70. Fig. 574. Find lines of intersection and develop surfaces.

Group XII. Surfaces Cut by Planes.

71, 72, 73, 74, 75. Fig. 575. Complete the views, finding lines of intersection. Make separate views of sections on planes indicated.

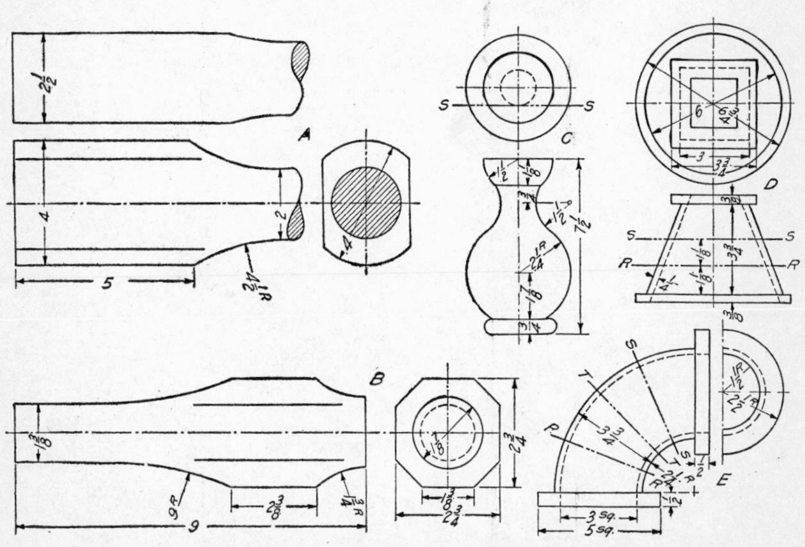

Fig. 575.—Surfaces cut by planes (Probs. 71 to 75).

CHAPTER XIV

PICTORIAL REPRESENTATION

246. In the study of the theory of projection in Chapter VI it was found that perspective projection shows the object as it appears to the eye but that its lines cannot be measured directly, while orthographic projection, with two or more views, shows it as it really is in form and dimensions but requires a trained imagination to visualize the object from the views. To combine the pictorial effect of perspective drawing with the possibility of measuring the principal lines directly, several forms of one-plane projection or conventional picture methods have been devised, in which the third dimension is taken care of by turning the object in such a way that three of its faces are visible. With the combined advantages are some serious disadvantages which limit their usefulness. The distorted effect is often unreal and unpleasant; only certain lines can be measured; the execution requires more time, particularly if curved lines occur, and it is difficult to add many figured dimensions, but even with their limitations a knowledge of these methods is extremely desirable and they can often be used to great advantage. Mechanical or structural details not clear in orthographic projection may be drawn pictorially or illustrated by supplementary pictorial views. Technical illustrations, patent office drawings and the like are made advantageously in one-plane projection; layouts and piping plans may be drawn, as in Fig. 411, and many other applications will occur to draftsmen who can use these methods with facility. One of the most important reasons for learning them is for their use in making freehand sketches.

247. Divisions.—Aside from perspective drawing there are two general divisions of pictorial projection: first, *axonometric*, with its divisions into isometric, dimetric and trimetric; second, *oblique* projection, with several variations. Other methods not theoretically correct, but effective, are sometimes used.

248. Axonometric projection, as shown in the tabular classification on page 79, is, theoretically, simply a form of orthographic projection in which only one plane is used, with the object turned so that three faces show. Imagine a transparent vertical plane with a cube behind it, one face of the cube being parallel to the plane. The projection on the plane, that is, the front view of the cube, will be a square. Rotate the cube about its vertical axis through any angle (less than 90°); the front view will now show two faces, both foreshortened. From this position tilt the cube forward any amount less than 90°. Three faces will now be visible on the front view. Thus there can be an infinite number of axonometric positions, only a few of which are ever used for drawing. The simplest of these is the "isometric" (equal measure) position, where the three faces are foreshortened equally, which is the basis for the isometric system.

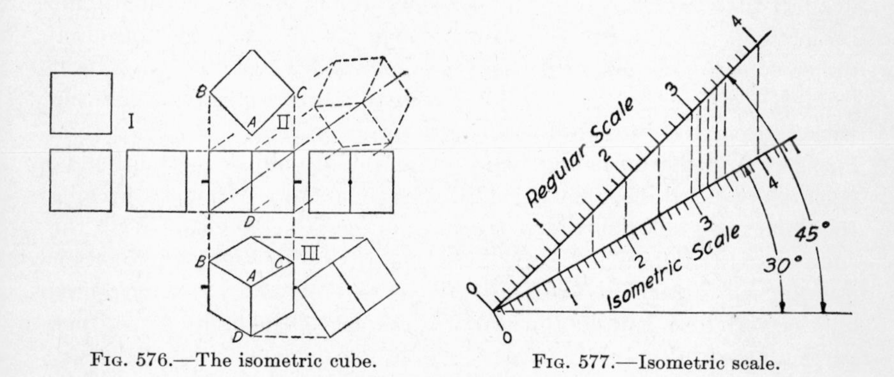

FIG. 576.—The isometric cube.

FIG. 577.—Isometric scale.

249. Isometric Projection.—If a cube in position I, Fig. 576, be rotated about a vertical axis through 45° as shown at II, then tilted forward as at III until the edge AD is foreshortened equally with AB and AC, the front view in this position is said to be in *isometric projection* (the cube has been tilted forward until the body diagonal from A is horizontal, making the top face slope 35° 16′ approximate).[1] The three lines of the front corner, AB, AC and AD, make equal angles with each other and are called the "isometric axes." Since parallel lines have their projections parallel, the other edges of the cube will be respectively parallel to these axes. Any line parallel to an isometric axis is called an "isometric line." The planes of the faces of the cube and all planes parallel to them are called "isometric planes." In

[1] In paragraph 101 the statement is made that the only difference between revolution and auxiliary projection is that in the former the object is moved and in the latter the plane is moved. Thus an auxiliary view on a plane perpendicular to a body diagonal of the cube in position II would be an isometric projection, as illustrated by the dotted view.

isometric projection the isometric lines have been foreshortened to approximately $^{81}/_{100}$ of their length, and an isometric scale to this proportion *might* be made graphically as shown in Fig. 577 if it ever became necessary to make an isometric projection to theoretical size.

250. Isometric Drawing.—In all practical use of the isometric system this foreshortening of the lines is disregarded and the full lengths laid off on the axes. This gives a figure slightly larger but of exactly the same shape, Fig. 578. The effect of increased size is usually of no consequence, and as the advantage of measuring the lines directly is of such great convenience isometric drawing is used almost exclusively instead of isometric projection.

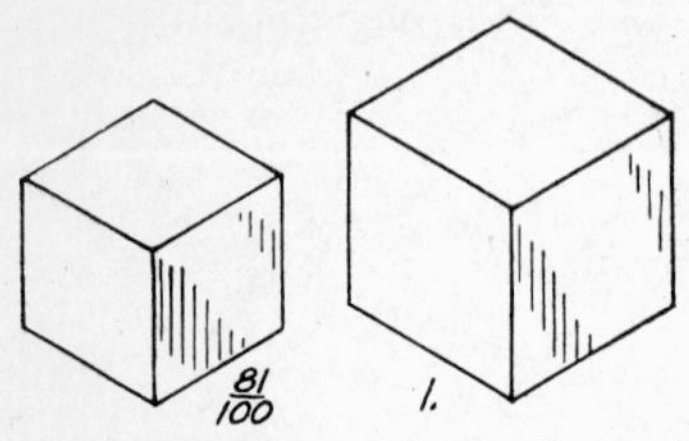

Fig. 578.—Isometric projection and isometric drawing.

251. To Make an Isometric Drawing.—If the object is rectangular, start with a point representing a front corner and draw from it the three isometric axes 120° apart, drawing one vertical, the two others with the 30° triangle, Fig. 579. On these three lines measure the length, breadth and thickness of the object, as indicated; through these points draw lines parallel to the axes, completing the figure. To draw intelligently in isometric it is only necessary to remember the direction of the three principal isometric planes. Hidden lines are always omitted except when necessary for the description of the piece.

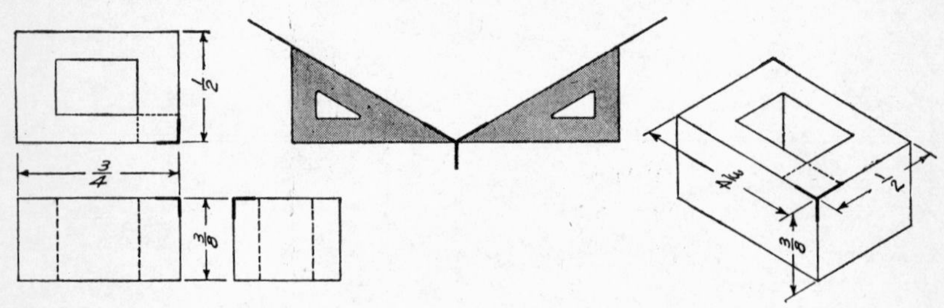

Fig. 579.—Isometric axes; first position.

It is often more convenient to start from a lower front corner, drawing axes as illustrated in Fig. 580.

Lines not parallel to one of the isometric axes are called non-isometric lines. The one important rule is *measurements can be made only on isometric lines;* and, conversely, measurements cannot be made on non-isometric lines. For example, the diagonals of the face of a cube are non-isometric lines and, although equal in length, will evidently be of very unequal length on the isometric drawing of the cube.

252. Objects Containing Non-isometric Lines.—Since a non-isometric line does not appear in its true length, its extremities must be located and the line found by joining these points. In Fig. 580, *AB* is a non-isometric line, found by drawing the two perpendicular isometric lines and joining their ends.

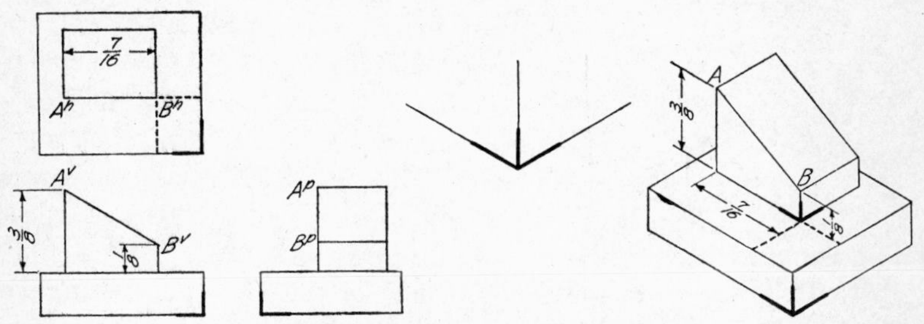

FIG. 580.—Isometric axes; second position.

When the object contains many non-isometric lines, it is drawn either by the "boxing" method or the "offset" method. In the first method the object is enclosed in a rectangular box, which is drawn in isometric and the object located in it by its points of contact, as in

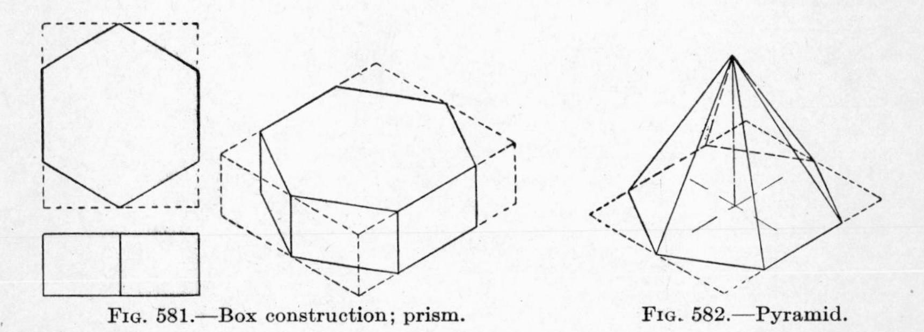

FIG. 581.—Box construction; prism. FIG. 582.—Pyramid.

Figs. 581 and 583. It should be noted that lines which are parallel on the object are parallel on the isometric view. Knowledge of this may often be used to save a large amount of construction, as well as to test for accuracy. Figure 581 might be drawn by putting the top face into isometric and drawing vertical lines equal in length to the edges downward from each corner.

It is not always necessary actually to enclose the whole object in a rectangular "crate." The pyramid, Fig. 582, would have its base enclosed in a rectangle and the apex located by erecting a vertical axis from the center.

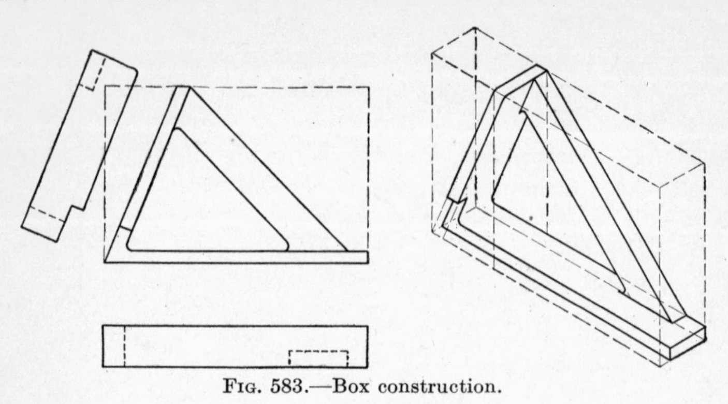

Fig. 583.—Box construction.

The object shown in Fig. 583 is composed almost entirely of non-isometric lines. In such cases the isometric view cannot be drawn without first making the orthographic views necessary for boxing. In general the boxing method is adapted to objects which have the non-isometric lines in isometric planes.

Offset Method.—When the object is made up of planes at a number of different angles, it is better to locate the ends of the edges by the

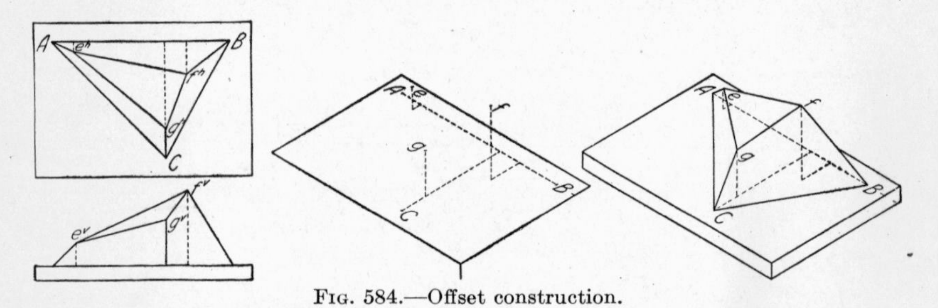

Fig. 584.—Offset construction.

"offset" method. In this method perpendiculars are dropped from each point to an isometric reference plane. These perpendiculars, which are isometric lines, are located on the drawing by isometric coordinates, the dimensions being taken from the orthographic views. In Fig. 584 the line AB of the figure is used as a base line and measurements made from it as shown. Figure 585 is another example of offset construction, working from a vertical plane.

Of course, angles in isometric drawing cannot be measured in degrees, so it is necessary to locate the direction of the including sides by ordinates, as in Fig. 586. This is well illustrated in Fig. 583.

253. Objects Containing Curved Lines.—It is obvious that a circle or any curve on the face of a cube will lose its true shape when the cube

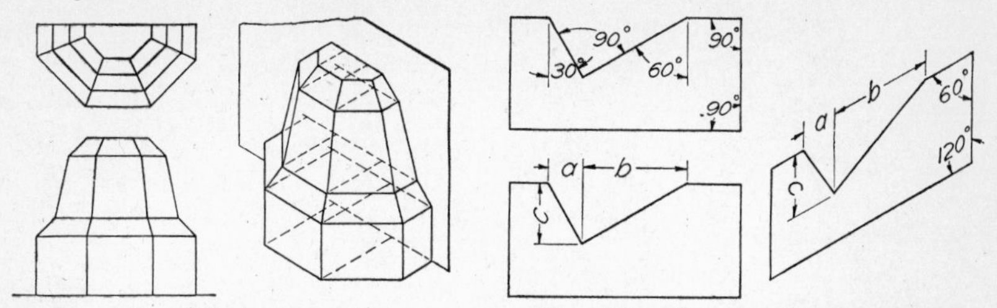

FIG. 585.—Offset construction. FIG. 586.—Construction for angles.

is drawn in isometric. A circle on any isometric plane will be projected as an ellipse.

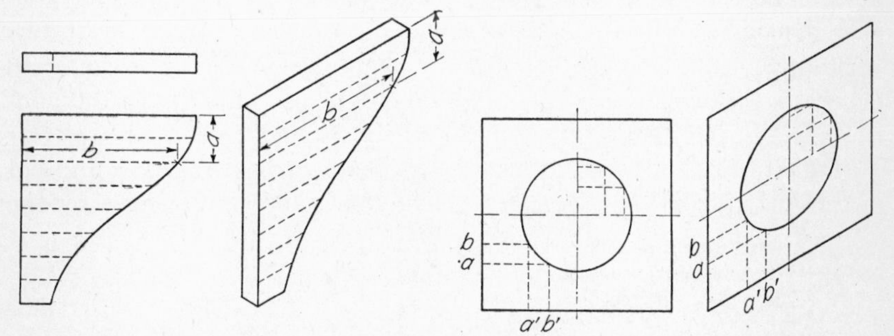

FIG. 587.—Construction for curves. FIG. 588.—Circle, points plotted.

Any curve may be drawn by plotting points on it from isometric reference lines, as in Fig. 587. A circle plotted in this way is shown in Fig. 588.

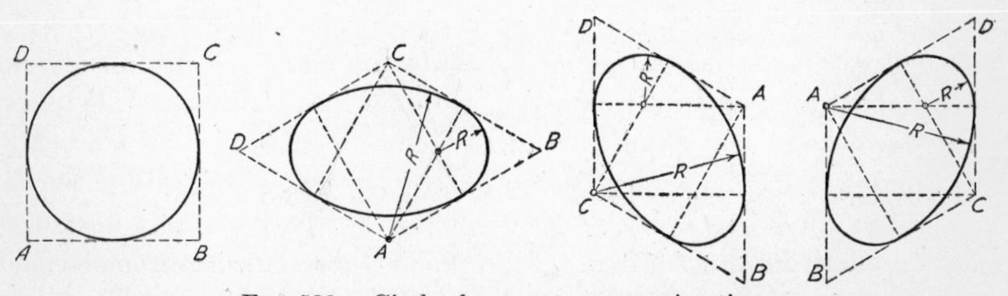

FIG. 589.—Circle, four-center approximation.

254. Isometric circles are usually drawn by a four-centered approximation, which is sufficiently accurate for all ordinary work.

The center for any arc tangent to a straight line lies on a perpendicular from the points of tangency. If perpendiculars be drawn from the middle point of each side of the circumscribing square, the intersections of these perpendiculars will be centers for arcs tangent to two sides, Fig. 589. Two of these intersections will evidently fall at the corners A and C of the square, as the lines are altitudes of equilateral triangles. The construction of Fig. 589 may thus be made by simply drawing 60° lines from the corners A and C.[1] To draw any circle arc, the isometric square of its diameter should be drawn in the plane of its face, with as much of this construction as is necessary to find centers for the part of the circle needed. Thus for a quarter circle, measure the true radius of the circle from the corner on the two isometric lines and draw actual perpendiculars from these points, Fig. 590. Their intersection will be the required center for the isometric radius.

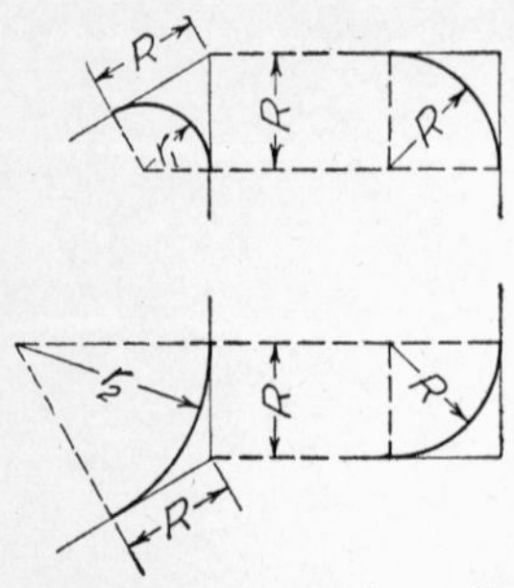

Fig. 590.—Isometric radii.

The isometric drawing of a *sphere* would be a circle with its diameter equal to the long axis of the ellipse inscribed in the isometric square of the real diameter of the sphere, as this ellipse would be the isometric of a great circle of the sphere.

255. Reversed Axes.—It is often desirable to show the lower face of an object by tilting it back instead of forward, thus reversing the axes to the position of Fig. 592. The construction is just the same, but the directions of the principal isometric planes must be kept in mind. The figure shows the application of circle-arc construction on the three visible faces of a reversed axis drawing. A practical use of reversed axis construction is in the representation of such architectural features as are naturally viewed from below. Figure 593 is an example.

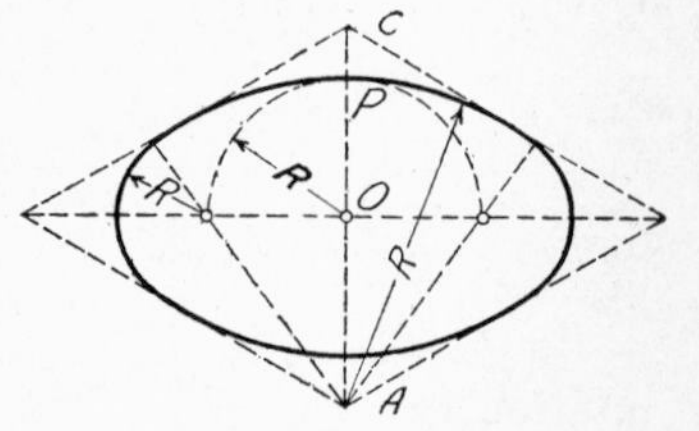

Fig. 591.—The "Stevens Method."

[1] Note.—If a true ellipse be plotted in the same square as this four-centered approximation it will be a little longer and narrower, and of more pleasing shape, but in the great majority of drawings the difference is not sufficient to warrant the extra expenditure of time required in execution. A closer approximation may be made by the "Stevens method," a very simple four-centered method shown in Fig. 591. Draw the arcs from A and C as before, extending them a little past the tangent point. With O as center and radius OP draw a semi-circle intersecting the long diagonal at points to be used as centers for the end arcs.

Sometimes a piece may be shown to better advantage with the main axis horizontal, as in Fig. 594

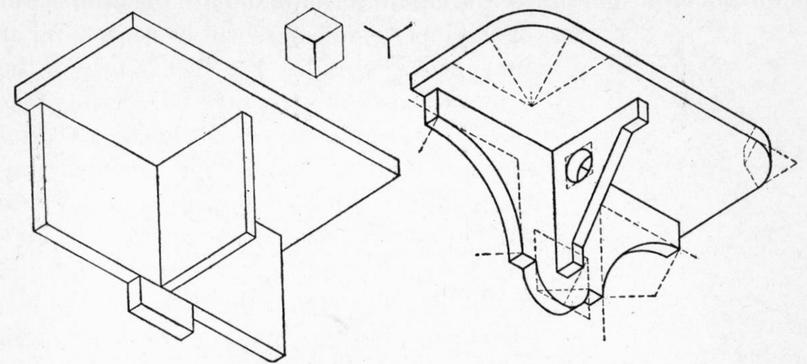

Fig. 592.—Construction with reversed axes.

256. Isometric Sections.—Isometric drawings are, from their pictorial nature, usually outside views, but sometimes a sectional view may be employed to good advantage to show a detail of shape or

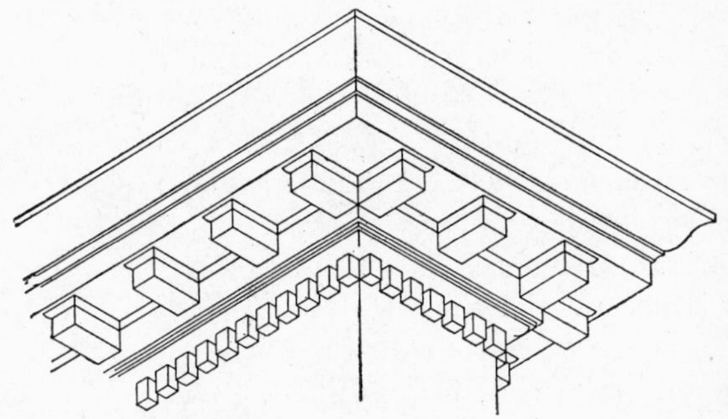

Fig. 593.—Architectural detail on reversed axes.

interior construction. The cutting planes are taken as isometric planes and the section-lining done in a direction to give the best effect. As a general rule a half section would be made by outlining the figure

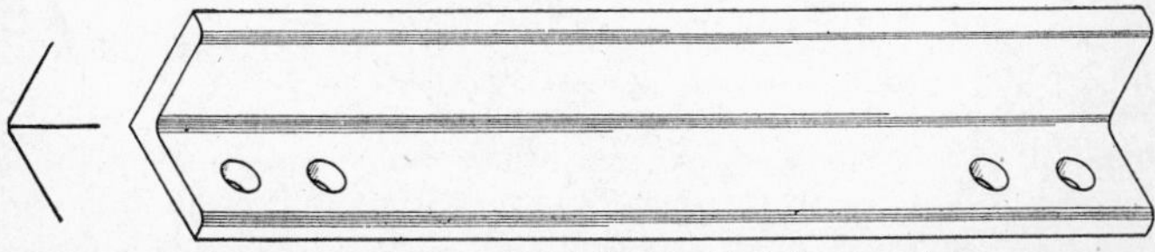

Fig. 594.—Isometric with main axis horizontal.

in full, then cutting out the front quarter by two isometric planes as in Fig. 595, while for a full section the cut face would be drawn first and the part of the object behind it added afterward, Fig. 596.

257. Dimetric Projection.—The reference cube might be revolved into any number of positions where two edges would be equally foreshortened, and the direction of axes and proportion of foreshortening of any one of these positions might be taken as a basis for a system of dimetric drawing. A simple dimetric position is one with the ratios 1:1:½. In this position the tangents of the angles are ⅛ and ⅞, making the angles approximately 7° and 41°. Figure 597 shows a drawing in this system, and Fig. 802 a convenient special triangle for it.

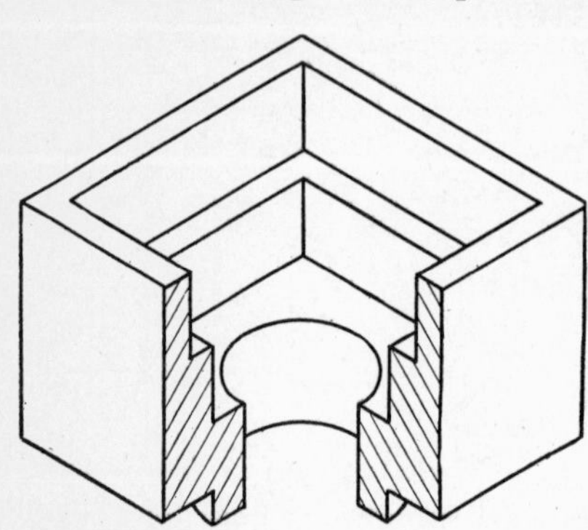

FIG. 595.—Isometric half section.

258. Trimetric Projection.—Any position with three unequal axes would be called trimetric. While with some of these positions the effect of distortion might be lessened, the added time required makes trimetric drawing impractical. The nearest approach to it is in clinographic projection, a special oblique form described on page 301.

259. Oblique Projection.—When the projectors make an angle other than 90° with the picture plane the resulting projection is called oblique projection (refer to the tabular classification on page 79). The projectors are usually taken at 45°, to which the special name of cavalier projection is given, although it is often called by the general name oblique projection or oblique drawing. The principle is as follows: Imagine a vertical plane with a rectangular block behind it, having its long edges parallel to the plane. Assume projecting lines making an angle of 45° with the picture plane, in any direction (they could be parallel to any one of the elements of a 45° cone with its base in V). Then the face of the block parallel to the plane would be projected in its true size and the edges perpendicular to the plane would be projected in their true length. Figure 598 illustrates this principle. The first panel shows the regular orthographic projection of a rectangular block with its front face in the vertical plane. An oblique projector from the back corner B will be the hypotenuse of a 45° right triangle of which AB will be

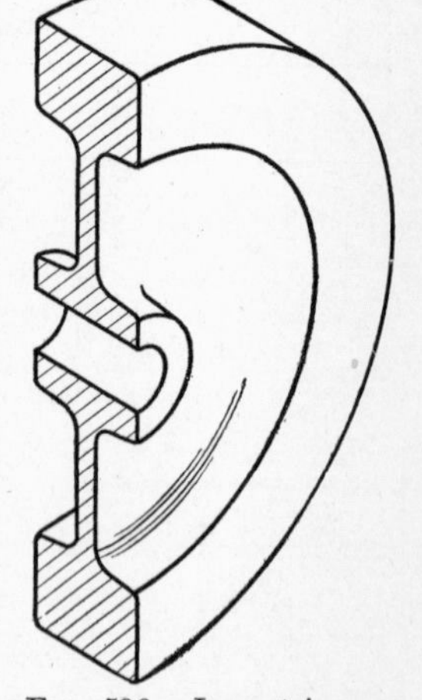

FIG. 596.—Isometric section.

one side and the projection of AB on the plane the other side. When this triangle is horizontal the projection on the plane will be AC. If the triangle be revolved about AB to any angle β, C will revolve to C_1 and $A^vC_1^v$ will be the oblique projection of AB. Since $A^vC^v = A^hC^h$, $A^vC^v = AB$.

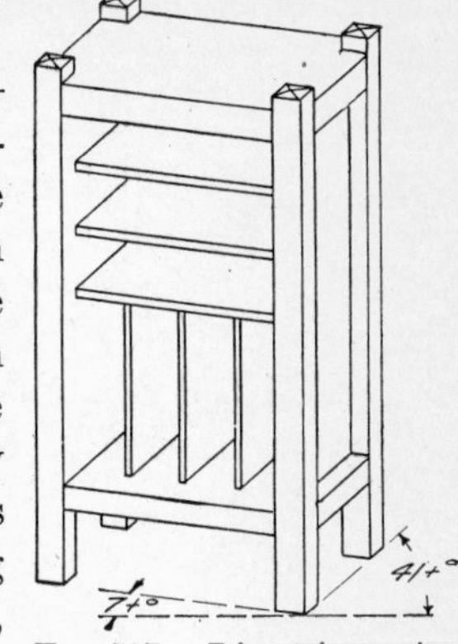

FIG. 597.—Dimetric projection.

260. To Make an Oblique Drawing.—Oblique drawing is similar to isometric drawing in having three axes representing three mutually perpendicular lines upon which measurements can be made. Two of the axes would always be at right angles to each other, being in a plane parallel to the picture plane. The third or cross-axis may be at any angle, 30° or 45° being generally used. It is thus more flexible than isometric drawing (see Fig. 599). For a rectangular object, Fig. 600, start with a point representing a front corner and draw from it the three oblique axes. On these three lines measure the length, breadth and thickness of the object.

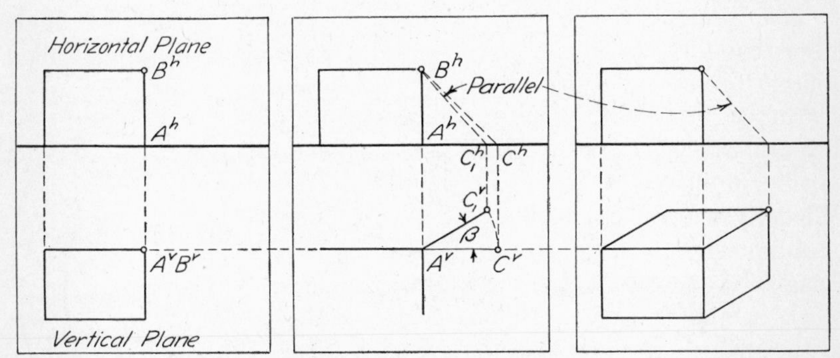

FIG. 598.—Oblique projection and the picture plane.

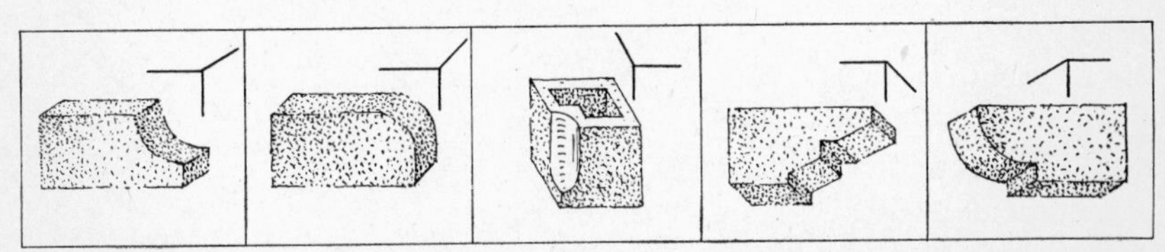

FIG. 599.—Various positions of oblique axes.

Any face parallel to the picture plane will evidently be projected without distortion, an advantage over isometric of particular value in the representation of objects with circular or irregular outline.

The first rule for oblique projection is *place the object with the irregular outline or contour parallel to the picture plane.* Note in Fig. 601 the distortion of *B* and *C* over that of *A*.

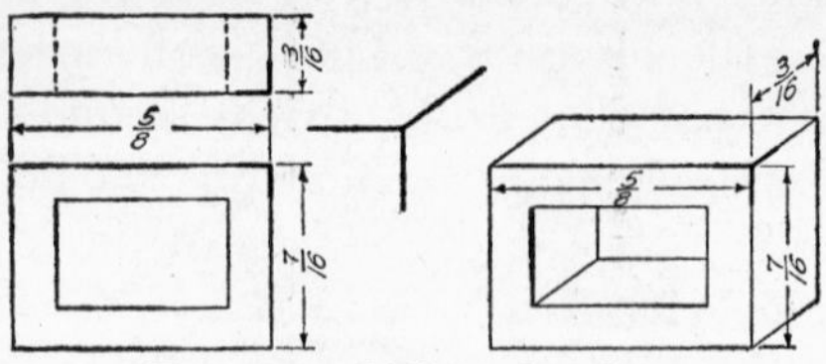

Fig. 600.—Oblique drawing.

One of the greatest disadvantages in the use of either isometric or oblique drawing is the effect of distortion produced by the lack of

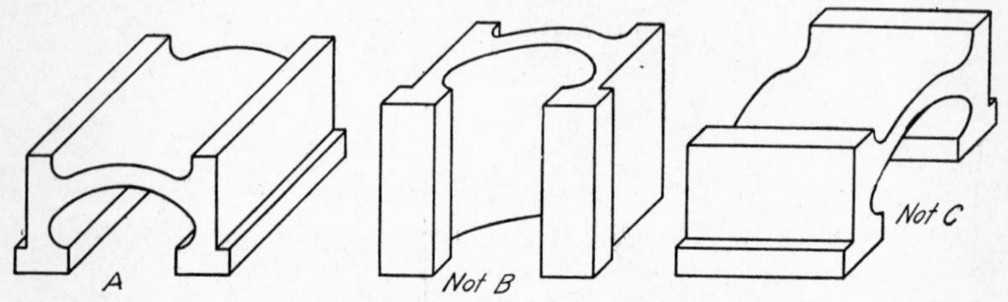

Fig. 601.—Illustration of first rule.

convergence in the receding lines—the violation of perspective. This in some cases, particularly with large objects, becomes so painful as

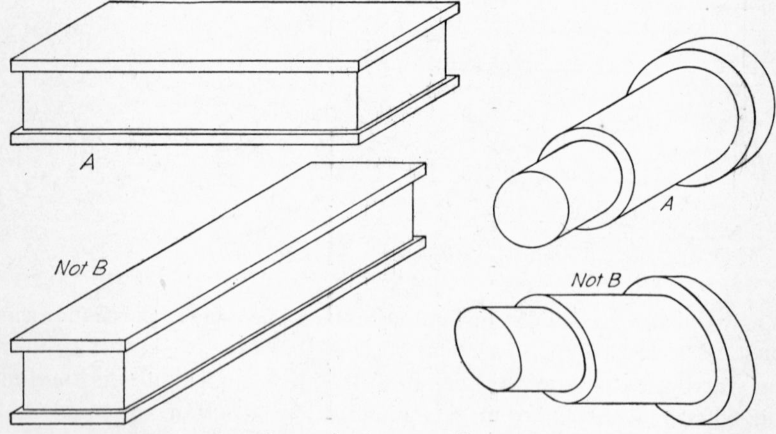

Fig. 602.—Illustration of second rule.

Fig. 603.—Precedence of first rule.

practically to prohibit the use of these methods. It is perhaps even more noticeable in oblique than in isometric and, of course, increases with the length of the cross-axis. Hence **the second rule**: *preferably have the longest dimension parallel to the picture plane.* In Fig. 602, *A* is preferable to *B*.

In case of conflict between these two rules the first should always have precedence, as the advantage of having the irregular face without distortion is greater than that gained by the second rule, as illustrated in Fig. 603. The precedence of the first rule should be followed even

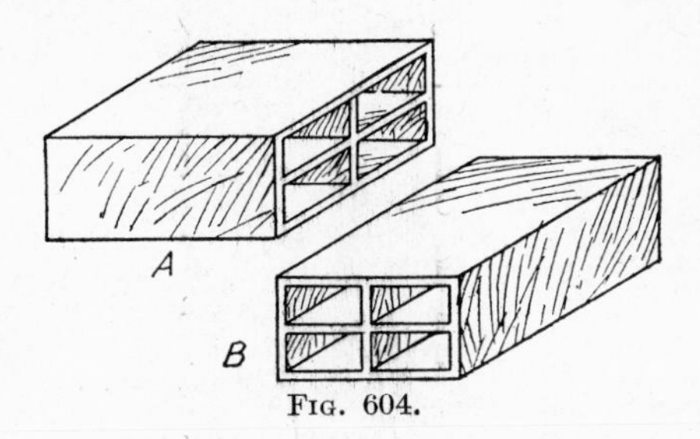

FIG. 604.

with shapes that are not irregular if in the draftsman's judgment the distortion can be lessened, as in the example of Fig. 604, where *B* is perhaps preferable to *A*.

261. Starting Plane.—It will be noted that so long as the front of the object is in one plane parallel to the plane of projection, the front face of the oblique projection is exactly the same as the orthographic.

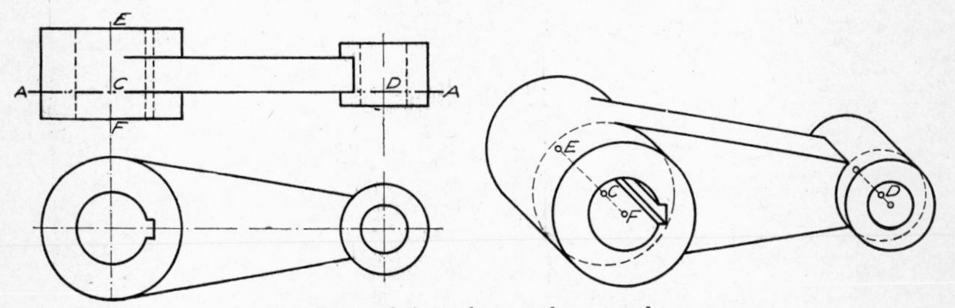

FIG. 605.—Offsets from reference plane.

When the front is made up of more than one plane, particular care must be exercised in preserving the relationship by selecting one as the starting plane and working from it. In such a figure as the link, Fig. 605, the front bosses may be imagined as cut off on the plane *A-A*, and the front view, that is, the section on *A-A*, drawn as the front of the oblique projection. On axes through the centers *C* and *D* the distances *CE* behind and *CF* in front may be laid off. When an object has no face perpendicular to its base it may be drawn in a similar way by cutting a right section and measuring offsets from it as in Fig. 606.

This offset method, previously illustrated in the isometric drawings, Figs. 584 and 585, will be found to be a most rapid and convenient

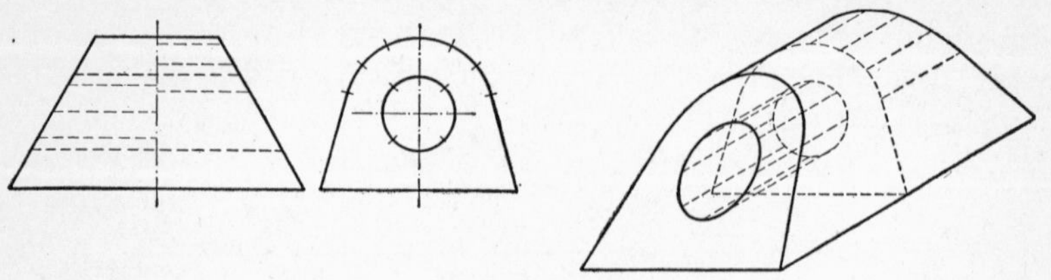

Fig. 606.—Offsets from right section.

way for drawing almost any figure, and it should be studied carefully.

When it is necessary to draw circles on oblique faces they either may be plotted or may be drawn approximately, on the same principle as Fig. 589, by erecting perpendiculars at the middle points of the containing square. In isometric it happens that one intersection falls in the corner of the square, and advantage is taken of the fact. In oblique its position depends on the angle of the cross-axis. Figure 607 shows three oblique squares at different angles and their inscribed circles.

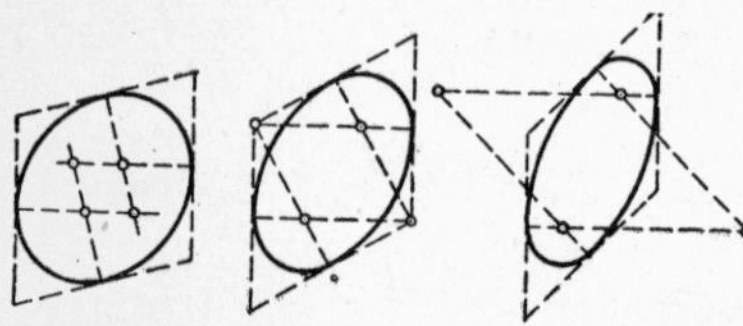

Fig. 607.—Oblique circle construction.

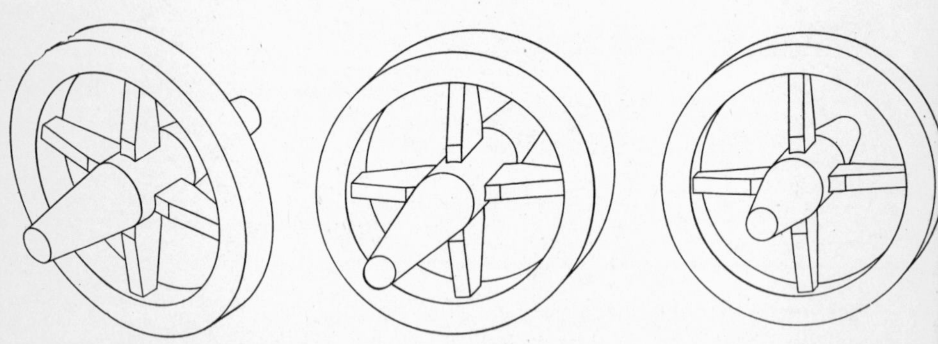

Fig. 608.—Isometric, oblique and cabinet drawing compared.

262. Cabinet drawing is an oblique projection assumed from such direction that all measurements parallel to the cross-axis are reduced one-half, so as to overcome the appearance of excessive thickness produced in cavalier projection. The cross-axis may be at any angle but is usually taken either 30° or 45°. The comparative appearances of isometric, cavalier and cabinet drawing are illustrated in Fig. 608.

263. Other Forms.—Cabinet drawing, explained above, is popular because of the easy ratio, but the effect is often too thin. Other

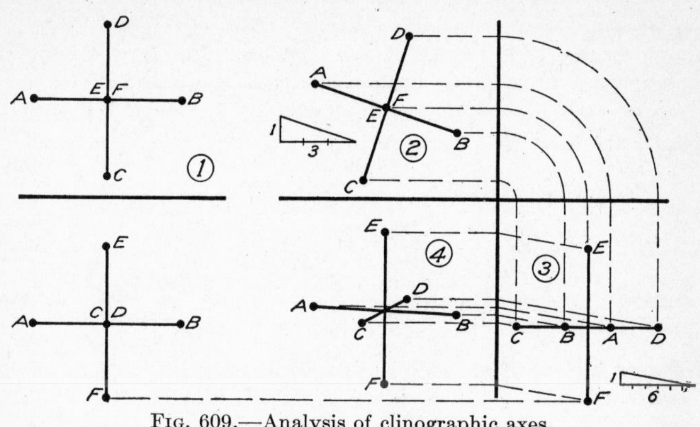

FIG. 609.—Analysis of clinographic axes.

oblique drawing ratios such as ⅔ or ¾ may be used with pleasing effect.

Pictorial drawings are sometimes made without reference to the theory of projection, on axis combinations of 15° and 30°, 15° and 45°, 15° and 15°, 20° and 20°.

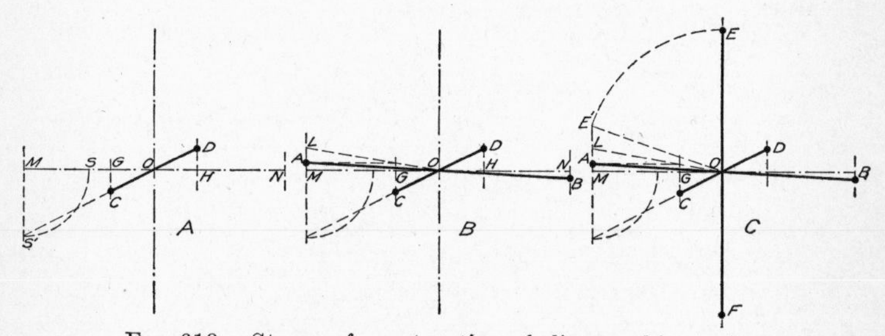

FIG. 610.—Stages of construction of clinographic axes.

264. Clinographic Projection.—This system was devised for the drawing of crystal figures in mineralogy to get a position in which no faces of the many crystal forms would be projected as a line. It is a form of oblique projection in which the figure is imagined as revolved about a vertical axis through an angle whose tangent is ⅓; then the eye (at an infinite distance) is elevated through an angle whose tangent is ⅙. Figure 609 is a graphic explanation: 1 represents the top and front views of the three axes of a cube; 2 is the top view revolved through the angle whose tangent is ⅓; 3 is the side view of 2; 4 is a front view projected from 3 and 2, the projection from 3 being at the angle whose tangent is ⅙.

When used in crystallography a diagram of the axes is usually constructed very accurately on cardboard and used as a templet or stencil, the center and terminal points being transferred by pricking through to the sheet on which the drawing is to be made. Figure 610 shows, in stages, a method of constructing this diagram, which as will be seen is simply a combination in one view of 2, 3 and 4 of Fig. 609. Take *MON* of convenient length, divide it into three equal parts, at *G* and *H*, and draw perpendiculars as shown. Make $MS = \frac{1}{2}\ MO$ and draw *S′OD*. Then *CD* will be one horizontal axis. Make $ML = \frac{1}{2}OG$ and draw *LO*. Project the point of intersection of *LO* and *GC* back horizontally to *LM* at *A*; then *AOB* will be the other horizontal axis. To obtain length of vertical axis make $ME = OG$, and lay off *OE* and *OF* equal to *OE*.

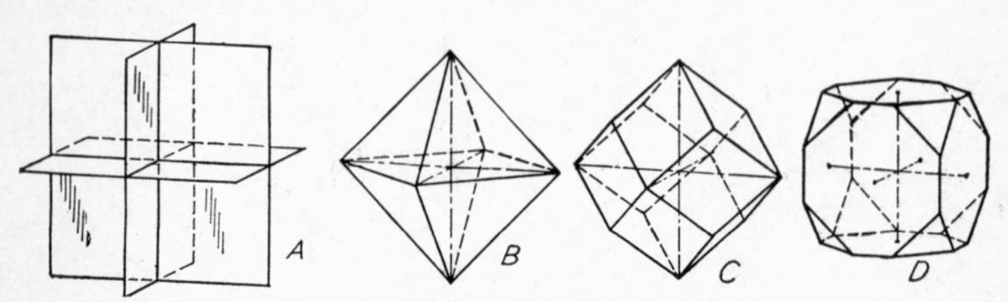

Fig. 611.—Crystals in clinographic projection.

The axial planes, and some crystals drawn on these axes, are shown in Fig. 611. These axes are for the cubic or isometric system of crystals. Axes for the other crystal systems may be constructed graphically in the same way, by drawing their orthographic projections, revolving, and projecting to the vertical plane with oblique projectors as was done in Fig. 609.

265. Sketching.—One of the valuable uses of the pictorial methods is in making freehand sketches, either to illustrate some object or detail of construction or dimensioned to form working drawings. The next chapter discusses pictorial sketching, emphasizing such points as flattening the axes (the beginner's usual mistake is in drawing them too steep, thereby spoiling the appearance of his sketch), keeping parallel lines parallel and vertical lines vertical, always blocking in squares before sketching circles, not confusing the drawing with dotted lines, etc.

PROBLEMS

266. The following problems are intended to serve two purposes: first, for practice in the various methods of pictorial representation; second, for practice in reading and translating orthographic projections.

In reading a drawing remember that a line on any view always means an edge or change in direction and that one must always look at another view to find out what kind of change it is. Do not try or expect to read a whole drawing at one glance.

The problems are arranged in groups for convenience in selection and assignment. Figures from previous chapters may be used for a further variety of problems.

Do not show hidden lines except where necessary to explain construction.

Group I. Isometric Drawing.—Figs. 612 to 634. Probs. 1 to 23.

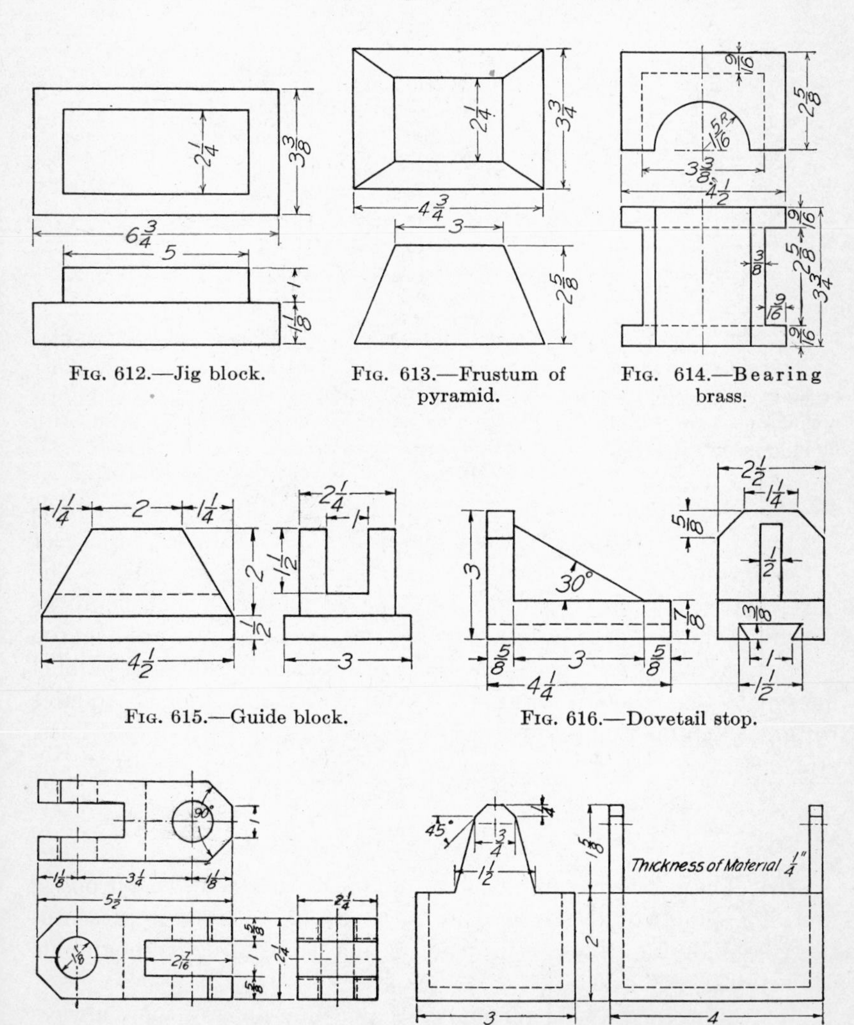

Fig. 612.—Jig block.

Fig. 613.—Frustum of pyramid.

Fig. 614.—Bearing brass.

Fig. 615.—Guide block.

Fig. 616.—Dovetail stop.

Fig. 617.—Swivel block.

Fig. 618.—Hanging box.

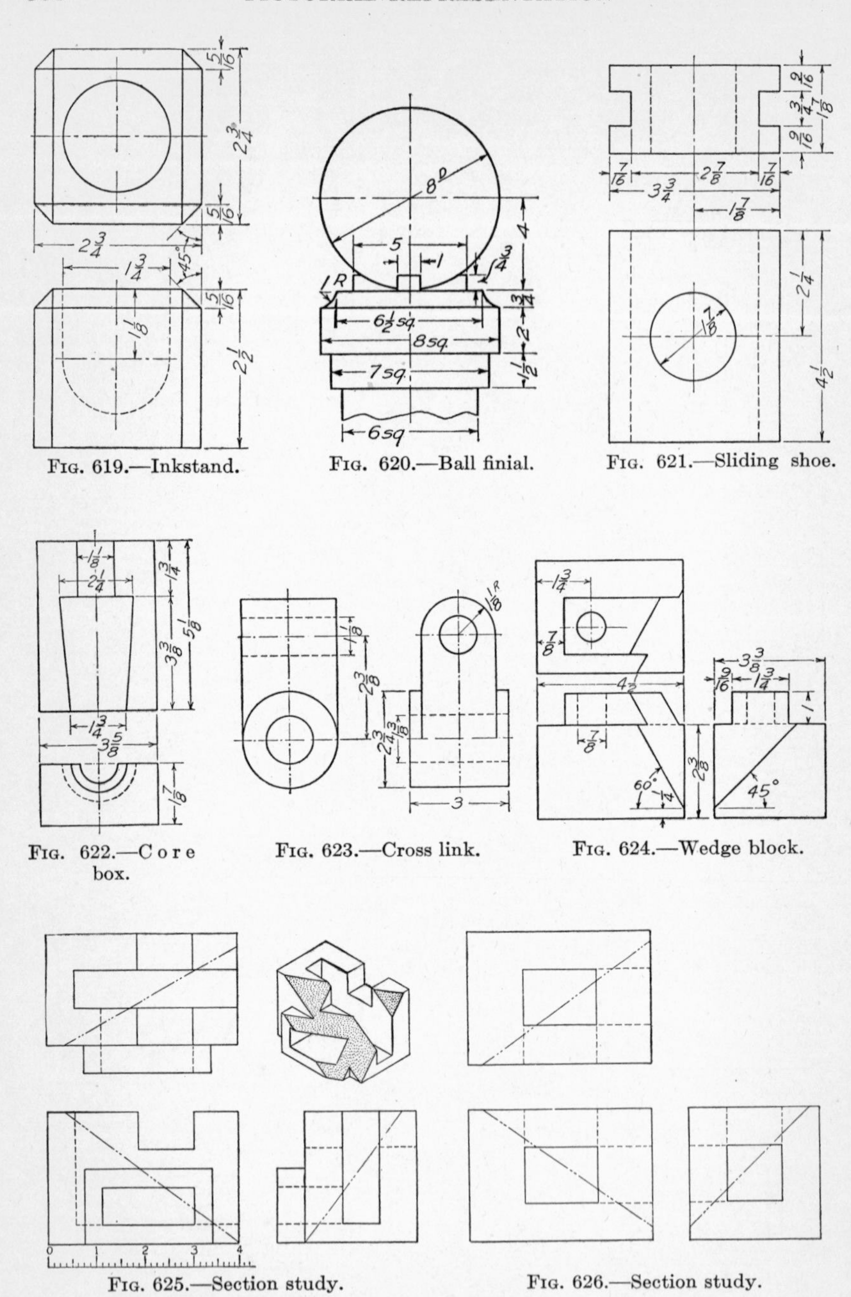

FIG. 619.—Inkstand.

FIG. 620.—Ball finial.

FIG. 621.—Sliding shoe.

FIG. 622.—Core box.

FIG. 623.—Cross link.

FIG. 624.—Wedge block.

FIG. 625.—Section study.

FIG. 626.—Section study.

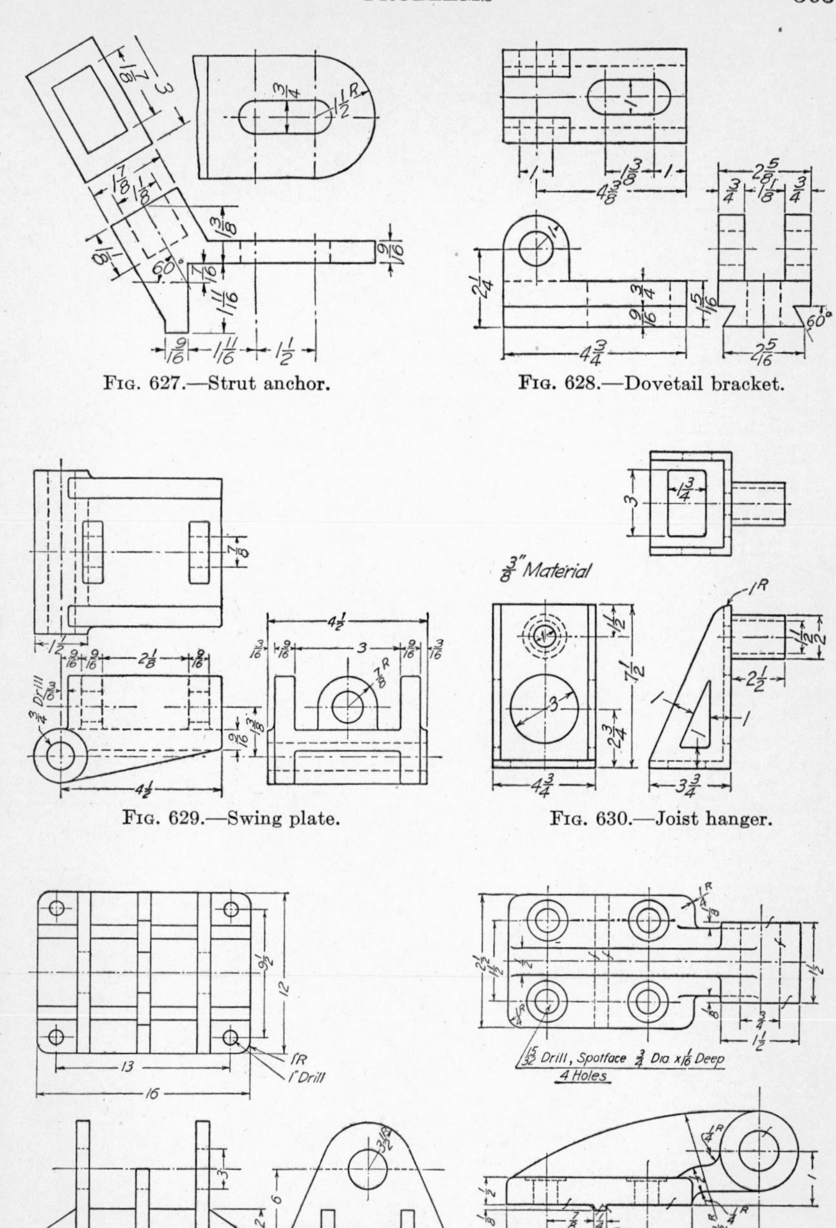

Fig. 627.—Strut anchor.

Fig. 628.—Dovetail bracket.

Fig. 629.—Swing plate.

Fig. 630.—Joist hanger.

Fig. 631.—Hinged shoe.

Fig. 632.—Offset side bracket.

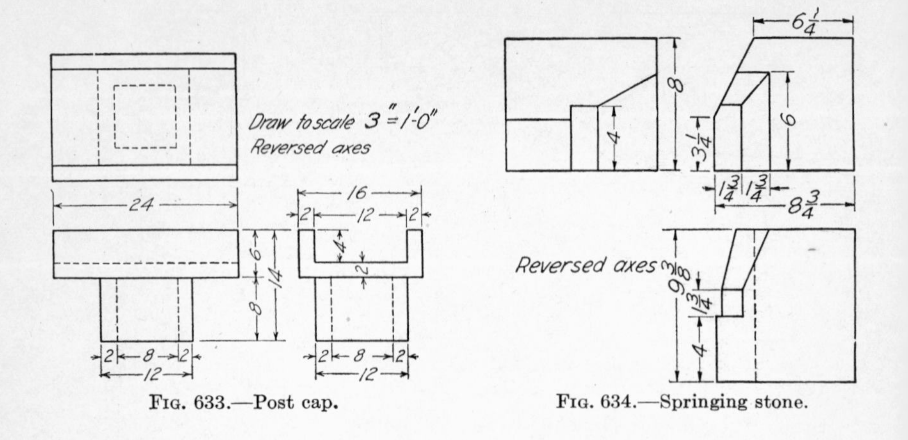

Fig. 633.—Post cap.

Fig. 634.—Springing stone.

Group II. Isometric Sections.—Figs. 635 to 642. Probs. 24 to 31.

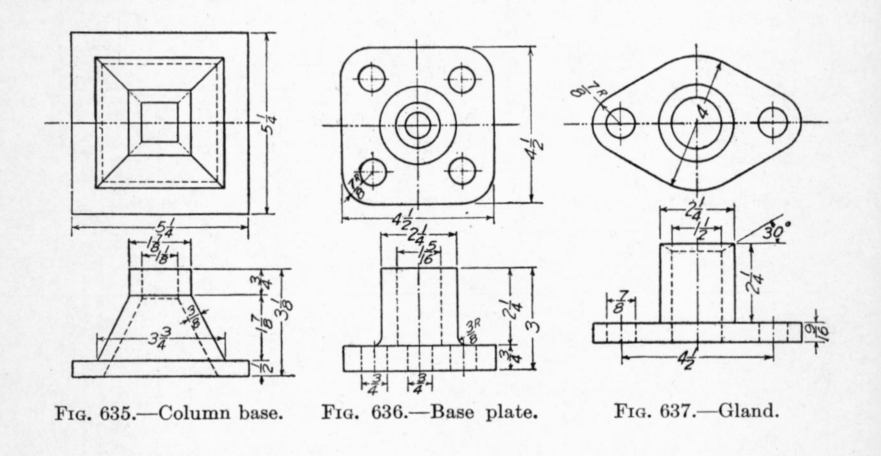

Fig. 635.—Column base.

Fig. 636.—Base plate.

Fig. 637.—Gland.

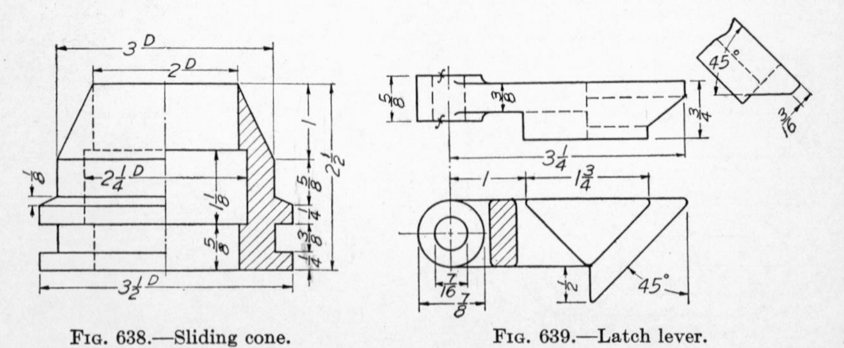

Fig. 638.—Sliding cone.

Fig. 639.—Latch lever.

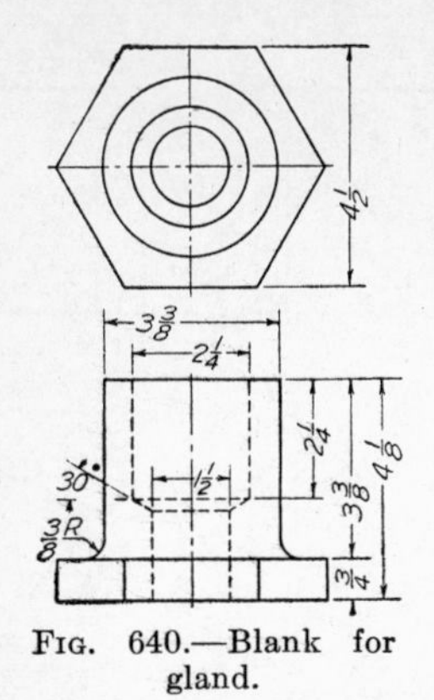

FIG. 640.—Blank for gland.

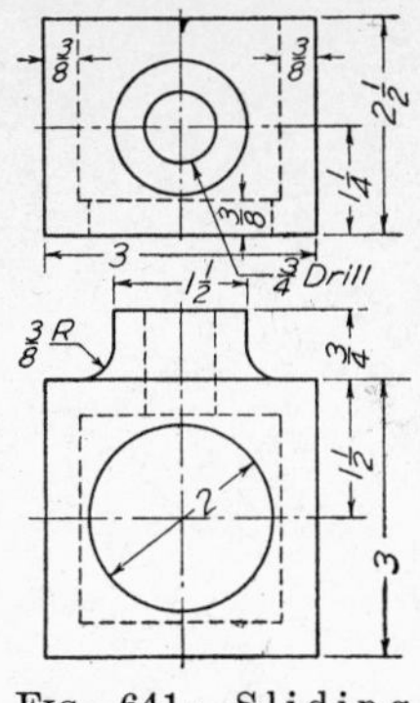

FIG. 641.—Sliding cover.

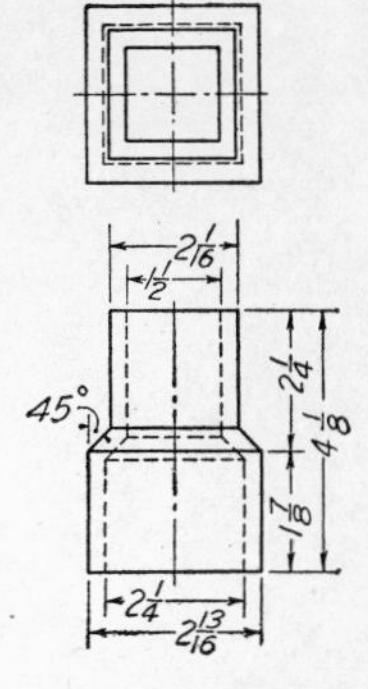

FIG. 642.—Socket wrench.

Group III. Oblique Drawing.—Figs. 643 to 661. Probs. 32 to 50.

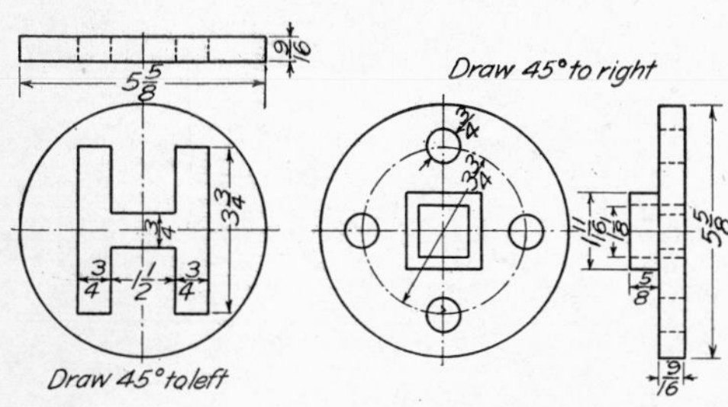

FIG 643.—Letter die. FIG. 644.—Guide plate.

Draw to scale 1"=1' and 30° to right

FIG. 645.—Monument.

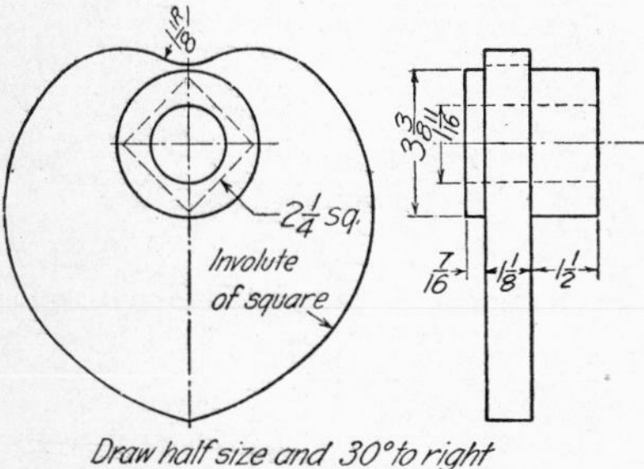

FIG. 646.—Heart cam.

Draw 45° to left

FIG. 647.—Ratchet wheel.

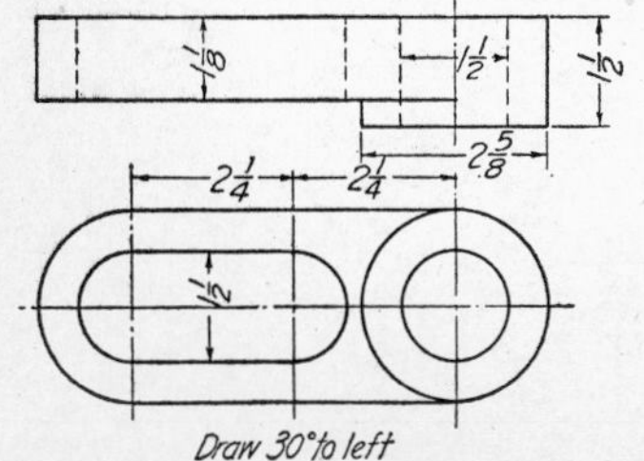

FIG. 648.—Slotted link.

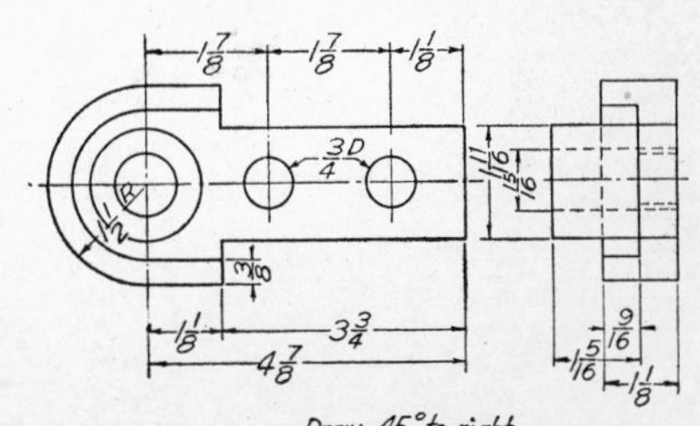

FIG. 649.—Swivel plate.

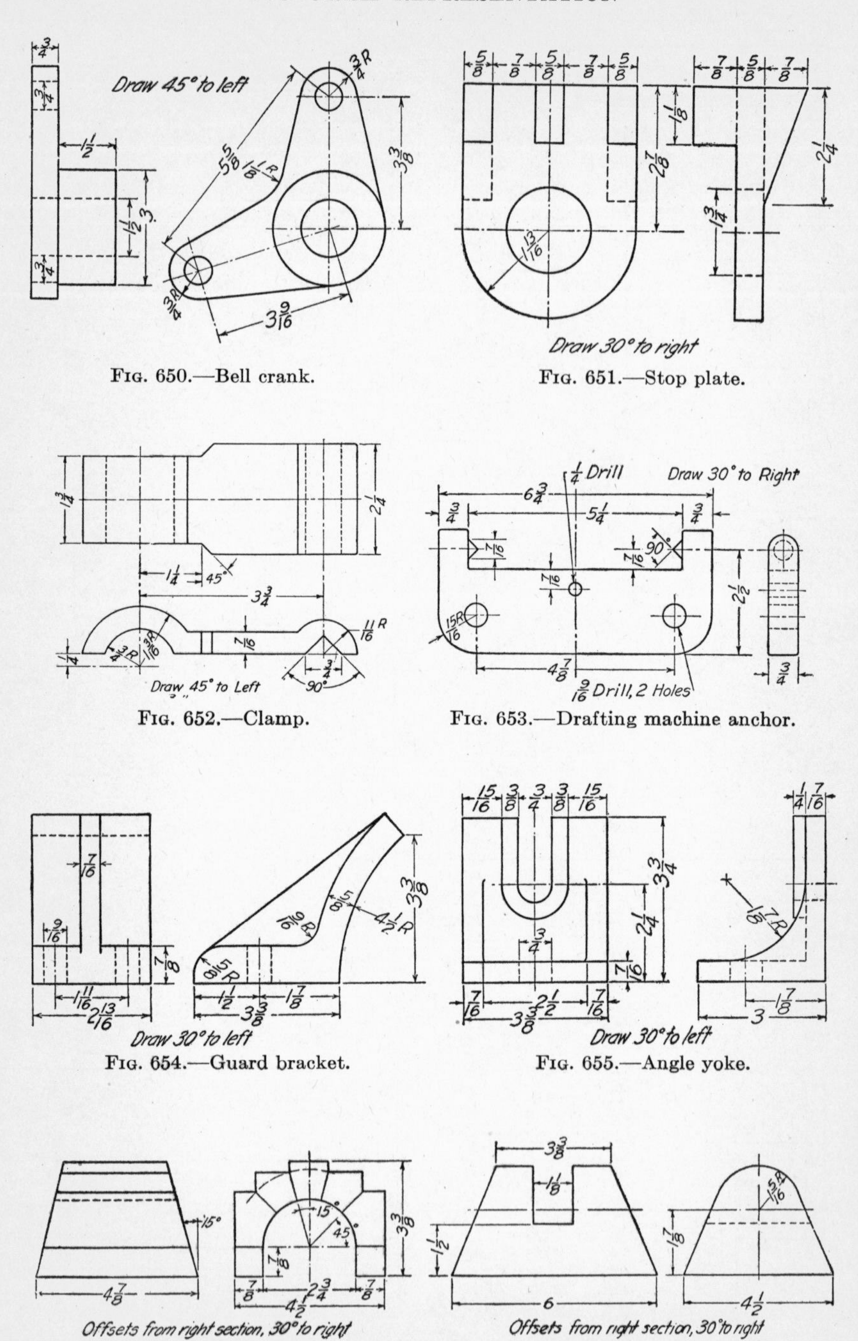

Fig. 650.—Bell crank.

Fig. 651.—Stop plate.

Fig. 652.—Clamp.

Fig. 653.—Drafting machine anchor.

Fig. 654.—Guard bracket.

Fig. 655.—Angle yoke.

Fig. 656.—Culvert model.

Fig. 657.—Slotted guide.

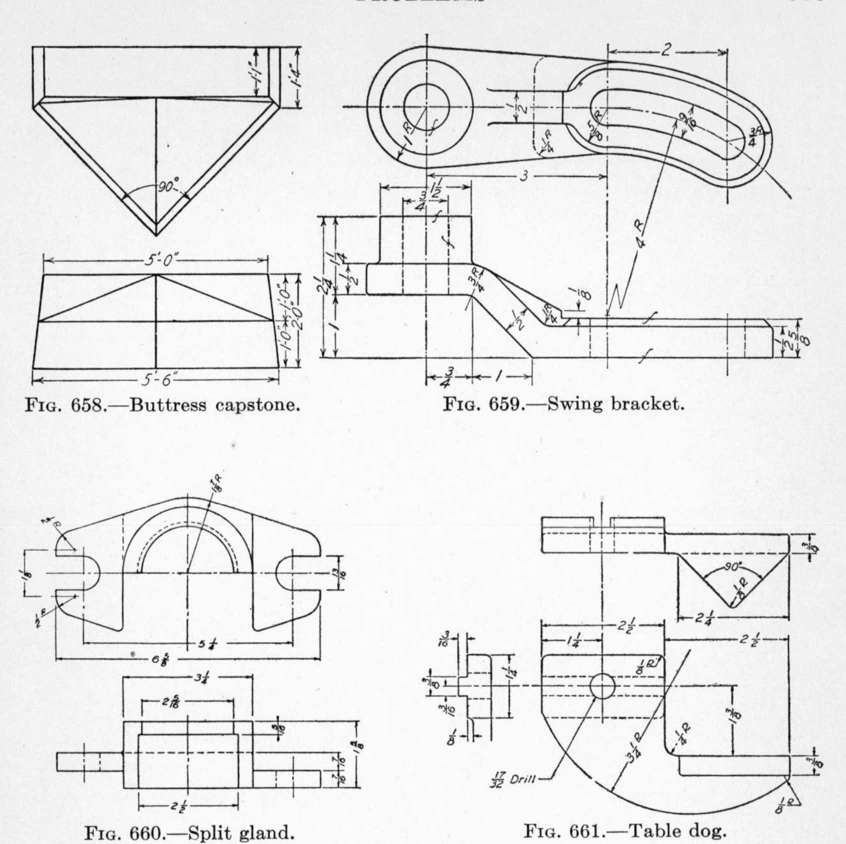

Fig. 658.—Buttress capstone.

Fig. 659.—Swing bracket.

Fig. 660.—Split gland.

Fig. 661.—Table dog.

Group IV. Oblique Sections or Half Sections.—Figs. 302 to 308 and 662, 663. Probs. 51 to 60.

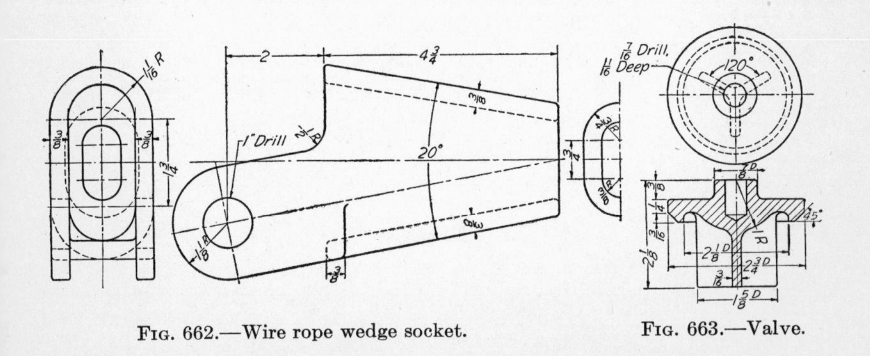

Fig. 662.—Wire rope wedge socket.

Fig. 663.—Valve.

Group V. Cabinet and Dimetric Drawing.—Use Figs. 618, 631, 633, 635.

Group VI. Reading Exercises.—Figs. 664, 665, 666. These figures are to be sketched freehand in one of the pictorial systems, as a test in the ability to read orthographic projections. They may also be used as reading problems by requiring other orthographic views, particularly the figures with two views given. Note that *C*-4 has warped surfaces on the sides.

Find three solutions of figure *Y* and two solutions each for *Z*-1, *Z*-2, *Z*-3 and *Z*-4. In the last row of Figs. 666, *A*-*A* to *E*-*E*, each problem has several solutions.

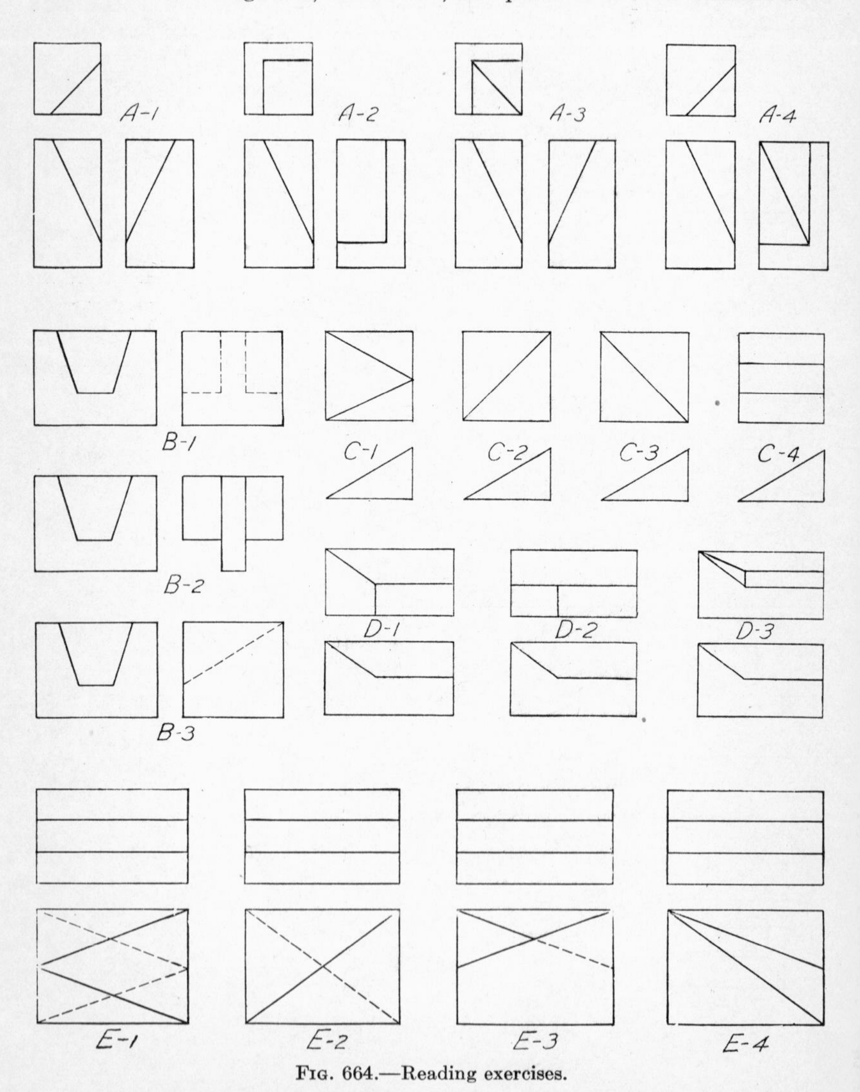

Fig. 664.—Reading exercises.

FIG. 665.—Reading exercises.

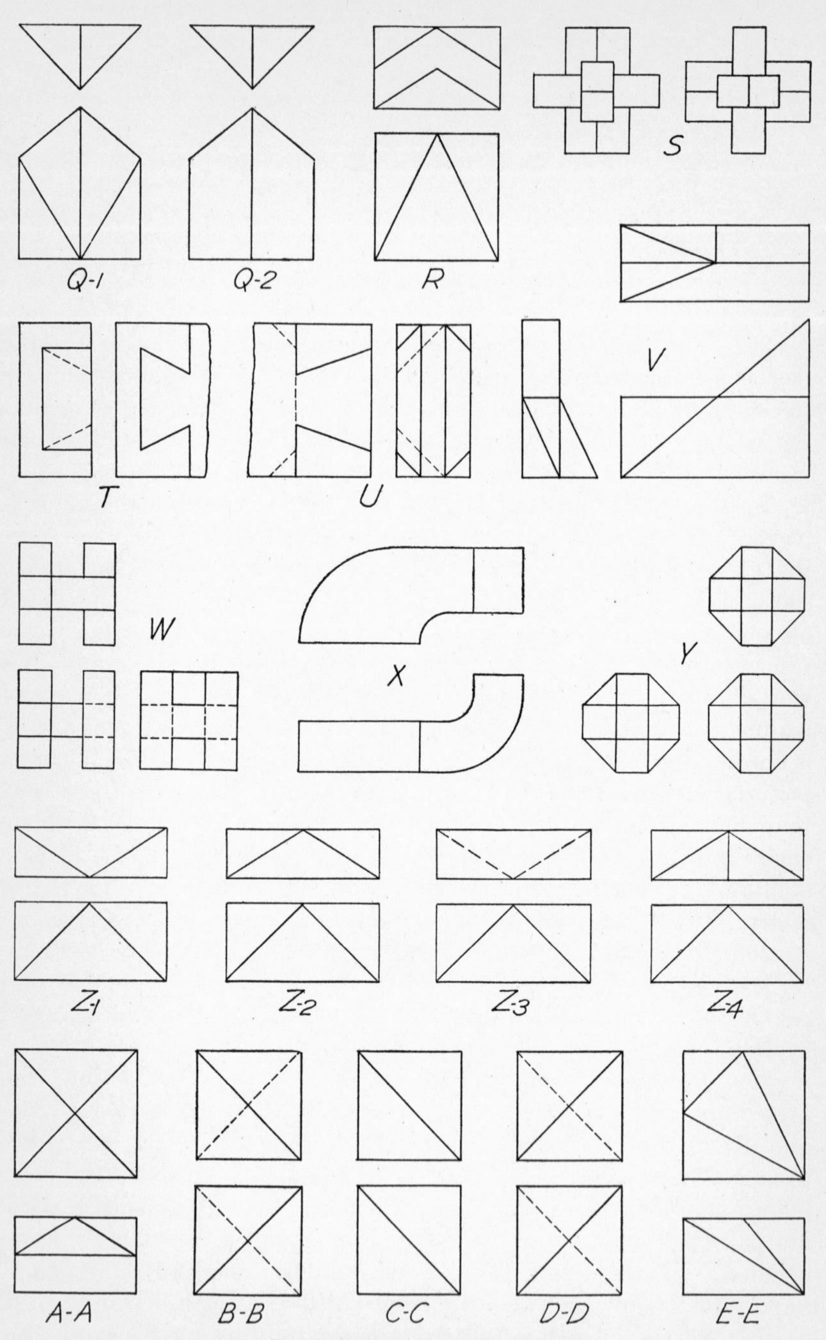

FIG. 666.—Reading exercises.

CHAPTER XV

PICTORIAL SKETCHING

267. The necessity to the engineer of training in freehand sketching has been emphasized in Chapter XII. While this referred particularly to sketching in orthographic projection it must be extended to include the ability to sketch pictorially with skill and facility, before the engineer can be called adequately equipped to use the graphic language.

In designing and inventing, the first ideas come into the mind in pictorial form, and preliminary sketches made in this form preserve the ideas as visualized. Then the preliminary orthographic design sketches are made. A pictorial sketch of an object or of some detail of construction can often be used to explain it when the orthographic projection cannot be read intelligently by a client or workman. If a working drawing is difficult to understand, one of the best ways of reading it is to start a pictorial sketch of it. Usually before the sketch is finished the orthographic drawing is perfectly clear. Often, again, a pictorial sketch may be made more quickly and serve as a better record than orthographic views of the same piece would do. The young engineer should not be deterred by any fancied lack of "artistic ability." An engineer's sketch is a record of information, not a "work of art." The one requirement common to both is *good proportion.*

268. Methods.—Although not an accurate classification, there may be said to be three pictorial methods, axonometric, oblique and perspective. The mechanical construction of the first two has been explained in detail in the previous chapter.

269. Axonometric Sketching.—After a clear visualization, the first procedure is to select the best position from which to view the object and thus determine the direction of axes. By referring back to page 288 on axonometric drawing it is remembered that there is an infinite number of positions for the three axes representing three mutually perpendicular lines and that the simplest was the isometric position. Sketches may be made on isometric axes, but, unless it is important to show some feature from the top, a much better effect is gained and the distortion greatly lessened by drawing the cross-axes at a much smaller angle with the horizontal, Fig. 667. Since measurements are not made on sketches the axes may be foreshortened until satisfactory to the eye and the effect of distortion may be overcome still further by slightly converging the receding lines. Objects of rectangular outlines are best adapted to sketching in axonometric projection.

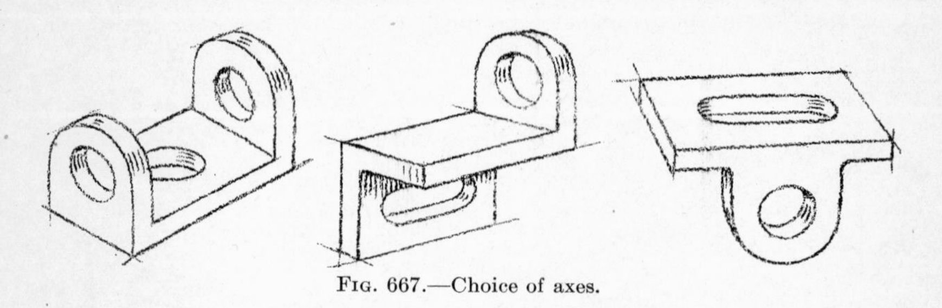

FIG. 667.—Choice of axes.

A successful method of establishing axes used by George J. Hood is to sketch first a horizontal ellipse (with a little practice this can be done with a free sweep of the arm), Fig. 668. At some point, draw a

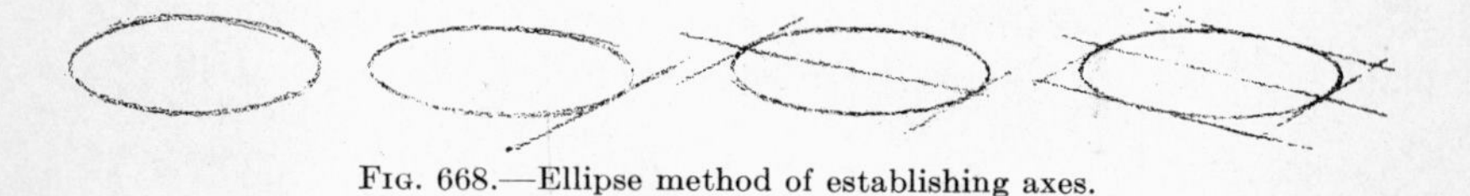

FIG. 668.—Ellipse method of establishing axes.

tangent. Through this point and the center of the ellipse draw one of the conjugate diameters and at the other end of this diameter

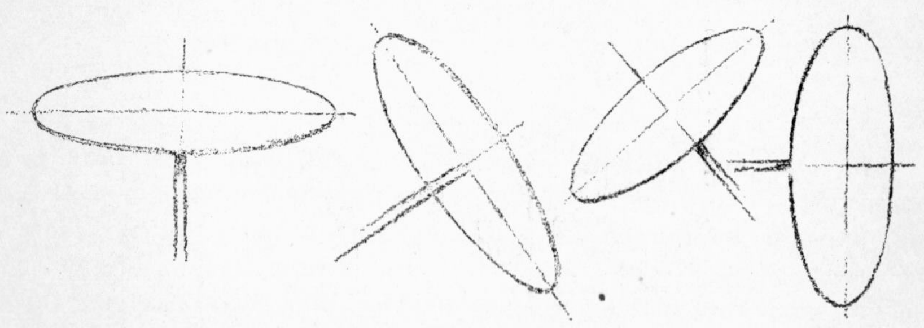

FIG. 669.—Relation of ellipse axes.

a second tangent parallel to the first. Complete the square by drawing the other two sides parallel to the diameter.

After setting the axes the sketch should be blocked in by drawing the principal outlines, boxing the cylindrical parts in their enclosing square prisms. A circle in pictorial drawing is always an ellipse whose major axis is at right angles to the shaft or rotation axis of the circle. Thus its minor axis coincides on the drawing with the shaft axis, Fig. 669. Locate these axes and carry the sketch on as suggested in Fig. 670, preserving the proportions by completing the main outlines before adding any minor details. Do not use any hidden lines unless necessary for the description of the piece.

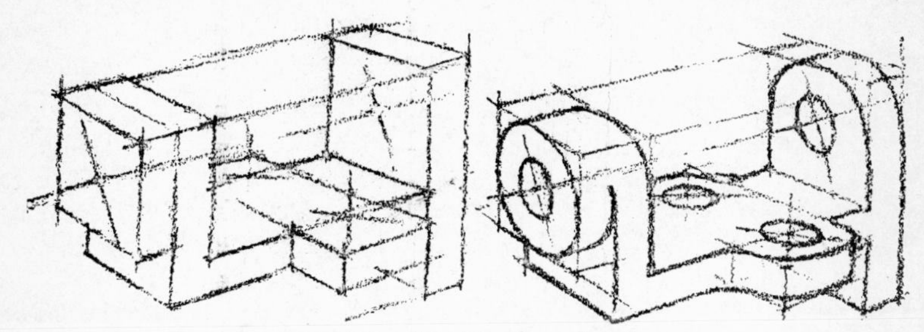

Fig. 670.—Blocking-in a sketch.

Some care must be exercised in adding dimensions to a pictorial sketch. The extension lines must be either in or perpendicular to the plane on which the dimension is being given (see paragraph 150).

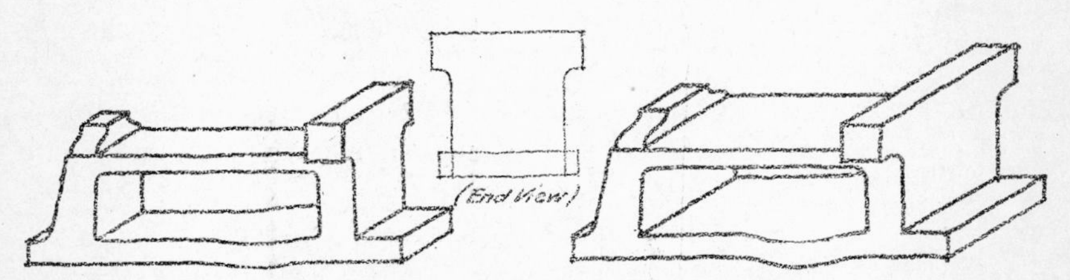

Fig. 671.—Oblique, with and without foreshortening.

270. Oblique Sketching.—The advantage of oblique projection in preserving one face without distortion is of particular value in sketching, and the painful effect of distortion in oblique drawing done mechanically may be greatly lessened in sketching, by foreshortening the cross-axis to a pleasing proportion, Fig. 671. By converging the lines parallel to the cross-axis the effect of parallel perspective is obtained. This converging in either axonometric or oblique is sometimes called "fake perspective."

271. Perspective Sketching.—A sketch made in perspective gives by far the most pleasing effect pictorially. For constructing a perspective drawing of a proposed structure from its plans and elevations a knowledge of the principles of perspective drawing is required, but for making a perspective sketch from the object one may get along by observing the ordinary phenomena of perspective which affect everything we see—the fact of objects appearing smaller in proportion to their distance from the eye, of parallel lines appearing to converge as they recede, of horizontal lines and planes "vanishing" on the horizon.

In sketching in perspective from the model the drawing is made simply by observation, the directions and proportionate lengths of lines being estimated by sighting and measuring on the pencil held at arm's length, with the knowledge of perspective phenomena used as a check.

With the drawing board or sketch pad held in a comfortable drawing position, *perpendicular* to the "line of sight" from the eye to the object, the direction of a line is tested by holding the pencil at arm's length *parallel* to the board, rotating the arm until the pencil appears to coincide with the line on the model, then moving it parallel to this position back to the board.

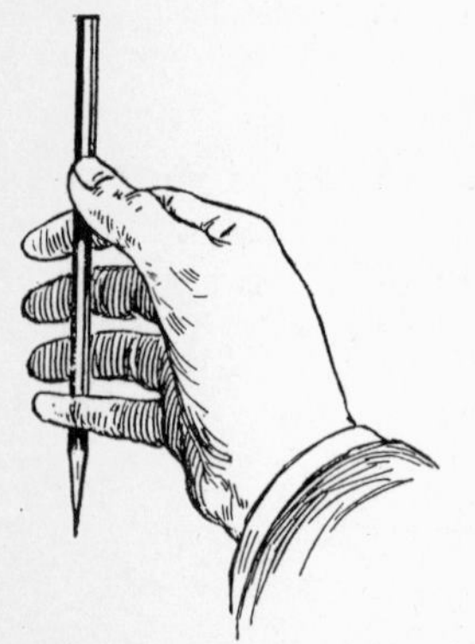

Fig. 672.—Estimating proportion.

The apparent lengths of lines are estimated in the same way, holding the pencil in a plane perpendicular to the line of sight, marking with the thumb the length of pencil which covers a line of the model, rotating the arm with the thumb held in position until the pencil coincides with another line, and estimating the proportion of this measurement to the second line, Fig. 672.

The sketch should be made lightly, with free sketchy lines, and no lines erased until the whole sketch has been blocked in. Do not make the mistake of getting it too small.

In starting a sketch from the object, set it in a position to give the most advantageous view, and sketch the directions of the principal lines, running the lines past the limits of the figure toward their vanishing points. Block in the enclosing squares for all circles and circle arcs and proceed with the figure, drawing the main outlines first and adding details later, then brighten the sketch with heavier lines. A good draftsman often adds a few touches of surface shading but the beginner should be cautious in attempting it. Figure 673 shows the general appearance of a "one-point" perspective sketch before the construction lines have been erased. Figure 674 is a sketch in angular perspective.

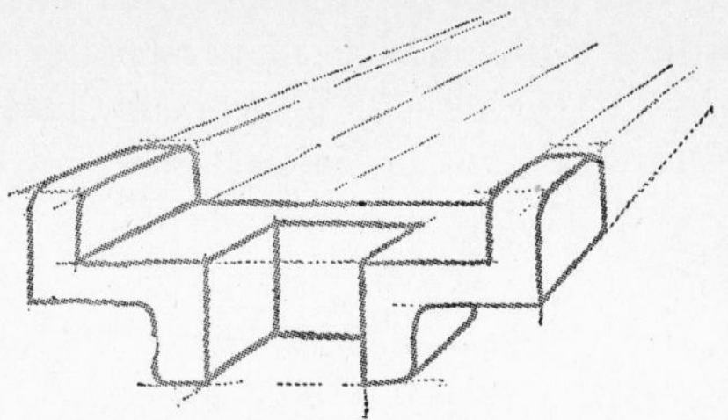

Fig. 673.—Parallel perspective sketch.

272. Sketching from Memory.—After one has become proficient in sketching, the memory for form may be strengthened and the capacity for "stored observation" greatly increased by systematic

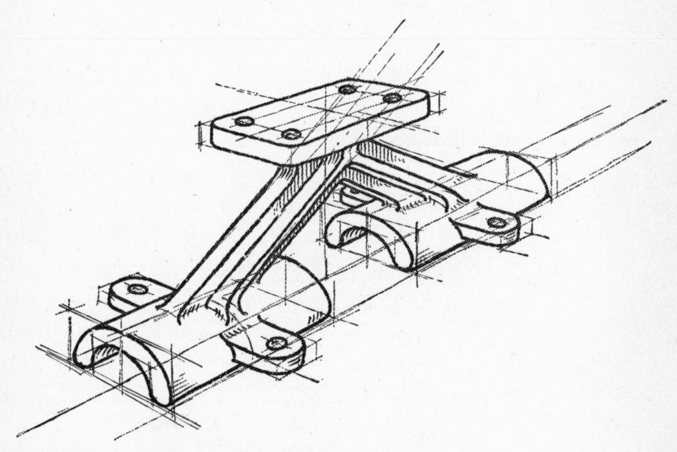

Fig. 674.—Angular perspective sketch.

and regular practice in sketching from memory. The order of this study should be graded carefully; first, easy pictorial drawings to be "read," then "copied" exactly from memory; second, orthographic drawings to be read and copied; third, pictorial drawings to be memorized, then drawn in orthographic; fourth, castings and machines to be studied and drawn in orthographic; fifth, orthographic drawings to be studied, then translated from memory into pictorial sketches.

Study the drawing with close concentration until every detail is stored for future visualization (the time required for this observation should be noted, although it is not the important factor). Then make an accurate sketch of the object from memory. When finished, com-

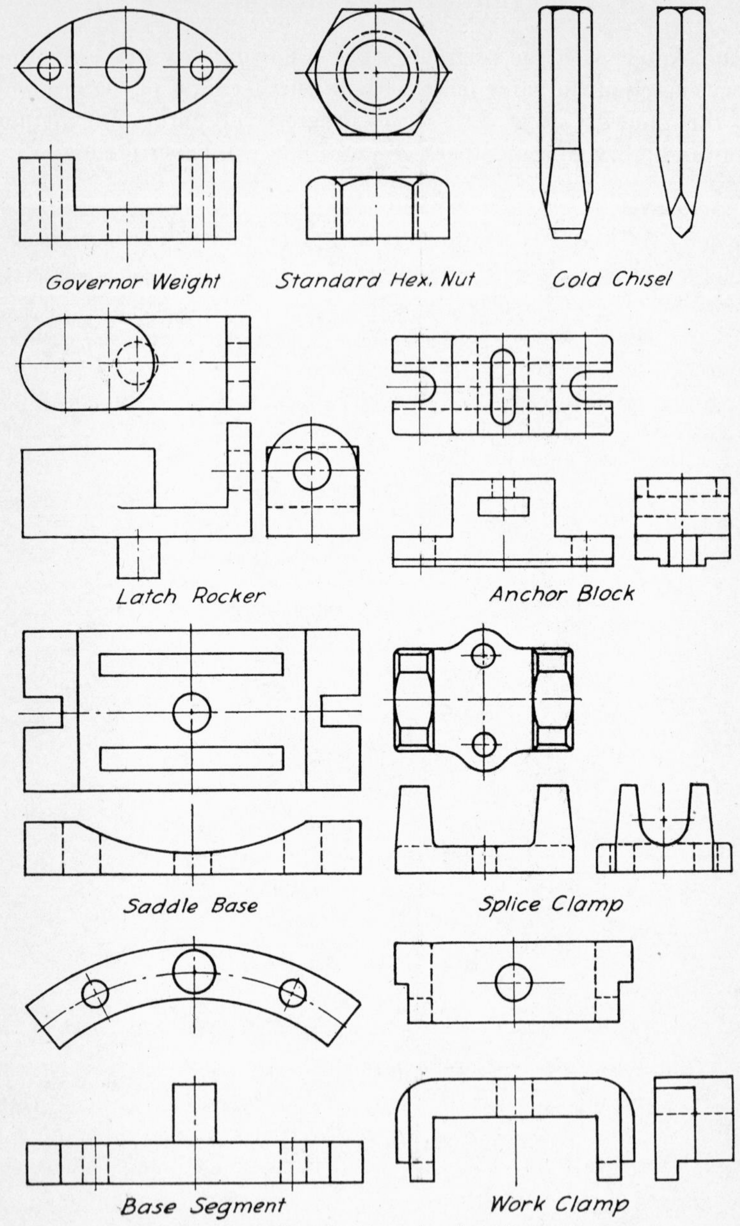

FIG. 675.—Problems for sketching.

pare the sketch with the original. The following day make another memory sketch of the same piece without further sight of the original. Carry this practice along with pieces progressively more difficult and the gain in ability to remember form and line will be surprising.

PROBLEMS

Group I.—Fig. 675. Make pictorial sketches of the pieces shown in this figure.

Group II.—Select from Figs. 612 to 663 some not previously drawn and make freehand sketches in perspective.

Group III.—Select one of the objects from Fig. 536, study it with concentration for 20 seconds, close the book and reproduce it.

Group IV.—Select one of the pieces from Figs. 664 to 666. Study it for from 10 to 30 seconds, close the book, make a memory sketch of the orthographic projection, then make a pictorial sketch.

CHAPTER XVI

PERSPECTIVE DRAWING

273. Perspective drawing is the representation of an object as it actually appears to an observer located at a particular station point. Geometrically it is the figure resulting when the cone of rays from the eye to the object is intersected by a vertical "picture plane." There is a distinction between "artists' perspective" and "geometrical perspective" in that the artist draws the object as he sees it projected on the spherical surface of the retina of his eye, while geometrical, or mechanical, perspective is projected on a plane as in a photograph, but except in wide angles of vision the difference is not noticeable.

In a technical way, perspective is used more in connection with architecture than in other branches, but every engineer will find it of advantage to know the principles of the subject.

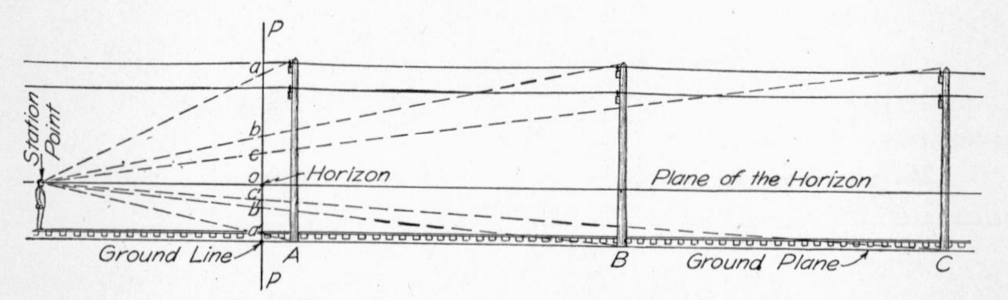

FIG. 676.—The observer and the picture plane.

274. Elementary Concepts of Perspective.—Let the student imagine himself standing on a long straight railroad track as in Fig. 676, with a perpendicular transparent plane erected between him and the view ahead. This plane is called the picture plane (*P.P.*) and upon it the picture is conceived to be projected. Rays from the observer's eye to the ends of the telegraph pole *A* intercept a distance *aa'* on *P.P.* Similarly rays from pole *B* intercept *bb'*, a lesser distance. The intercept *cc'* from *C* is still less. These distances *aa'*, *bb'*, *cc'*, etc., correspond in proportion to the heights of the images made upon the retina of the eye by the respective poles *A*, *B* and *C* and agree with our everyday experience—that the farther away an object is, the smaller it appears. It is evident from the figure that, as the succeeding poles in the line are considered, the projection of each upon the picture plane will be shorter than the preceding one. Thus a pole far away on the horizon would show only as a point at *o*. The horizontal plane through this point *o* and the observer's eye is called the plane of the horizon, and the horizontal line of intersection of this plane with the picture plane is called simply the *horizon*. Similarly the intersection of the ground plane with the picture plane is called the *ground* line. In drawing large objects the horizon is usually taken at a distance of 5½ feet above the ground plane since that is about the height of a man's eye. The position of the observer is called the *station point*. To avoid a distorted picture it should not be closer to the picture plane than twice the width or height of the object to be drawn.

Figure 677 shows the picture as seen by the observer in Fig. 676. The plane of the paper is the picture plane. The intercepts *aa′*, *bb′*, *cc′*, etc., of Fig. 676 show in the perspective as the heights of the respective poles as they diminish in size and disappear on the horizon. In a similar way the rails converge and vanish. It is evident that all horizontal planes vanish on the horizon line. Therefore *any horizontal line will vanish at some point on the horizon.* A system of parallel horizontal lines vanishes at a single point; thus, as with the telegraph wires and track, *horizontal lines perpendicular to the picture plane vanish at the center of vision*, a point on the horizon directly in front of the observer.

Vertical lines, being parallel to the picture plane, pierce it at an infinite distance and therefore do not vanish but show vertical in the picture.

275. Classes of Perspective Drawings.—Ordinary perspective drawings may be divided into two classes: (1) angular perspective and (2) parallel perspective, although the latter is simply a special case of the former.

When the object is so situated that none of its principal vertical planes are parallel to the picture plane, it is said to be in *angular perspective*. It may be turned at any angle (30° is very often used). If the angularity is reduced to 0° the face becomes parallel to the picture plane, making *parallel perspective* drawing. Figure 677 is in parallel perspective since the cross-arms and railroad ties are parallel to the picture plane.

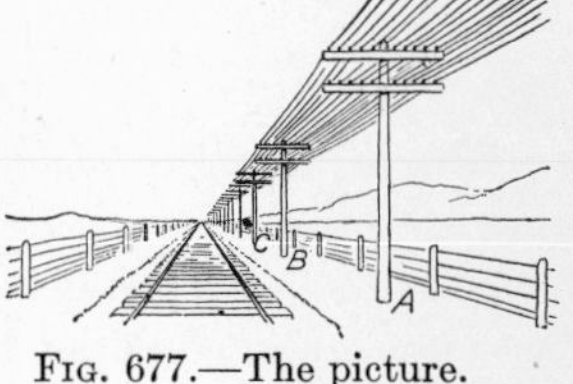

FIG. 677.—The picture.

276. To Make an Angular Perspective Drawing.—Let it be required to make an angular perspective of the monument, Fig. 678, having given two orthographic views, as in insert. Assume the picture plane to be set up against the front corner of the base, at an angle of

30° with the long side, and the observer 12 feet away directly in front of the corner, with a 5½ foot horizon.

The upper part of Fig. 678 may be thought of as the top view, and the lower part as the front or elevation view of the perspective drawing, the picture plane having been detached and moved forward, then laid down into the plane of the paper. The top view is used for

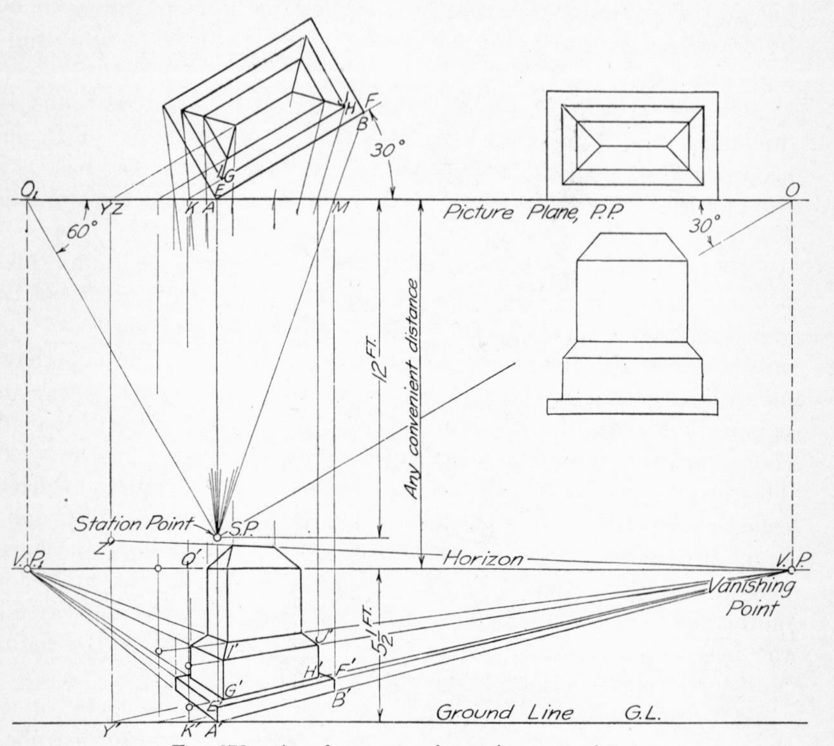

Fig. 678.—Angular perspective, using cone of rays.

construction purposes only and in practical work will usually be on a separate piece of paper held in position by thumb tacks.

With reference to the top view, visual rays from the station point *S.P.* (which is the top view of the observer's eye, 5½ feet above the ground) to the horizontal line *AB* of the long side of the base give on the picture plane an intercept *AM*. Imagine the line *AB* as moving to the right along the ground but still making 30° with *P.P.* Its intercept will become less and less, reaching zero value at some point *O*. This point is evidently on a 30° line from the *S.P.* and becomes the *vanishing point* for all horizontal 30° lines. Thus the vanishing point for any set of horizontal lines is found by drawing a line parallel to them from the *S.P.* to the *P.P.* Now imagine the picture plane, whose top view or edge only has been thus far considered, to be moved forward any convenient distance and revolved into the plane of the paper about the ground line *G.L.* The horizon will fall 5½ feet above the *G.L.* and the vanishing point *O* of the plan, being on the horizon, will fall at *V.P.* Find the vanishing point for the horizontal lines at 60° by drawing a 60° line from *S.P.* to the picture plane at O_1 and drop a perpendicular to $V.P._1$.

The perspective of the line *AB* of the plan would be found by drawing a line from *A'* (which is in the picture plane) to *V.P.* and dropping a perpendicular from *M*. Since the corner of the base is in the picture plane, *A'E'* will show its actual height and the top edge *E'F'* of the base will be drawn as shown.

277. Vertical Measurements.—With reference again to Figs. 676 and 677, it is evident that on account of the convergence of the visual rays all lines back of the picture plane are shortened and that only lines lying in the picture plane show in their true length. Hence *all measurements must be made in the picture plane.* Thus, to get the perspective of the face *GHJI*, imagine on the plan a vertical plane containing this face, extended until it cuts the picture plane at *K*. This intersection on the front view becomes the line *Q'K'*, which is called a *measuring line.* On it measure the actual heights of *G* and *I* from the ground. Lines vanished to *V.P.* from these measured heights and intersected by perpendiculars dropped from the intercepts on the plan will give the perspective of the face. In the same way find the perspective of the face of the die block, and finish the figure. Notice that *Z'Y'* is the measuring line for the ridge.

278. Summarizing.—(1) Draw the top view of the object, at the desired angle with *P.P.*; (2) locate the station point and draw from it the cone of rays, obtaining the intercept of each line of the plan; (3) find the top view of the two vanishing points by drawing from *S.P.* lines parallel to the sides of the object; (4) draw the horizon and ground line for the picture; (5) drop the vanishing points to the horizon; (6) start the picture, building from the ground up.

Usually, for compactness on the paper the picture is located in the space between the station point and the picture plane, as in Fig. 679. Pins, or preferably sewing needles, set at the *V.P.* and *S.P.* are convenient aids in drawing converging lines quickly and accurately.

279. Parallel Perspective.—For objects having circles or other curves in a vertical plane, parallel perspective is very convenient as the curves are drawn in their true shape. It is also suitable for interiors, street vistas and similar views where considerable depth is to be represented.

280. To Make a Parallel Perspective Drawing.—Fig. 679. As in angular perspective, the position of the observer's eye is chosen with reference to the picture plane and ground plane, and the plan drawn to scale. The top view of the object is so placed that the planes containing the principal contours are parallel to the picture plane. Consequently all horizontal lines in these planes will be horizontal in the picture and have no vanishing point. Horizontal lines perpendicular to the picture plane will vanish at the center of vision, as in Fig. 677. (Since there is only one vanishing point this is sometimes called "one-point" perspective.) Except for interior views the *S.P.* is generally located to the right or left of the object. For convenience, one face of the object is usually placed in the picture plane and is thus not reduced in size in the perspective.

In Fig. 679 the end of the hub is in the picture plane; thus the center O' is directly below O of the plan, and the circles are drawn in their true size. From O' draw the center line $O'X'$ to $C.V.$ To find the perspective of the center line MN pass a vertical plane through MN intersecting the picture plane in the measuring line GH. Draw a horizontal line from O' intersecting GH, thus locating M', and draw from M' the center line $M'N'$.

By using these two center lines as a framework the remaining construction is simplified. A ray from *S.P.* to B pierces the picture plane at J, which projected down to the center line locates B', and a horizontal line $B'Z$ through B' is the center line of the front face of the nearer arm. The intercept IJ projected down gives the perspective radius $A'B'$. The circular hole of radius CB on the plan has an intercept PJ, giving $C'B'$ as the perspective radius. The arc $Q'Y$ has its center on $O'X'$ at Z. On drawing the tangents $L'Q'$ and KY the face F is completed.

The remaining construction for the arms is exactly the same as that of face F, moving the centers back on the center lines and finding the radii from their corresponding intercepts on the picture plane.

281. The Revolved Plan Method.—This method, sometimes called the method of diagonals and perpendiculars, may often be used to advantage in parallel perspective instead of the cone of rays method. It depends on the principle that the perspective of any point can be found by drawing the perspectives of two lines through it, one perpendicular to the picture plane and one at 45°. One essential feature in drawing by this method is that the picture plane, instead of being detached and moved before revolving, is revolved where it stands, so that the line representing the edge of the picture plane in the plan view becomes the ground line of the pictorial view. Thus in Fig. 680 the phantom *ABCD* is the plan location of a tiled floor, and the picture plane has been revolved down over it. All the lines of the

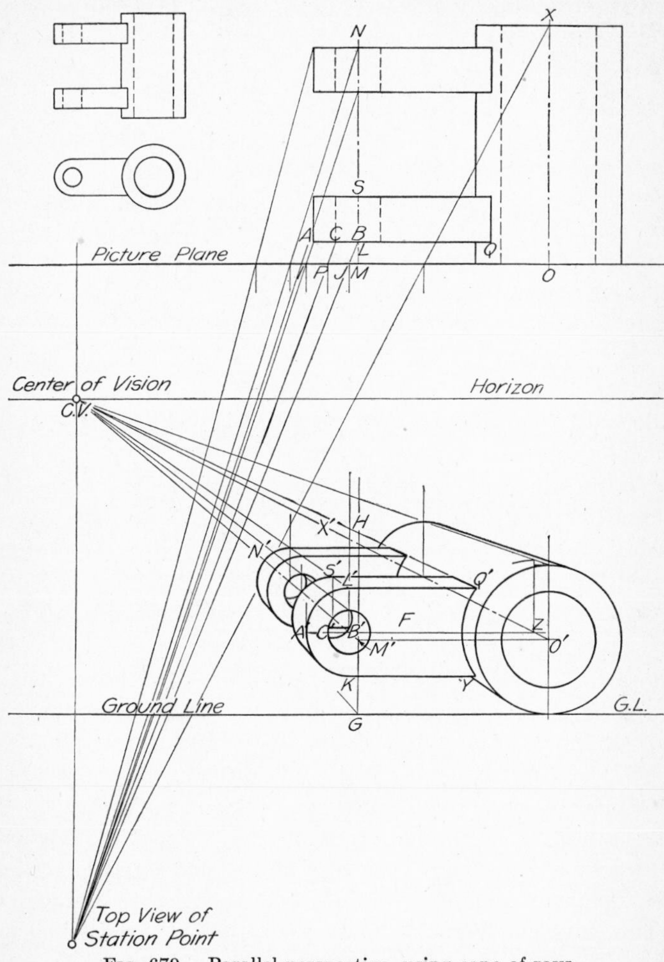

Fig. 679.—Parallel perspective, using cone of rays.

pattern which are perpendicular to the picture plane will vanish at the center of vision *C.V.* The lines at 45°, such as *EP*, will vanish at a point found as in angular perspective by drawing a line through *S.P.*, parallel to *EP*, to *M* and projecting to the horizon at *V*. To avoid the confusion resulting from the perspective falling on the plan, *the plan is not drawn behind the picture plane but is revolved through* 180° and drawn in front in reversed form at AB_rC_rD. The line EP thus reverses to E_rP.

282. To Draw by the Revolved Plan Method.—Fig. 680. Draw a ground line and horizon line. Assume $S.P.$ and from it draw 45° lines locating V and V_1. Draw the revolved plan AB_rC_rD, the front edge against the ground line. Draw a diagonal and a perpendicular

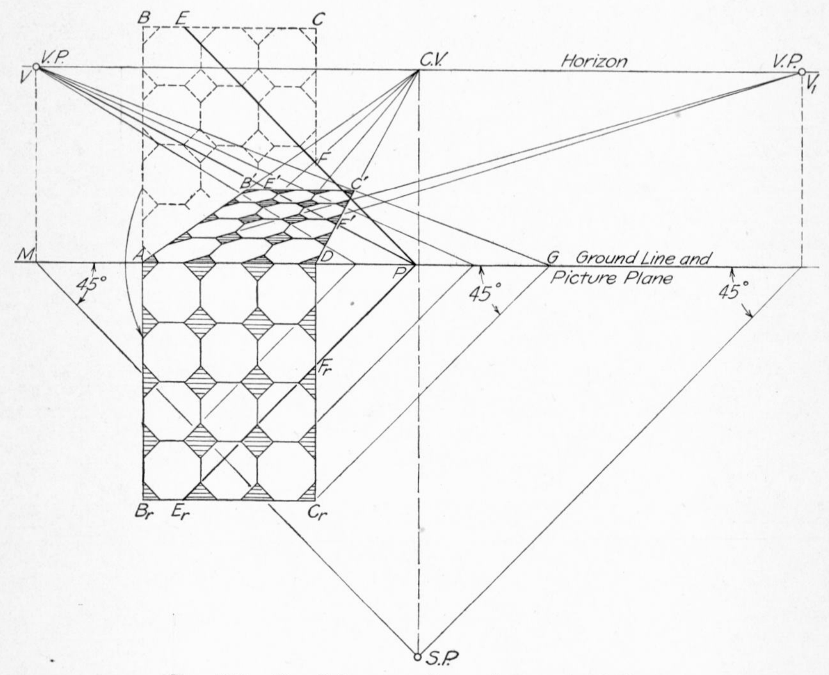

FIG. 680.—Parallel perspective, using revolved plan.

from each point to the ground line. Vanish all the perpendiculars to $C.V.$ and the diagonals to V. Their intersections will locate the perspective. The other system of 45° lines on the pattern would vanish at V_1. The points V and V_1 are called "distance points" since they are the same distance from $C.V.$ as $S.P.$ is from $P.P.$ The perspective could be made without drawing the plan at all, by simply measuring distances on the ground line. Thus the length of DC might have been measured from D to G, and GV would intersect the perspective of the perpendicular giving DC' as the perspective of DC.

283. Measuring Points.—In the same way, angular perspective may be drawn without using the cone of rays and projecting from the ray intercept on the picture plane, by making horizontal measurements through the use of "measuring points." The measuring point method has some advantage in laying off a series of measurements, such as a row of windows, as it avoids a confusion of intercepts on the picture plane and the inaccuracies due to long projection lines. It will be found of advantage, when the cone of rays method is used, to use measuring points for some measurements, and as a check on the first method.

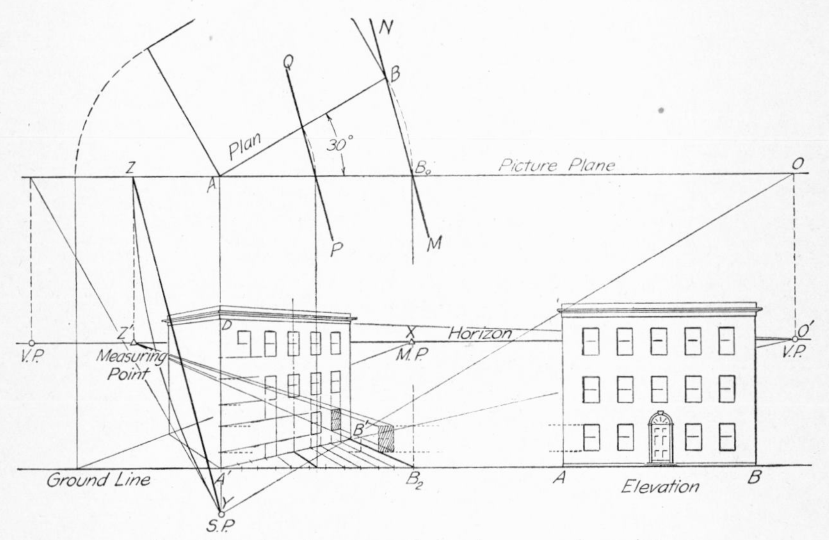

Fig. 681.—Angular perspective, using measuring points.

In the measuring point method the wall AB, Fig. 681, is conceived to be revolved to AB_o for measurement purposes. AB_o, showing below as $A'B_2$, lies in the picture plane and measurements may be made on it directly as shown. In projecting these divisions to $A'B'$ in the perspective drawing, an extra vanishing point is needed for such lines as MN and PQ which connect the two positions of the face. By drawing as usual a line from $S.P.$ to $P.P.$ parallel to MN and projecting to the horizon, the vanishing point Z' is found. Such a point is called a *measuring point* and may be defined as the vanishing point for lines joining corresponding points of the actual and revolved positions of the face concerned.

The divisions on the line $A'B_2$ are therefore projected to $A'B'$ by lines converging to the measuring point Z' and the work completed as under the other method. For work on the end of the building, revolve the end wall as indicated and find another measuring point X, proceeding in the same manner as outlined above for the front wall.

The triangles ABB_o and OZY are similar, since their sides are respectively parallel. Since $AB = AB_o$, then $OY = OZ = O'Z'$. Therefore, a measuring point is as far from the corresponding vanishing point as the station point is from the picture plane, measuring parallel to the face concerned. Practically, a measuring point is located by swinging an arc, with O as a center, from $S.P.$ to Z and projecting to Z'. Nevertheless, the fundamental idea must always be kept in mind that the measuring point is the vanishing point for lines joining the actual and revolved positions of the wall.

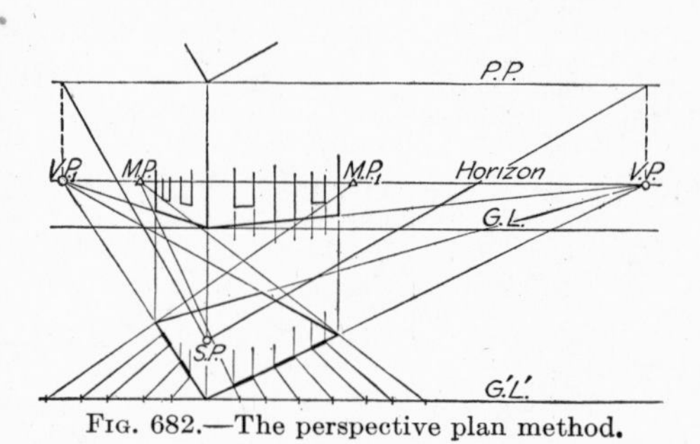

Fig. 682.—The perspective plan method.

The *elevation* or front view in Fig. 681 has been erected on the ground line so that vertical distances or heights may be obtained by projecting horizontally to the measuring line $A'D$. This method is convenient not only in architectural work but in many other cases where a perspective is to be made from two (or more) orthographic views. In fact, all three views may be utilized and held in place by thumb tacks while the perspective is being made, avoiding much laborious transferring of dimensions.

284. Perspective Plan Method.—In practical work it will be found very advantageous to make all horizontal measurements on a *perspective plan* below the ground line as if the plan were laid out on a basement floor. This not only gives better intersections of the lines to the vanishing and measuring points but keeps the construction work off the drawing. The method is suggested in Fig. 682.

285. Inclined Lines.—Thus far attention has been directed to finding the perspective of horizontal and vertical lines. Inclined lines comprise all those lines that are neither parallel nor perpendicular to the horizontal or ground plane. Because they are inclined to the horizontal plane they do not vanish on the horizon but at a point some distance above or below the horizon, depending on their inclination.

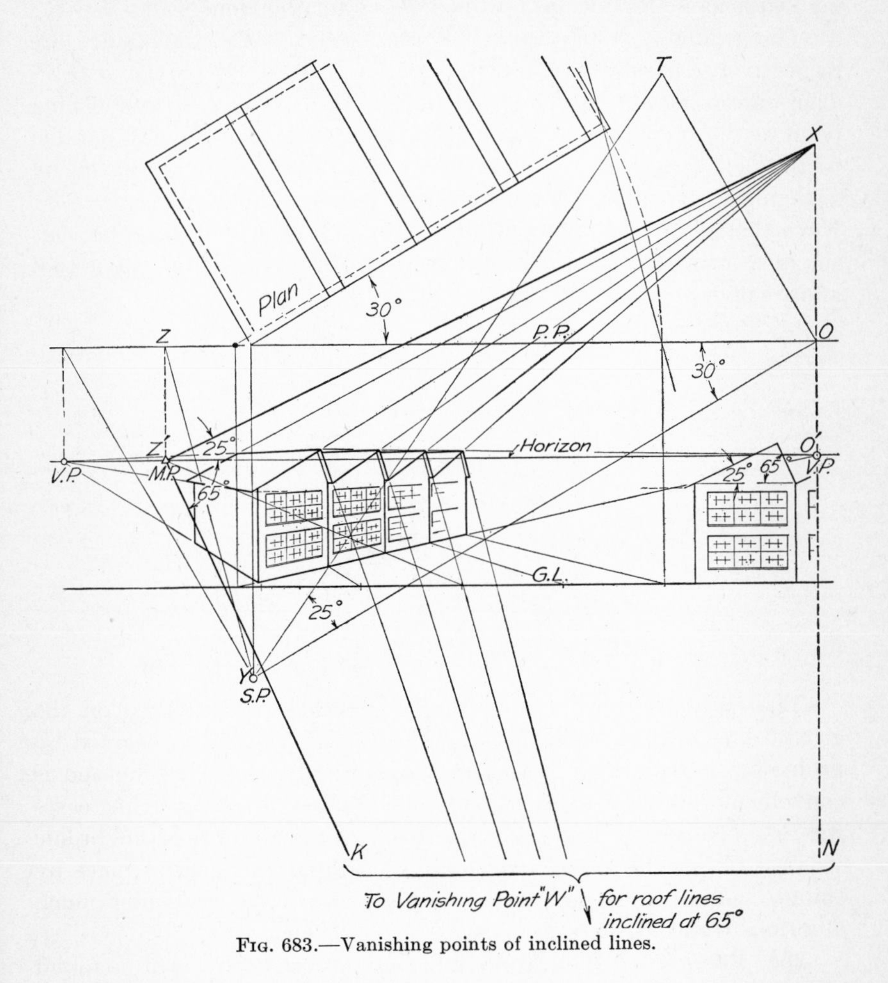

FIG. 683.—Vanishing points of inclined lines.

The perspective of an inclined line *may* be drawn by finding the perspective of two points on it. If many inclined lines are to be drawn in perspective this become laborious. As parallel inclined lines often occur in groups, it is usually more convenient to find vanishing points for them. *A system of parallel inclined lines vanishes at a single vanishing point.*

Figure 683 illustrates the application of the inclined vanishing point in finding the perspective of a factory building having a "saw-tooth" roof. Because of the repeating nature of the construction, measuring points have been used in the solution. The new situation with which we are confronted is that of finding the vanishing points for the two systems of inclined lines (25° and 65°).

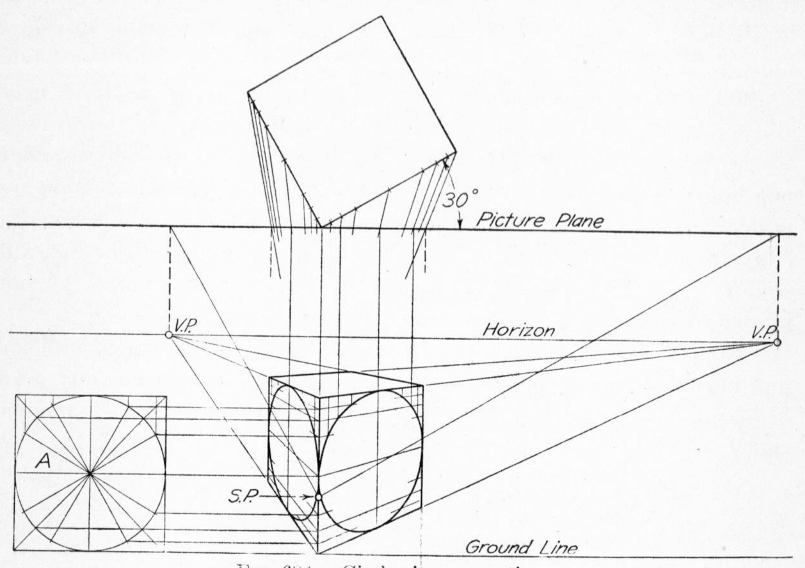

FIG. 684.—Circles in perspective.

The line YO is the horizontal distance (at 30°) from the $S.P.$ to the $P.P.$ O, projected to the horizon, gives the 30° vanishing point O'. An inclined line lying in the same vertical plane as OY but sloping upward at 25° will vanish at a point that is some distance directly above O'. This distance or rise of the vanishing point may be found by constructing the right triangle YOT. The 25° angle corresponds to the inclination of the line with the horizontal and the side OT will be the distance that the inclined $V.P.$ is above O'. By making $O'X = OT$ the vanishing point X for the lines inclined at 25° is located.

Second Method.—Consider the right triangles YOT and $Z'O'X$. $OT = O'X$, $Z'O' = YO$ since $YO = ZO = Z'O'$. Therefore, the two triangles are equal and the angle $O'Z'X$ equals 25°. This means that the vanishing point X may be found by drawing from the measuring point Z' a line inclined by an amount equal to the slope of the roof lines (25°). The point X will be where it intersects a vertical line through the horizontal vanishing point O'. This method is convenient when measuring points have already been located in connection with the other parts of the problem. The former method, it should be remembered, did not employ the measuring point.

The steeper side of the roof, inclined at 65°, may be found in the same manner. Draw from the measuring point Z' a line $Z'K$ inclined at 65°; where it intersects the vertical line $O'N$ (beyond the limits of the figure) will be the vanishing point W for the system of lines inclined at 65°.

286. Circles in Perspective.—The perspective of a circle is an ellipse whose axes usually fall at odd angles not easily determined. Consequently the geometrical methods for ellipse construction should not be attempted; rather, the circle should be plotted in perspective point by point (see Fig. 684). Although any points may be taken, it is convenient to choose points that are on the diagonals of the enclosing square or on 30°, 60° lines, etc., as at A. By using points at such known angles, two or more points may be gotten at a time.

Any curve may be drawn in perspective by plotting a sufficient number of points, locating them by their coordinates from any given or assumed reference lines and using a French curve to connect them.

CHAPTER XVII

THE ELEMENTS OF ARCHITECTURAL DRAWING

287. Architecture is classed as one of the fine arts and it is entirely beyond the scope of this book to take up architectural designing. But in the application by the architect of engineering drawing as a language, there are idioms and peculiarities of expression with which all engineers should be familiar, as in the interrelation of the professions they are often required to read or work from architects' drawings, or to make drawings for special structures.

288. Characteristics of Architectural Drawing.—The general principles of drawing are the same for all kinds of technical work. Each profession requires its own special application of these principles and the employment of particular methods, symbols and conventions. In architectural drawing the necessary smallness of scale requires that the general drawings be made up largely of conventional symbols indicating the various parts. Also so many notes of explanation and information regarding material and finish are required that it is not possible to include all of them on the drawings, so they are written separately in a document called the *specifications.* These specifications are complementary to the drawings and have equal importance and weight.

In the make-up of an architect's drawings there is an evidence of artistic feeling, produced in part by the freehand work and lettering, in part by the use of finer lines, that gives them an entirely different appearance from that of a set of machine drawings. One peculiarity found in many architectural drawings is the tendency to overrun corners. This, in an experienced draftsman's work, gives a certain snap and freedom, but it must not be taken by the beginner as a license for carelessness.

In arrangement of views, third angle projection is standard American practice for all branches of drawing, although now and then an architectural detail is seen made in the first angle. Sometimes it is advantageous to use what might be called second angle projection, superimposing one view over another. This is often done in stair detailing, as illustrated in Fig. 696.

Reflected Views.—A distinctively architectural feature is in the occasional use of the "reflected view," the drawing, usually a part view, as of a soffit or ceiling, being made as if reflected in a mirror on the ground. It should not be confused with another architectural term, the "view looking up," often used to show the under face of a cornice, etc.

Profiling.—Another architectural drawing characteristic, shown in Fig. 696, is that of "profiling" or "silhouetting" the important outline with a heavier line than the other lines of the drawing, which aids greatly in both appearance and ease of reading. It is of particular value on sectional drawings, both assembly and detail, to bring out the sectional outline distinctly from the parts beyond the cutting plane.

289. Kinds of Drawings.—Architectural drawings may be divided into three general classes: (1) preliminary studies, (2) presentation drawings, (3) working drawings.

290. Preliminary Studies.—In an architectural project the first step taken consists in the making of a program embodying all the necessary requirements for the proposed building, after a careful inquiry into the owner's demands, function of the building, materials of construction and character of the site. As the designer studies the various conditions and requirements as outlined in the program, the problem begins to take form and the ideas first find expression in rough sketch studies. Such studies are usually made with soft pencil on tracing paper, as one sketch may be made over another, thus saving time in the layout and enabling the preservation of all the different solutions. They are free, spontaneous drawings indicating the composition of the required elements. A favorite expression of one of our able architects is "keep the idea fluid at this stage." Many variations are studied in this form and eventually one is selected as the "*parti*" or scheme for the design of the building. From this stage the preliminary drawings of plans, elevations and often perspectives are developed, to describe the proposed scheme more fully for approval by the owner. They are made on tracing paper and are often mounted for display. For effectiveness they are sometimes rendered in color.

291. Presentation Drawings.—The object of presentation drawings is to give a realistic and effective representation of the design of a proposed building for illustrative or competitive purposes. They may consist of plans and elevations or to be more thorough may include perspective drawings, but in either case they will contain little or no structural information. For legibility and attractiveness they are generally rendered in water color, pen and ink, crayon or pencil, giving the effect of color, light and shade. Such accessories as human

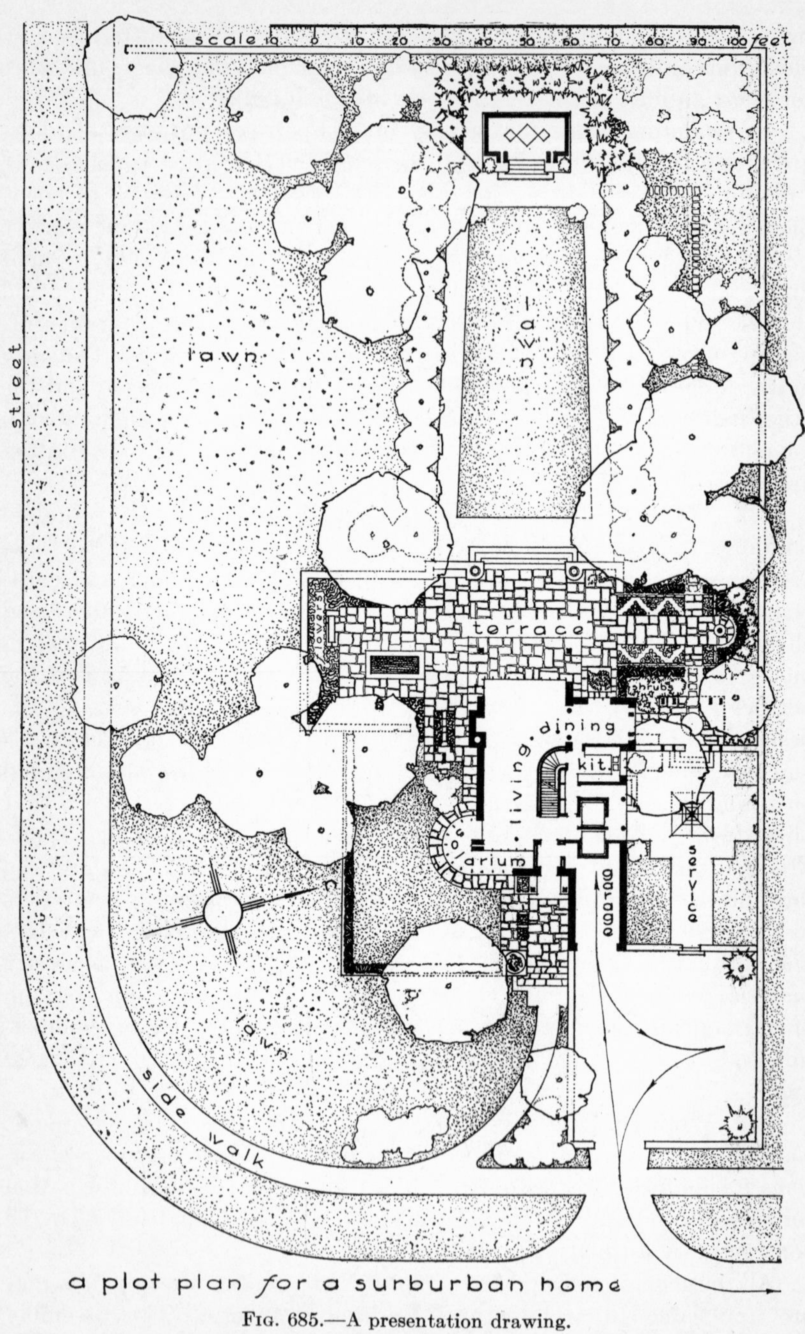

a plot plan for a surburban home

FIG. 685.—A presentation drawing.

figures, adjacent buildings, foliage, etc., are often introduced in elevations and perspectives, not so much for pictorial effect, but more for *scale*, an idea of the relative size of the building.

In rendering plans for display or competitive purposes shadows are often used to show the plan in relief. The terms "poché" and "mosaic" are used in connection with this type of drawing, poché meaning simply the blackening of the walls to indicate their relative importance in the competition, and mosaic the rendering in light lines and tints of the floor design, furniture, etc., on the interior and the entourage of walks, drives and planting on the exterior, representing the grounds immediately surrounding the building. Frequently in a symmetrical room one-half is shown with a floor mosaic and the other half with the ceiling mosaic as a reflected view. A pen rendered lot plan is shown in Fig. 685. Figures 686 and 687 are presentation drawings of the plans and elevations of the same house.

292. Models.—There is an increasing use of models for proposed buildings. Formerly the work of a modeler in plaster-of-paris, these are now made in the drawing room, using drawing paper and cardboard, and gaining over the white plaster model a greatly increased effect of realism in color and texture. The advantage of such a model in showing the appearance of the completed building and the perspective effect from any angle is of obvious value both to the designer and to the client. In making paper models the different walls and roofs are laid out in developed form, rendered, folded and mounted on a board base. The particularly important point to observe is that all features, such as moldings, railings, planting, etc., be kept to scale. Much artistic ability may be evidenced in their construction, and the ingenuity of the modeler is exhibited in the use of various materials in the entourage. Tinted sponges for trees, rubber sponge for hedges and shrubbery, sawdust and sand in glue, and various other accessory material will be thought of. For reproduction purposes, a photograph of the model is used instead of a perspective drawing, sometimes superimposed on one of the site, with adjacent buildings, made at the same angle.

293. Working Drawings.—Under this term are included *plans, elevations, sections* and *detail drawings*, which taken with the *specifications* for details of materials and finish give the working information for the contract and erection of the building. Their first use is by the contractors in estimating for bids.

All the general principles of Chapter XI regarding working drawings are applicable to architectural working drawings. The assembly drawings are usually made with only one plan or elevation on a sheet,

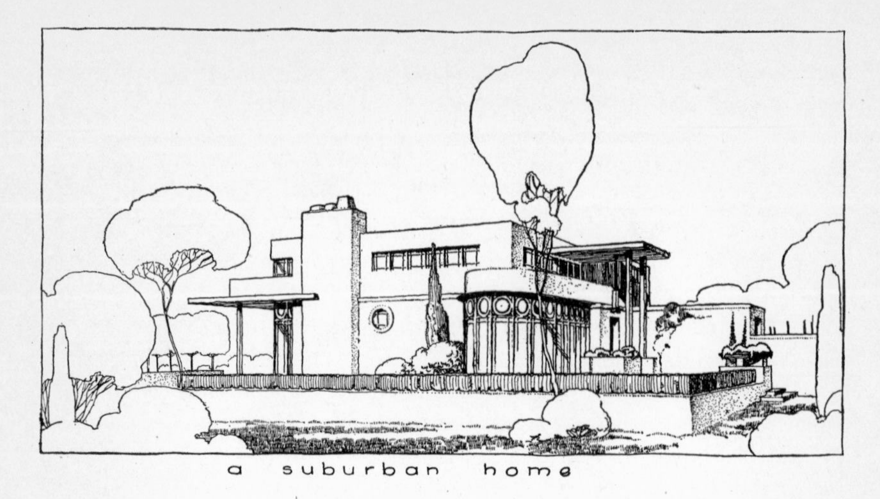

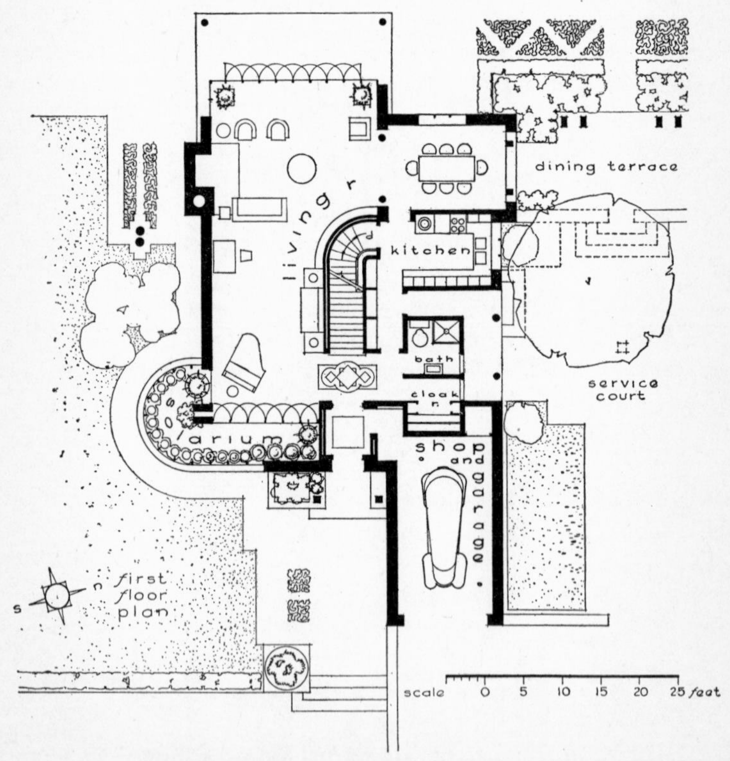

FIG. 686.—A presentation drawing.

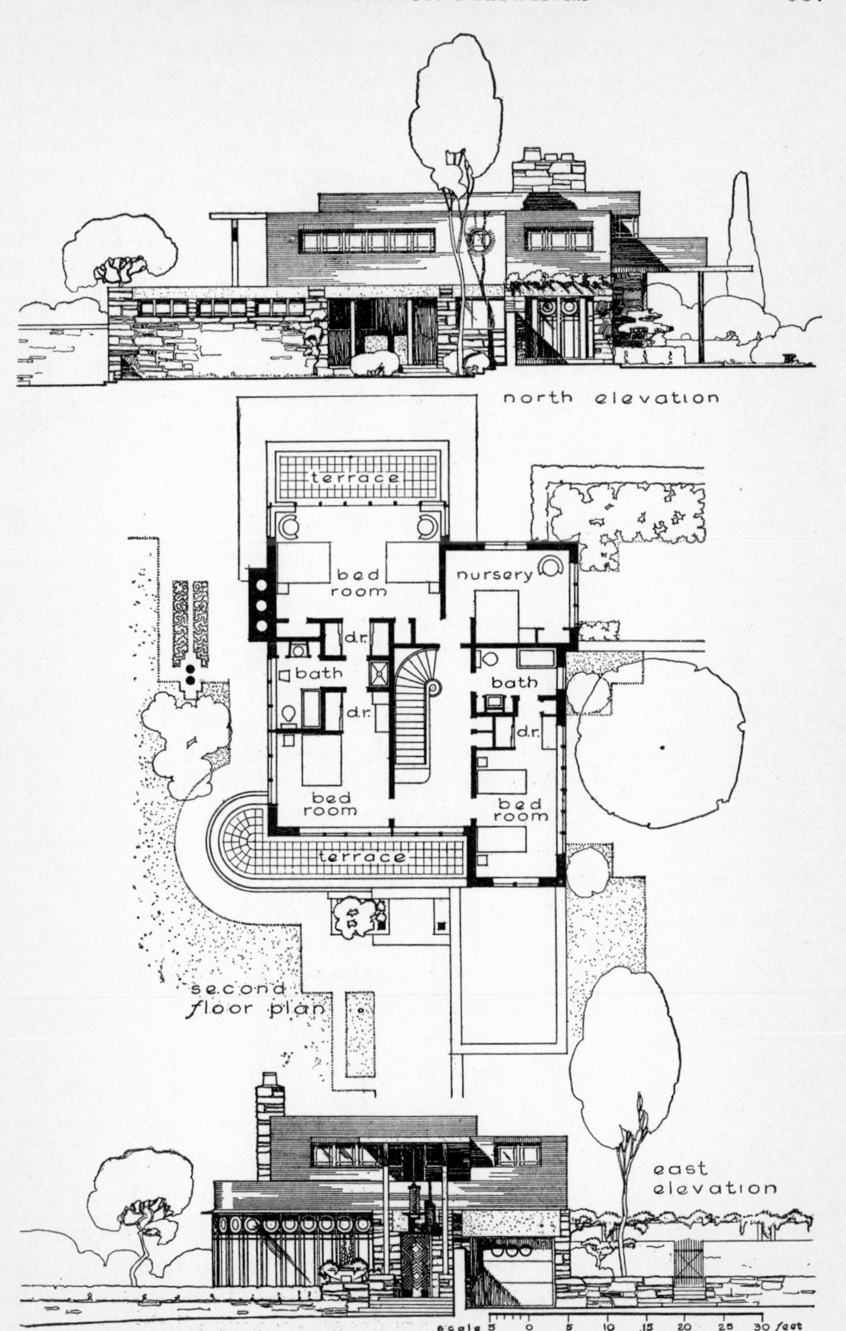

Fig. 687.—A presentation drawing.

in order to keep the drawings to convenient working size. The most frequent scale used on these drawings is ⅛″ = 1′, or, as often expressed, "one inch equals eight feet." For small buildings, perhaps up to 60 feet long, ¼″ = 1′ is used.

As a general rule things which are related should be shown together and information concerning each craft should be grouped, so far as possible. Many present-day buildings are so complicated that it is advantageous to draw special plans for each of the several crafts, in addition to the general plans, as for structural steel, heating, plumbing and wiring.

In making working drawings the draftsman must be familiar with local and state building codes, and the legal requirements as to approval, permits and restrictions.

294. Plan of Site.—Before designing any structure of importance a site plan is made, giving the property line, contours, available utilities, as sewer, gas, water, location of trees and other features, and the building is designed to fit the site. This drawing is completed by locating on it the building, approaches and contours of finished grades. For an ordinary residence, dimensions placed on the basement plan showing the distances of the building from the lot lines usually fulfill building permit requirements.

295. Floor Plans.—Figs. 688, 689, 690. A floor plan is a horizontal section at a distance above the floor varying so as to cut the walls at a height which will best show the construction. The cut will thus evidently cross all openings, no matter at what height they are from the floor. On account of the small scale compared with the actual size of the building, plans are largely made up of conventional symbols, with notes referring to detail drawings of different items. Walls, doors, windows, fixtures, etc., are all indicated by conventional representation, using symbols which are readily understood by the contractors who read the drawings. A floor plan contains, in general, the information for the space between the floor represented and the floor above, even though some items noted are above the cutting plane. The plan will show the location of all doors, windows, partition walls, radiators, built-in fixtures, ducts and flues, outlets for lighting and heating, material of floor, and information concerning the ceiling above, as beams, light outlets, etc. The joist framing of the floor above is indicated except when separate framing plans are necessary. The framing of a simple building is usually left to the contractor. In the case of special framing for heavy or concentrated loads, such as mill buildings, separate framing plans are drawn showing all the details of

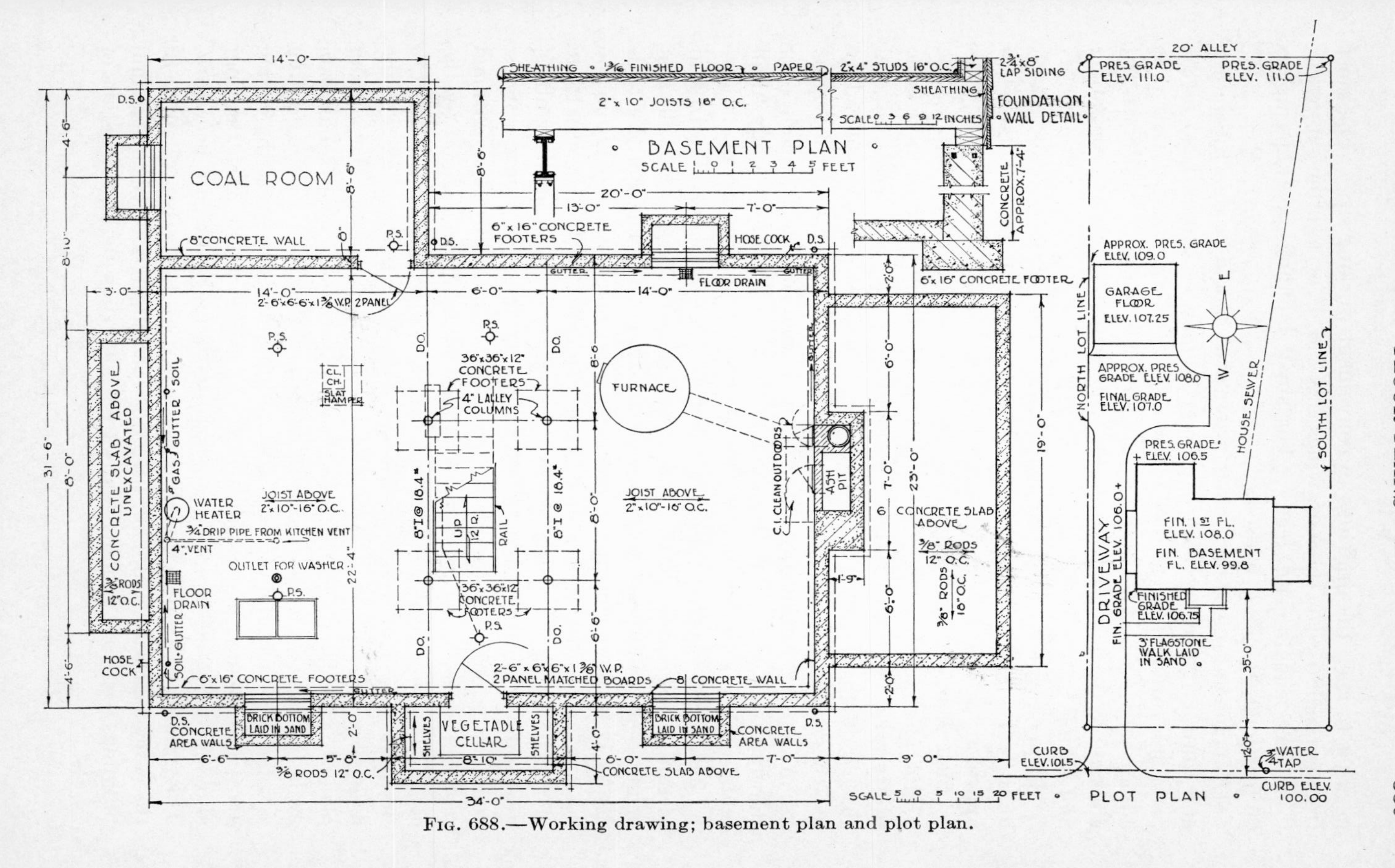

FIG. 688.—Working drawing; basement plan and plot plan.

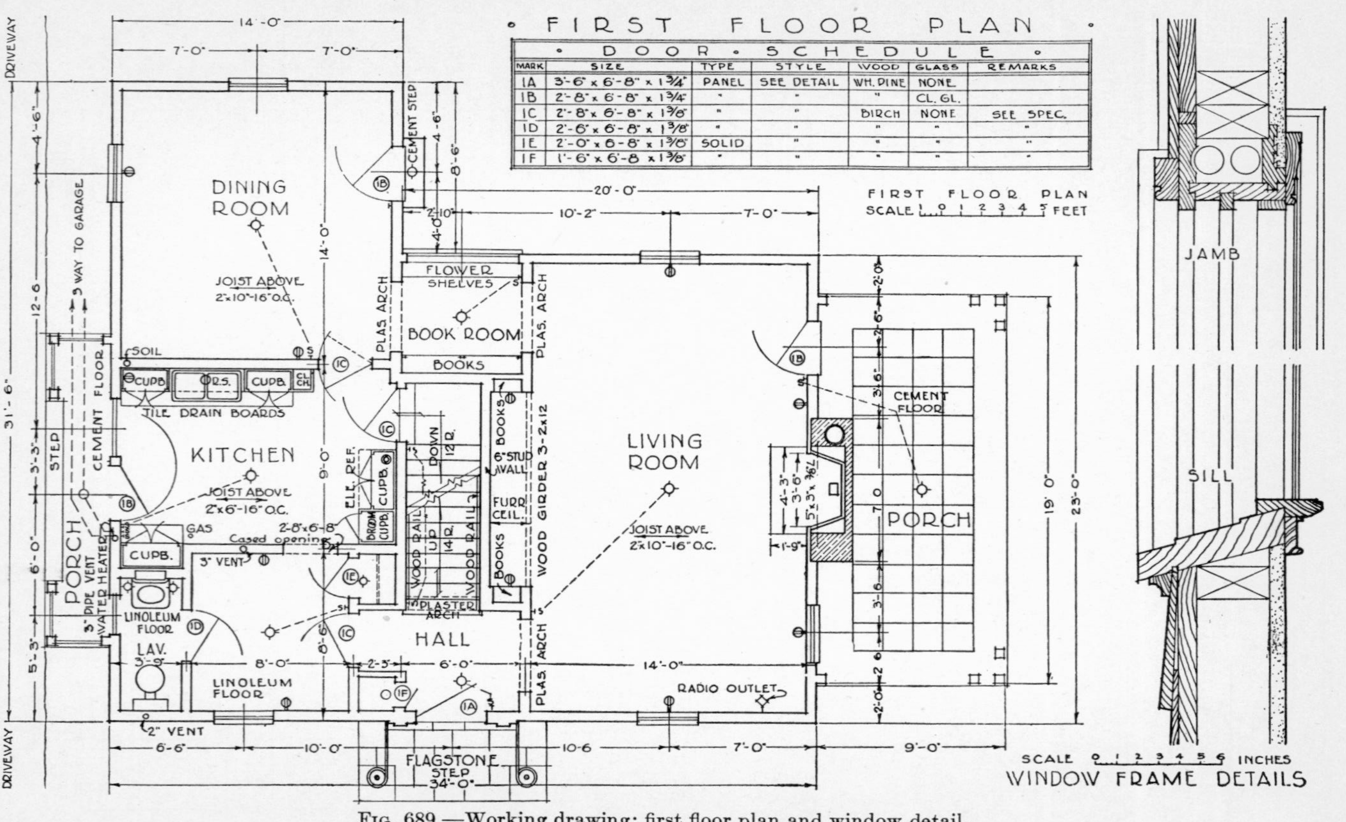

DOOR SCHEDULE

MARK	SIZE	TYPE	STYLE	WOOD	GLASS	REMARKS
1A	3'-6" x 6'-8" x 1 3/4"	PANEL	SEE DETAIL	WH. PINE	NONE	
1B	2'-8" x 6'-8" x 1 3/4"	"	"	"	CL. GL.	
1C	2'-8" x 6'-8" x 1 3/8"	"	"	BIRCH	NONE	SEE SPEC.
1D	2'-6" x 6'-8" x 1 3/8"	"	"	"	"	"
1E	2'-0" x 6'-8" x 1 3/8"	SOLID	"	"	"	"
1F	1'-6" x 6'-8 x 1 3/8"	"	"	"	"	"

Fig. 689.—Working drawing; first floor plan and window detail.

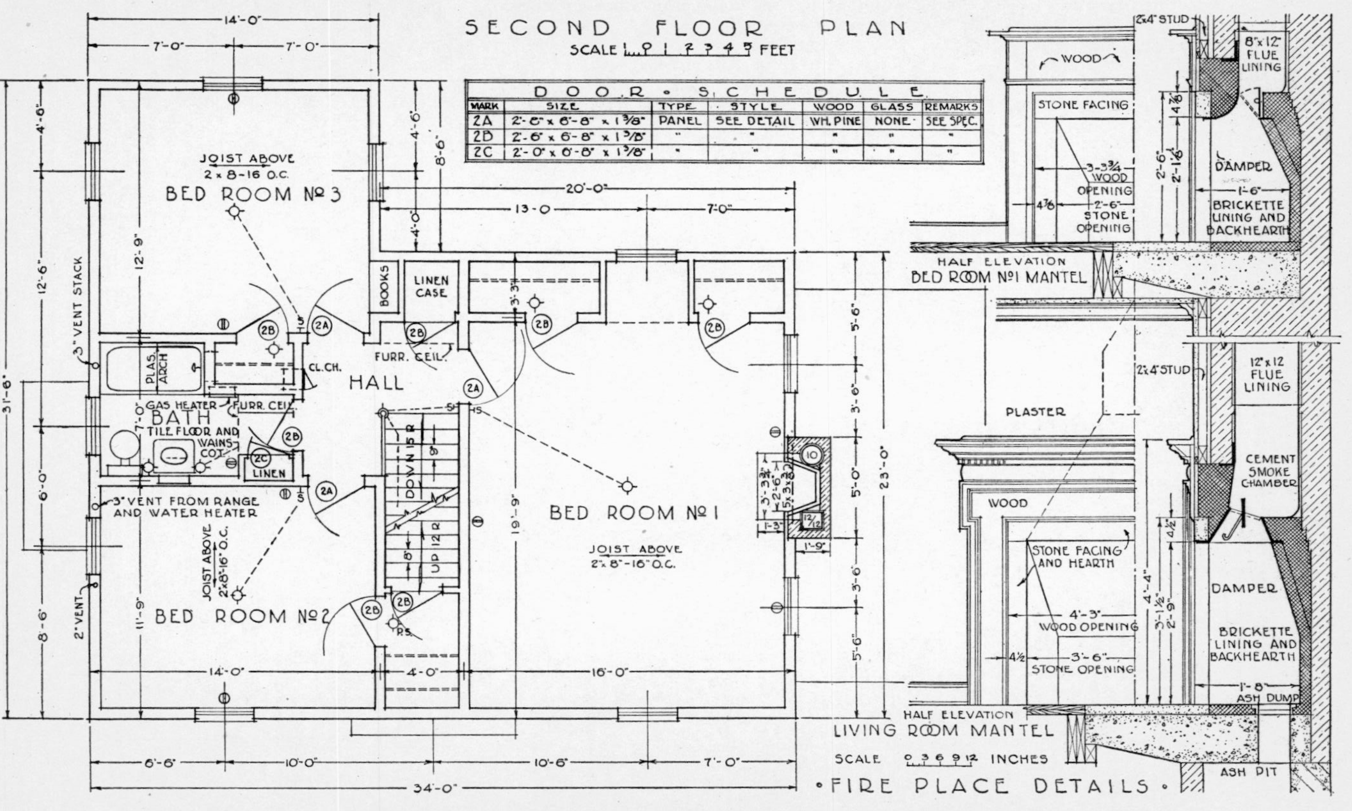

FIG. 690.—Working drawing; second floor plan and fireplace datails.

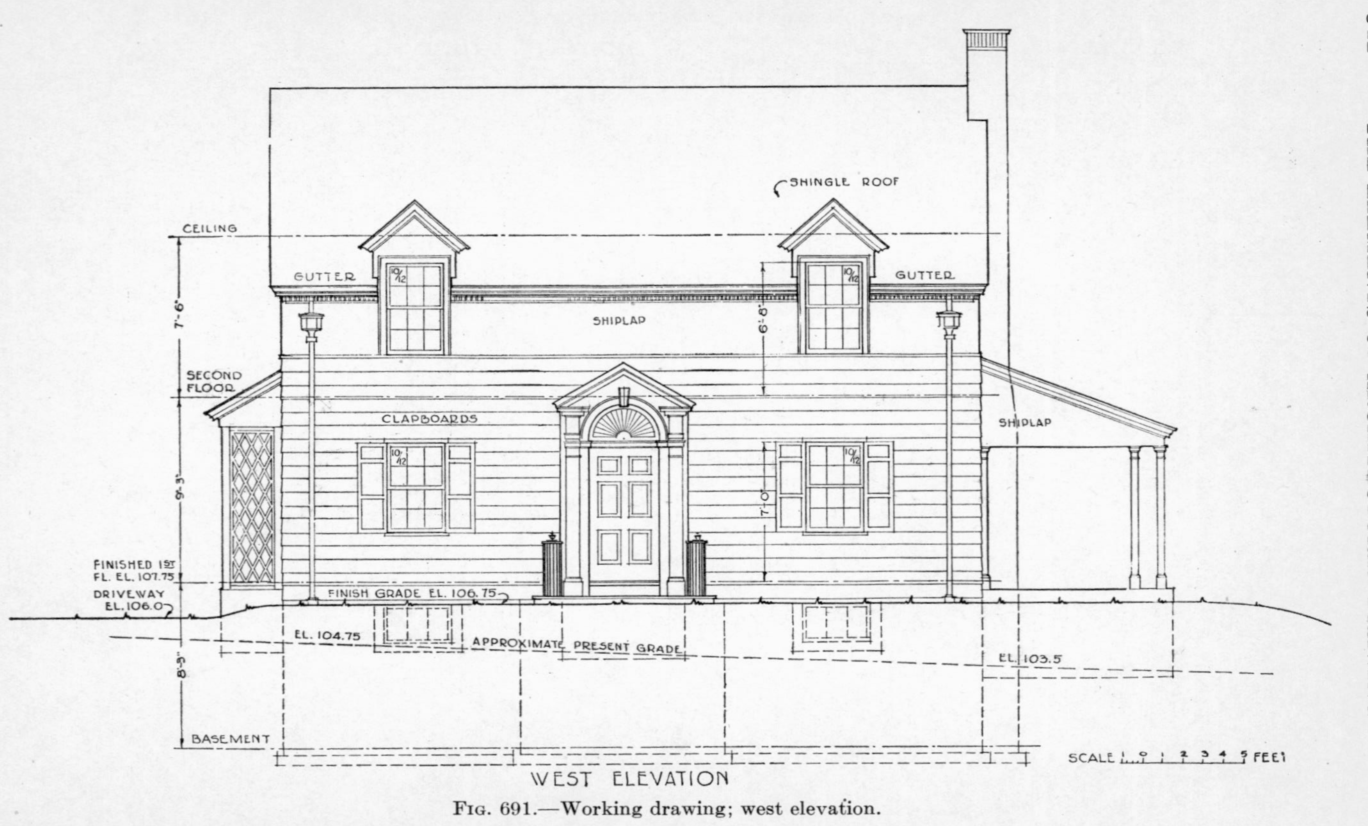

FIG. 691.—Working drawing; west elevation.

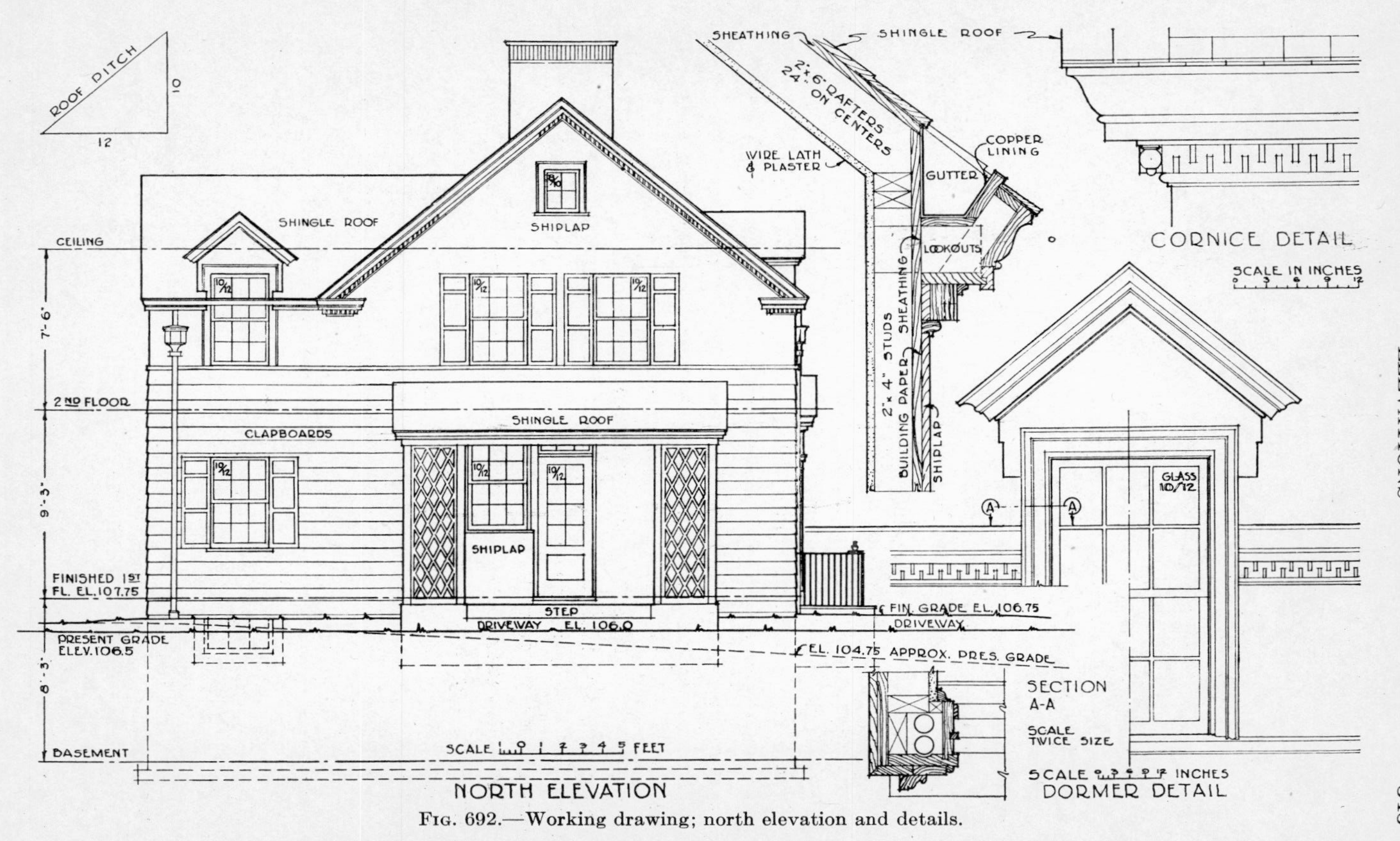

FIG. 692.—Working drawing; north elevation and details.

construction. A separate plan might be needed also for location and foundations for machinery.

296. Drawing a Plan.—A plan is always laid out with the front of the building at the bottom of the sheet. After selecting the scale ($\frac{1}{4}''$ = 1′ for ordinary house plans) draw and measure a line representing the outside face of the front wall. If the plan is symmetrical draw the main axis. The axes of a plan correspond to the center lines of a machine drawing and have a very important place in design. Complete the exterior walls and interior partitions (frame walls are drawn 6″ thick, brick walls 9″, 13″, 17″, etc.), then locate stairways, doors and other interior construction. In drawing the stairway, first make a diagram to find the number of steps and space required (for this the architect always uses the scale as shown in Fig. 115). The rise, or height from one step to the next, is between $6\frac{1}{2}$–$7\frac{1}{2}$ inches, and the tread is proportioned so that the sum of rise and tread is about $17\frac{1}{2}$ inches. One well-known rule makes the tread plus twice the rise equal 25 inches. On the plan the lines drawn represent the edges of the risers and are as far apart as the width of the tread. The entire flight is not drawn on the plan but is stopped about halfway up so as to show what is under it. Each floor plan thus shows part of the stairways leading both up and down from the floor represented. Always indicate the direction and number of risers in the stairway by an arrow and note (as in Fig. 689). The windows are not drawn until the elevations have been designed, but if their position in the wall is known their center lines are indicated. The first floor plan is usually made first and the outlines for basement plan, second floor plan and roof plan traced or drawn from it.

297. Elevations.—An elevation is a vertical projection showing the front, side or rear view of a structure. When a plan is irregular other elevations parallel to the walls are necessary. The elevation gives the floor heights, openings and exterior treatment. The visualizing power must be exercised to imagine the actual appearance or perspective of a building from its elevations. Roofs in elevation are thus often misleading to persons unfamiliar with drawings as their appearance in projection is so different from the real appearance of the building when finished. Figures 691 and 692 illustrate what features are shown and what dimensions are given on elevations. The pump house, Fig. 693, shows the typical treatment of plan and elevation of this class of buildings.

298. Drawing an Elevation.—First draw a wall section at the side of the sheet, starting with the foundation and showing grade line, floor heights, sill and head of windows, cornice and pitch of roof and thick-

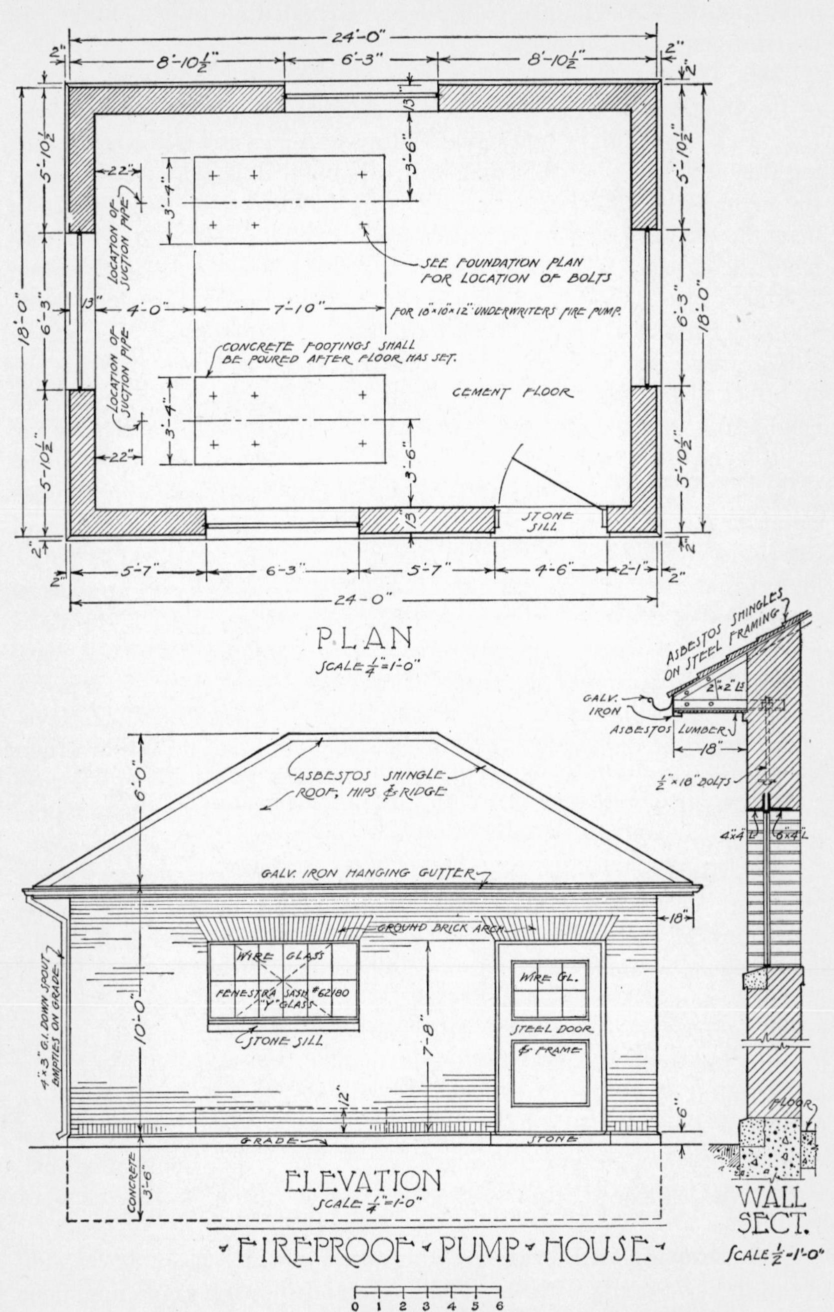

FIG. 693.—A pump house.

ness of walls. Carry the grade line across the sheet as the working base line. Project the floor and ceiling lines across lightly. With the plan sheet placed above the elevation project down for widths. Locate the windows, and complete the elevations as shown in the figures.

299. Sections.—A general section is an interior view on a vertical cutting plane to show interior construction and architectural treatment. This cutting plane, as with the horizontal, need not be continuous but may be staggered so as to include as much information as possible. In a simple structure a part section or "wall section" shown with the elevation, either to the same scale or larger, is often sufficient to give the required vertical dimensions. Part sections to larger scale are often used in connection with drawings, as, for example, in Figs. 689, 690 and 692, the usual cutting plane line indicating the location and direction of the sectional view.

300. Detail Drawings.—A set of drawings will contain, in addition to the plans, elevations and sections, larger scale drawings of such parts as are not indicated with sufficient definiteness on the small-scale drawings. Stair details and detail sections of various items, such as footings, windows, framing, etc., may be shown clearly to the scales of $\frac{3}{4}''$ or $1\frac{1}{2}''$ to $1'$. Details are best grouped so that each sheet contains the references made on one sheet of the general drawings.

As the building progresses the drawings are supplemented by full-size drawings of moldings and millwork details, ornamental iron, etc., usually made in soft pencil on tracing paper and blue printed, all of which must be checked carefully by measurements on the building. In these drawings revolved sections are used freely.

Figure 696 illustrates a method of combining views sometimes used for compactness and convenience in projecting.

301. Details of Building Construction.—The engineer and architect are mutually dependent. In building, such questions as strength, mechanical apparatus and construction are engineering problems, while plan and exterior design are architectural problems.

In the design of a building for engineering or manufacturing purposes there are many considerations involved which the architect cannot be expected to know. The young engineer should be able to prepare preliminary layouts or to make drawings for simple plant buildings. A few parts of such drawings are included here to suggest the method of representation, and the names of the different pieces are given.

Different forms of foundation, floor and wall construction, for buildings without basement, are shown in Fig. 694. Details of the method of making connection between walls and different kinds of roofs are shown in Fig. 695. Column details may be represented as in Fig. 697 where the lower and upper end floor connections are illustrated. Part of the details for large openings in both brick and frame walls are given in Fig. 698.

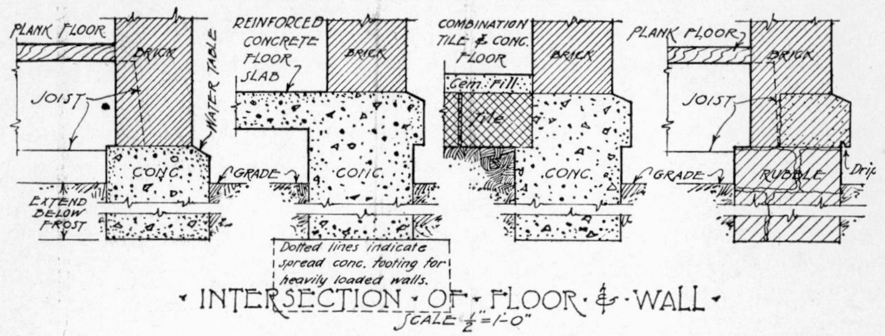

Fig. 694.—Foundation details.

A part of an elevation of one "bent" of a wooden factory building, showing the sizes and locations of the different timbers, is shown in Fig. 699. Similar drawings may be required for floor and roof framing. The extent of detail on such drawings varies, but in all cases it is necessary to have all the information either on the drawings or in the specifications so that there will be no possibility of misunderstanding after the work is started.

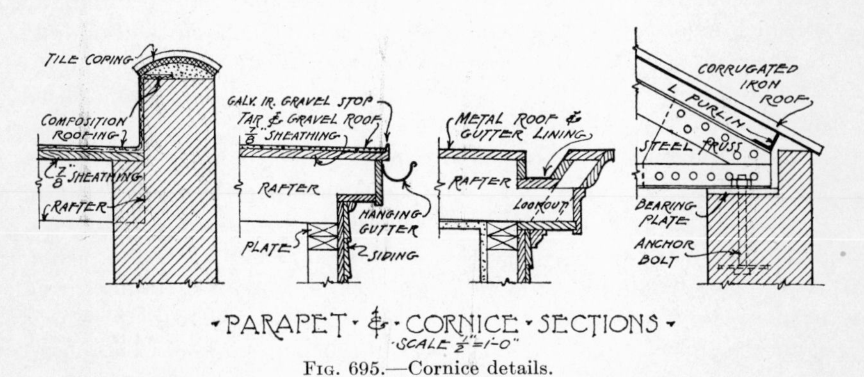

Fig. 695.—Cornice details.

302. Special Features.—In modern building construction many parts are used which are manufactured by firms specializing in one particular item. As an example, steel sash details vary with different makes. The architect gets full-size details from the makers and draws his building to conform. Similarly, other items such as ventilating

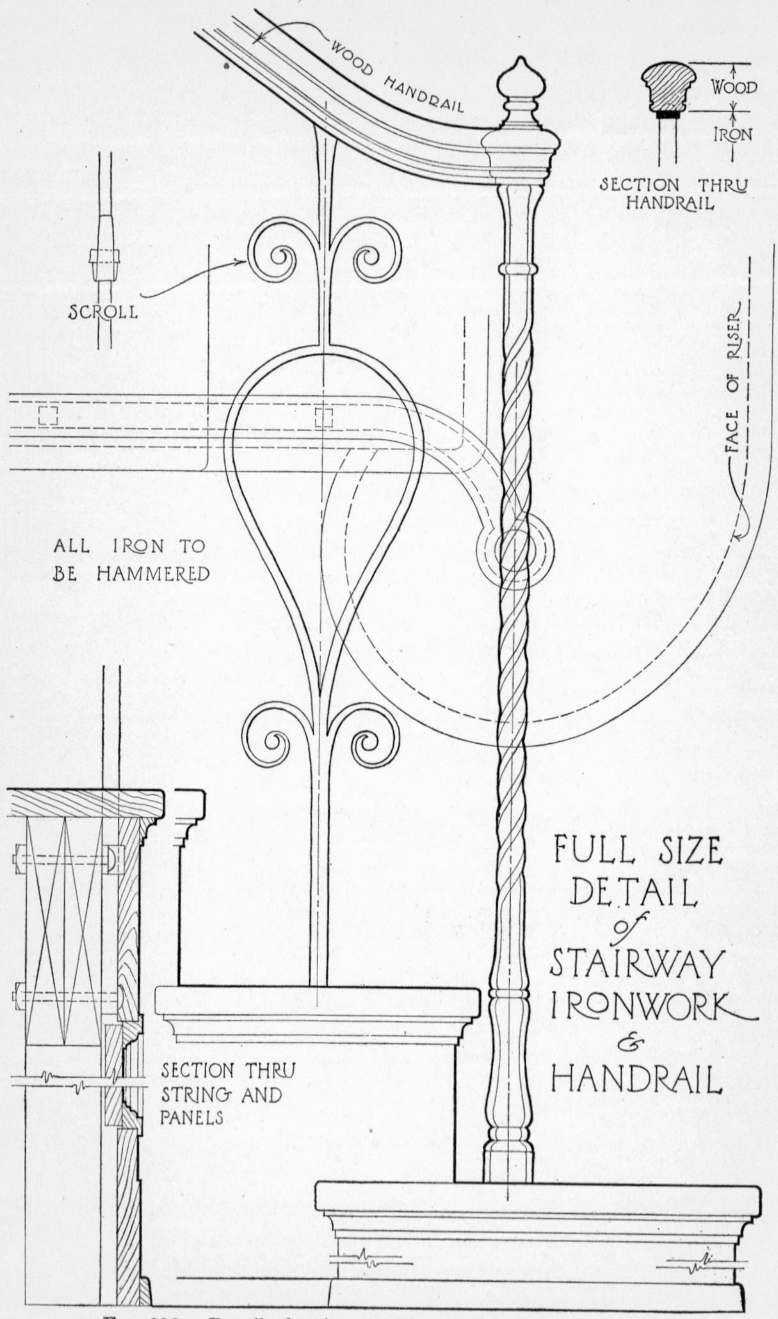

FIG. 696.—Detail showing superimposed view and profiling.

fans, stock stairways, fire doors and many other special features are always worked out from drawings furnished by the manufacturers of the equipment.

303. Symbols.—As heretofore stated, plans are largely made up of symbols. Walls are shown by double lines giving their thickness. Symbols for walls in plan and elevation are shown in Fig. 700. The conventional method of representating windows and their derivation

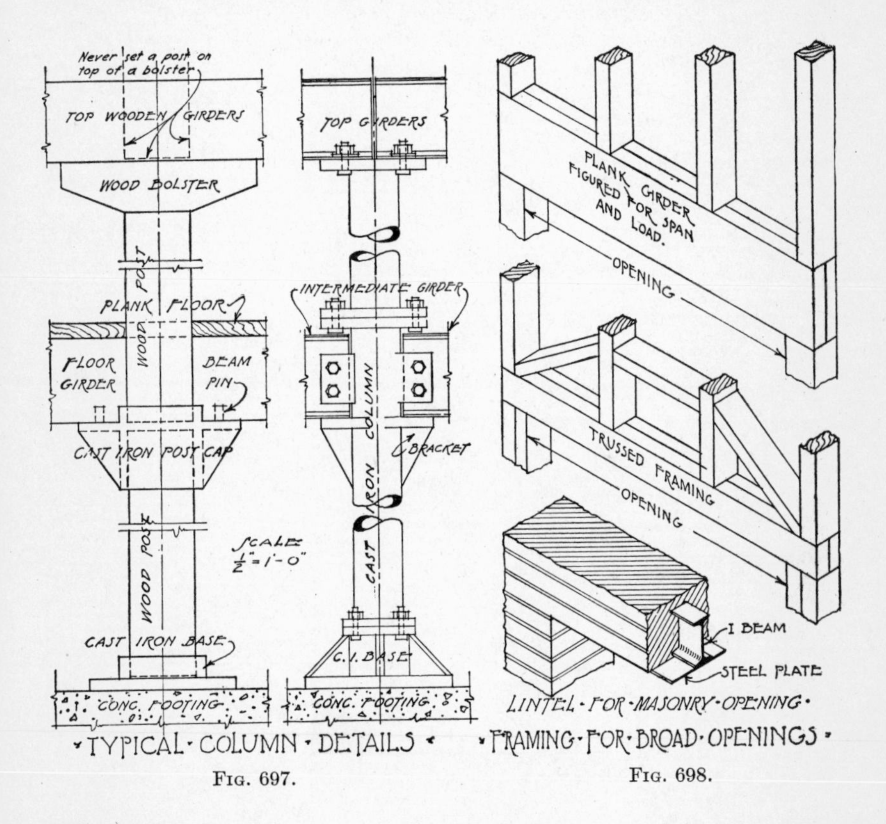

Fig. 697.

Fig. 698.

from the actual sections are shown in Fig. 701. Doors and casement windows are given in Fig. 702. The standard symbols for wiring plans will be found on page 461. Symbols for toilets, sinks, floor drains, etc., may be found on the floor plans, Figs. 688, 689, 690.

304. Dimensioning.—The correct dimensioning of an architectural drawing requires first of all a knowledge of the methods of building construction. The dimensions should be placed so as to be the most convenient for the workman, should be given to and from accessible points and should be chosen so that commercial variation in the sizes of materials will not affect the general dimensions. The principles of dimensioning found in Chapter IX are in general applicable to architectural drawing. A study of the dimensioning on the drawings in this chapter will be of much value. It will be noted that dimensions are kept outside the plans; that they are given to the outside face of

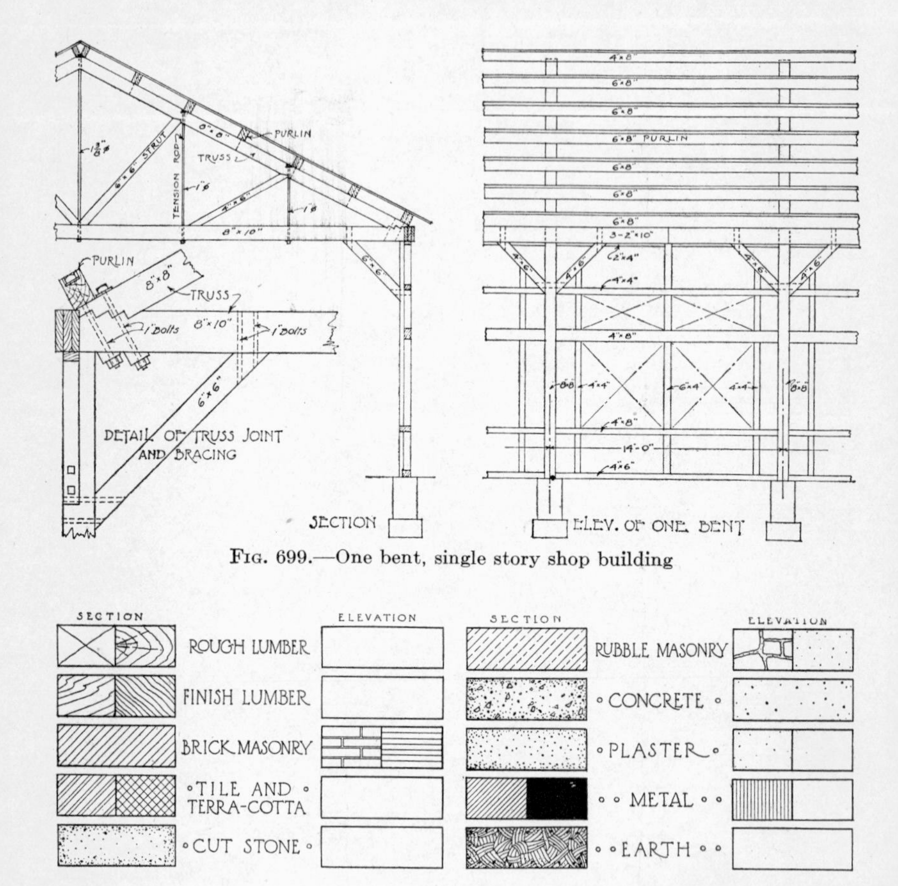

Fig. 699.—One bent, single story shop building

Fig. 700.—Symbols for materials.

masonry walls; to the center lines of door and window openings, frame partitions, beams and columns; to the outside of studs in outside frame walls; and that vertical dimensions and glass sizes are given on elevations.

305. Notes and Specifications.—The statement that the specifications contained the notes of explanation does not imply that no notes are to be placed on the drawings. On the other hand, there should be

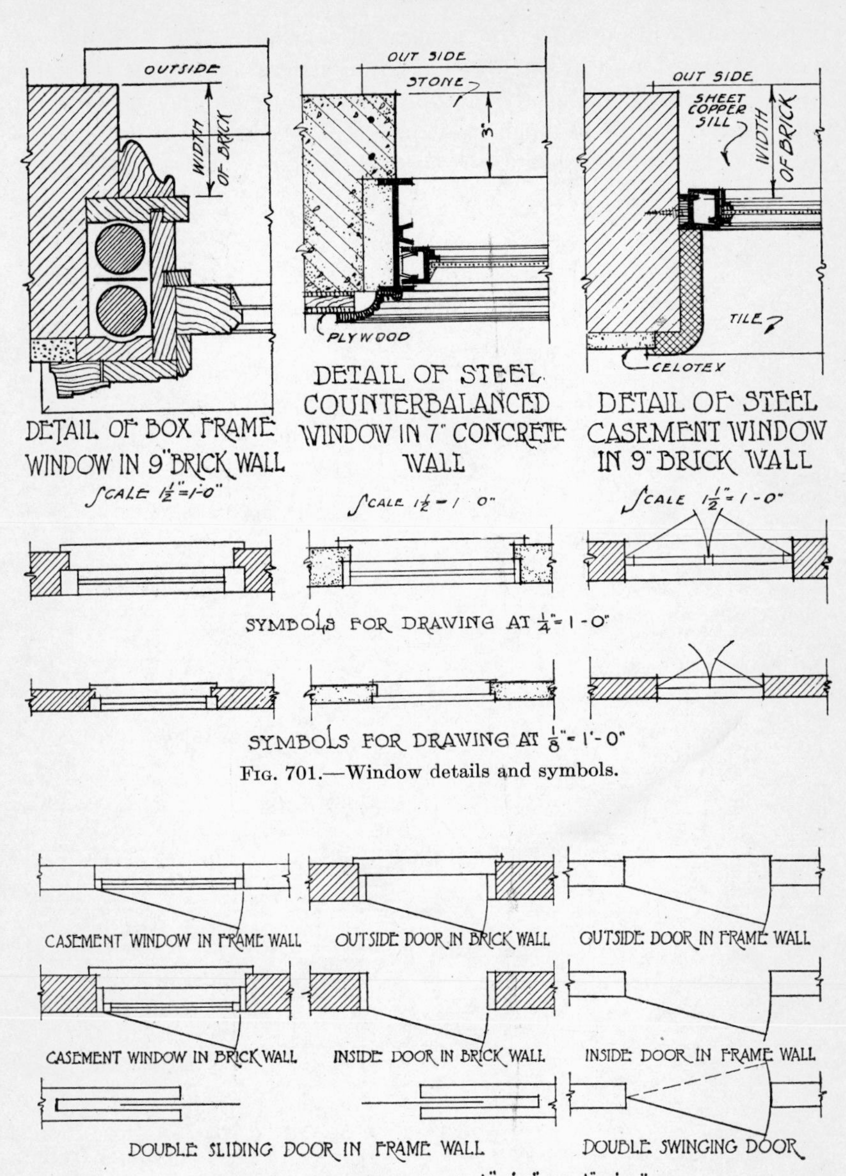

Fig. 701.—Window details and symbols.

Fig. 702.—Window and door symbols.

on architectural working drawings clear, explicit notes in regard to material, construction and finish even though repeated more fully in the specifications. The builders are apt to overlook a point mentioned only in the specifications but as they are using the drawings constantly will be sure to see a reference or note on the drawing of the part in question. Recent practice has introduced, as an item on the drawings, the "schedule," a systematic method of presenting such notes. This gives in tabular form detailed information taken from the specifications, thus making this required information easily accessible to the craftsmen. Of particular value is the *finish schedule*, placed on a plan drawing and giving specifications for all rooms shown on that plan. An example is shown in Fig. 703. A door schedule, or door-list, the forerunner of other schedules, is on Figs. 689 and 690.

FINISH SCHEDULE • FIRST FLOOR ROOMS								
ROOM NO.	ROOM NAME	FLOOR	BASE	WALLS & CEILING	WAINSCOT	TRIM	CORNICE	REMARKS
101	HALL	YEL. PINE	BIRCH	PLASTER	———	BIRCH	PICT MLD.	OAK STAIR TREADS & PLATFORM
102	LIVING RM.	"	"	"	———	"	"	SEE DETAILS
103	DINING RM.	"	"	"	———	"	"	" "
104	LAVATORY	TILE	4" TILE	"	KEENE'S CEM.	POPLAR	———	OAK STEPS-BIRCH WDW. STOOLS
105	KITCHEN	YEL. PINE	POPLAR	"		"	———	SEE DET'LS- " " "
106	STAIR	Y.P. TREADS	Y.P.	"		Y.P.	———	FINISH TO BOTTOM 1ST FLOOR JOISTS
NOTE - FINISH CLOSETS SAME AS ROOMS FROM WHICH THEY OPEN ∘ ∘ ∘ ∘ ∘								

Fig. 703.—Finish schedule.

306. Checking.—Architectural drawings require careful checking. As the draftsman develops the drawings he checks back and forth continually. Before going to the tracer the design of all structural parts should be checked for strength and fitness, the drawings checked for accuracy of draftsmanship, and to see that all special requirements of the client are embodied (these should be on record in writing).

Tracings should be checked by a responsible checker, marking all dimensions with a check mark in soft or blue pencil, checking mistakes with red pencil or correcting when found. All checking should be done in a definite order, following each item through separately and systematically. This order will be dictated by the checker's preference or by conditions of the problem. The following is suggested as a guide:

1. Check main over-all dimensions on the plans, seeing that all plans agree.
2. Check location dimensions on plans, seeing that openings line up vertically, and that plan axes (center lines) "carry through" with openings designed to be on axes.
3. See that dimensions of construction and finish on details correspond to those on plans and fit into adjacent features. Large-scale details made as the work progresses must be checked to measurements made at the building.
4. Check stair dimensions carefully both as to "rise" and "run" and to "head-room" at close places.

5. Check all vertical dimensions on elevations and vertical sections.

6. Check glass sizes of windows and glazed doors.

7. Check all door sizes, and see that doors are completely described by note, drawing or specification.

8. Check design, length and notation of steel lintels over windows and doors as shown on elevations, and compare with large-scale details.

9. Check sizes and locations of all ducts and flues.

10. Check location and kind of wiring outlets.

11. Check for clearances for all mechanical equipment, including heating, ventilating, plumbing, wiring.

12. See that all notes are complete and accurate.

13. Check the titles for correctness of statement and spelling.

14. Check specifications for typographical errors.

15. Check the specifications with the drawings. While the specifications ordinarily take precedence over the drawings there should be no discrepancy.

16. Check specifications to see that all fixtures and apparatus for plumbing, heating and lighting systems are specified.

17. Check for conformity with building codes and laws.

307. Lettering.—There are two distinct divisions in the use of lettering by the architect: the first, *office lettering,* including all the titles and notes put on the drawings for information, the second, *design lettering,* covering drawings of letters to be executed in stone or bronze or other material in connection with design.

The Old Roman is the architect's one general-purpose letter which serves him, with a few exceptions, for all his work in both divisions. It is a difficult letter to execute properly, and the draftsman should make himself thoroughly familiar with its construction, character and beauty before attempting to design inscriptions for permanent structures or even titles.

308. Titles.—Titles on display drawings are usually made in careful Old Roman in either outline or solid. One alphabet is given in Fig. 102. On working drawings a rapid single stroke based on Old Roman such as Fig. 104 is used.

An architectural title should contain part or all of the following items:

1. Name and location of structure.
2. Kind of view, as roof plan, (sometimes put elsewhere on sheet).
3. Name and address of client.
4. Date.
5. Scale.
6. Name and address of architect.
7. Number (in set).
8. Key to materials.
9. Office record.
10. For public buildings, space for signed approval of authority.

Three examples of working drawing titles are given in Fig. 704. the first a drawn title, the second a stamp title, such as is made for a large project where hundreds of drawings are required, the third a finished title in roman letters.

RESIDENCE FOR
MR. & MRS. RODERICK H. WILLCOX
COM. 274
31 S. COLUMBIA AVE. BEXLEY OHIO
SCALE ¼"=1'-0"
SHEET 7
SOUTH ELEVATION
DATE 2/7/35
BENHAM & RICHARDS - ARCHITECTS
167 E. STATE ST. COLUMBUS OHIO

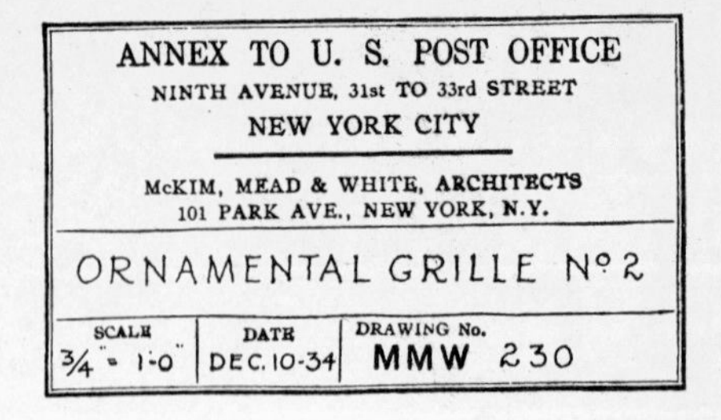

Fig. 704.—Working drawing titles.

PROBLEMS

309. The following problems are suggested for practice in architectural drawing. The student should have ready access to information on present-day building materials. Use ¼" scale for plans and elevations, ¾" for wall sections and 1½" for details.

1. Draw the south elevation of the house shown in Figs. 688 to 692, getting the information from these drawings.

2. Draw the east elevation of foregoing house.

3. Fig. 705. Make floor plan, elevations and roof framing plan for week-end cottage. In its construction it is suggested that the walls be solid masonry of rough-faced field stone. Roof timbers of old barn timbers or beams hewed to fit from trees on the site. Flagstone floor with cement joints. Roof of heavy slate or large shakes. Woodwork of barn boards or unfinished lumber, stained.

4. Fig. 706. Make set of working drawings for vacation cottage. Foundation of field stone.

5. Fig. 707. Make working drawings for hunting lodge. Field stone foundation, hewn timber construction and sod roof.

6. Fig. 708. Make working drawings for house shown. Concrete foundation. Walls of stucco, sheetrock or metal, backed with insulation. Fireproof construction and steel sash preferred.

7. Fig. 709. Make working drawings for house shown, with choice of building materials.

8. Figs. 686, 687. Make working drawings for house shown. First floor limestone, second floor brick to match. First floor lintels reinforced concrete. Fireproof floor, partitions and roof.

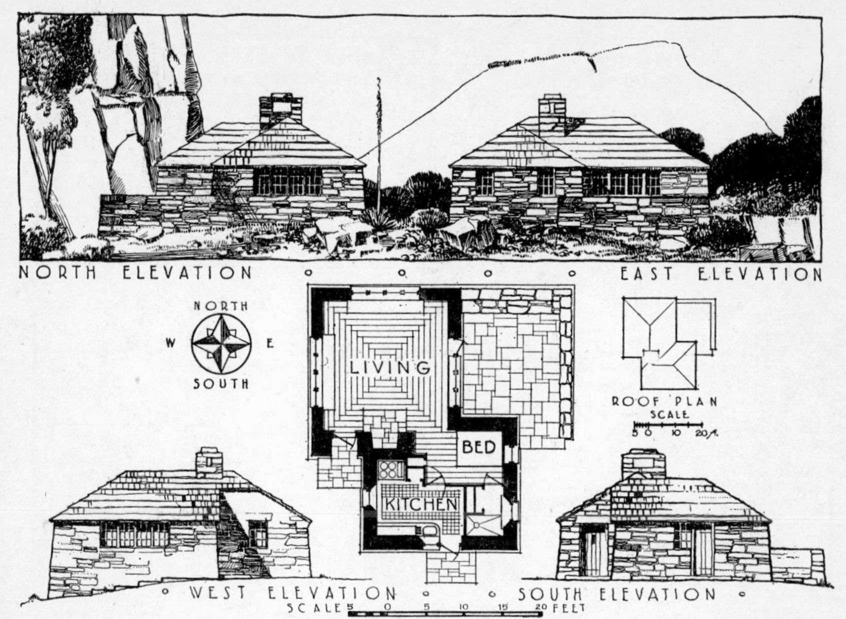

FIG. 705.—A week-end cottage.

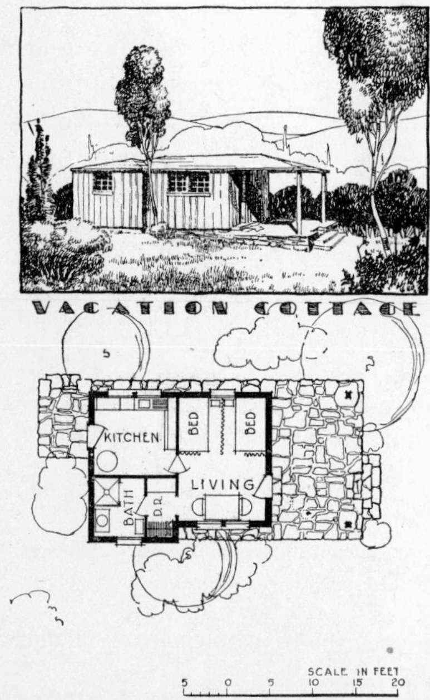

FIG. 706.—A vacation cottage.

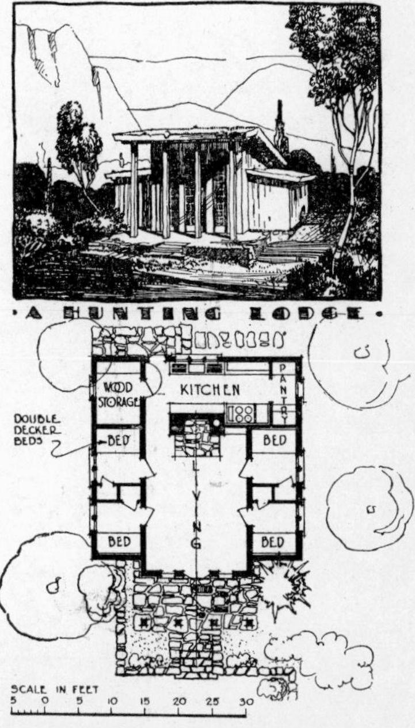

FIG. 707.—A hunting lodge.

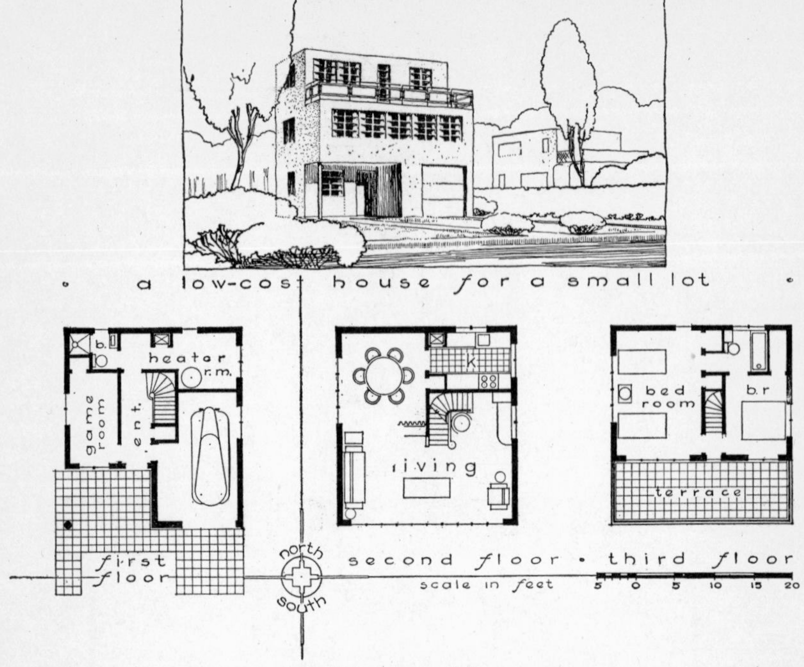

FIG. 708.—A small house.

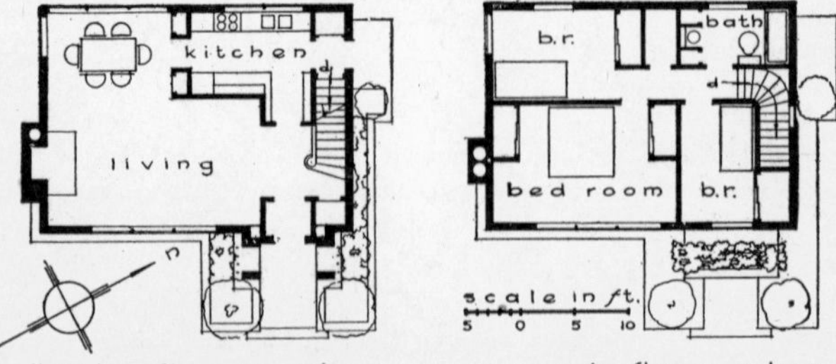

FIG. 709.—A modern house.

CHAPTER XVIII

THE ELEMENTS OF STRUCTURAL DRAWING

310. Structural drawings differ from other drawings only in certain details and practices which have developed as peculiar to the materials worked with and their method of fabrication. The differences are so well established that it is essential for any engineer to know something of the methods of representation in use in structural work.

Steel structures are made up of "rolled shapes" put together permanently by riveting or welding. The function of a structural drawing is to show the shapes and sizes used and the details of fastening. Sections of the usual structural shapes are shown in Fig. 710.

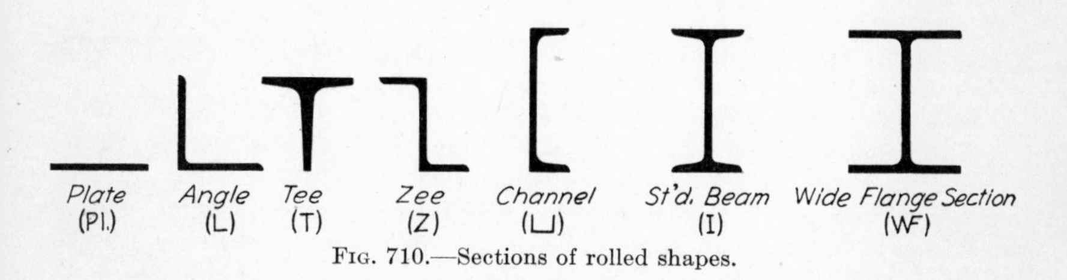

Fig. 710.—Sections of rolled shapes.

The dimensions of the various sizes of standard steel shapes, together with much other information with which the structural draftsman must be familiar, are given in the various structural steel handbooks. For wooden structures, where the parts are not so completely standardized, complete details and dimensions of every part are desirable.

A glossary of terms used in structural drawing is given in the Appendix, page 469.

311. Classification.—Professor Ketchum[1] has classified and described the drawings for structures as follows:

(1) **General Plan.**—This will include a profile of the ground; location of the structure; elevations of ruling points in the structure; clearances; grades; (for a bridge) direction of flow, high water, and low water; and all other data necessary for designing the substructure and superstructure.

(2) **Stress Diagram.**—This will give the main dimensions of the structure, the loading, stresses in all members for the dead loads, live loads, wind loads, etc.,

[1] "Structural Engineers' Handbook" by Milo S. Ketchum.

itemized separately; the total maximum stresses and minimum stresses; sizes of members; typical sections of all built members showing arrangement of material; and all information necessary for the detailing of the various parts of the structure.

(3) **Shop Drawings.**—Shop detail drawings should be made for all steel and iron work and detail drawings of all timber, masonry and concrete work.

(4) **Foundation or Masonry Plan.**—The foundation or masonry plan should contain detail drawings of all foundations, walls, piers, etc., that support the structure. The plans should show the loads on the foundations; the depth of footings; the spacing of piles where used; the proportions for the concrete; the quality of masonry and mortar; the allowable bearing on the soil, and all data necessary for accurately locating and constructing the foundations.

(5) **Erection Diagram.**—The erection diagram should show the relative location of every part of the structure; shipping marks for the various members; all main dimensions; number of pieces in a member; packing of pins; size and grip of pins; and any special feature or information that may assist the erector in the field. The approximate weight of heavy pieces will materially assist the erector in designing his falsework and derricks.

(6) **Falsework Plans.**—For ordinary structures it is not common to prepare falsework plans in the office, this important detail being left to the erector in the field. For difficult or important work erection plans should be worked out in the office and should show in detail all members and connections of the falsework and also give instructions for the successive steps in carrying out the work. Falsework plans are especially important for concrete and masonry arches and other concrete structures, and for forms for all walls, piers, etc. Detail plans of travelers, derricks, etc., should also be furnished the erector.

(7) **Bills of Material.**—Complete bills of material showing the different parts of structure with its mark and the shipping weight should be prepared. This is necessary in checking up the material to see that it has all been shipped or received and to check the shipping weight.

(8) **Rivet List.**—The rivet list should show the dimensions and number of all field rivets, field bolts, spikes, etc., used in the erection of the structure.

(9) **List of Drawings.**—A list should be made showing the contents of all drawings belonging to the structure.

312. General Drawings.—The general drawings correspond in many respects to the design drawings and assembly drawings of the mechanical engineer and include the general plan, stress diagram and erection diagram. In some cases the design drawing is worked out completely by the engineer, giving the sizes and weights of members and the number and spacing of all rivets, but in most cases the general dimensions, positions and sizes of the members and the number of rivets are shown, leaving the details to be worked out in the shop or to be given on separate complete detail shop drawings.

In order to show the details clearly the structural draftsman often uses two scales in the same view, one for the center lines or skeleton of the structure, showing the shape, and a larger one for the parts composing it. The scale used for the skeleton is determined by the size of the structure as compared with the sheet; ¼″, ⅜″ and ½″ to 1′ are

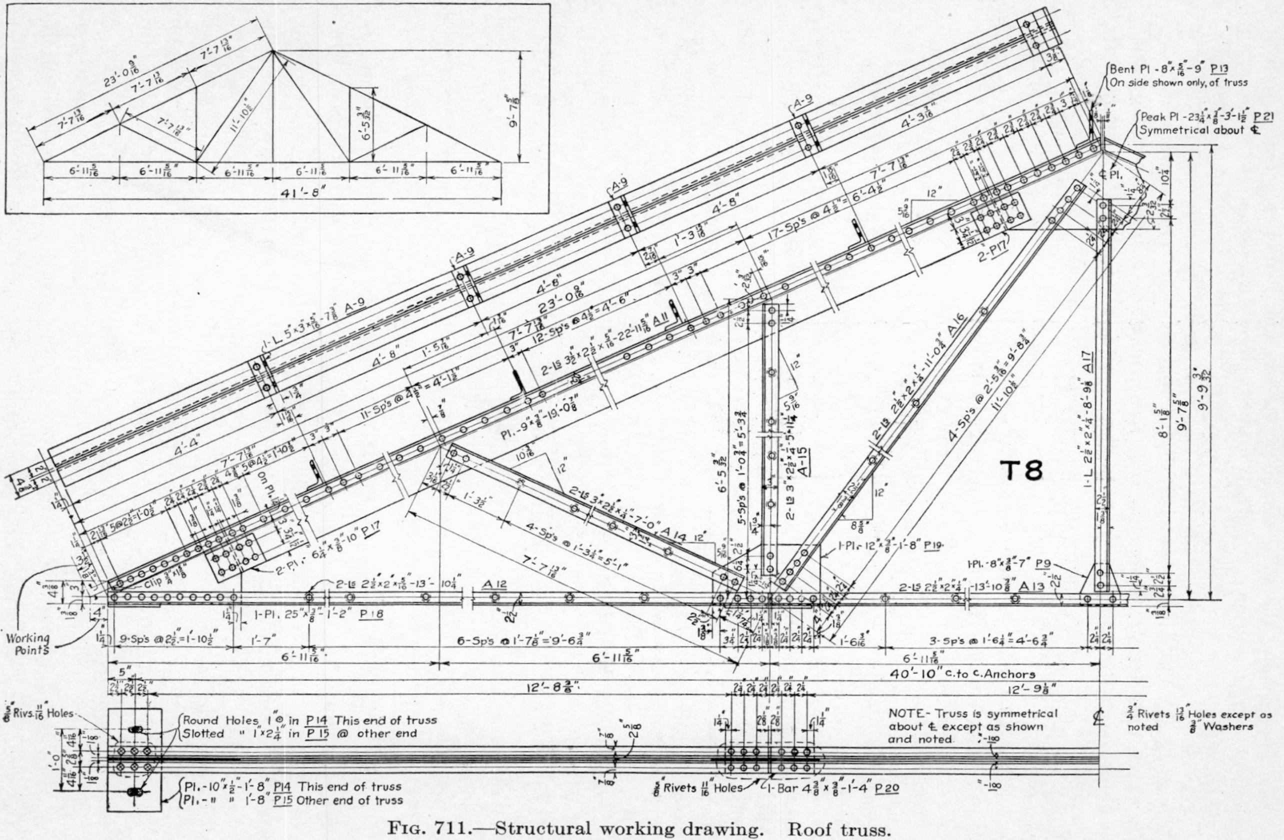

FIG. 711.—Structural working drawing. Roof truss.

commonly used. Shop details are made ¾″, 1″ or 1½″, and for small details 3″, to the foot. Figure 711 is a typical drawing of a small roof truss, giving complete details. Such drawings are made about the working lines which were used in calculating the stresses and sizes of the members. These lines are usually the gravity lines of the members and form the skeleton, as illustrated separately to small scale in the box on the figure. The intersections of these lines are called *working points* and are the points from which all distances are figured. The length of each working line is computed accurately, and from it the intermediate dimensions are obtained.

The erection diagram is often put on the same sheet as the truss.

When one-half of a truss only is shown, it is always the left end, looking toward the side on which the principal connections are made.

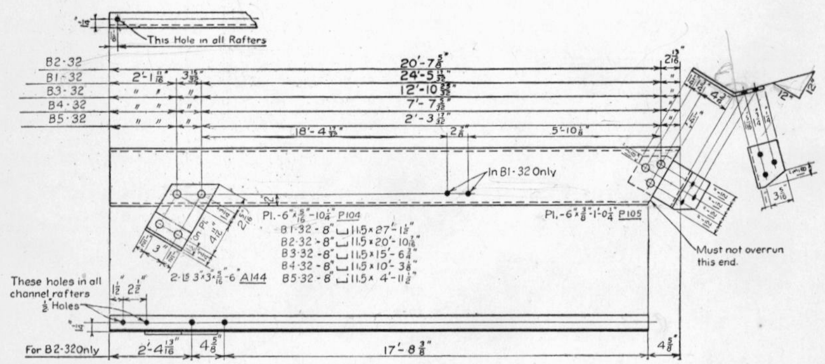

Fig. 712.—Beam detail.

In building construction a beam schedule and a column schedule, giving the detailed information concerning these members, should be added on the drawings.

313. Detail Drawings.—Separate drawings made to a sufficiently large scale to carry complete information are called "shop detail drawings." All parts are shown to scale, and it should be noted particularly that rivets and rivet heads are drawn accurately to scale. When possible, all members are shown in the position which they will occupy in the completed structure, vertical, horizontal or inclined. Long vertical or inclined members may be drawn horizontally, a vertical member always having its lower end at the left, and an inclined member drawn in the direction it would fall. Except in plain building work a diagram to small scale, showing by a heavy line the relative position of the member in the structure, should be drawn on every detail sheet.

Figure 712 is a beam detail, giving all the information for five different beams in one drawing, and illustrating the method of representing a bent plate. It is obvious that in such a drawing the lengths are not to scale.

As the various members are detailed they are given a mark, such as B1-32 (B, for beam; 1, the shop number and 32, the sheet number of the detail drawing), for identification in assembling.

314. Structural Drawing Practice.—All drawings in an office should be made to standard sizes. Half-inch borders are generally used. Inked outlines should be of sufficient weight to make the main material stand out distinctly, while dimension lines and gage lines are made in very fine full lines in black. Some prefer red ink for dimension and gage lines. This makes the tracing somewhat easier to read but the prints are not so satisfactory and it is difficult to get a permanent red ink. When new work is to be attached to old, the old is often drawn in red.

Dimensions are always placed over the dimension line instead of in a space left in the line. Lengths of 10″ and over are given in feet and inches, thus, 0-10″, 1′-2½″. Care should be taken that dimensions are given to commercial sizes of materials. Sizes of members are specified by figures parallel to them as 2 L-2½ × 2 × ¼ × 7′-3″, which means two angles having unequal legs of 2½″ and 2″, ¼″ thick and 7′-3″ long. Angle or bevel cuts, as for gussets, are indicated by their tangents on a 12″ base line, shown on a small triangle adjacent to the angle.

The dimensions necessary for the sections of Fig. 710, with the abbreviations for sections to be used on drawings, as adopted by the American Institute of Steel Construction (1934) are as follows:

Plates.—Width × thickness × length (Pl 18 × ½).

Equal Leg Angles.—Size of legs × thickness × length (L3 × 3 × ¼).

Unequal Leg Angles.—Size of long leg × short leg × thickness × length (L7 × 4 × ½).

Tees.—Height × width × weight per foot × length (T3 × 3 × 6.7).

Zees.—Height × thickness × weight per foot × length (Z6 × 3½ × 15.7).

Standard Channels.—Height × weight per foot × length (9 ⊔ 13.4).

Standard I-beams.—Height × weight per foot × length (15 I 42.9).

Wide Flange Sections.—Height × weight per foot × length (24WF74).

Checking is usually indicated by a dot in red ink placed under the dimension. Elevations, sections and other views are placed by the theory of third angle projection except that when a view is given under a front view, as in Figs. 711 and 712, it is made as a section taken above the lower flange, looking down, instead of as a regular bottom view looking up. Large sections of materials are shown with uniform cross-hatching. Small-scale sections are blacked in solid, with white spaces left between adjacent pieces.

Rivets are spaced along "gage lines," measured from the backs of angles and channels and from center to center on I-beams. The distance between rivets measured along the gage line is called the "pitch." The gages and pitch for various angles are shown in Fig. 713.

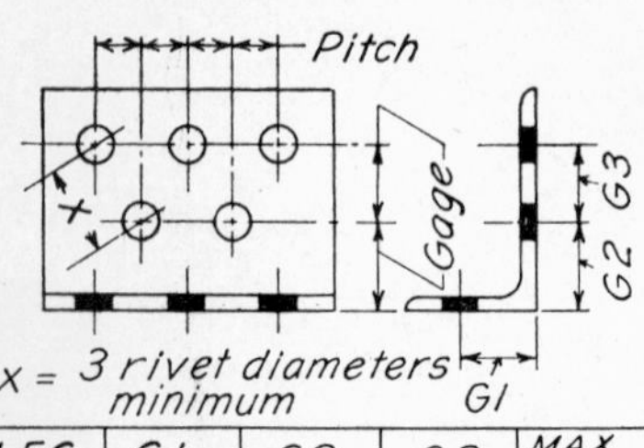

LEG	G1	G2	G3	MAX RIVET
8	4½	3	3	1⅛
7	4	2½	3	1⅛
6	3½	2½	2¼	1
5	3	2	1¾	1
4	2½			⅞
3½	2			⅞
3	1¾			⅞
2½	1⅜			¾
2	1⅛			⅝
1¾	1			½
1½	⅞			⅜
1⅜	⅞			⅜
1¼	¾			⅜
1	⅝			¼
¾	½			¼

Fig. 713.—Gage and pitch.

The size of most structures prevents their being completed in the shop so they are "fabricated" as large as transportation facilities allow, and the necessary connections made where the structure is erected. The holes for these "field rivets" are always indicated in solid black to scale on the drawing, while shop rivets are indicated by circles of the diameter of the rivet head. A bill of field rivets is always furnished. In drawing rivets, the drop pen, Fig. 787, is a favorite instrument.

A general note is usually added to all detail drawings, giving rivet sizes, size of open holes and edge distance (unless noted) and painting instructions, as "Paint one coat of red lead (or black graphite) in shop. Paint all parts in contact before assembly."

Figure 714 shows the Standard symbols for riveting, formerly called the Osborn symbols, which are so universally used that no key on the drawing is necessary. Figure 715 shows rivets to larger scale.

There is a growing use of arc welding instead of riveting for structural work (see page 200).

Bent plates should be developed and the "stretchout" length of bent forged bars given. The length of a bent plate may be taken as the inside length of the bend plus half the thickness of the plate for each bend.

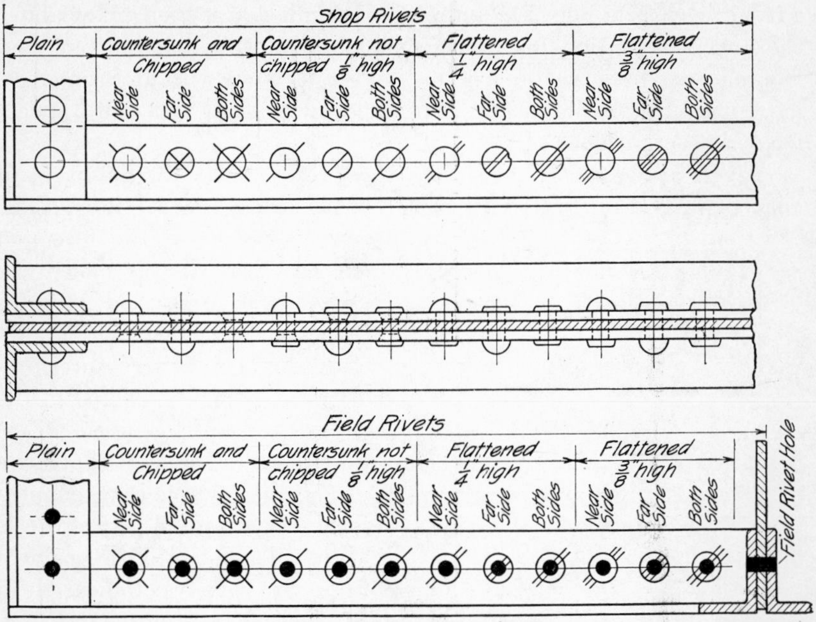

Fig. 714.—Standard rivet symbols.

A **bill of material** always accompanies a structural drawing. This may be put on the drawing but the best practice is to attach it as a separate "bill sheet" generally on 8½″ × 11″ paper.

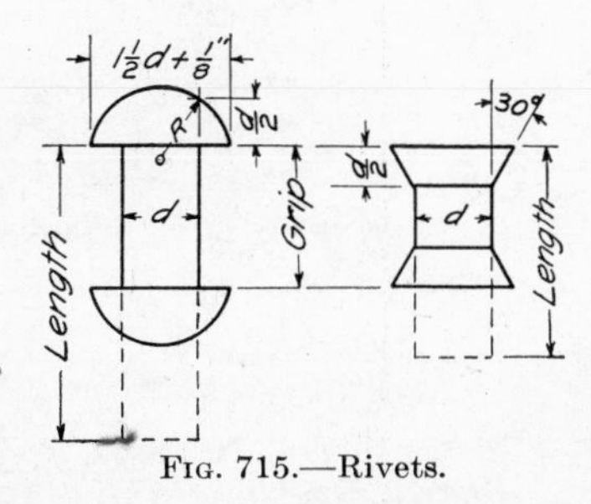

Fig. 715.—Rivets.

Each member of a structure is given a shipping mark consisting of a capital letter and a number, which appears on the drawings and on the bill sheet (see Figs. 711 and 712).

Lettering is done in rapid single stroke either inclined or vertical. An example of a printed title form is given in Fig. 716.

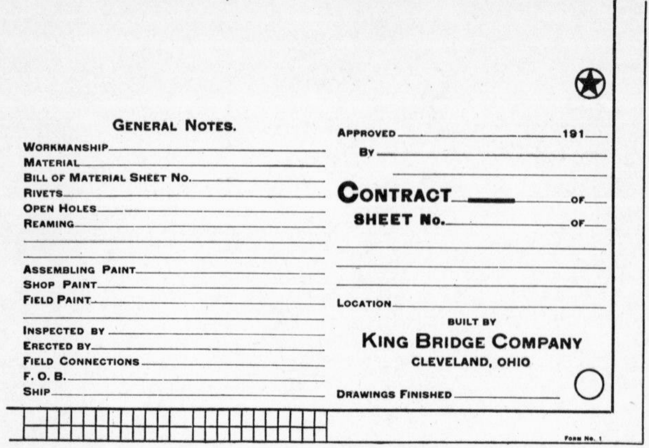
GENERAL NOTES.
WORKMANSHIP
MATERIAL
BILL OF MATERIAL SHEET NO.
RIVETS
OPEN HOLES
REAMING

ASSEMBLING PAINT
SHOP PAINT
FIELD PAINT

INSPECTED BY
ERECTED BY
FIELD CONNECTIONS
F. O. B.
SHIP

APPROVED 191
BY

CONTRACT OF
SHEET No. OF

LOCATION
BUILT BY
KING BRIDGE COMPANY
CLEVELAND, OHIO
DRAWINGS FINISHED

Fig. 716.—A printed title form.

315. Timber Structures.—The representation of timber framed structures involves no new principles but requires particular attention to details. Timber members are generally rectangular in section and

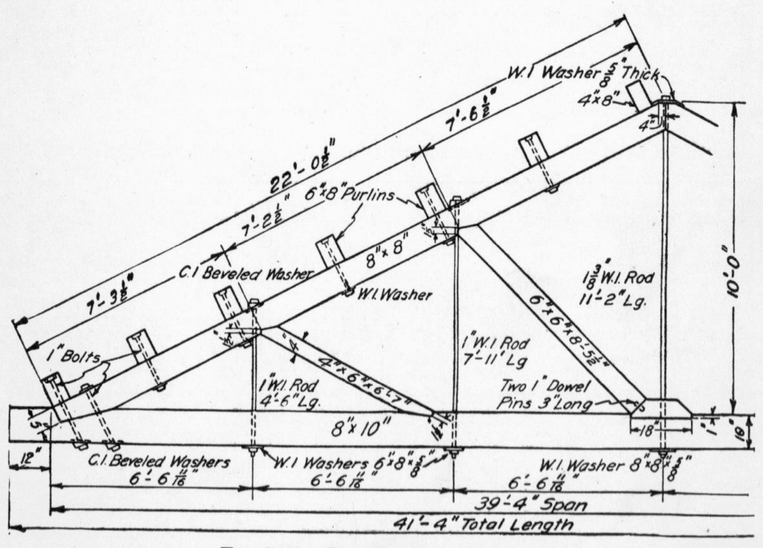

Fig. 717.—Timber truss drawings.

are specified to nominal sizes in even inches, as 8″ × 12″. As nominal sizes are generally larger than the actual dimensions the general drawing must give center and other important distances accurately.

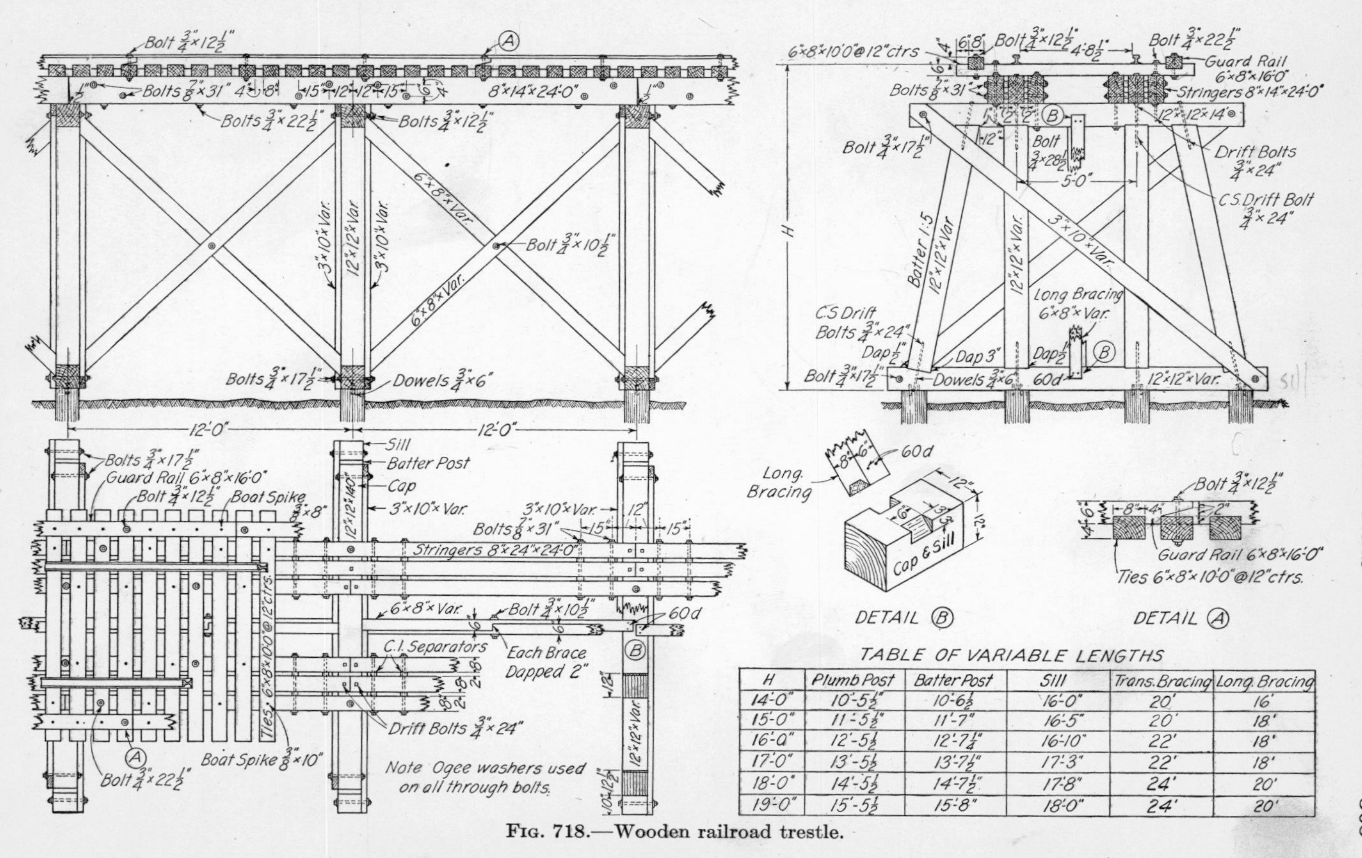

TABLE OF VARIABLE LENGTHS

H	Plumb Post	Batter Post	Sill	Trans. Bracing	Long. Bracing
14'0"	10'-5½"	10'-6½"	16'-0"	20'	16'
15'0"	11'-5½"	11'-7"	16'-5"	20'	18'
16'0"	12'-5½"	12'-7¼"	16'-10"	22'	18'
17'0"	13'-5½"	13'-7½"	17'-3"	22'	18'
18'0"	14'-5½"	14'-7½"	17'-8"	24'	20'
19'0"	15'-5½"	15'-8"	18'-0"	24'	20'

FIG. 718.—Wooden railroad trestle.

Details drawn to larger scale give specific information as to separate parts. Sizes of wood members vary so much that nothing should be left to "guess in" when erecting. The particulars of joints, splices, methods of fastening, etc., should be given in full. As this requires a specialized knowledge of wood-framing construction, acquired only

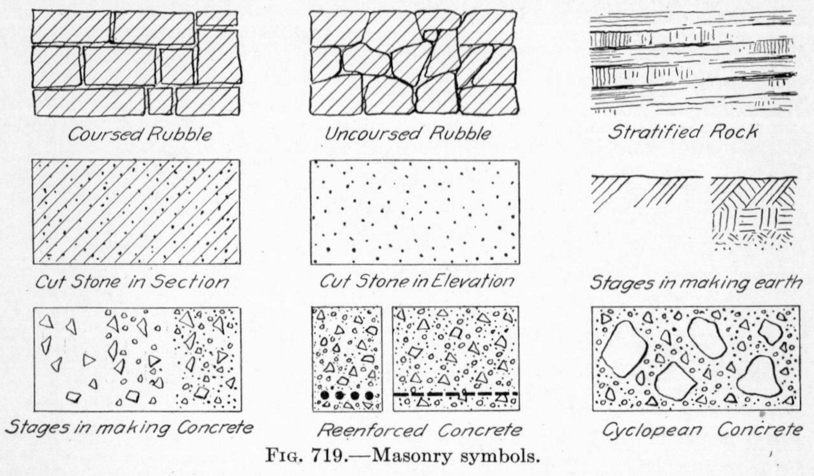

FIG. 719.—Masonry symbols.

through large experience in this class of work, it should not be attempted by the novice.

Two scales may sometimes be used to advantage on the general drawing, as was done in Fig. 717.

Figure 718 shows the construction of a wooden trestle on piles. Timbers of the sizes shown are used for heights up to 20 feet. Complete notes are an essential part of such drawings, especially when an attempt at dimensioning the smaller details would result in confusion.

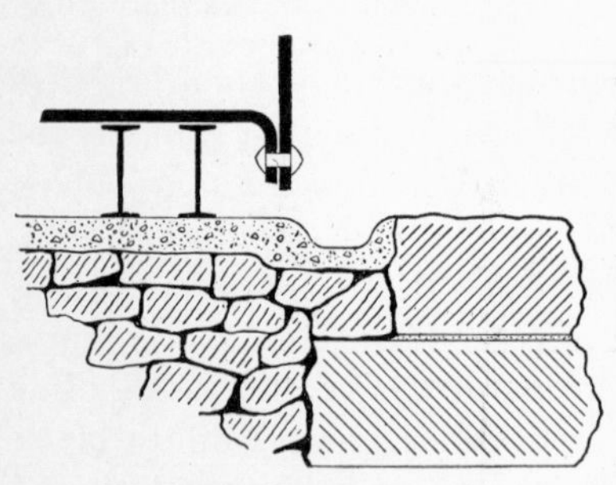
FIG. 720.—Masonry section.

316. Masonry Structures.—In drawing masonry the symbols used bear some resemblance to the material represented. Figure 719 gives those in common use and shows the stages followed to secure uniformity of effect in rendering earth and concrete. An effective method of cross-hatching, leaving a white line around the edge of the stone is shown in Fig. 720. Drawings for piers, foundations for machines and other structures are met with in all kinds of engineering work. Grade levels, floor levels and other fixed heights should be given, together with accurate location dimensions for foundation bolts. All materials should be marked plainly with name or notes. A pier is illustrated in Fig. 721.

317. Reinforced concrete is an important division of masonry construction needing careful attention in representation. It is almost impossible to show definitely the shapes of reinforcing bars in concrete by the usual orthographic views, without a systematic scheme of marking. In Fig. 722 the various bars are designated by reference letters and numbers on horizontal and vertical center lines. Note the horizontal lines *G* and *F*, and the vertical lines numbered 1, 2, 3, 4, 5. The first bar in the line *G* is called *G*1, the second *G*2, etc., similarly for bars *F*1, *F*2. Each of the bars is marked with its same combination of letter and figure in the other views, and they are detailed in separate bending diagrams, thus completely defining their location and shape. Sometimes the attempt is made to give bending dimensions in the views of the structure but, as this greatly increases the difficulty of reading the drawing, it is not good practice.

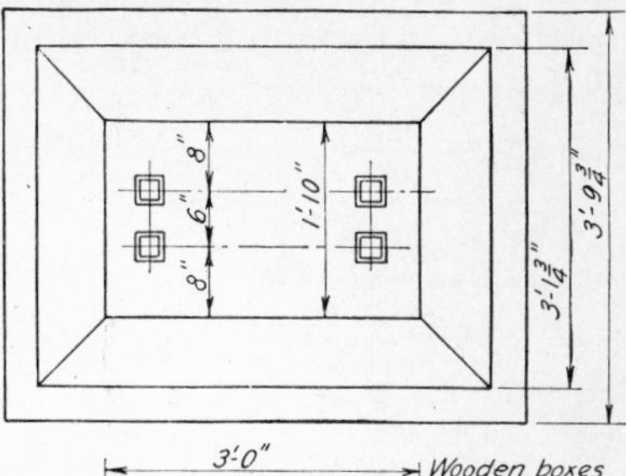

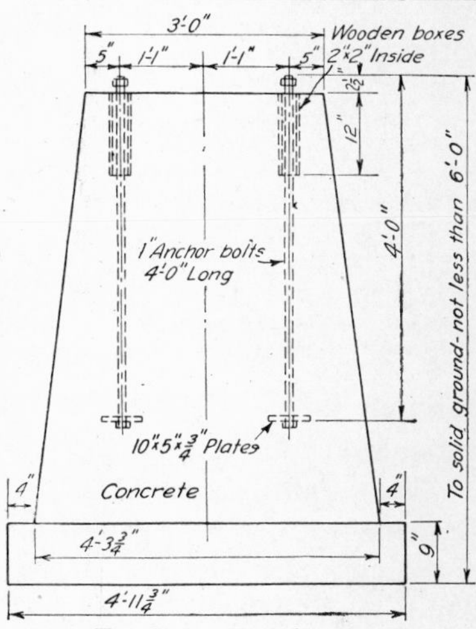

FIG. 721.—Pier drawing.

The usual symbol for concrete in section is used very commonly for reinforced concrete, adding the reinforcing bar sections in heavy black dots, with dashed or full lines for the bars parallel to the section. This, however, gives a very confused appearance. The reinforcing bars can be shown in place much more clearly if the concrete is represented by an even tint instead of using the regular symbol. This tint may be made by section lining in colored ink or in very dilute black ink or, if the tracing is made on the smooth side of the cloth, by stumping the back with soft pencil. Any one of these methods gives a light blue tint on the blue print and enables the details of the reinforcing, which is the important item, to be shown clearly. The two methods are shown side by side in Fig. 722.

Drawings of reinforced concrete structures should contain, in tabular form, beam schedules, slab schedules and column schedules as well as bar schedules.

Certain classes of engineering structures involve much freehand rendering, and the ease of reading (usefulness) depends upon the care with which this rendering is done.

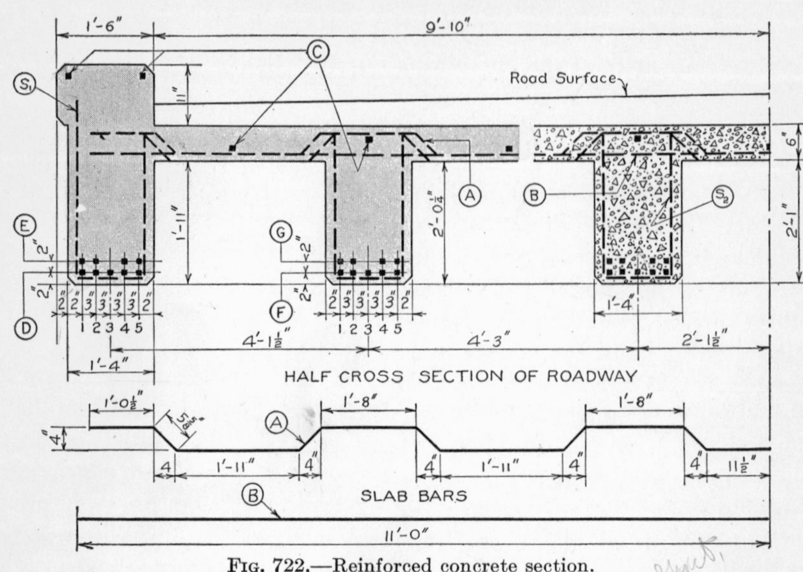

FIG. 722.—Reinforced concrete section.

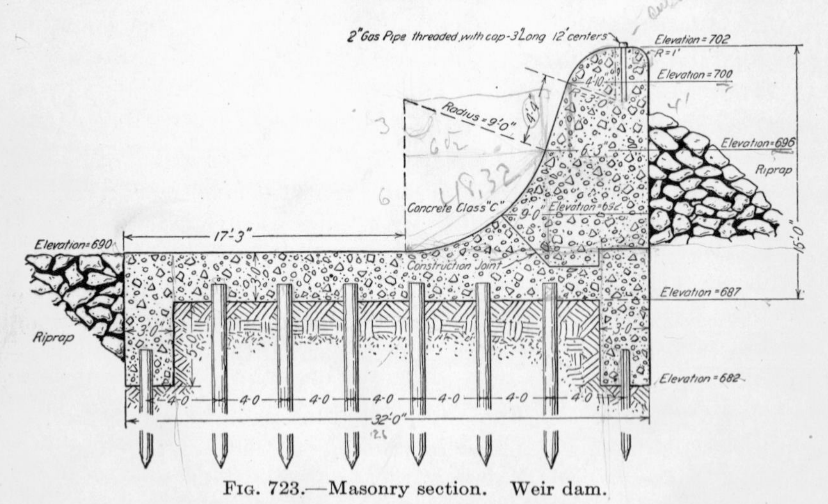

FIG. 723.—Masonry section. Weir dam.

The section of a submerged weir, Fig. 723, is an example of this, where there is comparatively little mechanical execution. Any means of "bringing out" the construction, such as surface shading or use of solid black, is legitimate.

CHAPTER XIX

MAP AND TOPOGRAPHIC DRAWING

318. Thus far in our consideration of drawing as a graphic language we have had to represent the three dimensions of an object either pictorially or, in the usual case, by drawing two or more views of it. In map drawing, the representation of features on parts of the earth's surface, there is the distinct difference that the drawing is complete in one view, the third dimension, the height, being either represented on this view or omitted as not required for the particular purpose for which the map was made.

The surveying and mapping of the site is the first preliminary work in improvements and engineering projects, and it is desirable that all engineers should be familiar with the methods and symbols used in this branch of drawing. Without considering the practice of surveying and plotting or the various methods used by the cartographers in projecting the curved surface of the earth on a plane, we are interested in the use and details of execution of plats and topographic maps.

319. Classification.—The content or information on maps may be classified in general under three divisions:

(1) The representation of imaginary lines, such as divisions between areas subject to different authority or ownership, either public or private; or lines indicating geometric measurements on the ground. In this division may be included plats or land maps, farm surveys, city subdivisions, plats of mineral claims.

(2) The representation of real or material features or objects within the limits of the tract, showing their relative location or size and location, depending upon the purpose of the map. When relative location only is required the scale may be small, and symbols employed to represent objects, as houses, bridges or even towns. When the size of the objects is an important consideration the scale must be large and the map becomes a real orthographic top view.

(3) The representation of the relative elevation of the surface of the ground. Maps with this feature are called relief maps or, if contours are used with elevations marked on them, contour maps.

Various combinations of these three devisions are required for different purposes. Classified according to their purpose, maps may be (*a*) geographic, (*b*) topographic, (*c*) cadastral, (*d*) engineering.

Geographic maps include large areas and consequently must be to small scale. They would contain under division (1) political boundaries and under (2) the more important towns and cities, streams and bodies of water. Symbols for mountain ranges might be classed under (3).

Topographic maps are complete descriptions of certain areas and would thus include, to larger scale, items under (1) and (2) and contours under (3).

Cadastral maps are very accurate control maps for cities and towns, made to large scale with all features drawn to size, and used to control city development and operation, particularly taxation.

Engineering maps are working maps for engineering projects and contain accurate property lines, all objects on the site and contour lines.

320. Plats.—A map plotted from a plane survey, and having the third dimension omitted, is called a "plat" or "land map." It is used in the description of any tract of land when it is not necessary to show relief, as in such typical examples as a farm survey or a city plat.

The plotting is done from field notes, (1) by latitudes and departures, (2) by bearings and distances, (3) by deflection angles and distances, (4) by coordinates or the total latitude and departure from some fixed origin and for each separate point (important in mine engineering), (5) by azimuth and distances. Angles are laid off by bearings, by plotting tangents of the angle or sine of half the angle or by an accurate protractor.

The first principle to be observed in the execution of this kind of drawings is *simplicity*. Its information should be clear, concise and direct. The lettering should be done in single stroke, and the north point and border be of the simplest character. The day of the intricate border corner, elaborate north point and ornamental title is, happily, past, and all such embellishments are rightly considered not only as a waste of time but as being in very bad taste.

321. Plat of a Survey.—The plat of a survey should give clearly all the information necessary for the legal description of the parcel of land. It should contain

1. Lengths and bearings of the several sides.
2. Acreage.
3. Location and description of monuments found and set.
4. Location of highways, streams, etc.
5. Official division lines within the tract.
6. Names of owners of abutting property.
7. Title and north point.
8 Certification.

Figure 724 illustrates the general treatment of this kind of drawing. It is almost always traced and blue printed, and no water-lining of streams or other elaboration should be attempted. It is important to

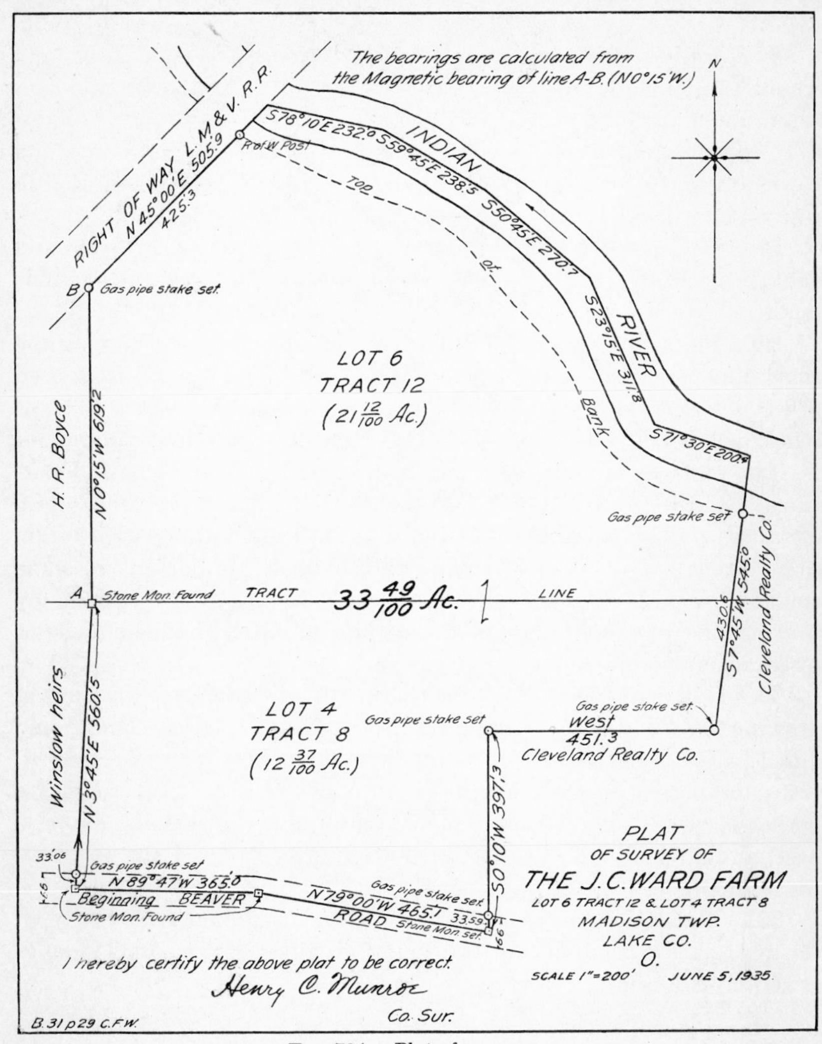

FIG. 724.—Plat of a survey.

observe that the size of the lettering used for the several features must be in proportion to their importance.

322. A Railroad Property Map.—Of the many kinds of plats used in industrial work one only is illustrated here, the portion of a railway

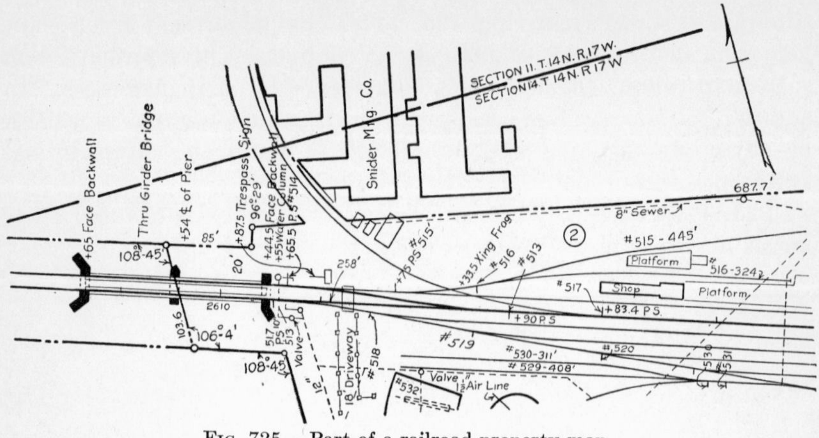

Fig. 725.—Part of a railroad property map.

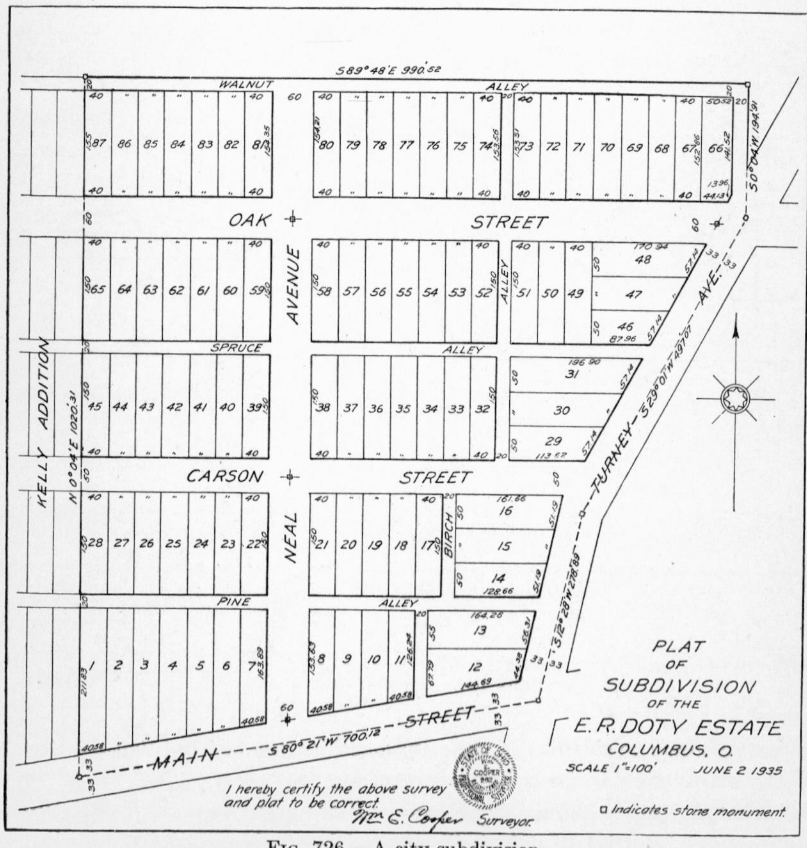

Fig. 726.—A city subdivision.

situation or station map, Fig. 725. This might represent also a plant valuation map, a type of plat often required. The information on such maps varies to meet the requirements of particular cases. In addition to the preceding list, it might include such items as pipe lines, fire hydrants, location and description of buildings, railroads and switch points, outdoor crane runways, etc.

323. Plats of Subdivisions.—The plats of subdivisions and allotments in cities are filed with the county recorder for record and must

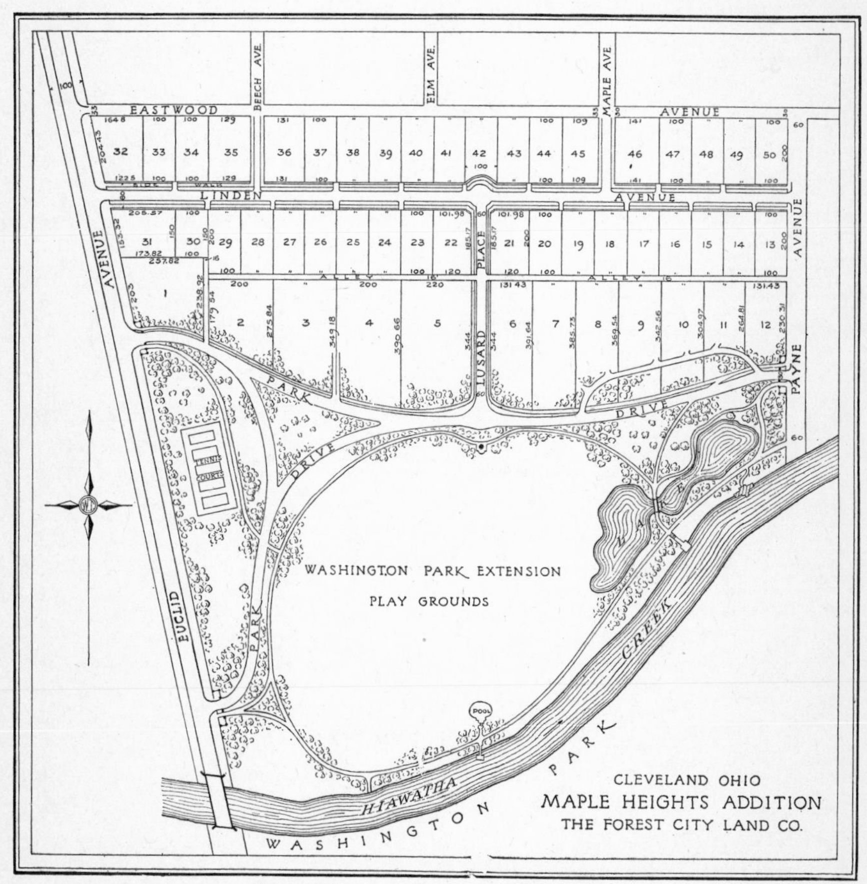

FIG. 727.—A real estate display map.

be very complete in their information concerning the location and size of the various lots and parcels composing the subdivisions, Fig. 726. All monuments set should be shown and all measurements of lines and angles given, so that it will be possible to locate any lot with precision.

Sometimes landowners desire to use these maps in display to prospective buyers, and some degree of embellishment is allowable, but care must be taken not to overdo the ornamentation. These drawings are usually finished as blue prints. Figure 727 is an example showing an acceptable style of execution and finish.

324. City Plats.—Under this head are included chiefly maps or plats drawn from subdivision plats or other sources for the record of

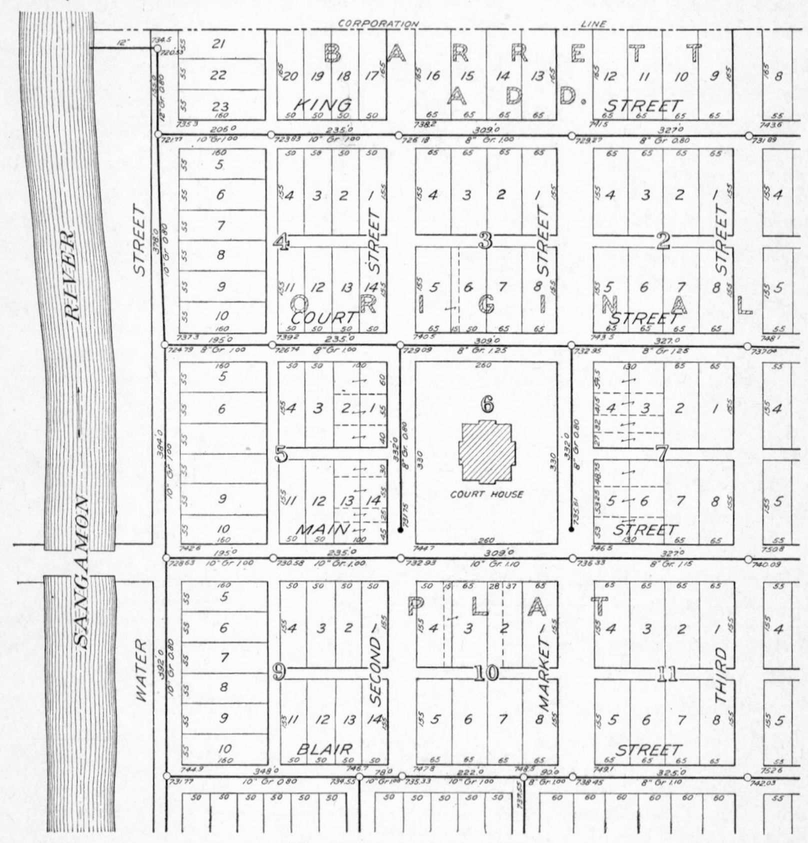

FIG. 728.—A sewer map.

city improvements. These plats are used for the record of a variety of information, such as, for example, the location of sewers, water mains, street railways and street improvements.

One valuable use is the levying of assessments for street paving, sewers, etc. As they are made for a definite purpose they should not contain unnecessary information and hence will not include all the details as to sizes of lots, location of monuments, etc., which are given on subdivision plats. They are usually made on mounted paper and should be to a scale large enough to show clearly the features required, 100′ and 200′ to the inch are common scales, and as large as 50′ is sometimes used. For smaller cities the entire area may be covered by one map; in larger cities the maps are made in convenient sections so as to be filed readily.

A study of Fig. 728, a sewer map, will show the general treatment of such plats. The appearance of the drawing is improved by adding shade lines on the lower and right-hand side of the blocks, that is, treating the streets and water features as depressions. A few of the more important public buildings are shown, to facilitate reading. The various wards, subdivisions or districts may be shown by large outline letters or numerals as illustrated in the figure. Contours are often put on these maps in red or brown ink, either on the original or sometimes on a positive print from it.

325. Topographic Drawing.—As before defined, a complete topographic map would contain:

1. The imaginary lines indicating the divisions of authority or ownership.
2. The geographical position of both the natural features and the works of man. They may also include information in regard to the vegetation.
3. The relief, or indication of the relative elevations and depressions. The relief, which is the third dimension, is represented in general either by contours or by hill shading.

326. Contours.—A contour is an imaginary line on the surface of the ground which, at every point, passes through the same elevation; thus the shore line of a body of water represents a contour. If the water should rise one foot the new shore line would be another contour, with one foot "contour interval." A series of contours may thus be illustrated approximately by Fig. 729.

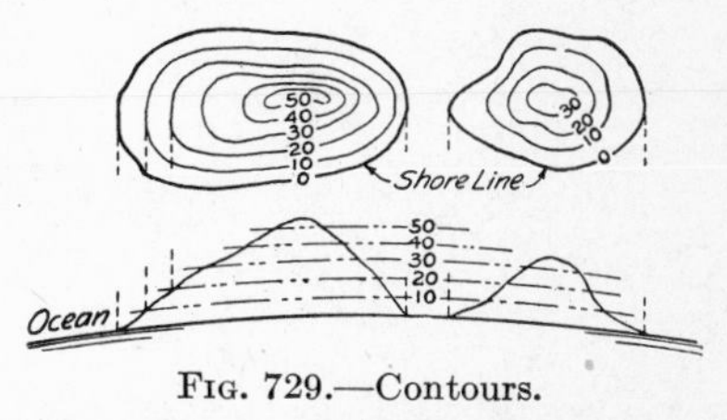

Fig. 729.—Contours.

Figure 730 is a perspective view of a tract of land. Figure 731 is a contour map of this area, and Fig. 732 is the same surface shown with hill shading by hachures. Contours are drawn as fine, full lines, with every fifth one of heavier weight, and the elevations in feet marked on them at intervals, usually with the sea level as datum. They may be drawn with a swivel pen, Fig. 789. Alteneder's is recommended or a fine pen such as Gillott's 170. On paper drawings they are usually made in brown.

FIG. 730.—Perspective view.

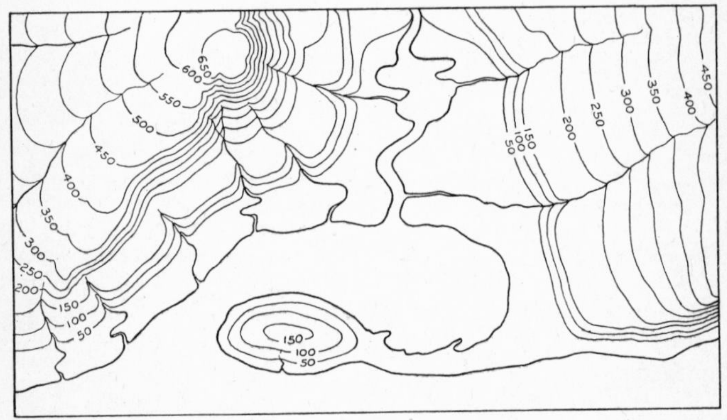

FIG. 731.—Application of contour lines.

FIG. 732.—Application of hachures for hill shading.

Figure 733 is a topographic map of the site of a proposed filtration plant and illustrates the use of the contour map as the necessary preliminary drawing in engineering projects. Often on the same drawing there are shown, by lines of different character, both the existing contours and the required finished grades.

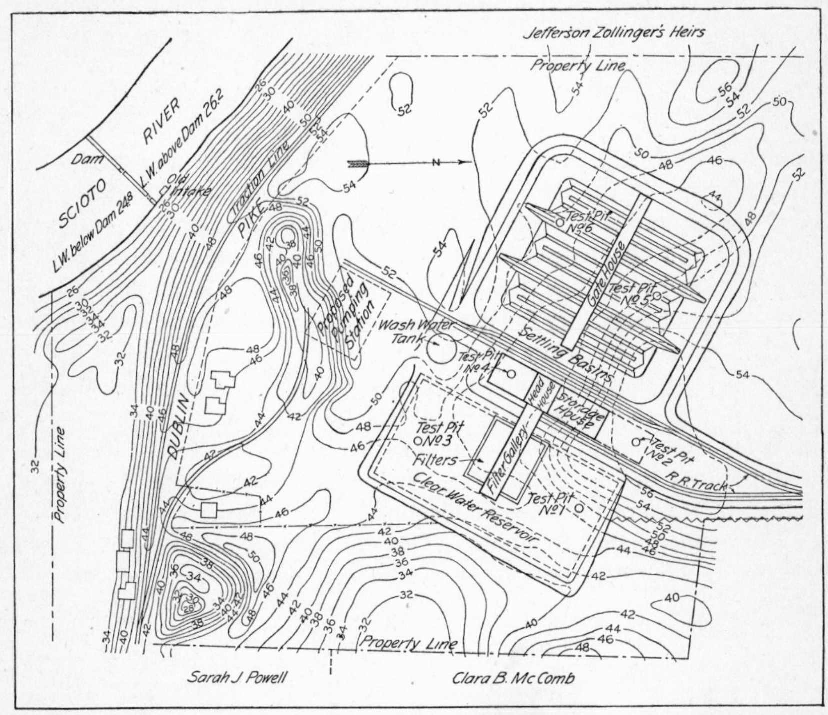

Fig. 733.—Contour map for engineering project.

327. Hill Shading.—The showing of relief by means of hill shading gives a pleasing effect but this is very difficult of execution, does not give exact elevations and would not be applied on maps to be used for engineering purposes. It may sometimes be used to advantage in reconnaissance maps or in small-scale maps for illustration. There are several systems, of which hachuring, as shown in Fig. 732, is the commonest. The contours are sketched lightly in pencil and the hachures drawn perpendicular to them, starting at the summit and grading the weight of line to the degree of slope. A scale of hachures to use for reference is often made, graded from black for 45° to white for horizontal. The rows of strokes should touch the pencil line to avoid white streaks along the contours. Two other systems in use are the horizontal, or English, drawing graded lines parallel to the contours, and the oblique illumination, or French, using hachures graded to give sunlight effect as well as the degree of slope.

328. Water-lining.—On topographic maps made for display or reproduction the water features are usually finished by "water-lining," running a system of fine lines parallel to the shore lines, either in black or in blue (it must be remembered that blue will not photograph for reproduction or print well from a tracing). Poor water-lining will ruin the appearance of an otherwise well-executed map, and it is better to omit it rather than do it hastily or carelessly. The shore line is drawn first, and the water-lining done with a fine mapping pen, as Gillott's 170 or 290, always drawing toward the body and having the preceding line to the left. The first line should follow the shore line very closely, and the distances between the succeeding lines gradually increased and the irregularities lessened. Sometimes the weight of lines is graded as well as the intervals but this is a very difficult operation and is not necessary for the effect. A common mistake is to make the lines excessively wavy or rippled.

In water-lining a stream of varying width, the lines are not to be crowded so as to be carried through the narrower portions, but corresponding lines should be brought together in the middle of the stream as illustrated in Fig. 732. Care should be taken to avoid spots of sudden increase or decrease in spacing.

329. Topographic Symbols.—The various symbols used in topographic drawing may be grouped under four heads:

1. Culture, or the works of man.
2. Relief—relative elevations and depressions.
3. Water features.
4. Vegetation.

When color is used the culture is done in black, the relief in brown, the water features in blue, and the vegetation in black or green.

These symbols, used to represent characteristics on the earth's surface, are made, when possible, to resemble somewhat the features or objects represented as they would appear either in plan or in elevation. No attempt is here made to give symbols for all the features that might occur in a map; indeed one may have to invent symbols for some particular locality.

Figure 734 illustrates a few of the conventional symbols used for culture or the works of man, and no suggestion is needed as to the method of their execution. When the scale used is large, houses, bridges, roads and even tree trunks can be plotted so that their principal dimensions can be scaled. A small-scale map can give by its symbols only the relative locations.

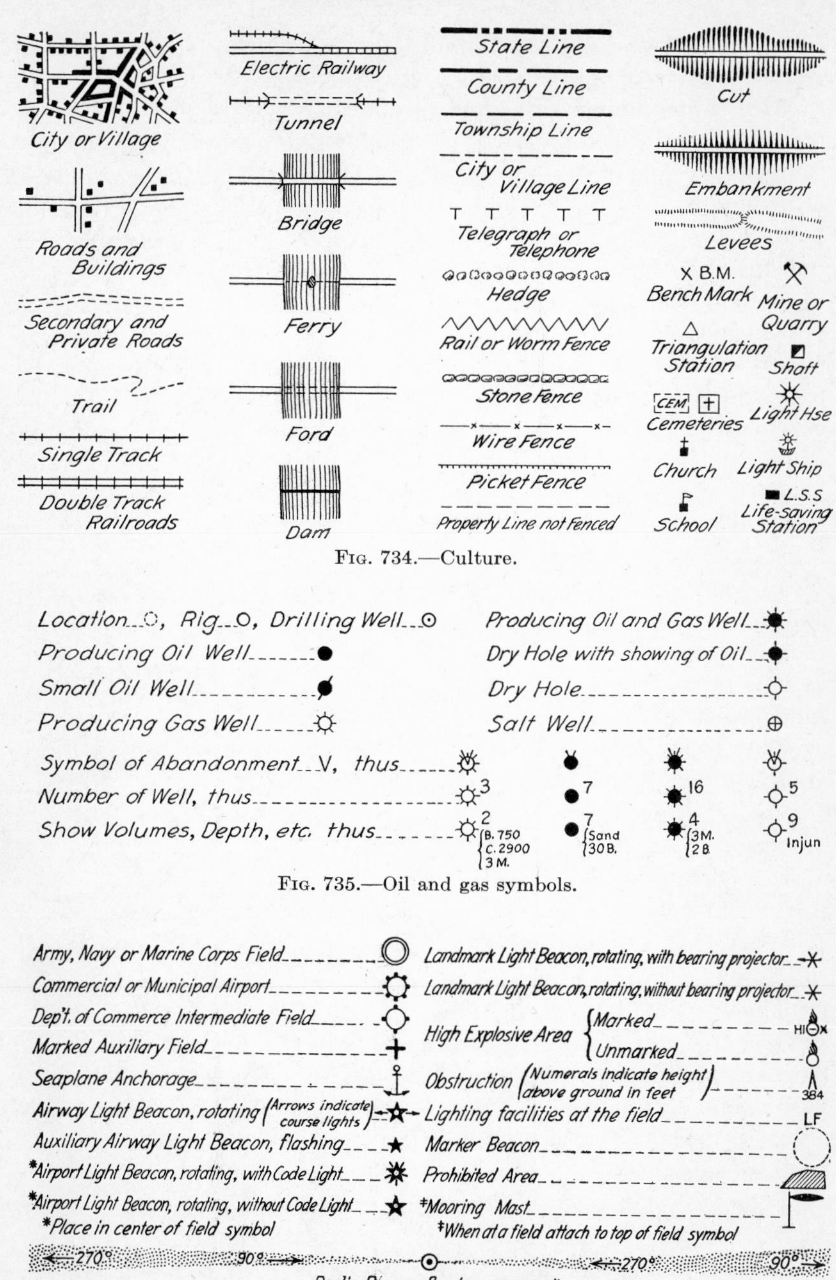
City or Village
Roads and Buildings
Secondary and Private Roads
Trail
Single Track
Double Track Railroads
Electric Railway
Tunnel
Bridge
Ferry
Ford
Dam
State Line
County Line
Township Line
City or Village Line
Telegraph or Telephone
Hedge
Rail or Worm Fence
Stone Fence
Wire Fence
Picket Fence
Property Line not Fenced
Cut
Embankment
Levees
X B.M.
Bench Mark
Mine or Quarry
Triangulation Station
Shaft
CEM
Cemeteries
Light Hse
Church
Light Ship
School
L.S.S
Life-saving Station
Location, Rig, Drilling Well
Producing Oil Well
Small Oil Well
Producing Gas Well
Producing Oil and Gas Well
Dry Hole with showing of Oil
Dry Hole
Salt Well
Symbol of Abandonment V, thus
Number of Well, thus
Show Volumes, Depth, etc. thus
3
7
16
5
2
B. 750
C. 2900
3 M.
7
Sand
30 B.
4
3M.
2 B
9
Injun
Army, Navy or Marine Corps Field
Commercial or Municipal Airport
Dep't. of Commerce Intermediate Field
Marked Auxiliary Field
Seaplane Anchorage
Airway Light Beacon, rotating (Arrows indicate course lights)
Auxiliary Airway Light Beacon, flashing
*Airport Light Beacon, rotating, with Code Light
*Airport Light Beacon, rotating, without Code Light
*Place in center of field symbol
Landmark Light Beacon, rotating, with bearing projector
Landmark Light Beacon, rotating, without bearing projector
High Explosive Area
Marked
Unmarked
HI
Obstruction (Numerals indicate height above ground in feet)
384
Lighting facilities at the field
LF
Marker Beacon
Prohibited Area
†Mooring Mast
†When at a field attach to top of field symbol
270°
90°
270°
90°
Radio Range, Bearings are magnetic
(All the above symbols to be drawn in red)

FIG. 734.—Culture.

FIG. 735.—Oil and gas symbols.

FIG. 736.—Aviation symbols.

In Fig. 735 the standard symbols used in the development of oil and gas fields are given; in Fig. 736 the symbols for aerial navigation of the U. S. Board of Surveys and Maps, adopted 1932; in Fig. 737 symbols

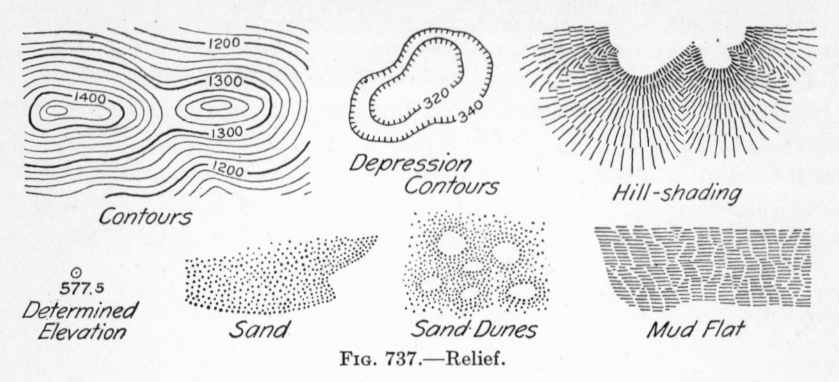

Fig. 737.—Relief.

used to show relief; in Fig. 738 water features; and in Fig. 739 some of the commoner symbols for vegetation and cultivation.

Draftsmen should keep in mind the purpose of the map, and the relative importance of features should be in some measure indicated by their prominence or strength, gained principally by the amount of

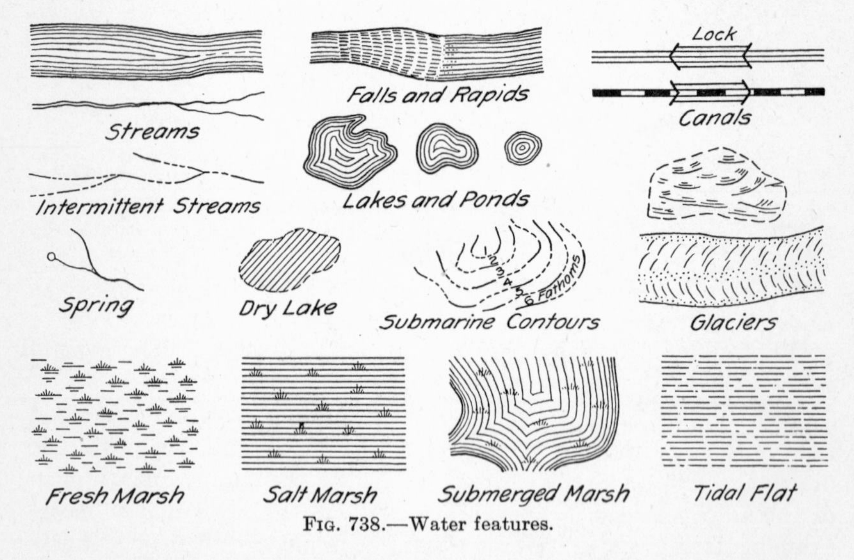

Fig. 738.—Water features.

ink used. For instance, in a map made for military maneuvering a cornfield might be an important feature; or in maps made to show the location of special features, such as fire hydrants, these objects would be indicated very plainly. The map of an airport or of a golf course would contain emphasized features. This principle calls for some originality to meet varying cases.

A common fault of the beginner is to make symbols too large. The symbols for grass, shown under "meadow," Fig. 739, if not made and spaced correctly will spoil the entire map. This symbol is composed of from five to seven short strokes radiating from a common center and starting along a horizontal line as shown in the enlarged form, each tuft beginning and ending with a mere dot. Always place the tufts with the bottom parallel to the border and distribute them uniformly over the space, but not in rows. A few incomplete tufts or rows of dots improve the appearance. Grass tufts should never be so heavy

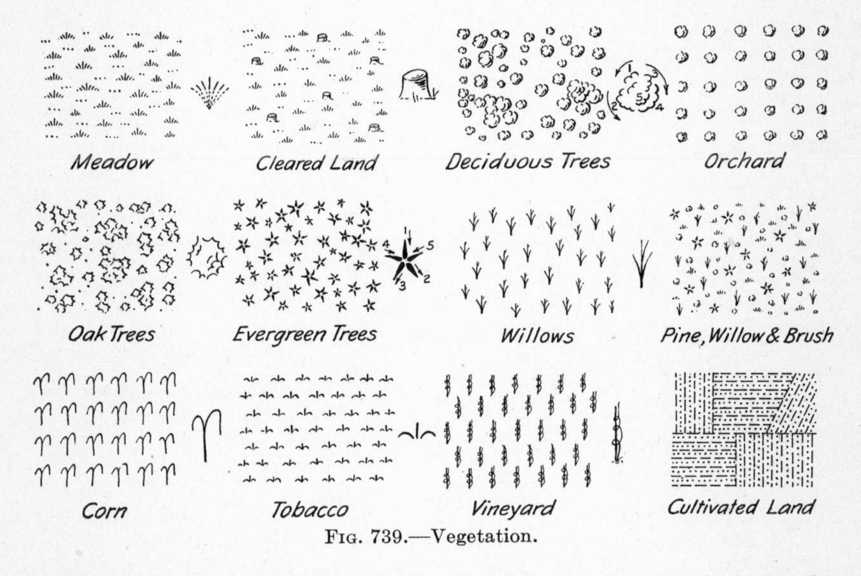

Fig. 739.—Vegetation.

as tree symbols. In drawing the symbol for deciduous trees the sequence of strokes shown should be followed.

The topographic map, Fig. 740, is given to illustrate the general execution and placing of symbols.

The well-known maps of the U.S. Coast and Geodetic Survey and the Geological Survey illustrate the application of topographic drawing. The quadrangle sheets issued by the topographic branch of the U. S. Geological Survey are excellent examples and so easily available that every draftsman should be familiar with them. These sheets represent 15 minutes of latitude and 15 minutes of longitude to the scale of 1:62,500 or approximately 1″ to the mile. The entire United States is being mapped by the department in cooperation with the different states, and in 1934 over 46 per cent had been completed, the amounts varying widely in different states, as 85.9 per cent of Pennsylvania, 10.1 per cent of Indiana, all of Ohio and 10 other states. This work is now facilitated by the application of aerial photography. Much territory in the West and South has been mapped ½ inch to the mile, and earlier some in the West was mapped ¼ inch to the mile. These maps may be secured for 10 cents each (not stamps) by addressing The Director, *U. S. Geological Survey, Washington, D.C.*, from whom information as to the completion of any particular locality or the progress in any state may be had.

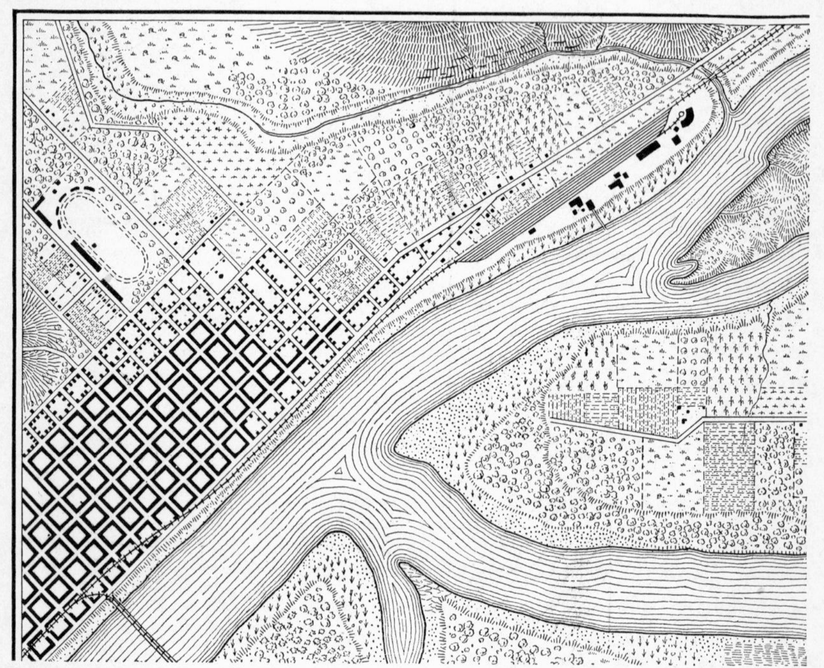

FIG. 740.—Part of a topographic map.

330. Landscape Maps.—A topographic map made to a relatively large scale and showing all details is called a "landscape map." Such maps are required by architects and landscape gardeners for use in planning buildings to fit the natural topographic features and for lamdscaping parks, playgrounds and private estates. These are generally maps of small areas, and a scale of 1″ = 20′ to 1″ = 50′, depending upon the amount of detail, is used.

The contour interval varies from 6 inches to 2 feet according to the ruggedness of the surface. The commonest interval is 1 foot. These maps are often reproduced in black line prints upon which contours in different color are drawn to show the landscape treatment proposed. Natural features and culture are added in more detail than on ordinary topographic maps. Trees are designated as to size, species and sometimes spread of branches and condition. It is often necessary to invent symbols suitable for the particular survey and to include a key or legend on the map. Roads, walks, streams, flower beds, houses, etc., should be plotted carefully to scale, so that measurements can be taken from them.

331. Colors.—Instead of using colored inks, which are thin and unsatisfactory to handle in the pen and neither photograph nor blue print well, it is much better to use water colors for contours, streams and other colored symbols in topographic mapping. For contours, burnt sienna, either straight or darkened with a drop of black, and mixed rather thick; for streams Prussian blue, and for red features alizarin crimson, all work well in either crowquill or contour pen and make good blue prints. Colors in tubes are more convenient than those in cakes or pans.

332. Lettering.—The style of lettering on a topographic map will depend upon the purpose for which the map is made. If it is for construction purposes, such as a contour map for the study of municipal problems, street grades, plants or railroads, the single-stroke Gothic and Reinhardt is to be preferred. For a finished map vertical Modern Roman letters for land features and inclined Roman and stump letters for water features should be used. The scale should always be drawn as well as stated.

333. Titles.—The standard letter for finished map titles is the Modern Roman. The design should be symmetrical, with the heights of the letters proportioned to the relative importance of the line. A map title should contain as many as are necessary of the following items:

1. Kind—"Map of," etc.
2. Name.
3. Location of tract.
4. Purpose, if special features are represented.
5. For whom made.
6. Engineer in charge.
7. Date (of survey).
8. Scale—stated and drawn.
9. Authorities.
10. Legend or key to symbols.
11. North point.
12. Certification.

334. Profiles.—Perhaps no kind of drawing is used more by civil engineers than the ordinary profile, which is simply a vertical section taken along a given line either straight or curved. Such drawings are indispensable in problems of railroad construction, highway and street

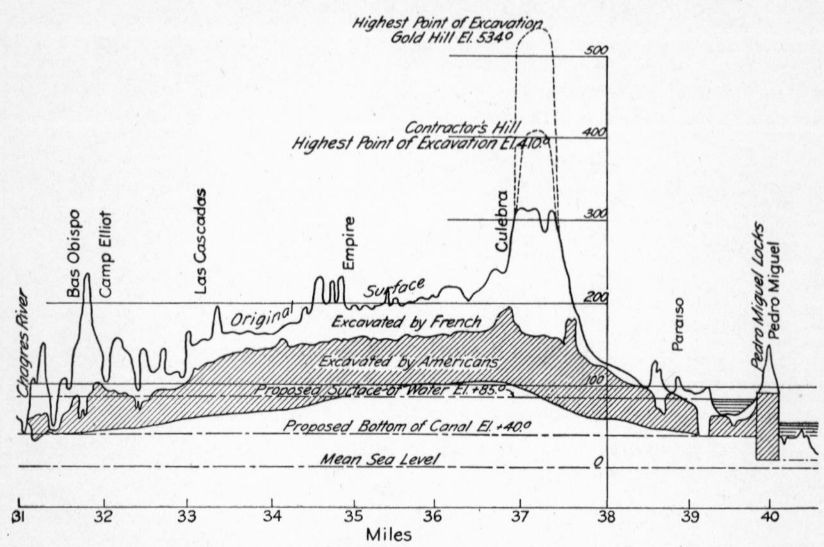

FIG. 741.—Profile (vertical scale 50 times horizontal).

improvements, sewer construction and many other problems where a study of the surface of the ground is required. Very frequently engineers other than civil engineers are called upon to make these drawings. Several different types of profile and cross-section paper

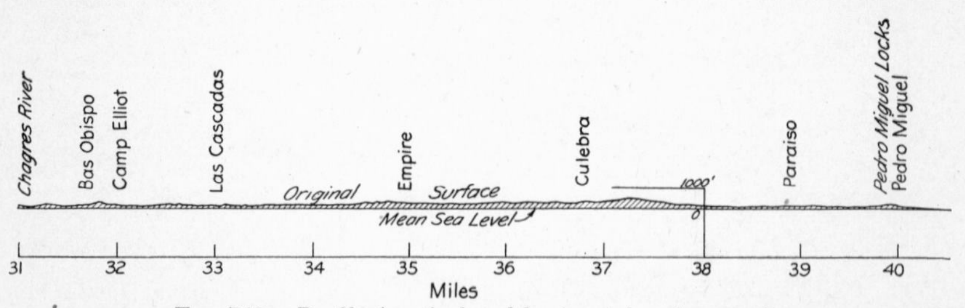

FIG. 742.—Profile (vertical and horizontal scales equal).

are in use and may be found in the catalogues of the various firms dealing in drawing materials. One type of profile paper in common use is known as "Plate A" in which there are 4 divisions to the inch horizontally and 20 to the inch vertically. Other divisions which are used are 4 × 30 to the inch and 5 × 25 to the inch. At intervals,

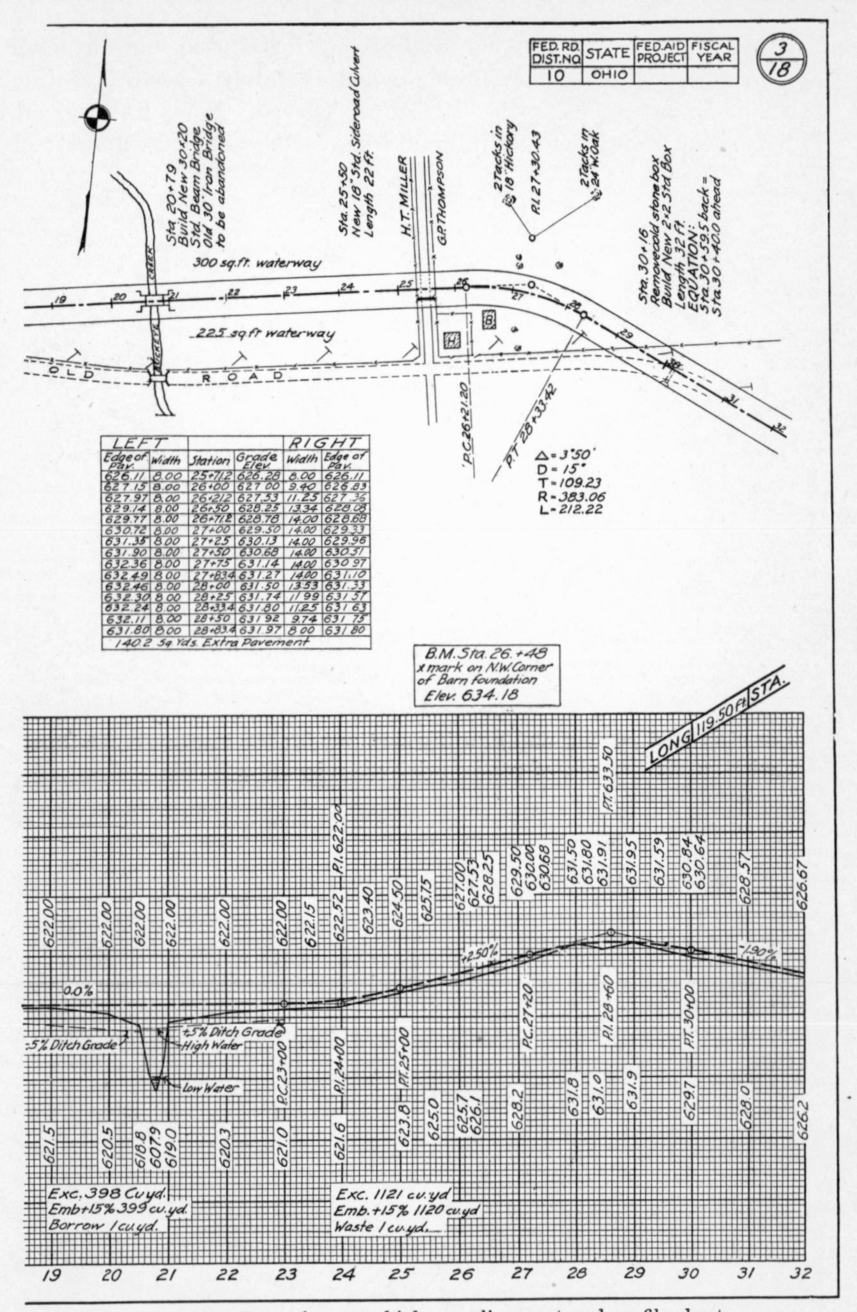

LEFT				RIGHT	
Edge of Pav.	Width	Station	Grade Elev.	Width	Edge of Pav.
626.11	8.00	25+71.2	626.28	8.00	626.11
627.15	8.00	26+00	627.00	9.40	626.83
627.97	8.00	26+21.2	627.53	11.25	627.36
629.14	8.00	26+50	628.25	13.34	628.08
629.77	8.00	26+71.2	628.78	14.00	628.68
630.72	8.00	27+00	629.50	14.00	629.33
631.35	8.00	27+25	630.13	14.00	629.96
631.90	8.00	27+50	630.68	14.00	630.51
632.36	8.00	27+75	631.14	14.00	630.97
632.49	8.00	27+83.4	631.27	14.00	631.10
632.46	8.00	28+00	631.50	13.53	631.33
632.30	8.00	28+25	631.74	11.99	631.57
632.24	8.00	28+33.4	631.80	11.25	631.63
632.11	8.00	28+50	631.92	9.74	631.75
631.80	8.00	28+83.4	631.97	8.00	631.80
140.2 Sq. Yds. Extra Pavement					

Fig. 743.—Part of a state highway alignment and profile sheet.

both horizontally and vertically, somewhat heavier lines are made in order to facilitate reading.

Horizontal distances are plotted as abscissas and elevations as ordinates. Since the vertical distances represent elevations, being plotted to larger scale, a vertical exaggeration is obtained which is very useful in studying the profile for the establishing of grades. The vertical exaggeration is sometimes confusing to the layman or inexperienced engineer, but ordinarily a profile will fail in the purpose for which it was intended if the horizontal and vertical scales are the same. Again the profile unless so distorted would be a very long and unwieldy affair, if not entirely impossible to make. The difference between profiles with and without vertical exaggeration is shown in Figs. 741 and 742.

Figure 743 is a portion of a typical State Highway *Alignment and Profile Sheet*, plotted to scale 1″ = 100′ with vertical scale of profile 1″ = 10′. Tracing cloth is furnished with the coordinates printed in red on the back so that any changes or erasures on the profile are brought out by erasing the lines on the back. This sheet is one of a set of drawings used for estimating cost, and by the contractor as a working drawing during construction. Other drawings in the set consist of *cross-sections* (taken every 100 feet or oftener), used for grading, and *working drawings* of bridges, culverts, guard rails, etc., as well as standard paving and grading sections for the various conditions met with in the stretch of road under consideration.

CHAPTER XX

CHARTS, GRAPHS AND DIAGRAMS

335. This chapter is given as an introduction to the use of graphical methods in tabulating data for analysis, solving problems and presenting facts. It will indicate to the prospective engineer the uses and value of this application of graphics and suggest his further study of the subject.

For the purpose of presenting a series of quantitative facts quickly, the graphical chart is the one best method. The statement "it is easier to see than to think" applies as meaning that with the majority of people the visual impression is the strongest form of appeal. It is not to be supposed that charts can be substituted for thinking, but they assist clear thinking by eliminating the tiring mental effort necessary in keeping in mind an involved series of figures. When properly constructed and thoroughly understood, charts, graphs and diagrams constitute a powerful tool for computation, analysis of engineering data and the presentation of statistics for comparison or prediction.

336. When classified as to use, charts, graphs and diagrams may be divided roughly into two classes: those used for purely technical purposes, and those for popular appeal in information or advertising. The engineer is concerned mainly with the first class, but he should have some acquaintance with the preparation and possibilities in influence of the second class. The aim here is to give a short study of the types with which engineers and those in allied professions should be familiar.

The construction of a graphical chart requires a fair degree of draftsmanship, but in engineering and scientific work the important considerations are judgment as to the proper selection of coordinates, accuracy in plotting points and drawing the graph and an understanding of the functions and limitations of the resulting chart.

It is assumed that the reader is familiar with the use of rectangular coordinates and that the meaning of such terms as "axes," "ordinates," "abscissas," "coordinates," "variables," etc., is understood.

337. Titles and Notation.—The title is a very important part of a chart. Its wording should be studied until it is clear and concise. In every case it should contain sufficient description to tell what the chart is, the source or authority, the name of the observer and the *date.*

Approved practice places the title at the top of the sheet, arranged in phrases symmetrically about a center line. If placed within the ruled space a border line or box will set it out from the sheet. Each sheet of curves should have a title and when more than one curve is shown on a sheet the different curves should be drawn so as to be easily distinguishable, by varying the character of the lines, using full, dotted and dot-and-dash lines, with a tabular key for identification, or by lettering the names of the curves directly along them. When not intended for reproduction, different colors of inks may be used.

338. Rectilinear Charts.—The rectilinear chart is made on a sheet ruled with equispaced horizontal lines crossing equispaced vertical

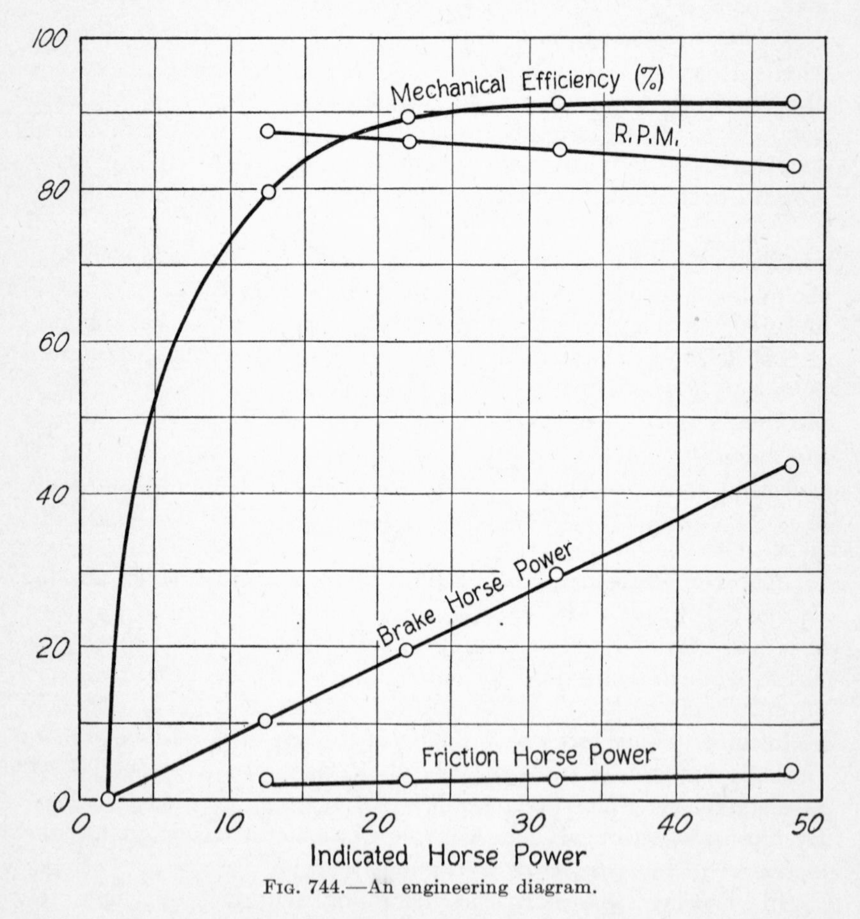

Fig. 744.—An engineering diagram.

lines. The spacing is optional but it is customary and convenient to use squares of one-twentieth of an inch with every fifth line heavier, to aid in plotting and reading. Sheets are printed with various other rulings, as 4, 6, 8, 12 and 16 divisions per inch.

As the majority of chart work in experimental engineering is done on rectilinear graph paper the student should become familiar with this form of chart early in his course.

It is universal practice to use the upper right-hand quadrant for plotting experimental curves, making the lower left-hand corner the origin. In case both positive and negative values of a function are to be plotted, as in the case of many mathematical curves, it is necessary to place the origin so as to include all desired values.

Figure 744 shows a usual form of rectilinear chart, such as might be made on 8½″ × 11″ paper to be included in a written report.

In drawing graphs from experimental data it is often a question whether the curve should pass through all the points plotted or strike a mean between them. In general the correct procedure is to locate the points by small circles and to draw a smooth curve striking the mean, since the deviations are probably due to observational errors.

339. Logarithmic Ruling.—A very important type of chart is that in which the divisions, instead of being equally spaced, are made proportional to the logarithms of the numbers at the margin instead of the numbers themselves. When ruled logarithmically in one direction and with equal spacing at right angles it is called semi-logarithmic.

Logarithmic spacing may be done directly from the graduations on one of the scales of a slide rule. Log paper in various combinations of ruling is sold. It may be had in one, two, three or more cycles, or multiples of 10, also in part-cycle and split-cycle form. In using log paper interpolations should be made logarithmically, not arithmetically as on rectangular coordinates, which with coarse divisions might lead to considerable error.

340. The Semi-logarithmic Chart.—This chart has equal spacing on one axis, usually the X-axis, and logarithmic spacing on the other axis. It is frequently called the "ratio chart" owing to a property by virtue of which the slope of the curve at any point is an exact measure of the rate of increase or decrease in the data plotted. It is extremely useful in statistical work as it shows at a glance the rate at which a variable changes. Karsten aptly calls it the "rate of change chart" as distinguished from the rectilinear or "amount of change chart." By the use of this chart it is possible to predict a trend, such as the increase of a business, growth of population, etc.

In choosing between rectilinear ruling and semi-log ruling the important point to consider is whether the chart is to represent *numerical* increases and decreases or *percentage* increases and decreases.

In many cases it is desired to emphasize the percentage or rate change, not the numerical change; hence a semi-log chart should be used.

An example of the use of the semi-log chart is illustrated in Fig. 745. This curve was drawn from data furnished by R. B. Prescott, Consulting Statistician, compiled for "Automotive Industries." The dash line is the actual production by years and the full line the trend curve, the extension of which predicts future production.

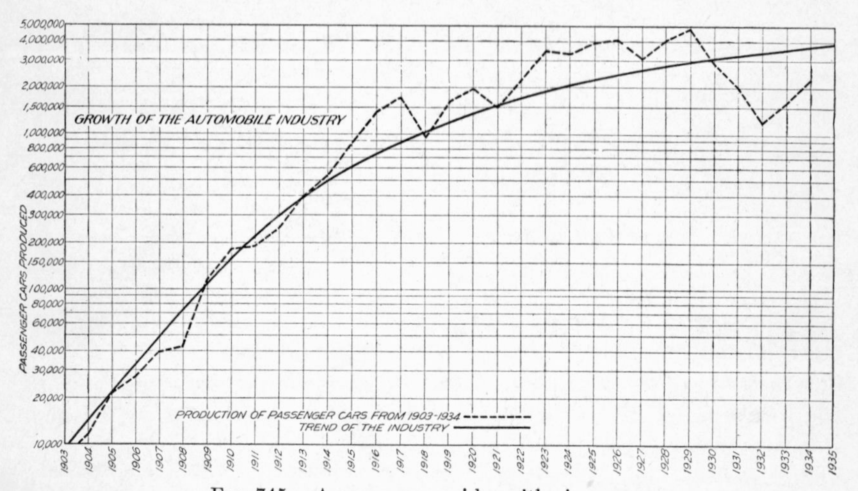

FIG. 745.—A curve on semi-logarithmic paper.

341. The function of a chart is to reveal facts. It may be entirely misleading if a wrong choice of paper or coordinates is taken. The growth of an operation plotted on a rectilinear chart might, for example, entirely mislead an owner analyzing the trend of his business, while if plotted on a semi-log chart it would give a true picture of conditions. Intentionally misleading charts have been used many times in advertising matter, the commonest form being the chart with a greatly exaggerated vertical scale.

342. Logarithmic charts with both abscissas and ordinates spaced logarithmically are used more for the solution of problems than for presenting facts. A property which distinguishes the logarithmic chart and accounts for its usefulness in so many cases is that the graphs of all algebraic equations representing multiplication, division, roots and powers are straight lines. If the equation $X^2Y = 16$ were plotted on ordinary rectangular coordinates the resulting curve would be a hyperbola with the X- and Y-axes as asymptotes. By taking the logarithms of both sides of the given equation it becomes $2 \log x + \log y = \log 16$. The equation now has the slope intercept form $y = mx + b$ and if so desired could be plotted on rectangular coordinates by substituting the logarithms of the variables. Obviously, it is easier to use logarithmic coordinates and plot the points directly than to take the logarithms of the variables and plot them on rectangular coordinates.

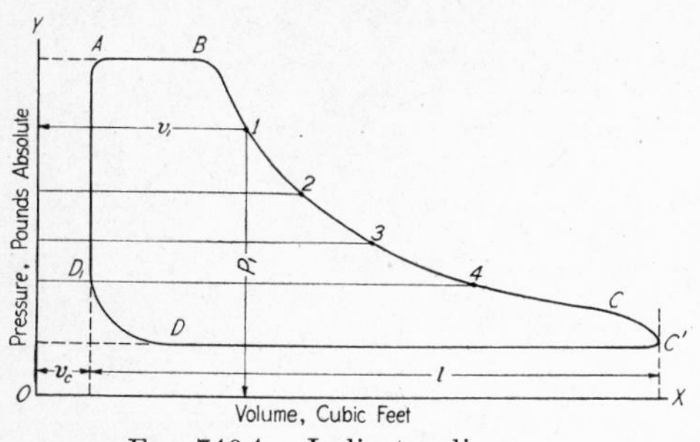

FIG. 746*A*.—Indicator diagram.

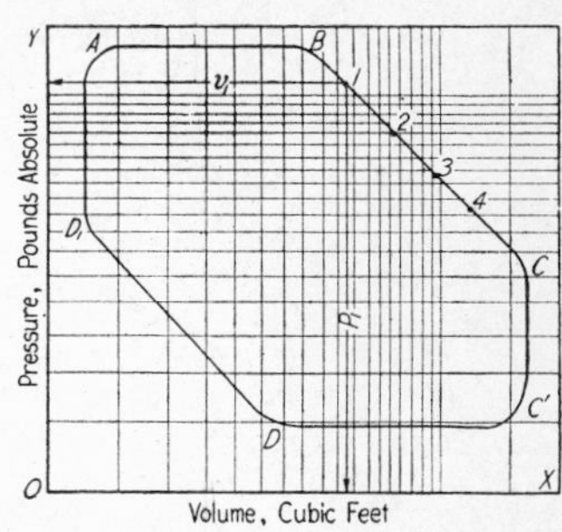

FIG. 746*B*.—Same on log paper.

A feature of the logarithmic chart which makes it valuable for the study of many problems is that the exponent in the equation may be determined by measuring the slope of the graph. An inspection of the foregoing equations will show that the slope m, as given by the slope intercept form, is -2. The value of this exponent may be determined by direct measurement of the slope, by using a uniformly graduated scale.

Figure 746 shows an example of the use of logarithmic charts in studying steam engine performance. When the indicator card A is plotted on log paper it takes the form B. The hyperbolas of a perfect card become straight lines, deviations from which indicate faults.

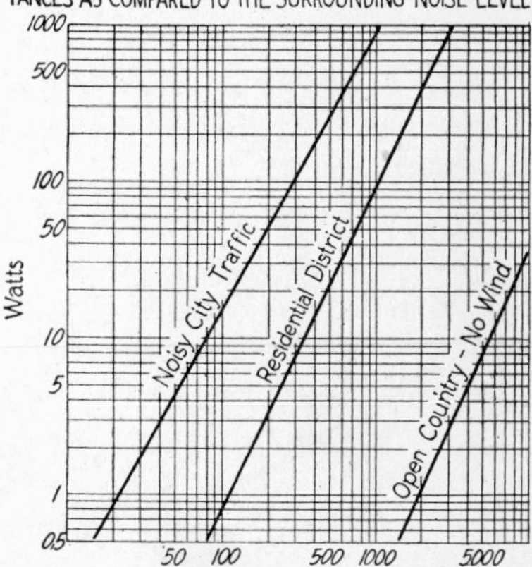

FIG. 747.—Multiple cycle ruling.

Figure 747 illustrates the use of multiple cycle paper.

343. The Polar Chart.—The use of polar coordinate paper for representing intensity of illumination, intensity of heat, polar forms of curves, etc., is common. Figure 748 shows two candle power distribution curves, A the curve for an ordinary Mazda B lamp and B for a certain type of reflector. The candle power in any given direction is determined by reading off the distance from the origin to the curve. Use of these curves enables the determination of the foot-candle intensity at any point.

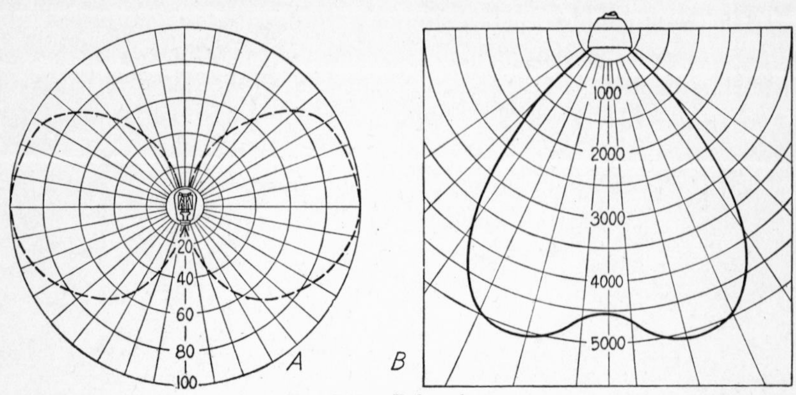

FIG. 748.—Polar charts.

344. The Trilinear Chart.—The trilinear chart, or triaxial diagram as it is sometimes called, offers a valuable means of studying the properties of chemical compounds consisting of three elements, alloys of three metals or compounds and mixtures containing three variables.

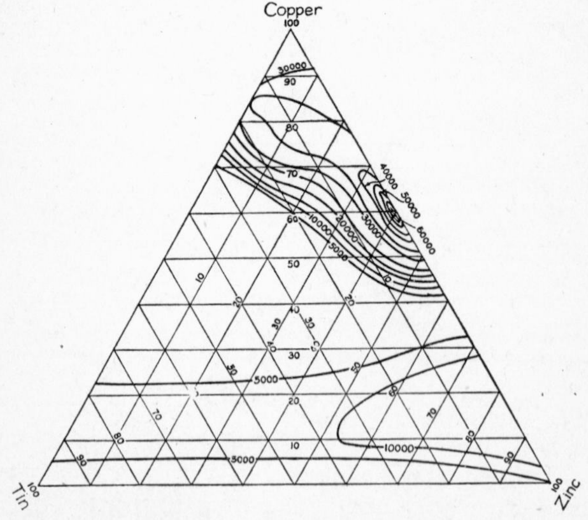

FIG. 749.—A trilinear chart.

The chart has the form of an equilateral triangle the altitude of which represents 100 per cent of each of the three constituents. Figure 749, showing the tensile strength of copper-tin-zinc alloys, is a typical example of its application. The use of such diagrams depends upon the geometrical principle that the sum of the perpendiculars to the sides from any point within an equilateral triangle is a constant and is equal to the altitude.

345. Nomographs.—The simplest form of nomograph is the *alignment chart,* consisting of three parallel lines graduated and spaced in such a manner that a straight line passing through known values on two of the scales gives the proper corresponding value at the inter-

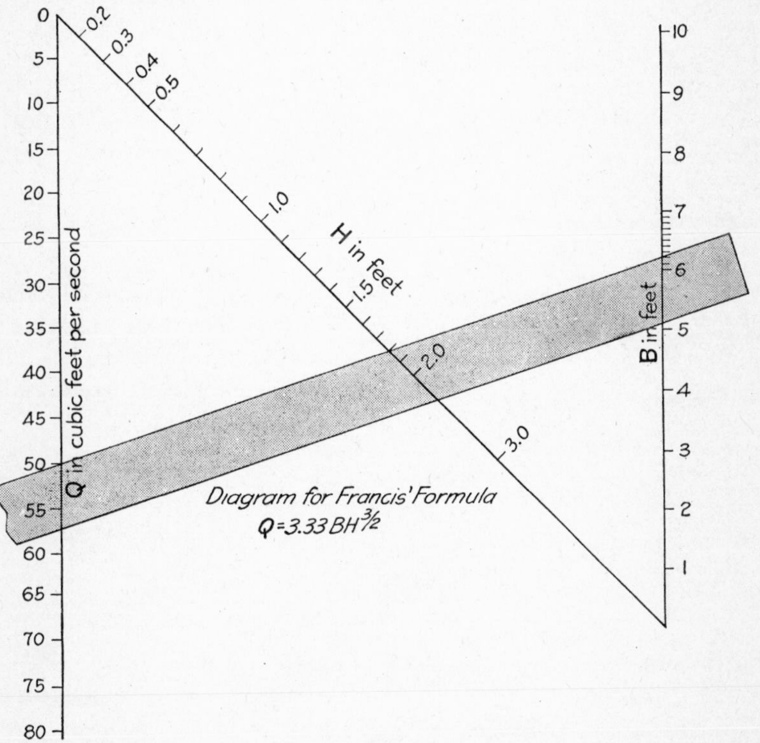

FIG. 750.—An alignment chart, or nomograph, of an equation. (*Redrawn from Hewes and Seward, The Design of Diagrams for Engineering Formulas.*)

section with the third scale. After an alignment is constructed, it is one of the easiest and most accurate means for the solution of the equation for which it is designed. It is beyond our scope here to explain the mathematics underlying the construction of nomographs as this chapter is only indicating and illustrating the various uses of graphic representation. The graduated lines in a nomograph need not be parallel, and any or all of them may be either curved or straight, depending upon the equation represented. Figure 750 is one form of an alignment chart sometimes called the "zigzag nomograph" from its appearance. The rectangular chart for the same equation is given in Fig. 751 for comparison. The simplicity of the alignment chart is obvious.

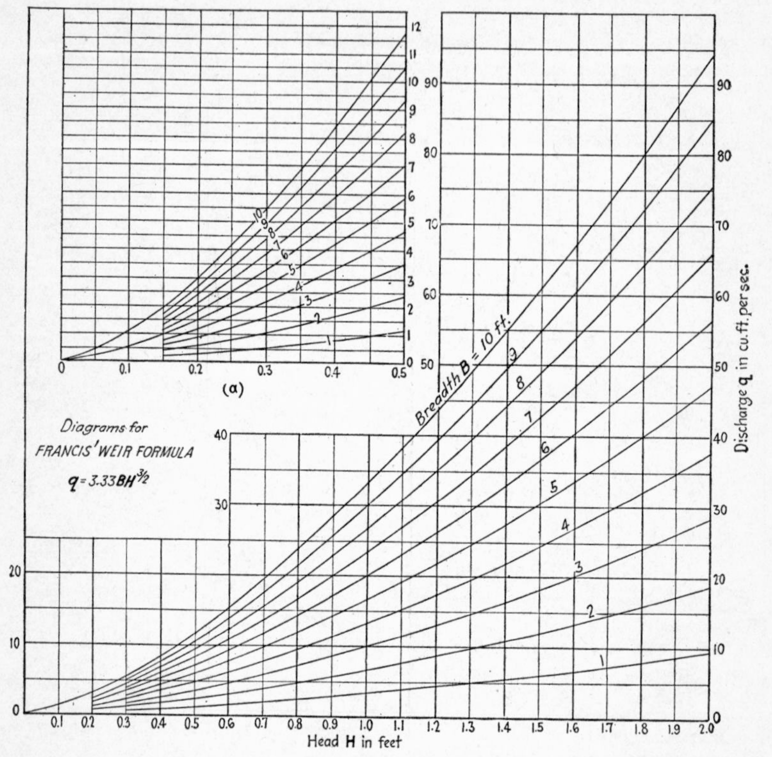

FIG. 751.—A rectilinear chart of an equation. (*Courtesy of Hewes and Seward, The Design of Diagrams for Engineering Formulas.*)

346. Classification Charts, Route Charts and Flow Sheets.—The uses to which the three named classes of charts may be put are widely different but their underlying principles are similar and they have thus been grouped for convenience.

A classification chart, as illustrated in Fig. 752, is intended to show the subdivisions of a whole, and interrelation of these parts with each other. Such a chart often takes the place of a written outline since it gives a better visualization of the facts than words alone would convey. A common application is an organization chart of a corporation or business. It is customary to enclose the names of the divisions in rectangles although circles or other shapes may be used. The rectangle has the advantage of being more convenient for lettering, while the circle may be drawn more quickly and possesses a popular appeal. Often a combination of both is used.

The *route chart* is used mainly for the purpose of showing the various steps in a process, either in manufacturing or in business transaction.

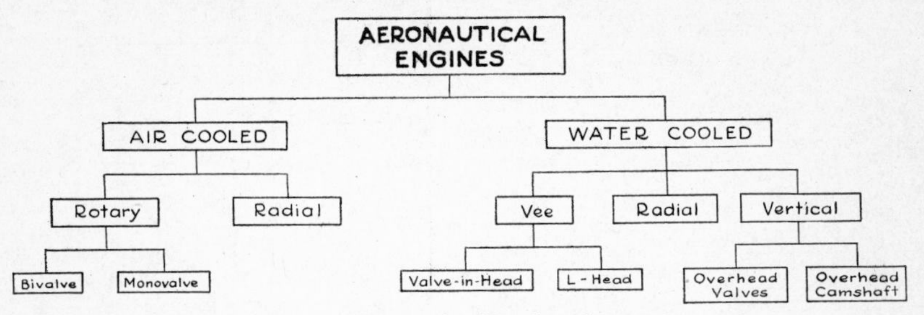

FIG. 752.—A classification chart.

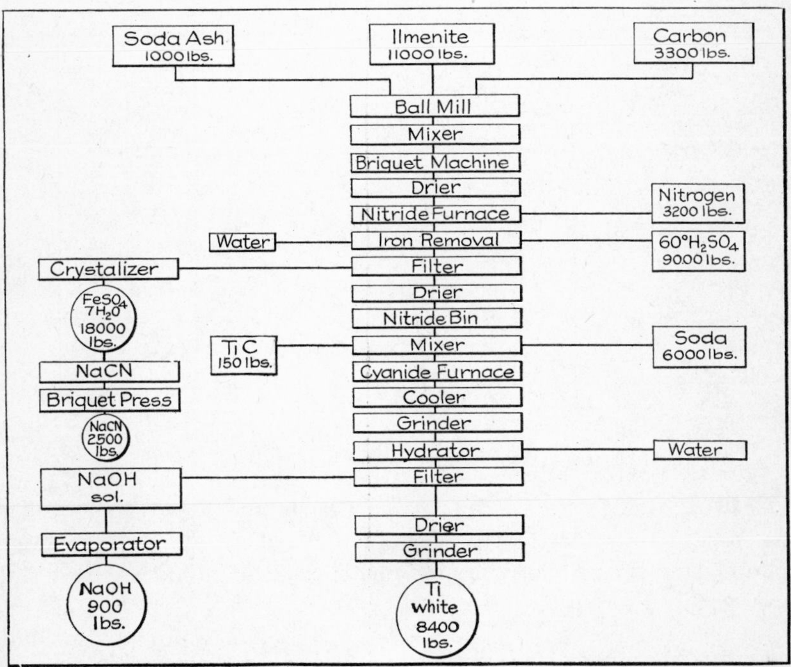

FIG. 753.—A flow sheet.

The *flow sheet* given in Fig. 753 is an example of a route chart applied to a chemical process. Charts of this type show in a dynamic way facts which might require some study to comprehend from written description. A different form of route chart is that of Fig. 441, showing the path of a drawing through the shops.

347. Popular Charts.—Engineers and draftsmen are frequently called upon to prepare charts and diagrams which will be understood by diversified and non-technical readers. In many cases it is not advisable to present the facts by means of curves drawn on coordinate paper, although the resulting chart may suffer somewhat in accuracy for the sake of greater effectiveness. In preparing charts for popular use particular care must be taken to make them so that the impression produced will be both quick and accurate. It is to be remembered that such charts are seldom studied critically but are taken in at a glance; hence the method of presentation requires the exercise of careful judgment and the application of a certain amount of psychology.

27% Absorbed in front wheels.
47% Absorbed in rear wheels axle and transmission.
26% Absorbed in wind resistance

POWER LOSSES IN THE AVERAGE AUTOMOBILE WHEN RUNNING 20 MI PER HR.

Fig. 754.—A 100 per cent bar.

348. Bar Charts.—The bar chart is a very easily understood type for the non-technical reader. One of its simplest forms is the *hundred per cent bar* for showing the relations of the constituents to a given total. Figure 754 is an example of this form of chart. The different segments should be cross-hatched, shaded or distinguished in some effective manner, the percentage represented placed on the diagram or directly opposite and the meaning of each segment clearly stated. These bars may be placed either vertically or horizontally, the vertical position giving an advantage for lettering.

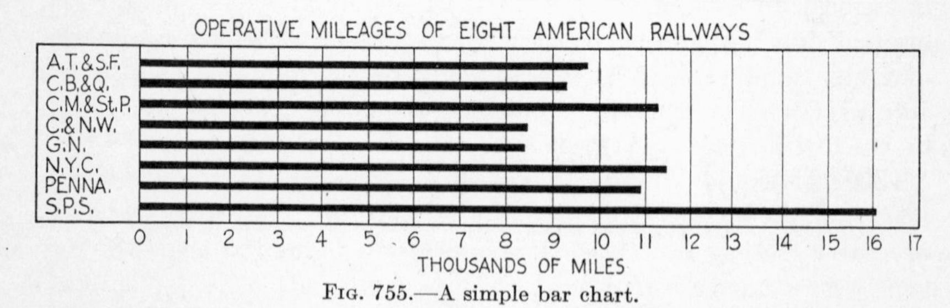

Fig. 755.—A simple bar chart.

Figure 755 is an example of a *simple bar chart* in which the length of each bar is proportional to the magnitude of the quantity represented. Means should be provided for reading numerical values represented by the bars. If it is necessary to give the exact value represented by the individual bars, these values should not be lettered at the ends of the bars since the apparent length would be increased. This type is made both horizontally, with the description at the base, and vertically. The vertical form is sometimes called the "pipe-organ chart." When vertical bars are drawn close together so as to touch along the sides the diagram is called a "staircase chart." This is made oftener as the "staircase curve," a line plotted on coordinate paper representing the profile of the tops of the bars.

A *compound bar chart* is made when it is desired to show two or more components in each bar. It is really a set of 100 per cent bars of different lengths set together either in pipe-organ or horizontal form.

349. Pie Charts.—The "pie diagram" or 100 per cent circle, Fig. 756, is much inferior to the bar chart but is used constantly because of its insistent popular appeal. It is a simple form of chart and, with the exception of the lettering, is easily constructed. It may be regarded as a 100 per cent bar bent into circular form. The circumference of the circle is divided into 100 parts and sectors are used to represent percentages of the total. To be effective, this diagram must be carefully lettered and the percentages marked on the sectors or at the circumference opposite the sectors. For contrast it is best to cross-hatch or shade the individual sectors. If the original drawing is to be displayed, the sectors may be colored and the diagram supplied with a key showing the meaning of each color. In every case the percentage notation should be placed where it can be read without removing the eyes from the diagram.

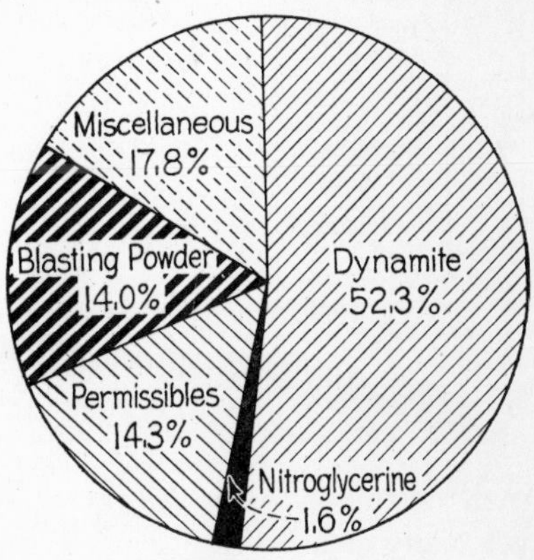

Fig. 756.—A pie chart.

350. Area and Volume Diagrams.—The use of area and volume diagrams has been very common, although they are usually the most deceptive method of graphic representation. Pictorial charts of this type were formerly much used for comparisons, such as of populations, standing armies, livestock and other products. It was customary to represent the data by human figures, whose heights were proportional to the numerical values, or by silhouettes of the animals or products concerned, whose heights or sometimes areas were proportional. Such charts are grossly misleading since volumes vary as the cubes of the linear dimensions. For such comparisons bar charts or even pie diagrams should be used.

There are occasions when area diagrams offer the most logical and effective method of presentation, as in Fig. 757. Such a chart may be regarded as a series of vertical 100 per cent bars placed side by side.

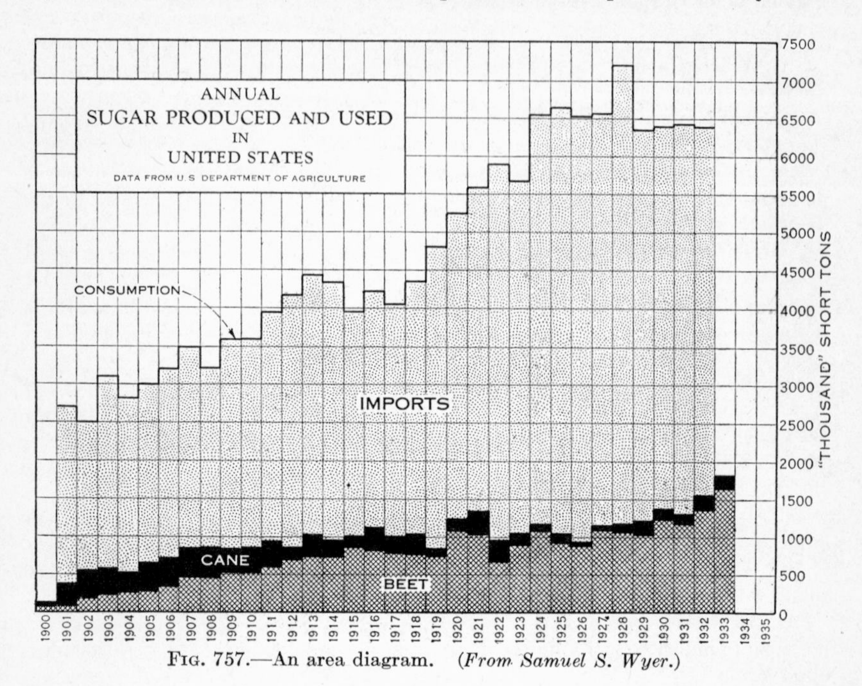

Fig. 757.—An area diagram. (*From Samuel S. Wyer.*)

351. To Draw a Chart.—In drawing a coordinate chart the general order would be (1) compute and assemble all data; (2) determine size and kind of chart best adapted and whether printed or plain paper will be used; (3) determine the scales for abscissas and ordinates from the limits of the data, and to give the best effect to the resulting curve; (4) lay off the independent variable (often *time*) on the horizontal or X-axis, and the dependent variable on the vertical or Y-axis; (5) plot points from the data and pencil the curves; (6) ink the curve; (7) compose and letter title and coordinates.

When the chart is drawn on a printed form, to be blue printed, the curve may be drawn on the reverse side of the paper, enabling erasures to be made without injuring the ruled surface.

Green is becoming the standard color for printed forms. Blue will not print or photograph and red is trying on the eyes.

If the curve is for purposes of computation it should be drawn with a fine accurate line. If for demonstration it should be fairly heavy, for contrast and effect.

The Joint Committee on Standards for Graphic Presentation recommends the following rules:

Standards for Graphic Presentations.

1. The general arrangement of a diagram should proceed from left to right.
2. Where possible represent quantities by linear magnitude as areas or volumes are likely to be misinterpreted.
3. For a curve the vertical scale, whenever practicable, should be so selected that the zero line will appear in the diagram.
4. If the zero line of the vertical scale will not normally appear in the curve diagram, the zero line should be shown by the use of a horizontal break in the diagram.
5. The zero lines of the scales for a curve should be sharply distinguished from the other coordinate lines.
6. For curves having a scale representing percentages, it is usually desirable to emphasize in some distinctive way the 100 per cent line or other line used as a basis of comparison.
7. When the scale of a diagram refers to dates, and the period represented is not a complete unit, it is better not to emphasize the first and last ordinates, since such a diagram does not represent the beginning and end of time.
8. When the curves are drawn on logarithmic coordinates, the limiting lines of the diagram should each be at some power of 10 on the logarithmic scale.
9. It is advisable not to show any more coordinate lines than necessary to guide the eye in reading the diagram.
10. The curve lines of a diagram should be sharply distinguished from the ruling.
11. In curves representing a series of observations, it is advisable whenever possible, to indicate clearly on the diagram all the points representing the separate observations.
12. The horizontal scale for curves should usually read from left to right and the vertical scale from bottom to top.
13. Figures for the scale of a diagram should be placed at the left and at the bottom or along the respective axes.
14. It is often desirable to include in the diagram the numerical data or formula represented.
15. If numerical data are not included in the diagram, it is desirable to give the data in tabular form accompanying the diagram.
16. All lettering and all figures in a diagram should be placed so as to be easily read from the base as the bottom or from the right-hand edge of the diagram as the bottom.
17. The title of a diagram should be made as clear and complete as possible. Subtitles or descriptions should be added if necessary to insure clearness.

352. Charts for Reproduction.—Charts for reproduction by zinc etching should be carefully penciled to about twice the size of the required cut. See "drawing for reproduction" on page 408. In inking, first ink circles around plotted points; second, ink the curves with strong lines. A border pen is useful for heavy lines, and a Payzant pen may be used to advantage particularly with dotted lines;

third, ink the title box and all lettering; fourth, ink the coordinates with fine black lines, putting in only as many as are necessary for easy reading, and breaking them wherever they interfere with title or lettering or cross plotted points.

353. Charts for Display.—Large charts for demonstration purposes are sometimes required. These may be drawn on sheets 22 × 28 or 28 × 44 known as printer's blanks. The quickest way to make them is with the show-card colors and single-stroke sign-writer's brushes. Large bar charts may be made with strips of black adhesive tape. Lettering may be done with the brush or with gummed letters.

PROBLEMS

354. The following problems are given as suggestive of various types for both technical and popular presentation.

1. During a certain chemical process the rise in temperature varied with the time as given in the following data:

Time	Temperature, °C.	Time	Temperature, °C.
0	0	7	136
1	33	8	139
2	66	9	142
3	93	10	143
4	110	11	144
5	123	12	155
6	131		

Using 8½″ × 11″ paper divided into inches and twentieths show graphically the relation between the time and the corresponding rise in temperature.

2. In a tension test of a machine steel bar the following data were obtained:

Applied Load, Pounds per Square Inch	Elongation per Inch of Length
0	0
3,000	0.00011
5,000	0.00018
10,000	0.00033
15,000	0.00051
20,000	0.00067
25,000	0.00083
30,000	0.00099
35,000	0.00115
40,000	0.00134
42,000	0.00142

Plot the foregoing data on rectangular coordinates using the elongation as the independent variable and the applied load as the dependent variable.

3. In testing a small 1-kilowatt transformer for efficiencies at various loads the following data were obtained:

Watts Delivered	Losses
948	73
728	62
458	53
252	49
000	47

Plot curves on rectangular coordinate paper showing the relation between percentage of load and efficiency, using watts delivered as the independent variable and remembering that efficiency = output + (output + losses).

4. The following data were obtained from a test of an automobile engine:

R.P.M.	Length of run, minutes	Fuel per run, pounds	Brake horsepower
1,006	11.08	1.0	5.5
1,001	4.25	.5	8.5
997	7.53	1.0	13.0
1,000	5.77	1.0	16.3
1,002	2.38	.5	21.1

Plot curves on rectangular coordinate paper showing the relation between fuel used per brake horsepower-hour and brake horsepower developed. Show also the relation between thermal efficiency and brake horsepower developed assuming the heat value of the gasoline at 19,000 British thermal units per pound.

5. During a certain year the distribution of bleaching powder by industries was as follows:

Industry	Tons
Pulp and paper	64,000
Textile	16,000
Water purification	9,000
Laundry	4,000
Miscellaneous	7,000

Show these facts by means of a 100 per cent bar, a pie diagram, and a bar chart. After having drawn these three charts determine which one you would use if you were presenting the information to the president of a manufacturing company; to the general public; to a group of engineers.

6. Make a semi-logarithmic chart showing the comparative rate of growth of the five largest American cities during the past 50 years. Data for this chart may be obtained from the U. S. Census Bureau Reports.

7. Make a compound bar chart showing the proportion of men and women students in your school in first, second, third and fourth years. Data from the registrar.

8. Make a compound bar chart comparison of the total foreign trade of the United States, Canada, France, Germany, Great Britain, Italy, Japan and the

Netherlands for one year, showing what proportion of the foreign countries' trade is with the United States. Data from "World Almanac."

9. Make a rectilinear chart showing the fluctuation of one active listed stock during the past month. The data for this may be obtained from the daily papers or from a stock broker.

10. Draw a chart showing the growth of life insurance in this country, in number of policies and in value, from 1900 to date. Data from "World Almanac."

11. Put the data of Fig. 756 into 100 per cent bar form.

12. Make an organization chart of (*a*) your city government, (*b*) the administration of your school, (*c*) a small manufacturing concern.

CHAPTER XXI

DUPLICATION AND DRAWING FOR REPRODUCTION

355. Several different processes are in use for duplicating drawings. The simplest and most generally used is blue printing from a tracing made on paper or tracing cloth. The best prints are made from tracings inked on cloth. Sometimes for economy tracings are inked on paper. A great many tracings are made in pencil on tracing paper and when the penciling is done carefully, with uniform lines, very good blue prints can be made from them.

356. Tracing cloth is a fine thread fabric, sized and transparentized with a starch preparation. The smooth side is considered by the makers as the right side but most draftsmen prefer to work on the dull side, which will take pencil marks. The cloth should be tacked down smoothly over the pencil drawing and its selvage torn off. It should then be dusted with chalk or prepared pounce (a blackboard eraser may be used) and rubbed off with a cloth, to remove the traces of grease which sometimes prevent the flow of ink.

357. Tracing.—To insure good printing, the ink should be perfectly black and the outline should be made with a bolder line than would be used on paper, as the contrast of a white line on the blue ground is not so strong as the black line on a white ground. Red ink should not be used unless it is desired to have some lines very inconspicuous on the print. Blue ink will not print well. Sometimes, in maps, diagrams, etc., to avoid confusion of lines, it is desirable to use colored inks on the tracing; if so, a little Chinese white added will render them opaque enough to print.

Sometimes, instead of section-lining, sections are indicated by rubbing a pencil tint over the surface on the dull side or by putting a wash of color on it. These tints will print in lighter blue than the background.

Ink lines may be removed from tracing cloth by rubbing with a pencil eraser, slipping a triangle under the tracing to give a harder surface. The rubbed surface should afterward be burnished with an ivory or bone burnisher or with the fingernail. In tracing a part that has been section-lined, a piece of white paper should be slipped under the cloth and the section-lining done without reference to the drawing underneath.

Tracing cloth is very sensitive to atmospheric changes, often expanding overnight so as to require restretching. If the complete tracing cannot be finished during the day some views should be finished and no figure left with only part of its lines traced.

In making a large tracing it is well to cut off the piece required from the roll and lay it exposed, flat, for a short time before tacking it down.

Water will ruin a tracing, and moist hands or arms should not come in contact with the cloth. The habit should be formed of keeping the hands off drawings. It is a good plan, in both drawing and tracing on large sheets, to cut a mask of drawing paper to cover all but the view being worked on. Unfinished drawings should always be covered overnight.

Sometimes it is desired to add an extra view or a title to a print without putting it on the tracing. This may be done by drawing the desired additions on another piece of cloth of the same size as the original and printing the two tracings together.

Tracings may be cleaned of pencil marks and dirt by rubbing over with a cloth or waste dipped in benzine or gasolene. To prevent smearing in cleaning, titles and border if printed from type on the tracing cloth should be printed in an ink not affected by benzine.

Soft cloths for penwipers may be made by washing the starch out of scrap tracing cloth.

The tracing is a "master drawing" and should never be allowed to be taken out of the office.

Pencil cloth is a transparentized fabric similar to tracing cloth except that its surface is prepared to take pencil. Thus the original drawing may be made on it and blue prints made either from the pencil drawing or after it has been inked.

358. Blue Printing.—Blue prints are made by exposing a piece of sensitized paper in contact with the tracing to sunlight or electric light in a printing frame made for the purpose. The blue print paper is a white paper free from sulphites, coated with a solution of citrate of iron and ammonia, and ferricyanide of potassium. On exposure to the light a chemical action takes place, which when fixed by washing in water gives a strong blue color. The parts protected from the light by the black lines of the tracing wash out, leaving the white paper. Blue print paper is usually bought ready sensitized and may be had in different weights and different degrees of rapidity. When fresh it is of a yellowish-green color, and an unexposed piece should wash out perfectly white. With age or exposure to light or air, it turns to a darker gray-blue color and spoils altogether in a comparatively short time. In some emergency, it may be necessary to prepare blue print paper. The following formula will give a paper requiring about three minutes' exposure in bright sunlight.

1. Citrate of iron and ammonia (brown scales) 2 ounces, water 8 ounces.
2. Red prussiate of potash 1½ ounces, water 8 ounces.

Keep in separate bottles away from the light.

To prepare paper take equal parts of 1 and 2 and apply evenly to the paper with a sponge or camel's-hair brush, by subdued light.

359. To Make a Blue Print.—Lay the tracing in the frame with the inked side toward the glass, and place the paper on it with its sensitized surface against the tracing. Lock up in the frame so there is a perfect contact between paper and cloth. See that no corners are turned under. Expose to the sunlight or electric light. If a frame having a hinged back is used, Fig. 758, one side may be opened for examination.

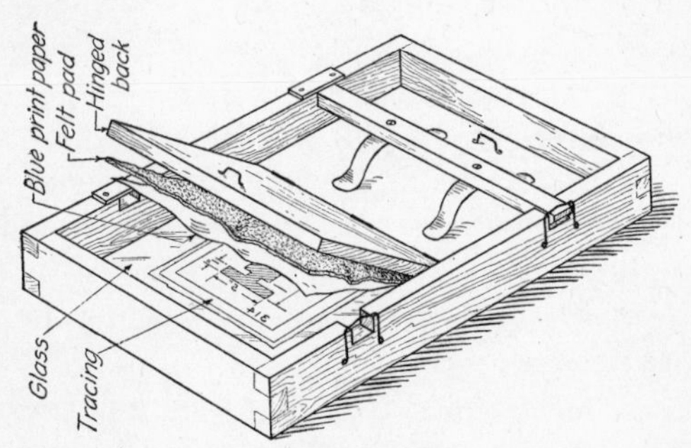

Fig. 758.—A blue print frame.

When the paper is taken from the frame it will be a bluish-gray color with the heavier lines lighter than the background, the lighter lines perhaps not being distinguishable. Put the print for about five minutes in a bath of running water, taking care that air bubbles do not collect on the surface, and hang up to dry. An overexposed print may often be saved by prolonged washing. The blue color may be intensified and the white cleared by dipping the print for a moment into a bath containing a solution of potassium bichromate (1 to 2 ounces of crystals to a gallon of water), and rinsing thoroughly. This treatment will bring back a hopelessly "burned" print. Sodium bichromate is a cheaper substitute sometimes used. Prints may be cleared successfully by dipping in a bath of hydrogen peroxide, 1 ounce to the gallon.

To be independent of the weather most concerns use electric printing machines, either *cylindrical*, in which a lamp is lowered automatically inside a glass cylinder about which the tracing and paper are placed, or *continuous*, in which the tracing and paper are fed through rolls, and in some machines printed, washed, "potashed" and dried in one operation. Figure 759 is a machine of this type.

Fig. 759.[1]—Electric blue printing machine with washing and drying equipment.

Blue print making is a recognized business, and blue print concerns are found in every city. Many manufacturers and architects find it more satisfactory and economical to send their tracings out for printing than to maintain a blue print room.

360. Changes are made on blue prints by writing or drawing with any alkaline solution, such as of soda or potash, which bleaches the blue. Potassium oxalate is the best. A little gum arabic will prevent spreading. A tint may be given by adding a few drops of red or other colored ink to the solution. Chinese white is sometimes used for white line changes on a blue print.

[1] Manufactured by the C. F. Pease Company, Chicago.

A blue print may be made from a drawing made in pencil or ink on bond paper or tracing paper, but with thick drawing paper the light will get under the lines and destroy the sharpness. A print may be made from Bristol or other heavy white paper by turning it with the ink side against the paper, thereby reversing the print, or by first making a Van Dyke negative, or it may be soaked in benzine and printed while wet. The benzine will evaporate and leave no trace.

A clear blue print may be made from a typewritten sheet which has been written with a sheet of carbon paper back of it, so that it is printed on both sides.

In an emergency it is possible to make a fair print by holding tracing and paper to the sunlight against a window pane.

Any white paper may be rendered sufficiently translucent to give a good blue print by transparentizing with a solution of paraffin cut in benzine or with a solution sold by drawing materials dealers.

A blue-line print may be taken from a blue print by fading the blue of the first print in weak ammonia water, washing thoroughly, then turning it red in a weak solution of tannic acid and washing again. Transparentizing at this stage will assist.

In printing a number of small tracings they may be fastened together at their edges and handled as a single sheet.

361. Other Printing Processes.—Van Dyke paper is a thin sensitized paper which turns dark brown on exposure and fixing by first washing in water, then in hyposulphite of soda and again thoroughly in water. A reversed negative of a tracing may be made on it by exposing with the inked side of the drawing next to the sensitized side of the paper, and this negative printed on blue print paper, giving a positive print with blue lines on white.

B W paper, giving black lines on a white ground directly from the original tracing is being used extensively when positive prints are desired.

Photostat prints are extensively used by large corporations. By this method a print with white lines on a dark background is made directly from any drawing or tracing, to any desired reduction or enlargement, through the use of a large specially designed camera. This print may be again photostated, giving a brown-line print with a white ground. The method is extremely useful to engineers for drawings to be included in reports, and for matching drawings of different scales, which may have to be combined into one.

The Ozalid process, still in use in some places, gives a direct print with dark reddish lines on a white ground. It has an advantage in avoiding distortion since the prints are not washed but developed dry by exposing to the fumes of strong aqua ammonia in an airtight tube or developing machine.

Duplicating Tracings.—Tracings having all the qualities of ordinary inked ones are made photographically from pencil drawings by using Eastman sensitized tracing cloth.

Lithoprinting.—When a number of copies of a drawing, say 50 or more, are needed they may be reproduced by lithoprinting, a simplified form of photolithography, at comparatively small cost.

Copying methods such as the mimeograph, neostyle, ditto machine and other forms of the hectograph or gelatine pad are often used for reproducing small drawings.

362. Drawing for Reproduction.—By this term is meant the preparation of drawings for reproduction by one of the photomechani-

Fig. 760.—Drawing for one-half reduction.

cal processes used for making plates, or "cuts," as they are often called, for printing purposes. Such drawings will be required in the preparation of illustrations for books and periodicals, for catalogues or other advertising and incidentally for Patent Office drawings, which are reproduced by photolithography.

Line drawings are usually reproduced by the process known as zinc etching, in which the drawing is photographed on a process plate, generally with some reduction, the negative film reversed and printed so as to give a positive on a sensitized zinc plate (when a particularly fine result is desired, a copper plate is used) which is etched with acid, leaving the lines in relief and giving, when mounted type-high on a wood base, a block which can be printed along with type in an ordinary printing press.

FIG. 761.—One-half reduction.

Drawings for zinc etching should be made on smooth white paper or tracing cloth in black drawing ink, and preferably larger than the required reproduction.

If it is desired to preserve the hand-drawn character of the original, the reduction should be slight; but if a very smooth effect is wanted, the

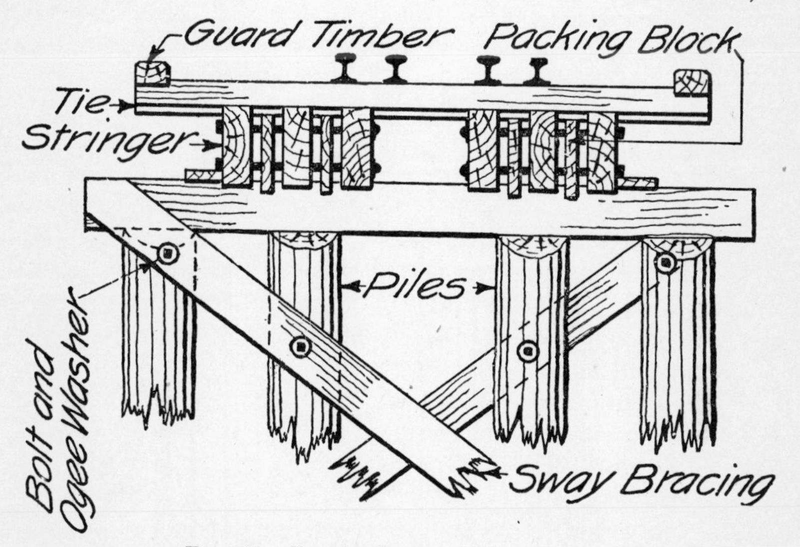

FIG. 762.—Drawing for two-thirds reduction.

drawing may be as much as three or four times as large as the cut. The best general size is from one and one-half to two times linear. Figure 760 illustrates the appearance of an original drawing and Fig. 761 the same drawing reduced one-half. Figure 762 is another original which has been reduced two-thirds, Fig. 763. The coarse appearance of these originals and the open shading should be noticed.

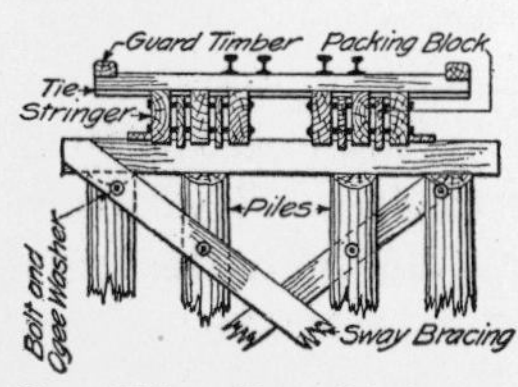

FIG. 763.—Two-thirds reduction.

A reducing glass, a concave lens mounted like a reading glass, is sometimes used to aid in judging the appearance of a drawing on reduction. If lines are drawn too close together the space between them will choke in the reproduction and mar the effect.

One very convenient thing not permissible in other work may be done on drawings for reproduction—any irregularities may be corrected by simply painting out with water-color white. If it is desired to shift a figure after it has been inked it may be cut out and pasted on in the required position. The edges thus left will not trouble the engraver, as they will be tooled out when the etching is finished. Reference letters and numbers, notes and other lettering are often cut out of a sheet printed in type of proper size and pasted on the drawing.

Wash drawings and photographs are reproduced in a similar way on copper by what is known as the half-tone process, in which the negative is made through a ruled "screen" in front of the plate, which breaks up the tints into a series of dots of varying size. Screens of different fineness are used for different kinds of paper, from the coarse screen newspaper half-tone of 80 to 100 lines to the inch, the ordinary commercial and magazine half-tone of 133 lines, to the fine 150 and 175 line half-tones for printing on very smooth coated paper.

Photographic prints for reproduction are often retouched and worked over, shadows being strengthened with water color, high lights accented with white and details brought out that would otherwise be lost. In catalogue illustration of machinery, etc., objectionable backgrounds or other features can be removed entirely. Commercial retouchers use the air-brush as an aid in this kind of work, spraying on color with it very rapidly and smoothly and securing results not possible in hand work.

So-called "phantom drawings" or "X-ray drawings" are made in this way, sometimes using a double exposure negative as a basis.

The "Ben Day" film is another aid in commercial illustration that is used very extensively. Figure 14 is a simple example of its use.

Line illustrations are sometimes made by the "wax process" in which a blackened copper plate is covered with a very thin film of wax, on which a drawing may be photographed and its outline scratched through the wax by hand with different-sized gravers. The lettering is set up in type and pressed into the wax; more wax is then piled up in the wider spaces between the lines and an electrotype taken. Drawings for this process need not be specially prepared, as the work may be done even from a pencil sketch or blue print. Wax plates print very clean and sharp and the type lettering gives them a finished appearance, but they lack the character of a drawing, are more expensive than zinc etching and often show mistakes due to the lack of familiarity of the engraver with the subject. Figure 764 shows the characteristic appearance of a wax plate.

Maps and large drawings are usually reproduced by lithography, in which the drawing is either photographed or engraved on a lithographic

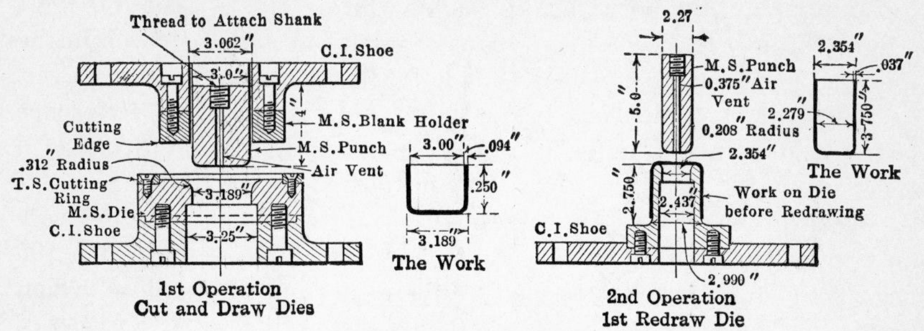

Fig. 764.—A wax plate.

stone and transferred from this either to another stone from which it is printed or, in the offset process, to a thin sheet of zinc which is wrapped around a cylinder, and prints to a rubber blanket which in turn prints on the paper.

CHAPTER XXII

SHADE LINES AND LINE SHADING

363. Shade Lines.—The general practice on working drawings is to use a uniform bold full line for visible outlines. In some special kinds of work an effective appearance of relief and finish is given, and the legibility of the drawing increased, by using two weights of lines, light and heavy. This is used to advantage in technical illustrations, advertising matter, etc., where the definition of *shape* is the important feature. Shade lines are required on Patent Office drawings and are used in a few shops on assembly drawings, but for ordinary shop drawings the advantage gained is much overbalanced by the increased cost.

Theoretically the shade line system is based on the principle that the object is illuminated from one source of light at an infinite distance,

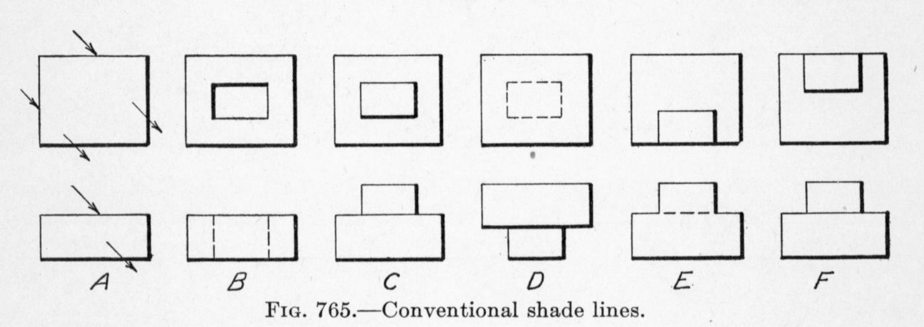

Fig. 765.—Conventional shade lines.

the rays coming from the left in the direction of the body diagonal of a cube, so that the two projections of any ray each make an angle of 45° with the ground line. Part of the object would thus be illuminated and part would be in shade. A shade line is a line separating a light face from a dark face. The strict application of this theory involves some trouble and it is not followed out in practice, but the one simple rule of shading the lower and right-hand lines of all views is observed, Fig. 765. The light lines should be comparatively fine and the shade lines about three times as wide. The width of the shade line is added outside the surface of the piece.

Figure 766 shows two pieces in combination. At *A* the faces of the parts 1 and 2 are in the same plane; the line of the joint is, consequently, a light line. At *B* and *C* the faces are not in the same plane. Hidden lines are never shaded.

In inking a shade line drawing it is important to follow the order of inking carefully. Ink (1) light arcs, (2) light to heavy arcs, (3) heavy arcs, (4) light lines, (5) heavy lines.

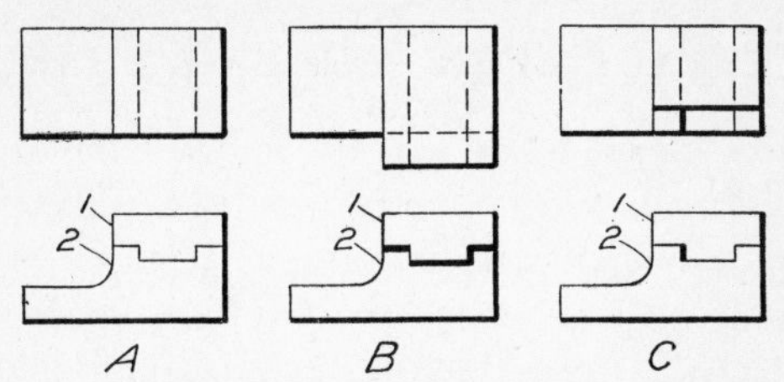

Fig. 766.—Shading two pieces in combination.

A circle may be shaded by shifting the center on a 45° line toward the lower right-hand corner, to an amount equal to the thickness of the shade line and drawing another semi-circular arc with the same radius, Fig. 767; or it may be done much more quickly, particularly with small circles, after the "knack" has been acquired, by keeping the needle in the center after drawing the circle, and springing the needle-point leg

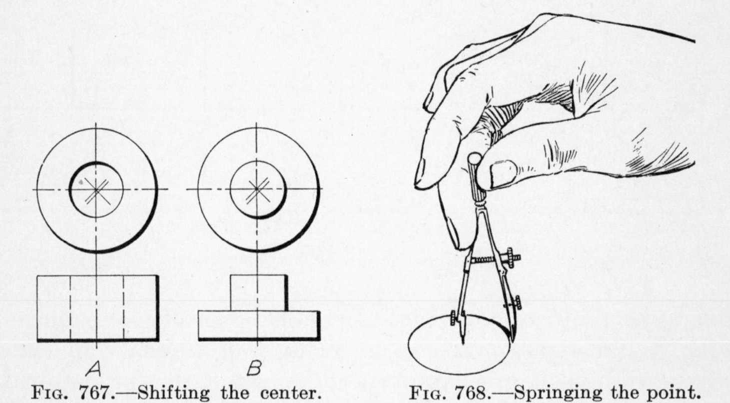

Fig. 767.—Shifting the center.

Fig. 768.—Springing the point.

out and back gradually while going over the half to be shaded, pressing with the middle finger in the position of Fig. 768. Never shade a circle arc so that it appears heavier than the straight lines.

364. Shade lines in isometric drawing have no value so far as aiding in the reading is concerned, but they may by their contrast add some attractiveness to the appearance. Assuming the light as coming from the left in the direction of the body diagonal of the isometric cube, and disregarding shadows, shade lines separating light from dark faces would appear as at *B* in Fig. 769. Another method popular among patent draftsmen and others using this kind of drawing for illustration is to bring out the nearest corners with heavy lines, as at *C*.

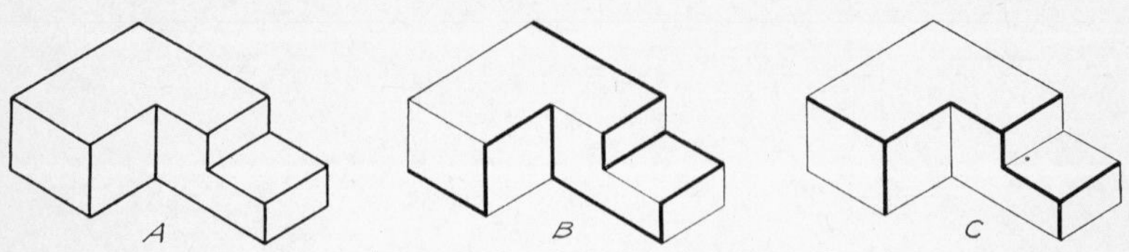

FIG. 769.—Two methods of shading isometric drawings.

365. Line Shading.—Line shading is a method of representing the effect of light and shade by ruled lines. It is an accomplishment not usual among ordinary draftsmen as it is not used on working drawings and the draftsman engaged in that work does not have occasion to apply it. It is used on display drawings, illustrations, Patent Office drawings and the like and is worthy of study if one is interested in this class of finished work.

To execute line shading rapidly and effectively requires continued practice and some artistic ability and, as much as anything else, good judgment in knowing when to stop. Often the simple shading of a shaft or other round member will add greatly to the effectiveness of a drawing and may even save making another view; or a few lines of "surface shading" on a flat surface will show its position and character. The pen must be in perfect condition, with its screw working very freely.

366. Theory of Line Shading.—The theoretical direction of the light is, as already mentioned, in the direction of the body diagonal of a cube. Thus the two projections of a ray of light would be as A^h and A^v, Fig. 770, and two visible faces of the hexagonal prism would be illuminated, while one is in shade. It is immediately observed that the theoretical shade lines differ from the conventional ones as used in the preceding discussion. The figure illustrates the rule that *an inclined illuminated surface is lightest nearest the eye and an inclined surface in shade is darkest nearest the eye.*

A cylinder would be illuminated as in Fig. 771. Theoretically the darkest place is at the tangent or "shade line" and the lightest part at the "brilliant line" where the light is reflected directly to the eye. Cylinders shaded according to this theory are the most effective, but often in practice the dark side is carried out to the edge, and in small cylinders the light side is left unshaded.

A method of finding the brilliant point and shade line of a sphere is shown in Fig. 772. An auxiliary view of the sphere and circumscribing cube is taken parallel to the body diagonal of the cube, and the angle between the ray of light and the center line to the eye bisected, giving the brilliant point. Tangents locate the shade line.

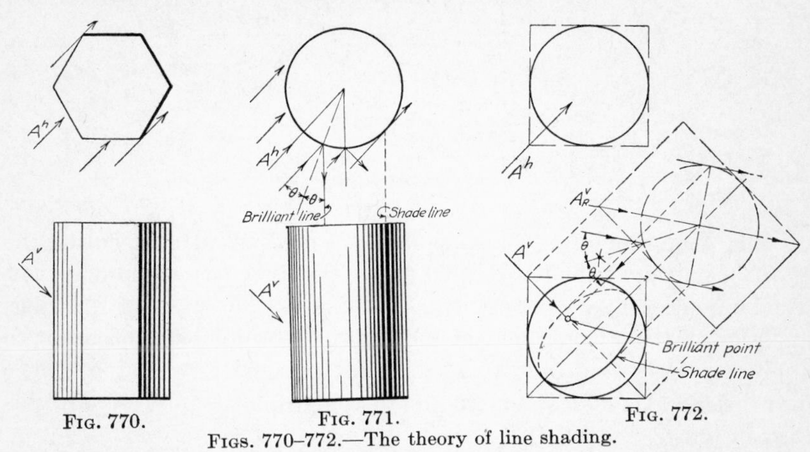

FIG. 770. FIG. 771. FIG. 772.

FIGS. 770–772.—The theory of line shading.

367. Practice.—Three preliminary exercises in flat and graded tints are given in Fig. 773. In these the pitch, or distance from center to center of lines, is equal. In wide-graded tints, as *B* and *C*, the setting of the pen is not changed for every line, but several lines are drawn, then the pen changed and several more drawn.

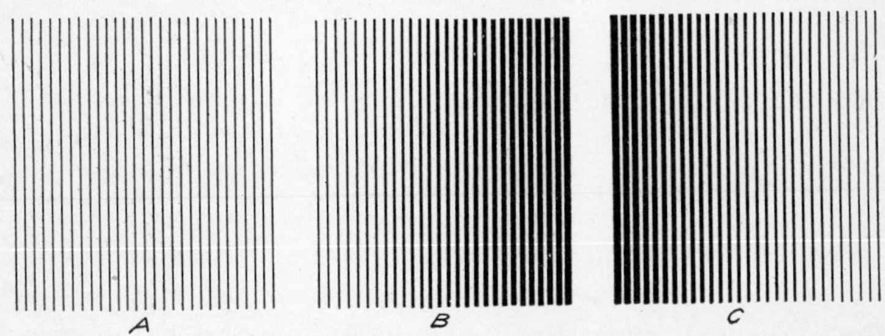

FIG. 773.—Flat and graded tints.

Figure 774 is a row of cylinders of different sizes. The effect of polish is given by leaving several brilliant lines, as might occur if the light came in through several windows. A conical surface may be shaded by driving a fine needle at the apex and swinging a triangle about it as in *A*, Fig. 775. To avoid a blot at the apex of a complete cone the needle may be driven on the extension of the side as in *B* or the lines may be drawn parallel to the sides as in *C*.

It is in the attempt to represent double-curved surfaces that the line shader meets his principal troubles. The brilliant line becomes a

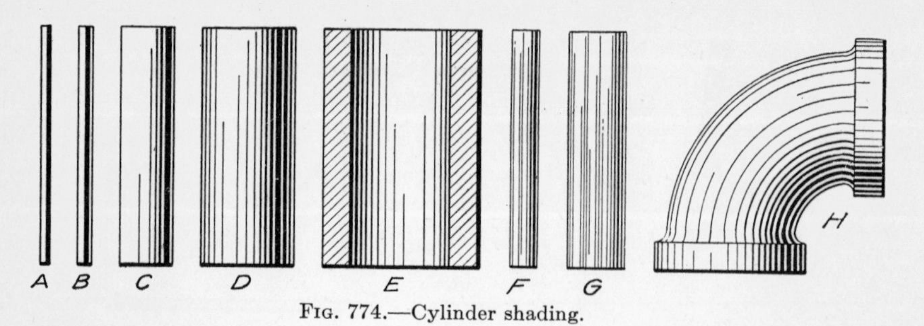

Fig. 774.—Cylinder shading.

brilliant point and the tangent shade line a curve, and to represent the gradation between them by mechanical lines is a difficult proposition.

Three methods of shading a sphere are shown in Fig. 776. The first one, *A*, is the commonest. Concentric circles are drawn from the

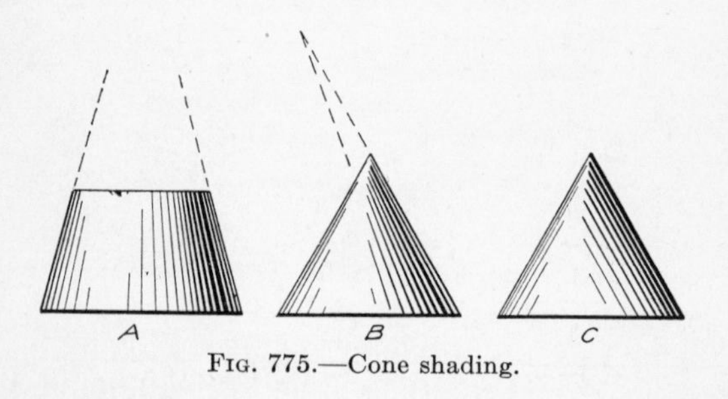

Fig. 775.—Cone shading.

center, with varying pitch, and shaded on the lower side by springing the point of the compasses. At *B*, the brilliant point, usually "guessed in," is used as a center. At *C*, the "wood cut" method, the taper on

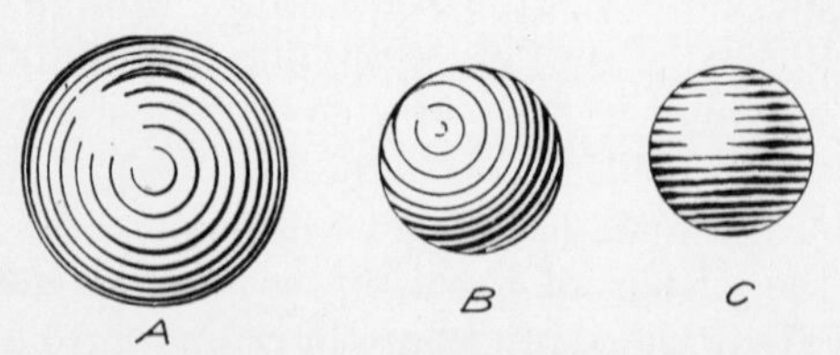

Fig. 776.—Sphere shading.

the horizontal lines is made by starting with the pen out of the perpendicular plane and turning the handle up as the line progresses.

Applications of shading on flat and curved surfaces are shown in Figs. 777 and 778.

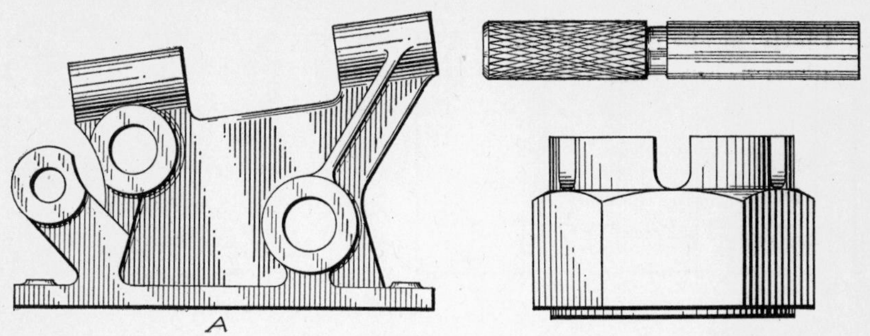

FIG. 777.—Applications of line shading.

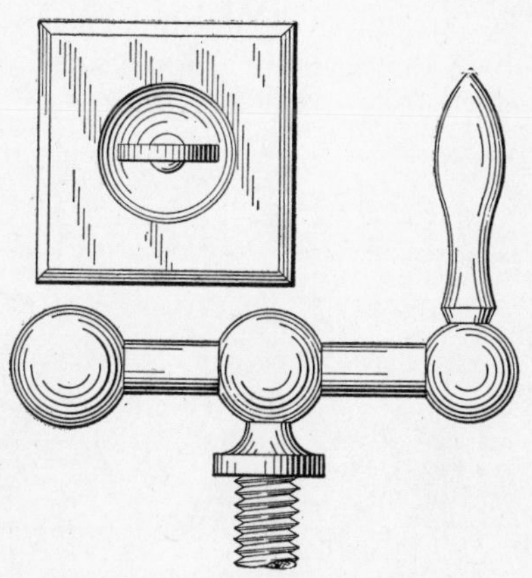

FIG. 778.—Applications of shading.

368. Patent Office Drawings.—In the application for letters patent on an invention or discovery there is required a written description called the "specification," and in case of a machine, manufactured article or device for making it, a drawing, showing every feature of the invention. If it is an improvement, the drawing must show the invention separately, and in another view a part of the old structure with the invention attached. A high standard of execution and conformity to the rules of the Patent Office must be observed. A pamphlet called the "Rules of Practice," giving full information and rules governing Patent Office procedure in reference to application for patents, may be had gratuitously by addressing the *Commissioner of Patents, Washington, D.C.*

The drawings are made on smooth white paper specified to be of a thickness equal to three-sheet Bristol board. Two-ply Reynolds board is the best paper for the purpose, as prints may be made from it readily, and it is preferred by the Office. The sheets must be exactly 10″ × 15″, with a border line 1″ from the edges. Sheets with border and lettering printed, as Fig. 779, are sold by the dealers but are not required to be used. A space not less than 1¼″ inside the top border must be left blank for the printed title added by the Office.

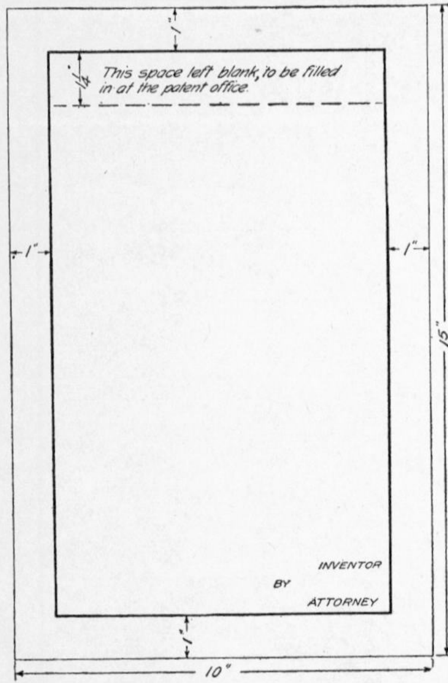

Fig. 779.—Blank for patent drawing.

Drawings must be in black ink and drawn for a reproduction to reduced scale. As many sheets as are necessary may be used. In the case of large views any sheet may be turned on its side so that the heading is at the right and the signatures at the left, but all views on the same sheet must stand in the same direction.

Patent Office drawings are not working drawings. They are descriptive and pictorial rather than structural; hence they will have no center lines, no dimension lines or figured dimensions, no notes or names of views. The scale chosen should be large enough to show the mechanism without crowding. Unessential details or shapes need not be represented with constructional accuracy, and parts need not be drawn strictly to scale. For example, the section of a thin sheet of metal drawn to scale might be a very thin single line, but it should be drawn with a double line and section-lined between.

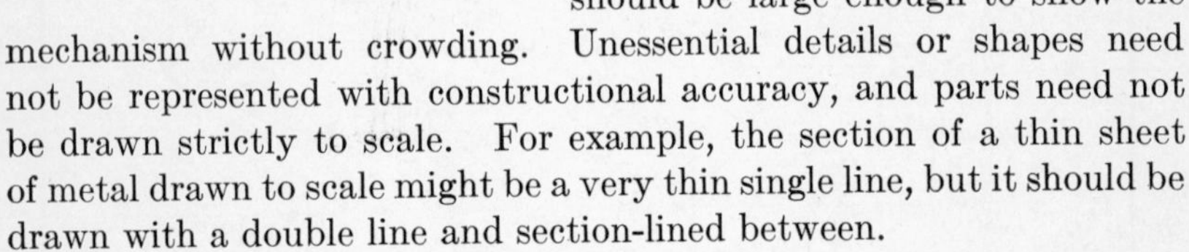

Section-lining must not be too fine. One-twentieth of an inch pitch is a good limit. Solid black should not be used except to represent insulation or rubber. Shade lines are always added, except in special cases where they might confuse or obscure instead of aid in the reading. Surface shading by line shading is used whenever it will aid to the legibility, but it should not be thrown in indiscriminately or lavishly simply to please the client.

Gears and toothed wheels must have all their teeth shown, and the same is true of chains, sprockets, etc., but screw threads may be represented by the conventional symbols. The "Rules of Practice" gives a chart of electrical symbols, symbols for colors, etc., which should be followed.

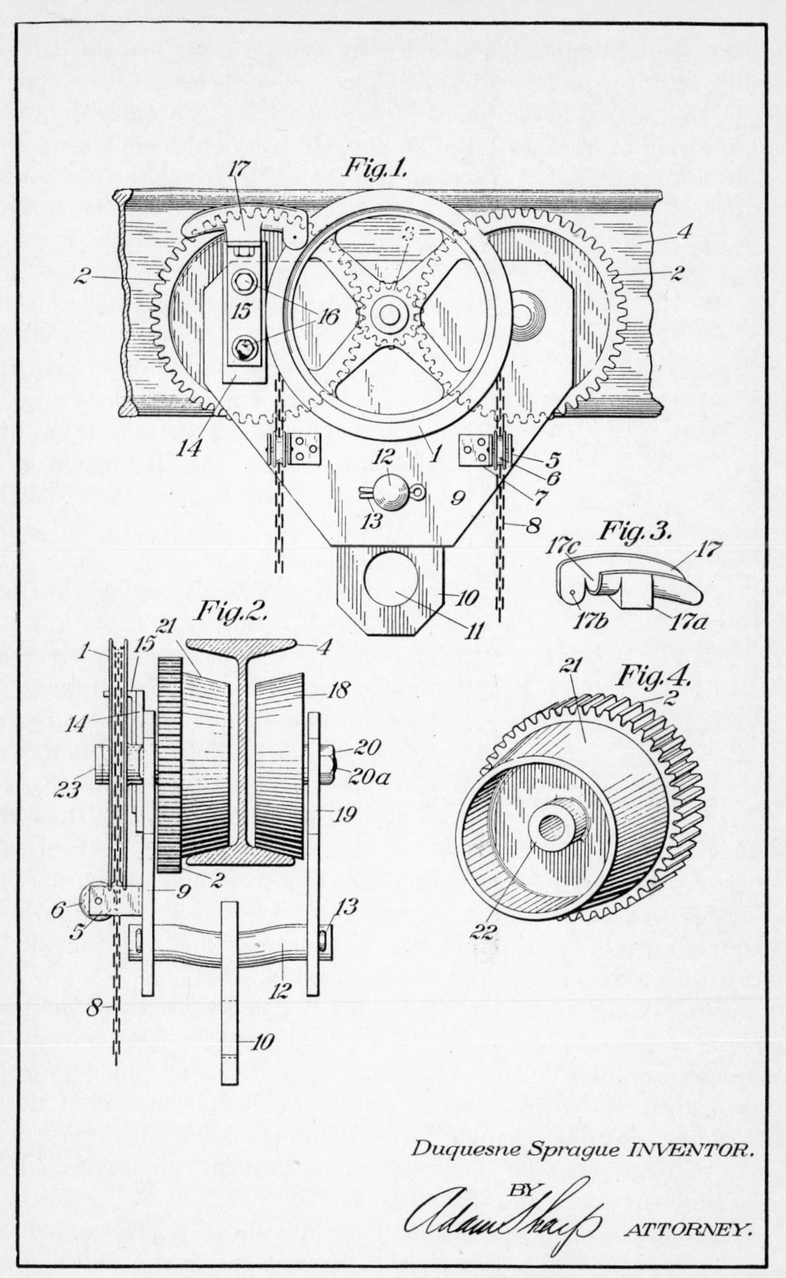

FIG. 780.—A patent office drawing (reduced one-half).

The drawings may be made in orthographic, axonometric, oblique or perspective. The pictorial system is used extensively, for either all or part of the views. The examiner is, of course, expert in reading drawings, but the client, and sometimes the attorney, may not be, and the drawing should be clear to them. In checking the drawing for completeness it should be remembered that in case of litigation it may be an important exhibit in the courts. Only in rare cases is a model of an invention required by the Office.

The views are lettered "Fig. 1," "Fig. 2," etc., and the parts designated by reference numbers through which the invention is described in the specification. One view, generally "Fig. 1," is made as a comprehensive view that may be used in the *Official Gazette* as an illustration to accompany the "claims."

The inventor signs the drawing in the lower right-hand corner. In case an attorney prepares the application and drawing, the attorney writes or letters the name of the inventor, signing his own name underneath as his attorney.

To avoid making tack holes in the paper it should be held to the board by the heads of the thumb tacks only.

The requirements for drawings for foreign patents vary in different countries, most countries requiring drawings and several tracings of each sheet.

Figure 780 is an example of a Patent Office drawing, reduced to one-half size.

CHAPTER XXIII

NOTES ON COMMERCIAL PRACTICE

369. There are many items of practical information of value to the student and draftsman which are not included in the ordinary course in drawing but are learned through experience. A few miscellaneous points are included here as suggestions of kinds of information which are worth collecting and preserving in notebook form.

370. Stretching Paper.—If a drawing is to be tinted the paper should be stretched on the board. First, dampen it thoroughly until limp, either with a sponge or under the faucet, then lay it on the drawing board face down, take up the excess water from the edges with a blotter, brush glue or paste about one-half inch wide around the edge, turn over and rub the edges down on the board until set, and allow to dry horizontally.

Drawings or maps on which much work is to be done, even though not to be tinted, may be made advantageously on stretched paper; but Bristol or calendered paper should not be stretched.

371. Tinting is done with washes made with water colors. The drawing may be inked (with waterproof ink) either before or preferably after tinting. The drawing should be cleaned and the unnecessary pencil marks removed with a very soft rubber, the tint mixed in a saucer and applied with a camel's-hair or sable brush, inclining the board and flowing the color with horizontal strokes, leading the pool of color down over the surface, taking up the surplus at the bottom by wiping the brush out quicky and picking up with it the excess color. Stir the color each time the brush is dipped into the saucer. Tints should be made in light washes, depth of color being obtained if necessary by repeating the wash. To get an even color it is well to go over the surface first with a wash of clear water. Diluted colored inks may be used for washes instead of water color.

372. Mounting Tracing Paper.—Tracings on paper are mounted for display, on white mounts, by either "tipping" or "floating." To tip a drawing, brush a narrow strip of glue or paste around the under edge, dampen the right side of the drawing by stroking with a sponge very slightly moistened and stretch the paper gently with the thumbs on opposite edges, working from the middle of the sides toward the corners.

To float a drawing make a *very thin* paste and brush a light coat over the entire surface of the mount, lay the tracing paper in position and stretch into contact with the board as in tipping. If air bubbles occur, force them out by rubbing from the center of the drawing out, laying a piece of clean paper over the drawing to protect it.

373. Mounting on Cloth.—As a protection to maps and drawings requiring much handling it is advisable to mount them on cloth. The method to be used depends largely upon the weight and quality of the material to be mounted. A method suitable for one case might fail in another, but by having a general idea of the requirements it is possible to vary the method to suit the case. There are two methods used, hot mounting and cold mounting. The adhesives used are photo library paste and liquid glue. The commercial products of each are so easily obtained that a formula for their preparation is unnecessary and the ones to be used are largely a matter of choice and availability.

Hot mounting is the most satisfactory for the average work because of the saving in time. The mounting cloth is usually a first grade of white light-weight sheeting. For small work dust-colored dress lining is well suited. This is stretched tightly, and tacked down, over a table which has been previously covered with cloth. The paste is prepared by heating with a small amount of water until the solution becomes clear. With a broad flat brush paste the back of the print quickly, working from the center toward the edges. Allow a moment for uniform expansion, then place face up on the cloth. Have iron hot enough not to scorch, work quickly with rotary motion and iron print from center out until edges are stuck. Remove tacks and raise from table to release steam. Iron until dry. Never iron on the back, as the steam formed will cause blisters. Keep the iron well paraffined and a good gloss will be produced on the print. Liquid glue diluted and heated will work quite as well, but the sheet will not be so flexible and will break if folded too often.

Cold paste may be used instead of hot and is quite satisfactory. The method is practically the same except that a photographic print roller is substituted for the hot iron and the print is allowed to become thoroughly dry before the tacks are removed.

For Mounting Thin Paper.—The cloth is tacked down in the same way as for hot or cold mounting except that several thicknesses of newspaper are placed directly under the cloth. The hot paste is applied directly to the cloth until the cloth is thoroughly filled with paste. The print to be mounted is rolled, face in, from each end toward the center, leaving an equal amount of paper in each roll. With one roll in each hand place the print in the center of the pasted area, allowing only a few inches to unroll. Iron quickly as for hot mounting, unrolling the print as the ironing proceeds.

Another successful method consists in rolling the print to be mounted, face in, on a roll of detail paper. Hot paste is applied beginning at one end, the print rolled off on the cloth, and followed up as fast as unrolled by a hot iron. It is inadvisable to apply paste to thin paper, unless supported as above, for it curls up so rapidly that it becomes unmanageable and results in the loss of the print.

374. Methods of Copying Drawings—Pricking.—Drawings are often copied on opaque paper by laying the drawing over the paper and pricking through with a needle point, turning the upper sheet back frequently and connecting the points. Prickers may be purchased or may be made easily by forcing a fine needle into a soft wood handle. They may be used to advantage also in accurate drawing, in transferring measurements from scale to paper.

375. Transfer by Rubbing.—This method, known as "frotté," is very useful, particularly in architectural drawing, in transferring any kind of sketch or design to the paper on which it is to be rendered.

The original is made on any paper and may be worked over, changed and marked up until the design is satisfactory. Lay a piece of tracing paper over the original and trace the outline carefully. Turn the tracing over and retrace the outline just as carefully on the other side, using a medium soft pencil with a *sharp* point. Turn back to first position and tack down smoothly over the paper on which the drawing is to be made, registering the tracing to proper position by center or reference lines on both tracing and drawing. Now transfer the drawing by rubbing the tracing with the rounded edge of a knife handle or other instrument (a smooth-edged coin held between thumb and forefinger and scraped back and forth is commonly used), holding a small piece of tracing cloth with smooth side up between the rubbing instrument and the paper, to protect the paper. Do not rub too hard, and be sure that neither the cloth nor paper moves while rubbing. Transfers in ink instead of pencil, useful on wash drawings, may be made by tracing with "encre a poncer," a rubbing ink made for this purpose

If the drawing is symmetrical about any axis the reversed tracing need not be made, but the rubbing can be made from the first tracing by reversing it about the axis of symmetry.

Several rubbings can be made from one tracing, and when the same figure or detail must be repeated several times on a drawing much time can be saved by drawing it on tracing paper and rubbing it in the several positions.

A very fine transfer of small details may be made by the engraver's method of tracing on a thin sheet of gelatine or celluloid, scratching the outline lightly with a sharp point, and rubbing colored crayon into the lines.

376. Glass Drawing Board.—Drawing tables with glass tops and having lights in reflecting boxes underneath are successful devices for copying drawings on opaque paper. A portable design is shown in Fig. 781. Drawings even in pencil may be copied readily on the

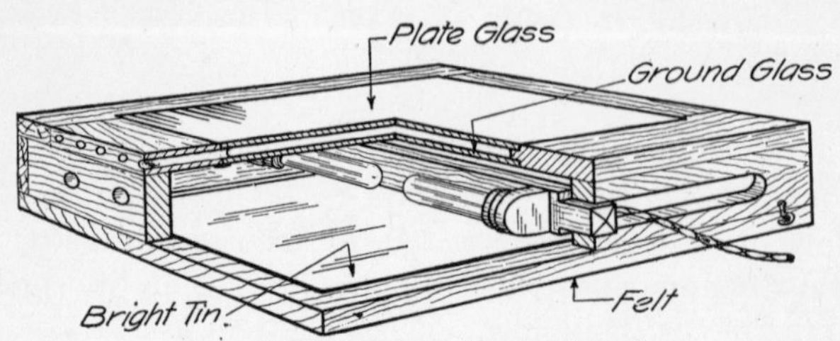

Fig. 781.—A glass drawing board.

heaviest paper or Bristol board by the use of a transparent drawing board.

377. Proportional Methods—The Pantograph.—The principle of the pantograph, used for reducing or enlarging drawings in any proportion, is well known. Its use is often of great advantage. It consists essentially of four bars, which for any setting must form a

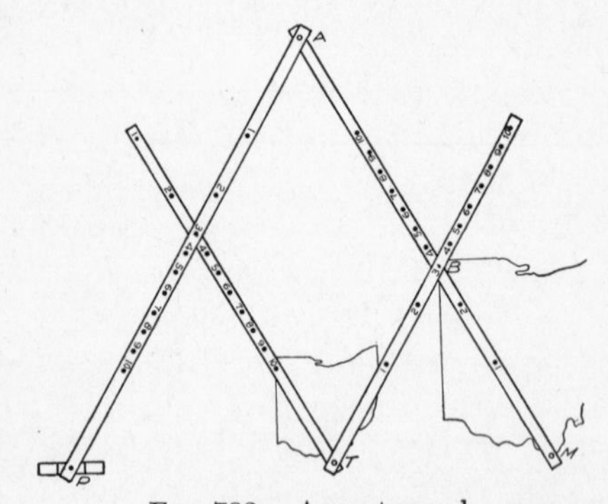

Fig. 782.—A pantograph.

parallelogram and have the pivot, tracing point and marking point in a straight line; and any arrangement of four arms conforming to this requirement will work in true proportion. With reference to Fig. 782 the scale of enlargement is $PM:PT$ or $AM:AB$. For corresponding reduction the tracing point and marking point are exchanged. The inexpensive wooden form of Fig. 782 is sufficiently accurate for ordinary outlining. A suspended pantograph with metal arms, for accurate engineering work, is shown in Fig. 783.

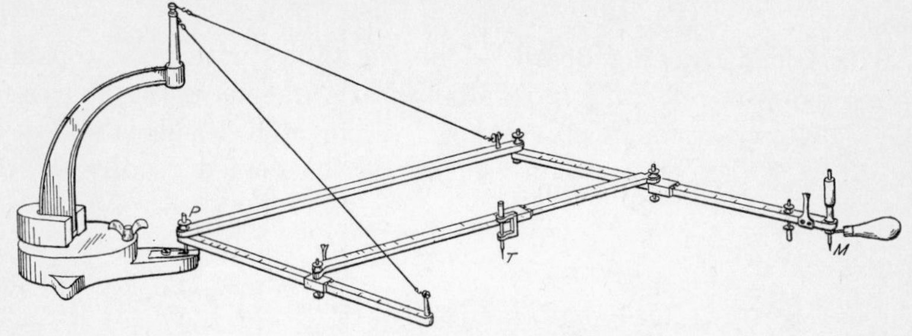

Fig. 783.—A suspended pantograph.

Drawings may be copied to reduced or enlarged scale by using the **proportional dividers,** illustrated in Fig. 784. The divisions marked

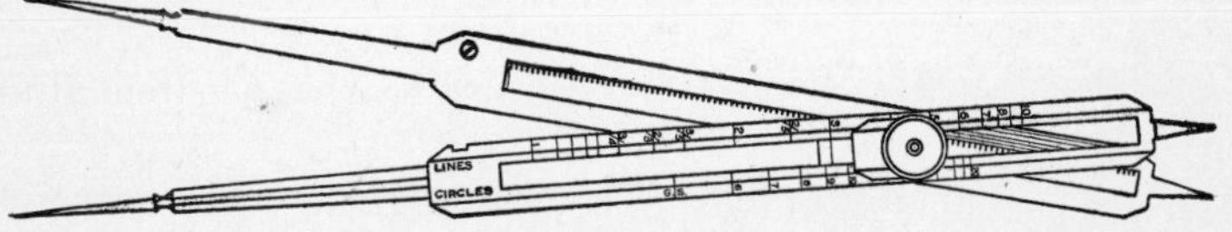

Fig. 784.—Proportional dividers.

"lines" are linear proportions, those marked "circles" give the setting for dividing a circle into a desired number of equal parts when the large end is opened to the diameter of the circle.

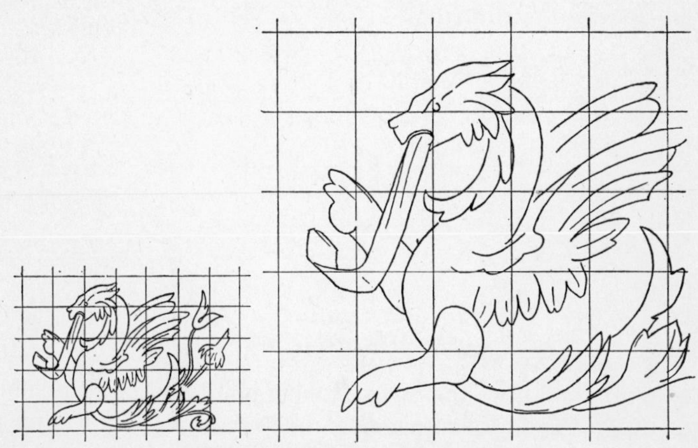

Fig. 785.—Enlargement by squares.

The well-known method of **proportional squares** is often used for reduction or enlargement. The drawing to be copied is ruled in squares of convenient size or, if it is undesirable to mark on the drawing, a sheet of ruled tracing cloth or celluloid is laid over it, and the copy made freehand on the paper, which has been ruled in corresponding squares, larger or smaller, Fig. 785.

In emergency the **rubber band method** of enlarging may be used. Using a band wide enough, mark along it the distances to be enlarged. When the band is stretched these distances will stretch proportionately.

378. Preserving Drawings.—A drawing, tracing or blue print which is to be handled much may be varnished with a thin coat of white shellac.

Pencil drawings may be sprayed with fixatif.

Prints made on sensitized cloth will withstand hard usage.

Blue prints for shop use are often mounted for preservation and convenience, by pasting on tar board or heavy press-board and coating with white shellac or Damar varnish. A coat of white glue under the varnish will aid still further in making the drawings washable.

Tracings to which more or less frequent reference will be made should be filed flat in shallow drawers. Sets of drawings preserved only for record are often kept in tin tubes numbered and filed systematically. A pasteboard tube with screw cover is also made for this purpose. It is lighter than tin and withstands fire and water even better.

Fireproof storage vaults should always be provided in connection with drafting rooms.

379. Special Instruments.—There are some instruments not in the usual assortment that are occasionally needed. Beam compasses are used for circles larger than the capacity of ordinary compasses with lengthening bar. A good form is illustrated in Fig. 786.

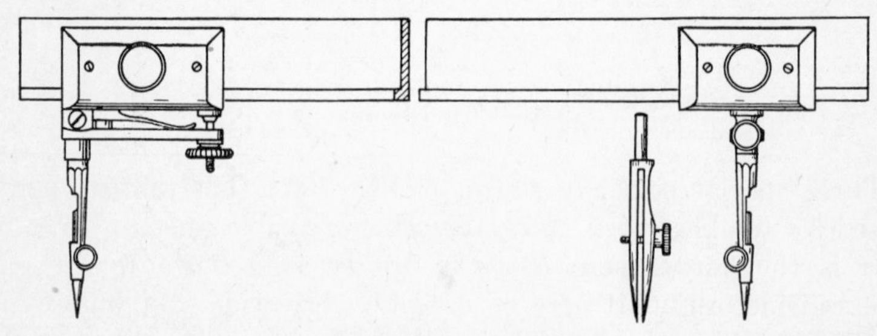

Fig. 786.—Beam compasses.

With the drop pen or rivet pen, Fig. 787, smaller circles can be made and made much faster than with the bow pen. It is held as shown, the needle point stationary and the pen revolving around it.

It is of particular convenience in bridge and structural work and in topographic drawing.

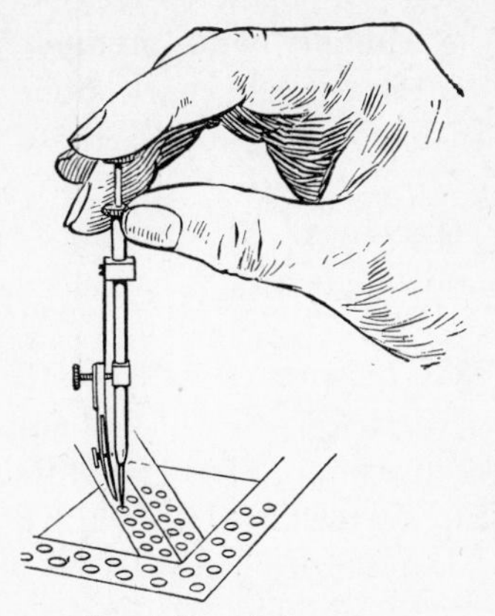

FIG. 787.—A drop pen.

Several instruments for drawing ellipses have been made. The ellipsograph, Fig. 788, is a very satisfactory one.

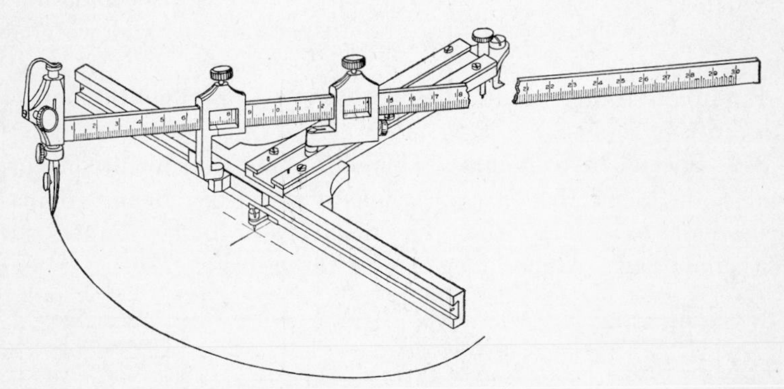

FIG. 788.—An ellipsograph.

Three special pens are shown in Fig. 789. The **railroad pen,** *A*, is used for double lines. A better pen for double lines up to ¼ inch apart is the **border pen,** *B*, as it can be held down to the paper more satisfactorily. It may be used for very wide solid lines by inking the middle space as well as the two pens. The **contour pen** or curve pen, *C*, made with a swivel is used in map work for freehand curves.

A **protractor** is a necessity in map and topographical work. A semi-circular brass or nickel-silver one, 6 inches in diameter, such as

Fig. 790, will read to half degrees. They may be had with an arm and vernier reading to minutes. Large circular paper protractors 8

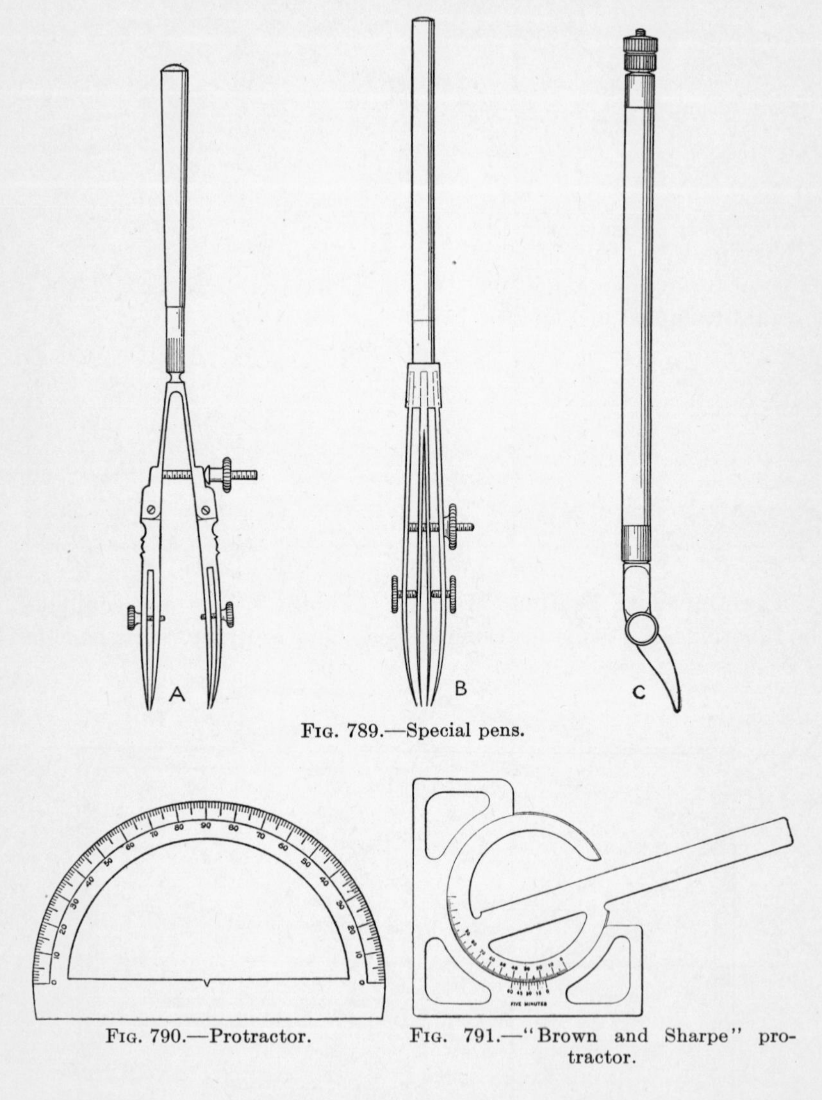

Fig. 789.—Special pens.

Fig. 790.—Protractor.

Fig. 791.—"Brown and Sharpe" protractor.

and 14 inches diameter reading to half and quarter degrees are used and preferred by some map draftsmen. Others prefer the "Brown and Sharpe" protractor of Fig. 791, reading to 5 minutes.

Two combinations of triangle and protractor popular with architects and draftsmen are shown in Figs. 792 and 793. Numerous

FIG. 792.—Lesh protractor triangle. FIG. 793.—New Facila set-square.

different forms of combination "triangles" have been devised, of which several are shown in Fig. 794.

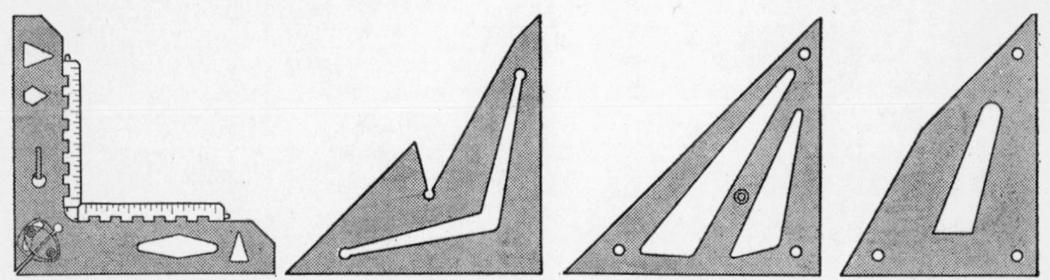

FIG. 794.—Ware angle-square, Crispin, Zange, and Rondinella "triangles."

The Universal Drafting Machine.—Figure 795, which combines the functions of T-square, triangles, scale and protractor, has had the

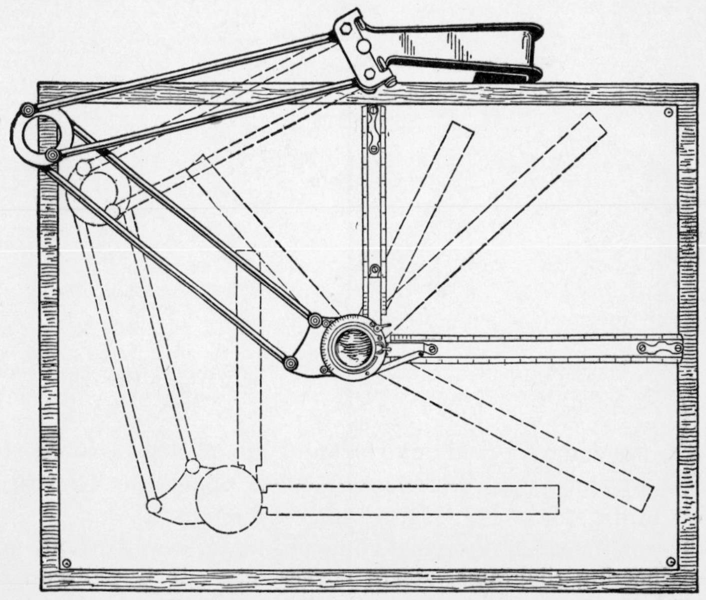

FIG. 795.—Universal drafting machine.

test of years of use and is used extensively in large drafting rooms and by practicing engineers and designers. It has been estimated that 35 per cent of time in machine drawing and over 50 per cent in civil engineering work is saved by its use.

Vertical drawing boards with sliding parallel straight-edges are preferred by some for large work.

Bottle holders prevent the possibility of ruining the drawing, table or floor by the upsetting of the ink bottle. Figure 796 shows a common

Fig. 796.—Bottle holders.

form and also a specialty of the Alteneder Company, by the aid of which the pen may be filled with one hand and time saved thereby.

Curves.—Some irregular curves were illustrated in Fig. 14. Many others are sold. Sometimes it is advisable for the draftsman to make his own templet for special or recurring curves. These may be cut out of thin holly or bass-wood, sheet lead, celluloid or even cardboard or pressboard. To make a paper curve, sketch the desired shape on the paper, cut out with scissors and sandpaper the edge. For inking, use it over a triangle or another piece of paper. Flexible curves of different kinds are sold. A copper wire or piece of wire solder can be used as a homemade substitute.

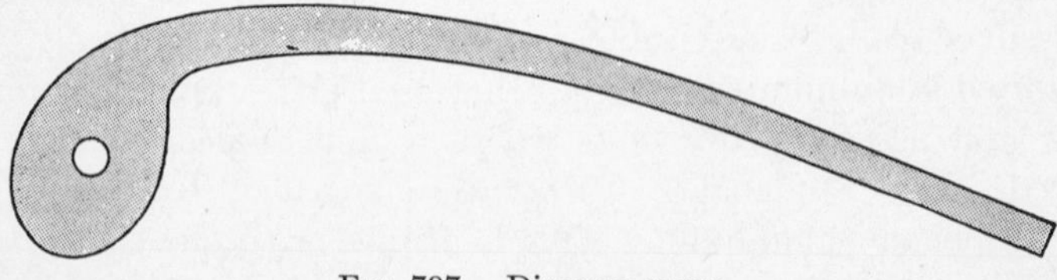

Fig. 797.—Diagram curve.

The curve illustrated in Fig. 797 has been found particularly useful for engineering diagrams, steam curves, etc. It is plotted on the polar equation $r = A \sec \theta + K$ in which A may be about $5\frac{1}{2}$ inches and K 8 inches.

If the glaze is removed from a celluloid irregular curve by rubbing with fine sandpaper, pencil marks may be made on it to facilitate drawing symmetrical curves.

380. Various Devices.—In making a drawing or map so large that it extends over the bottom edge of the board, a piece of halfround should be fastened to the board as in Fig. 798. to prevent creasing the

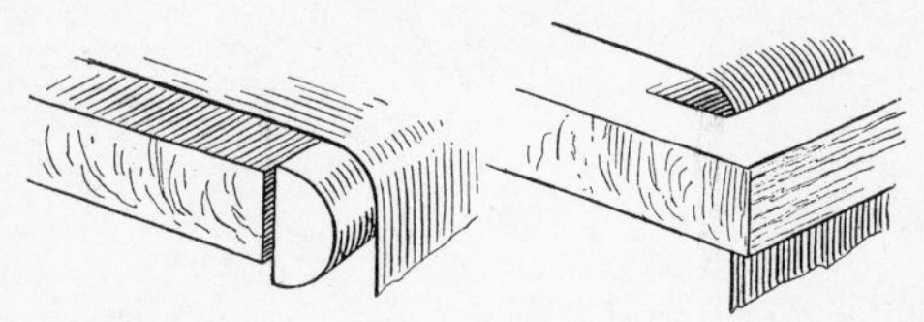

Fig. 798.—Rounded edges for large drawings.

paper. A drawing board made especially for this kind of work has a rounded slot near the front edge.

A steel edge for a drawing board may be made of an angle iron planed straight and set flush with the edge. A well-liked adjustable metal edge is made by L. S. Starrett & Company, Fig. 799. With a steel edge and steel T-square very accurate plotting may be done. These are often used in bridge offices.

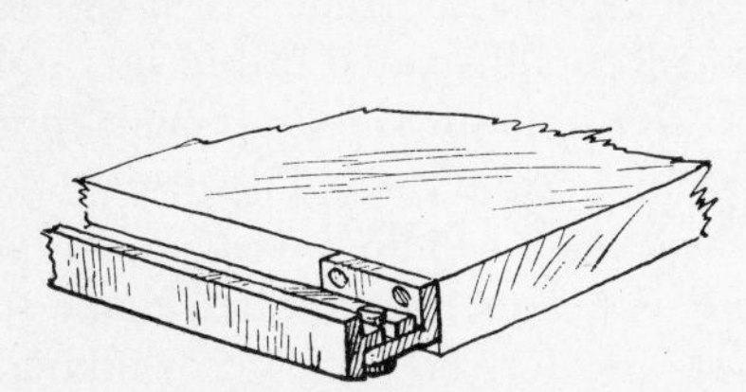

Fig. 799.—Starrett edge.

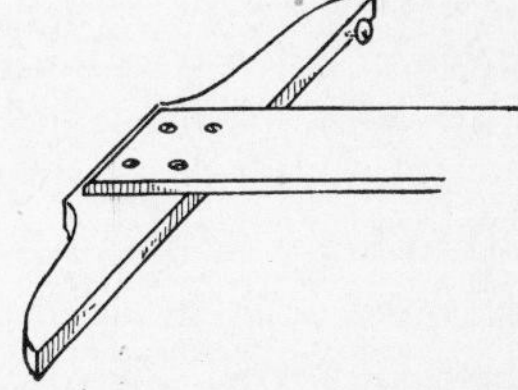

Fig. 800.—Temporary adjustment.

A temporary adjustment of a T-square may be made by putting a thumb tack in the head, Fig. 800.

If much ruling in red ink is done, a pen for the purpose with nickel-silver blades is advisable.

Painted aluminum sheets are being used instead of paper for large layout and assembly drawings where a fine degree of accuracy is required. The Studebaker Corporation specifies, for this, 14-gage "half-hardened" aluminum. This is primed with one coat of shellac and given eight coats of Acme no-luster white, then rubbed with fine "wetordry" sand paper and water.

Honed plate glass is being used instead of paper for accurate layouts in aeronautical drawing.

Section-lining or "cross-hatching" is a difficult operation for the beginner but is done almost automatically by the experienced draftsman. A number of instruments for mechanical spacing have been devised. For ordinary work they are not worth the trouble of setting up, and a draftsman should never become dependent upon them, although they are of occasional value in careful drawing for reproduction. Three ways of making a section-liner out of an ordinary triangle are shown in Fig. 801. The first two may be made of thin wood or

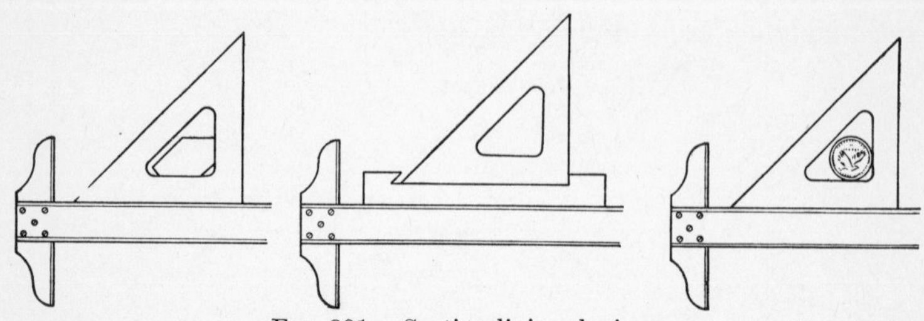

Fig. 801.—Section lining devices.

celluloid cut in the shapes indicated and used by slipping the block and holding the triangle, then holding the block and moving the triangle. A coin may be used for the same purpose.

Erasing shields of metal or celluloid permit an erasure to be made in a small space. Slots for the same purpose may be cut from sheet celluloid or tough paper.

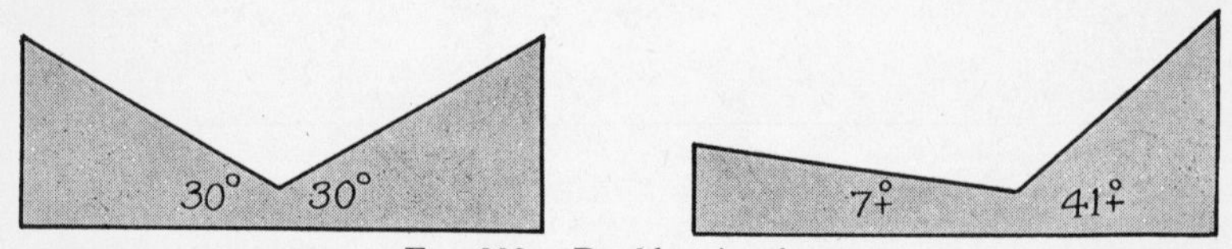

Fig. 802.—Double triangles.

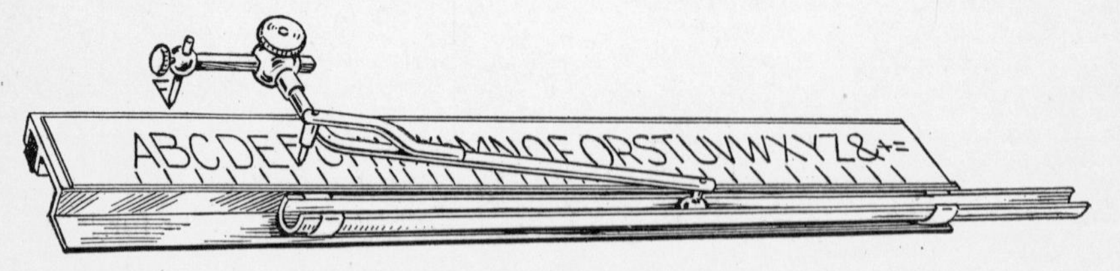

Fig. 803.—Edco lettering device.

Double triangles are very convenient in making pictorial drawings. Two forms are shown in Fig. 802, one for isometric and one for dimetric projection.

Mechanical lettering devices are being used to quite an extent in drafting rooms. Several forms are on the market, including the Wrico,

Edco, Normograph, Leroy and Minerva, all based on the principle of a stylographic pen guided by a sliding master plate. With their use very satisfactory display lettering can be done by unskilled labor. Figure 803 illustrates one of these instruments.

There are many other devices designed for labor saving and convenience in drafting rooms. The Bostich tacker is used instead of thumb tacks. Some draftsmen prefer to fasten paper to the board with Scotch tape. The Dexter "Draftsmen's Special" pencil sharpener removes the wood only, leaving a long exposure of lead. Electric erasing machines are popular.

CHAPTER XXIV

BIBLIOGRAPHY OF ALLIED SUBJECTS

The following short classified list of books is given to supplement this book, whose scope as a general treatise on the language of engineering drawing permitted only the mention or brief explanation of some subjects.

Abbreviations used for publishers' names:
Codex—Codex Book Company, Inc., New York.
Heath—D. C. Heath & Company, Boston.
Helb.—William Helburn, New York.
Ind. P.—Industrial Press, New York.
McG. H.—McGraw-Hill Book Company, Inc., New York.
Macm.—The Macmillan Company, New York.
P. P.—Pencil Points Library (Reinhold Publishing Corporation, New York).
Van N.—D. Van Nostrand Company, New York.
Wiley—John Wiley & Sons, Inc., New York.

Architectural Drawing

Clute, E.—Drafting Room Practice. 306pp. P. P., 1928.
Field, W. B.—Architectural Drawing. 161pp. 79pls. McG. H., 1922.
———.—An Introduction to Architectural Drawing. 103pp. McG. H., 1932.
Harbeson, J. F.—The Study of Architectural Design. 310pp. P. P., 1927.
Knobloch, P. G.—Good Practice in Construction. 114pp. P. P., 1931.
Ramsey and Sleeper.—Architectural Graphic Standards. 233pp. Wiley, 1932.
Voss and Varney.—Architectural Construction. 2 V. Wiley, 1927.

Cams

Furman, F. DeR.—Cams, Elementary and Advanced. 234pp. Wiley, 1921.

Charts, Graphs and Diagrams

Brinton, W. C.—Graphic Methods for Presenting Facts. 371pp. McG. H., 1914.
Dingman, C. F.—Plan Reading and Quantity Surveying. 201pp. McG. H., 1924.
Haskell, A. C.—How to Make and Use Graphic Charts. 539pp. Codex, 1920.
Hewes and Seward.—The Design of Diagrams for Engineering Formulas and the Theory of Nomography. 111pp. McG. H., 1923.
Karsten, K. G.—Charts and Graphs. 724pp. Prentice-Hall, 1923.
Knoeppel, C. E.—Profit Engineering. 326pp. McG. H., 1934.
Lipka, J.—Graphical and Mechanical Computation. 264pp. Wiley, 1918.

RIGGLEMAN, J. R.—Graphic Methods for Presenting Business Statistics. 231pp. McG. H., 1926.
SWETT, G. W.—Construction of Alignment Charts. 92pp. Wiley, 1928.

Descriptive Geometry

ANTHONY and ASHLEY.—Descriptive Geometry. 199pp. Heath, 1926.
CHERRY, F. H.—Descriptive Geometry. 127pp. Macm., 1933.
CHURCH, A. E.—Elements of Descriptive Geometry. 286pp. Am. Book Co., 1911.
CUTTER, L. E.—Descriptive Geometry. 244pp. McG. H., 1927.
HIGBEE, F. G.—The Essentials of Descriptive Geometry. 244pp. Wiley, 1930.
HOOD, GEORGE J.—Geometry of Engineering Drawing. 348pp. McG. H., 1933.
JORDAN and PORTER.—Descriptive Geometry. 349pp. Ginn & Co., 1929.
KIRCHNER and EGGERS.—Descriptive Geometry. 183pp. McG. H., 1928.
SCHUMANN, C. H.—Descriptive Geometry. 249pp. Van N., 1927.
SMITH, W. G.—Practical Descriptive Geometry. 281pp. McG. H., 1925.
WARNER, F. M.—Applied Descriptive Geometry. 214pp. McG. H., 1934.

Gears and Gearing

BEALE, O. J.—Practical Treatise on Gearing. Brown and Sharpe Mfg. Co., Providence.
BROWN and SHARPE MFG. CO.—Catalogue of Machinery and Tools. Providence.
BUCKINGHAM, E.—Spur Gears. 451pp. McG. H., 1928.
FELLOWS GEAR SHAPER CO.—Treatise on Commercial Gear Cutting. Springfield, Vt.
TRAUTSCHOLD, REGINALD—Standard Gear Book. 314pp. McG. H., 1935.

Handbooks

A great many "pocket-size" handbooks, with tables, formulas and information, are published for the different branches of the engineering profession, and draftsmen keep the ones pertaining to their particular line at hand for ready reference. Attention is called, however, to the danger of using handbook formulas and figures without understanding the principles upon which they are based. "Handbook designer" is a term of reproach applied not without reason to one who depends wholly upon these aids without knowing their theory or limitations.

Among the best known of these reference books are the following:

American Machinists' Handbook, Colvin and Stanley. 1,140pp. McG. H., 1932.
American Society of Heating and Ventilating Engineers' Guide (annually).
Architects' and Builders' Pocketbook, Kidder-Parker. 2,315pp. Wiley, 1931.
Civil Engineering Handbook, Urquhart. 885pp. McG. H., 1934.
Civil Engineers' Reference Book. 1,512pp. Trautwine Co., Phila., 1929.
Estimating Building Costs, F. E. Barnes. 656pp. McG. H., 1931.
General Engineering Handbook, O'Rourke. 931pp. McG. H., 1932.
Handbook of Building Construction, Hool and Johnson. 1,650pp. McG. H., 1929.

Handbook of various steel and other material companies, as Bethlehem, Carnegie, Aluminum Co. of America, Portland Cement Assoc., etc.

Handbook of Formulas and Tables for Engineers, Peirce, Carver and O'Rourke. 228pp. McG. H., 1929.

Highway Engineers' Handbook, Harger and Bonney. 1,721pp. McG. H., 1927.

Machinery's Handbook. 1,592pp. Ind. P., 1930.

Mechanical Engineers' Handbook, L. S. Marks. 2,264pp. McG. H., 1930.

Mechanical Engineers' Pocketbook, William Kent. 2,247pp. Wiley, 1923.

Standard Handbook for Electrical Engineers, F. F. Fowle. 2,816pp. McG. H., 1933.

Steel Construction. 352pp. Amer. Inst. of Steel Const., Inc., New York, 1934.

Lettering

FRENCH and MEIKLEJOHN.—The Essentials of Lettering. 94pp. McG. H., 1912.

FRENCH and TURNBULL.—Lessons in Lettering. 40pp. each. McG. H., 1922.

REINHARDT, C. W.—Lettering for Draftsmen, Etc. 39pp. Van N., 1917.

SVENSEN, C. L.—The Art of Lettering. 136pp. Van N., 1927.

WEISS, EGON—The Design of Lettering. 192pp. P. P., 1932.

Machine Drawing and Design

ALBERT, C. D.—Machine Design Drawing Room Problems. 320pp. Wiley, 1927.

BERARD and WATERS.—The Elements of Machine Design. 192pp. Van N., 1933.

BRADFORD and EATON.—Machine Design. 289pp. Wiley, 1934.

FAIRES, V. M.—Design of Machine Elements. 468pp. Macm., 1934.

HOFFMAN and SCIPIO.—Elements of Machine Design. 327pp. Ginn & Co., 1928.

HYLAND and KOMMERS.—Machine Design. 448pp. McG. H., 1929.

KIMBALL and BARR.—Elements of Machine Design. 446pp. Wiley, 1923.

LEUTWILER, O. A.—Elements of Machine Design. 607pp. McG. H., 1923.

NORMAN, C. A.—Principles of Machine Design. 710pp. Macm., 1925.

OLSEN, J. K.—Production Design. 211pp. McG. H., 1928.

SPOONER, H. J.—Machine Design, Construction and Drawing. 775pp. Longmans, Green, N. Y., 1927.

TOZER and RISING.—Machine Drawing. 317pp. McG. H., 1934.

Map and Topographic Drawing

DEETZ and ADAMS.—Elements of Map Projection. 173pp. U. S. Govt. Printing Office, 1931.

SLOANE and MONTZ.—Elements of Topographic Drawing. 188pp. McG. H., 1930.

STUART, E. R.—Topographical Drawing. 126pp. McG. H., 1917.

Mechanism and Kinematics

GUILLET, G. L.—Kinematics of Machines. 276pp. Wiley, 1934.

HAM and CRANE.—Mechanics of Machinery. 504pp. McG. H., 1927.

HECK, R. C. H.—Mechanics of Machinery—Mechanism. 550pp. McG. H., 1925.

KEOWN and FAIRES.—Mechanism. 242pp. McG. H., 1931.
PEARCE, C. E.—Principles of Mechanism. 283pp. Wiley, 1934.
SCHWAMB, MERRILL and JAMES.—Elements of Mechanism. 372pp. Wiley, 1930.
SMITH, W. G.—Engineering Kinematics. 343pp. McG. H., 1930.

Perspective

LUBCHEZ, B.—Perspective. 129pp. Van N., 1927.

Piping

WALKER and CROCKER.—Piping Handbook. 763pp. McG. H., 1931.
Industrial Piping. 286pp. Engineering Publications Inc., Chicago, 1933.

Rendering

GUPTIL, A. L.—Drawing with Pen and Ink. 444pp. P. P., 1928.
———.—Sketching and Rendering in Pencil. 200pp. P. P., 1922.
MAGONIGLE, H. V.—Architectural Rendering in Wash. 160pp. Scribners, 1926.

Shades and Shadows

BUCK, RONAN and OMAN.—Shades and Shadows for Architects. 134pp. McG. H., 1930.
McGOODWIN, H. K.—Architectural Shades and Shadows. 118pp. Helb., 1922.

Sheet-metal Drafting

KIDDER, F. S.—Triangulation Applied to Sheet Metal Pattern Cutting. 312pp. Sheet Metal Publ. Co., N. Y., 1930.
KITTREDGE, G. W.—The New Metal Worker Pattern Book. 518pp. Scientific Book Corp., 1927.
LONGFIELD, E. M.—Sheet Metal Drafting. 236pp. McG. H., 1921.

Shop Practice

BOSTON, O. W.—Engineering Shop Practice. V 1. 539pp. Wiley, 1933.
BURGHARDT, H. D.—Machine Tool Operation. 2 V. McG. H., 1922.
CINCINNATI MILLING MACHINE CO.—A Treatise on Milling and Milling Machines. 441pp. Cincinnati.
COLVIN and HAAS.—Jigs and Fixtures. 237 pp. McG. H., 1922.
DOWD and CURTIS.—Tool Engineering. 3 V. McG. H., 1925.
GWIAZDOWSKI and LORD.—Economics of Tool Engineering. 203pp. McG. H., 1932.
SMITH, R. H.—Advanced Machine Work. 829pp. Ind. Ed. Bk. Co., 1930.
TURNER, WILLIAM P.—Machine Tool Work. 424pp. McG. H., 1932.
VIALL, E.—Broaches and Broaching. 221pp. McG. H., 1918.
WENDT, R. E.—Foundry Work. 236pp. McG. H., 1928.

Slide Rule

CAJORI, F.—A History of the Logarithmic Slide Rule. 126pp. Eng. News Pub. Co., N. Y., 1909.
COOPER, H. O.—Slide Rule Calculations. 132pp. Oxford Univ. Press, 1931.

Structural Drawing and Design

BISHOP, C. T.—Structural Drafting. 362pp. Wiley, 1928.

HOOL and KINNE.—Structural Engineers' Handbook Library. 6 V. McG. H., 1924.

MORRIS, C. T.—Designing and Detailing of Simple Steel Structures. 279pp. McG. H., 1933.

SUTHERLAND and BOWMAN.—Structural Theory and Design. 318pp. Wiley, 1930.

TAYLOR, THOMPSON and SMULSKI.—Concrete, Plain and Reinforced. 2 V. Wiley, 1925.

Welding

CHAFFEE, W. J.—Arc Welding. 94pp. Hobart Bros., 1935.

HUBERT, E. H.—Manual of Electric Arc Welding. 163pp. McG. H., 1932.

McKENZIE and CARD.—The Welding Encyclopedia. 512pp. Welding Engineer Publ. Co., Chicago, 1932.

AMERICAN STANDARDS

The American Standards Association is working on a large number of standardization projects. Of its many publications the following approved standards having to do with the subjects in this book are available at the time of this printing and may be purchased at cost at its offices, 29 West Thirty-ninth Street, New York. A complete list of American Standards will be sent by the association on application.

A13—Identification of Piping Systems .... 50 cts.

A38—Steel Reinforcing Spirals .... 5 cts.

B1.1—Screw Threads for Bolts, Nuts, Machine Screws and Threaded Parts 65 cts.

B2—Pipe Thread .... 40 cts.

B4a—Tolerances, Allowances and Gages for Metal Fits .... 50 cts.

B5a—T-Slots, Their Bolts, Nuts, Tongues and Cutters .... 35 cts.

B6.1—Spur Gear Tooth Form .... 45 cts.

B6.2—Gear Materials and Blanks .... 50 cts.

B16a—Cast-iron Flanges and Flanged Fittings, Max. 125 lb .... 50 cts.

B16b—Cast-iron Flanges and Flanged Fittings, Max. 250 lb .... 50 cts.

B16b1—Cast-iron Flanges and Flanged Fittings for 800 lb. Hydraulic Pressure .... 35 cts.

B16b2—Cast-iron Flanges and Flanged Fittings for Max. 25 lb .... 40 cts.

B16c—Malleable-iron Screwed Fittings, Max. 150 lb .... 40 cts.

B16d—Cast-iron Screwed Fittings, Max 125 and 250 lb .... 35 cts.

B16e—Steel Flanged Fittings and Companion Flanges .... 65 cts.

B17.1—Shafting and Stock Keys .... 45 cts.

B17c—Design of Transmission Shafting .... 75 cts.

B17f—Woodruff Keys, Keyslots and Cutters .... 35 cts.

B18a—Small Rivets .... 30 cts.

B18c—Slotted Head Proportions, Machine Screws, Cap Screws, and Wood Screws .... 45 cts.

B18e—Round Unslotted Head Bolts .... 40 cts.

B18f—Plow Bolts .... 35 cts.

B18g—Tinners', Coopers', and Belt Rivets .... 35 cts.
B18.2—Wrench-head Bolts and Nuts and Wrench Openings .... 50 cts.
B26—Screw Threads for Fire Hose Couplings .... 25 cts.
B36.1—Welded and Seamless Steel Pipe .... 25 cts.
B36.2—Welded Wrought Iron Pipe .... 25 cts.
B36.3—Lap Welded and Seamless Steel Pipe for High Temperature Service 25 cts.
C10—Electrical Equipment of Buildings .... 20 cts.
Z10a—Mechanics, Structural Engineering and Testing Materials .... 25 cts.
Z10b—Symbols for Hydraulics .... 35 cts.
Z10c—Heat and Thermodynamics .... 30 cts.
Z10d—Photometry and Illumination .... 20 cts.
Z10e—Aeronautical Symbols .... 35 cts.
Z10f—Mathematical Symbols .... 30 cts.
Z10g1—Electrical Quantities, Letter Symbols .... 20 cts.
Z10g2—Electric Power and Wiring, Graphical Symbols .... 20 cts.
Z10g3—Radio, Graphical Symbols .... 20 cts.
Z10g5—Electric Traction, Including Railway Signalling, Graphical Symbols .... 40 cts.
Z10g6—Telephone and Telegraph, Symbols .... 20 cts.
Z10i—Abbreviations for Scientific and Engineering Terms .... 40 cts.
Z14.1—Drawings and Drafting Room Practice .... 50 cts.

APPENDIX

CONTENTS OF APPENDIX

APPENDIX

Tapers.—Taper means the difference in diameter or width in one foot of length, Fig. 804. *Taper pins,* much used for fastening cylindrical parts and for doweling, have a standard taper of ¼″ per foot.

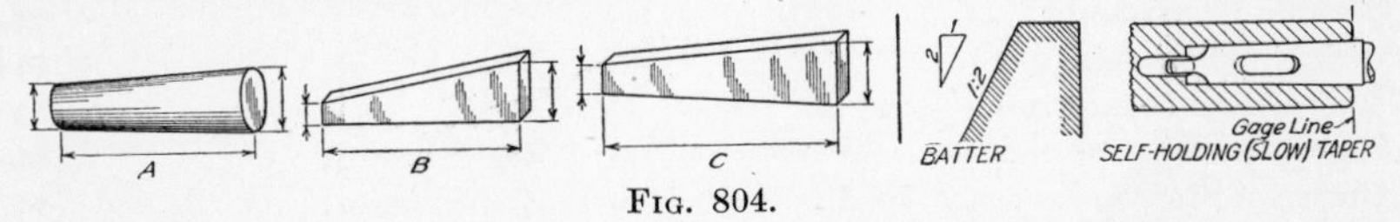

FIG. 804.

Machine Tapers.—The American Standard for self-holding (slow) machine tapers is designed to replace the various former standards. The table below shows its derivation. Detailed dimensions and tolerances for taper tool shanks and taper sockets will be found in A.S.A. B5.

DIMENSIONS OF TAPER PINS

Taper ¼″ per foot

Size No.	Diameter, large end	Drill size for reamer	Max. length
000000	0.072	53	⅝
00000	0.092	47	⅝
0000	0.108	42	¾
000	0.125	37	¾
00	0.147	31	1
0	0.156	28	1
1	0.172	25	1¼
2	0.193	19	1½
3	0.219	12	1¾
4	0.250	3	2
5	0.289	¼	2¼
6	0.341	9/32	3¼
7	0.409	11/32	3¾
8	0.492	13/32	4½
9	0.591	31/64	5¼
10	0.706	19/32	6
11	0.857	23/32	7¼
12	1.013	55/64	8¾
13	1.233	1 1/64	10¾

AMERICAN STANDARD MACHINE TAPERS[1]

SELF-HOLDING (SLOW) TAPER SERIES

Basic Dimensions

Origin of series	No. of taper	Taper per foot	Diameter at gage line	Means of driving and holding			
Brown and Sharpe taper series	0.239	0.500	0.239	Tongue drive with shank held in by friction			
	0.299	0.500	0.299				
	0.375	0.500	0.375				
Morse taper series	1	0.59858	0.475				
	2	0.59941	0.700		Tongue drive with shank held in by key		
	3	0.60235	0.938				
	4	0.62326	1.231				
	4½	0.62300	1.500				
	5	0.63151	1.748				
¾″ per foot taper series	20	0.750	2.000			Key drive with shank held in by key	Key drive with shank held in by drawbolt
	25	0.750	2.500				
	30	0.750	3.000				
	35	0.750	3.500				
	40	0.750	4.000				
	50	0.750	5.000				
	60	0.750	6.000				
	80	0.750	8.000				
	100	0.750	10.000				
	120	0.750	12.000				

[1] In process of adoption, March, 1935.

Decimal Equivalents of Fractions of an Inch

Fraction	Decimal	Fraction	Decimal	Fraction	Decimal	Fraction	Decimal
1/64	.015625	17/64	.265625	33/64	.515625	49/64	.765625
1/32	.03125	9/32	.28125	17/32	.53125	25/32	.78125
3/64	.046875	19/64	.296875	35/64	.546875	51/64	.796875
1/16	.0625	5/16	.3125	9/16	.5625	13/16	.8125
5/64	.078125	21/64	.328125	37/64	.578125	53/64	.828125
3/32	.09375	11/32	.34375	19/32	.59375	27/32	.84375
7/64	.109375	23/64	.359375	39/64	.609375	55/64	.859375
1/8	.125	3/8	.375	5/8	.625	7/8	.875
9/64	.140625	25/64	.390625	41/64	.640625	57/64	.890625
5/32	.15625	13/32	.40625	21/32	.65625	29/32	.90625
11/64	.171875	27/64	.421875	43/64	.671875	59/64	.921875
3/16	.1875	7/16	.4375	11/16	.6875	15/16	.9375
13/64	.203125	29/64	.453125	45/64	.703125	61/64	.953125
7/32	.21875	15/32	.46875	23/32	.71875	31/32	.96875
15/64	.234375	31/64	.484375	47/64	.734375	63/64	.984375
1/4	.25	1/2	.5	3/4	.75	1	1.0

Metric Equivalents

In converting inches to millimeters carry the millimeter equivalent to one *less* decimal place than the number to which the inch value is given.

In converting from millimeters to inches carry the inch equivalent to two *more* places than the number to which the millimeter value is given.

Millimeters to inches				Inches to millimeters			
Mm.	In.	Mm.	In.	In.	Mm.	In.	Mm.
1	.0394	17	.6693	1/32	.79	17/32	13.49
2	.0787	18	.7087	1/16	1.58	9/16	14.28
3	.1181	19	.7480	3/32	2.38	19/32	15.08
4	.1575	20	.7874	1/8	3.17	5/8	15.87
5	.1968	21	.8268	5/32	3.96	21/32	16.66
6	.2362	22	.8661	3/16	4.76	11/16	17.46
7	.2756	23	.9055	7/32	5.55	23/32	18.25
8	.3150	24	.9449	1/4	6.34	3/4	19.04
9	.3543	25	.9843	9/32	7.14	25/32	19.84
10	.3937	26	1.0236	5/16	7.93	13/16	20.63
11	.4331	27	1.0630	11/32	8.73	27/32	21.43
12	.4724	28	1.1024	3/8	9.52	7/8	22.22
13	.5118	29	1.1417	13/32	10.31	29/32	23.01
14	.5512	30	1.1811	7/16	11.11	15/16	23.81
15	.5906	31	1.2205	15/32	11.90	31/32	24.60
16	.6299	32	1.2598	1/2	12.69	1	25.39

AMERICAN STANDARD SCREW THREADS

American Standard Coarse and Fine[1] and S.A.E. Extra Fine Thread Series[2]

Size	Threads per inch		
	Coarse NC	Fine NF	Extra fine EF (S.A.E.)
0	....	80	
1	64	72	
2	56	64	
3	48	56	
4	40	48	
5	40	44	
6	32	40	
8	32	36	
10	24	32	
12	24	28	
1/4	20	28	36
5/16	18	24	32
3/8	16	24	32
7/16	14	20	28
1/2	13	20	28
9/16	12	18	24
5/8	11	18	24
3/4	10	16	20
7/8	9	14	20
1	8	14	20
1 1/8	7	12	18
1 1/4	7	12	18
1 3/8	6		
1 1/2	6	12	18
1 3/4	5	..	16
2	4 1/2	..	16
2 1/4	4 1/2	..	16
2 1/2	4	..	16
2 3/4	4	..	16
3	4	..	16
Over 3	....	..	16

[1] A.S.A. B1.1 1935.

[2] The extra fine screw thread series of the Society of Automotive Engineers is intended for aeronautical and other applications where screw threads finer than NF are necessary.

American Standard 8-pitch, 12-pitch, and 16-pitch Thread Series[1]

Size	Threads per inch		
	8-pitch N8	12-pitch N12	16-pitch N16
1/2 to 1 1/16[2]	..	12	
3/4 to 1 5/16[2]	..	12	16
1	8	12	16
1 1/16	..	12	16
1 1/8	8	12	16
1 3/16	..	12	16
1 1/4	8	12	16
1 5/16	..	12	16
1 3/8	8	12	16
1 7/16	..	12	16
1 1/2	8	12	16
1 9/16	..	..	16
1 5/8	8	12	16
1 11/16	..	..	16
1 3/4	8	12	16
1 13/16	..	..	16
1 7/8	8	12	16
1 15/16	..	..	16
2	8	12	16
2 1/16	..	..	16
2 1/8	8	12	16
2 3/16	..	..	16
2 1/4	8	12	16
2 5/16	..	..	16
2 3/8	..	12	16
2 7/16	..	..	16
2 1/2	8	12	16
2 5/8	..	12	16
2 3/4	8	12	16
2 7/8	..	12	16
3	8	12	16
3 1/8	..	12	16
3 1/4	8	12	16
3 3/8	..	12	16
3 1/2	8	12	16
3 5/8	..	12	16
3 3/4	8	12	16
3 7/8	..	12	16
4	8	12	16
4 1/4 to 6[3]	8	12	

[1] A.S.A. B1.1 1935.

[2] Size increments, 1/16″.

[3] Size increments, 1/4″.

American Standard Wrench Head Bolts and Nuts[1]

Diameter of bolt	REGULAR SERIES														
	Unfinished, square and hexagon					Semi-finished,[2] square and hexagon					Finished,[3] hexagon				
	Heads		Nuts			Heads		Nuts			Heads		Nuts		
	W	*H*	*W*	Regular *T*	Jam *T*	*W*	*H*	*W*	Regular *T*	Jam *T*	*W*	*H*	*W*	Regular *T*	Jam *T*
1/4	3/8	11/64	7/16	7/32	5/32	3/8	5/32	7/16	13/64	9/64	7/16	3/16	7/16	7/32	5/32
5/16	1/2	13/64	9/16	17/64	3/16	1/2	3/16	9/16	1/4	11/64	9/16	15/64	9/16	17/64	3/16
3/8	9/16	1/4	5/8	21/64	7/32	9/16	15/64	5/8	5/16	13/64	5/8	9/32	5/8	21/64	7/32
7/16	5/8	19/64	3/4	3/8	1/4	5/8	9/32	3/4	23/64	15/64	3/4	21/64	3/4	3/8	1/4
1/2	3/4	21/64	13/16	7/16	5/16	3/4	19/64	13/16	27/64	19/64	13/16	3/8	13/16	7/16	5/16
9/16	7/8	3/8	7/8	1/2	11/32	7/8	11/32	7/8	15/32	21/64	7/8	27/64	7/8	1/2	11/32
5/8	15/16	27/64	1	35/64	3/8	15/16	25/64	1	17/32	23/64	1	15/32	1	35/64	3/8
3/4	1 1/8	1/2	1 1/8	21/32	7/16	1 1/8	15/32	1 1/8	41/64	27/64	1 1/8	9/16	1 1/8	21/32	7/16
7/8	1 5/16	19/32	1 5/16	49/64	1/2	1 5/16	9/16	1 5/16	3/4	31/64	1 5/16	21/32	1 5/16	49/64	1/2
1	1 1/2	21/32	1 1/2	7/8	9/16	1 1/2	19/32	1 1/2	55/64	35/64	1 1/2	3/4	1 1/2	7/8	9/16
1 1/8	1 11/16	3/4	1 11/16	1	5/8	1 11/16	11/16	1 11/16	31/32	39/64	1 11/16	27/32	1 11/16	1	5/8
1 1/4	1 7/8	27/32	1 7/8	1 3/32	3/4	1 7/8	25/32	1 7/8	1 1/32	11/16	1 7/8	15/16	1 7/8	1 3/32	3/4
1 3/8	2 1/16	29/32	2 1/16	1 13/64	13/16	2 1/16	27/32	2 1/16	1 9/64	3/4	2 1/16	1 1/32	2 1/16	1 13/64	13/16
1 1/2	2 1/4	1	2 1/4	1 5/16	7/8	2 1/4	15/16	2 1/4	1 1/4	13/16	2 1/4	1 1/8	2 1/4	1 5/16	7/8
1 5/8	2 7/16	1 3/32	2 7/16	1 27/64	15/16	2 7/16	1 1/32	2 7/16	1 23/64	7/8	2 7/16	1 7/32	2 7/16	1 27/64	15/16
1 3/4	2 5/8	1 5/32	2 5/8	1 17/32	1	2 5/8	1 3/32	2 5/8	1 15/32	15/16	2 5/8	1 5/16	2 5/8	1 17/32	1
1 7/8	2 13/16	1 1/4	2 13/16	1 41/64	1 1/16	2 13/16	1 3/16	2 13/16	1 37/64	1	2 13/16	1 13/32	2 13/16	1 41/64	1 1/16
2	3	1 11/32	3	1 3/4	1 1/8	3	1 7/32	3	1 11/16	1 1/16	3	1 1/2	3	1 3/4	1 1/8
2 1/4	3 3/8	1 1/2	3 3/8	1 31/32	1 1/4	3 3/8	1 3/8	3 3/8	1 29/32	1 3/16	3 3/8	1 11/16	3 3/8	1 31/32	1 1/4
2 1/2	3 3/4	1 21/32	3 3/4	2 3/16	1 1/2	3 3/4	1 17/32	3 3/4	2 3/32	1 13/32	3 3/4	1 7/8	3 3/4	2 3/16	1 1/2
2 3/4	4 1/8	1 53/64	4 1/8	2 13/32	1 5/8	4 1/8	1 11/16	4 1/8	2 5/16	1 17/32	4 1/8	2 1/16	4 1/8	2 13/32	1 5/8
3	4 1/2	2	4 1/2	2 5/8	1 3/4	4 1/2	1 7/8	4 1/2	2 17/32	1 21/32	4 1/2	2 1/4	4 1/2	2 5/8	1 3/4

[1] A.S.A. B18.2 1933. [2] Finished under head only, plain or washer faced. [3] Finished all over, bearing surfaces washer faced.

American Standard Wrench Head Bolts and Nuts[1]

HEAVY SERIES

Diameter of bolt	Unfinished, square and hexagon					Semi-finished,[2] square and hexagon					Finished,[3] hexagon				
	Heads		Nuts			Heads		Nuts			Heads		Nuts		
	W	*H*	*W*	Heavy *T*	Jam *T*	*W*	*H*	*W*	Heavy *T*	Jam *T*	*W*	*H*	*W*	Heavy *T*	Jam *T*
1/2	7/8	7/16	7/8	1/2	5/16	7/8	13/32	7/8	31/64	19/64	7/8	7/16	7/8	1/2	5/16
9/16	15/16	15/32	15/16	9/16	11/32	15/16	7/16	15/16	35/64	21/64	15/16	1/2	15/16	9/16	11/32
5/8	1 1/16	17/32	1 1/16	5/8	3/8	1 1/16	1/2	1 1/16	39/64	23/64	1 1/16	9/16	1 1/16	5/8	3/8
3/4	1 1/4	5/8	1 1/4	3/4	7/16	1 1/4	19/32	1 1/4	47/64	27/64	1 1/4	11/16	1 1/4	3/4	7/16
7/8	1 7/16	23/32	1 7/16	7/8	1/2	1 7/16	11/16	1 7/16	55/64	31/64	1 7/16	13/16	1 7/16	7/8	1/2
1	1 5/8	13/16	1 5/8	1	9/16	1 5/8	3/4	1 5/8	63/64	35/64	1 5/8	15/16	1 5/8	1	9/16
1 1/8	1 13/16	29/32	1 13/16	1 1/8	5/8	1 13/16	27/32	1 13/16	1 7/64	39/64	1 13/16	1 1/16	1 13/16	1 1/8	5/8
1 1/4	2	1	2	1 1/4	3/4	2	15/16	2	1 3/16	1 1/16	2	1 3/16	2	1 1/4	3/4
1 3/8	2 3/16	1 3/32	2 3/16	1 3/8	13/16	2 3/16	1 1/32	2 3/16	1 5/16	3/4	2 3/16	1 5/16	2 3/16	1 3/8	13/16
1 1/2	2 3/8	1 3/16	2 3/8	1 1/2	7/8	2 3/8	1 1/8	2 3/8	1 7/16	13/16	2 3/8	1 7/16	2 3/8	1 1/2	7/8
1 5/8	2 9/16	1 9/32	2 9/16	1 5/8	15/16	2 9/16	1 7/32	2 9/16	1 9/16	7/8	2 9/16	1 9/16	2 9/16	1 5/8	15/16
1 3/4	2 3/4	1 3/8	2 3/4	1 3/4	1	2 3/4	1 5/16	2 3/4	1 11/16	15/16	2 3/4	1 11/16	2 3/4	1 3/4	1
1 7/8	2 15/16	1 15/32	2 15/16	1 7/8	1 1/16	2 15/16	1 13/32	2 15/16	1 13/16	1	2 15/16	1 13/16	2 15/16	1 7/8	1 1/16
2	3 1/8	1 9/16	3 1/8	2	1 1/8	3 1/8	1 7/16	3 1/8	1 15/16	1 1/16	3 1/8	1 15/16	3 1/8	2	1 1/8
2 1/4	3 1/2	1 3/4	3 1/2	2 1/4	1 1/4	3 1/2	1 5/8	3 1/2	2 3/16	1 3/16	3 1/2	2 3/16	3 1/2	2 1/4	1 1/4
2 1/2	3 7/8	1 15/16	3 7/8	2 1/2	1 1/2	3 7/8	1 13/16	3 7/8	2 13/32	1 13/32	3 7/8	2 7/16	3 7/8	2 1/2	1 1/2
2 3/4	4 1/4	2 1/8	4 1/4	2 3/4	1 5/8	4 1/4	2	4 1/4	2 21/32	1 17/32	4 1/4	2 11/16	4 1/4	2 3/4	1 5/8
3	4 5/8	2 5/16	4 5/8	3	1 3/4	4 5/8	2 3/16	4 5/8	2 29/32	1 21/32	4 5/8	2 15/16	4 5/8	3	1 3/4

[1] ASA B18.2 1933. [2] Finished under head only, plain or washer faced. [3] Finished all over, bearing surfaces washer faced.

American Standard Nuts[1]

Diameter of bolt	Light nuts[2] semi-finished, hexagon		Light castle nuts[2] semi-finished, hexagon				Machine screw[3] and stove bolt nuts, square and hexagon		
	W	T	W	Overall T	Slot				
					Width	Depth	Diameter	W	T
1/4	7/16	7/32	7/16	9/32	5/64	3/32			
5/16	1/2	17/64	1/2	21/64	5/64	3/32	No. 0	5/32	3/64
3/8	9/16	21/64	9/16	13/32	1/8	1/8	No. 1	5/32	3/64
7/16	5/8	3/8	5/8	29/64	1/8	1/8	No. 2	3/16	1/16
1/2	3/4	7/16	3/4	9/16	1/8	3/16	No. 3	3/16	1/16
9/16	7/8	31/64	7/8	39/64	5/32	3/16	No. 4	1/4	3/32
5/8	15/16	35/64	15/16	23/32	5/32	1/4	No. 5	5/16	7/64
3/4	1 1/16	21/32	1 1/16	13/16	5/32	1/4	No. 6	5/16	7/64
7/8	1 1/4	49/64	1 1/4	29/32	5/32	1/4	No. 8	11/32	1/8
1	1 7/16	7/8	1 7/16	1	5/32	1/4	No. 10	3/8	1/8
1 1/8	1 5/8	63/64	1 5/8	1 5/32	7/32	5/16	No. 12	7/16	5/32
1 1/4	1 13/16	1 3/32	1 13/16	1 1/4	7/32	5/16	1/4	7/16	3/16
1 3/8	2	1 13/64	2	1 3/8	7/32	5/16	5/16	9/16	7/32
1 1/2	2 3/16	1 5/16	2 3/16	1 1/2	1/4	3/8	3/8	5/8	1/4

[1] ASA B18.2, 1933.
[2] Usually supplied with fine threads, machined on bearing surface only.
[3] Top and bottom of square nuts and bottom of hexagon nuts shall be flat.

American Standard Finished Hexagonal Cap Screw Heads

Threads are Coarse Series

Diameter, D	Threads per inch, coarse	Width across flats, W	Height of head, H
1/4	20	7/16	3/16
5/16	18	1/2	15/64
3/8	16	9/16	9/32
7/16	14	5/8	21/64
1/2	13	3/4	3/8
9/16	12	13/16	27/64
5/8	11	7/8	15/32
3/4	10	1	9/16
7/8	9	1 1/8	21/32
1	8	1 5/16	3/4
1 1/8	7	1 1/2	27/32
1 1/4	7	1 11/16	15/16

American Standard Square Head Set Screw Heads

Threads Either Fine or Coarse Series

Diameter, D	Threads per inch		Width across flats, W	Height of head, H
	Coarse	Fine		
1/4	20	28	1/4	3/16
5/16	18	24	5/16	15/64
3/8	16	24	3/8	9/32
7/16	14	20	7/16	21/64
1/2	13	20	1/2	3/8
9/16	12	18	9/16	27/64
5/8	11	18	5/8	15/32
3/4	10	16	3/4	9/16
7/8	9	14	7/8	21/32
1	8	14	1	3/4
1 1/8	7	12	1 1/8	27/32
1 1/4	7	12	1 1/4	15/16
1 1/2	6	12	1 1/2	1 1/8

Dimensions of Slotted Head Cap Screws
Compiled from American Standard

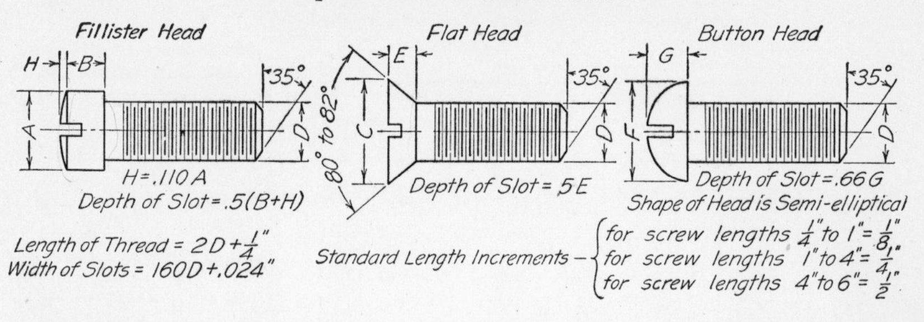

D Dia. of screw	1/4	5/16	3/8	7/16	1/2	9/16	5/8	3/4	7/8	1
A	3/8	7/16	9/16	5/8	3/4	13/16	7/8	1	1 1/8	1 5/16
B	11/64	13/64	1/4	19/64	21/64	3/8	27/64	1/2	19/32	21/32
C	1/2	5/8	3/4	13/16	7/8	1	1 1/8	1 3/8		
E	.146	.183	.220	.220	.220	.256	.293	.366		
F	7/16	9/16	5/8	3/4	13/16	15/16	1	1 1/4		
G (Nominal)	3/16	15/64	1/4	5/16	21/64	25/64	7/16	17/32		

Dimensions of Machine Screws
Compiled from Formulas of American Standards

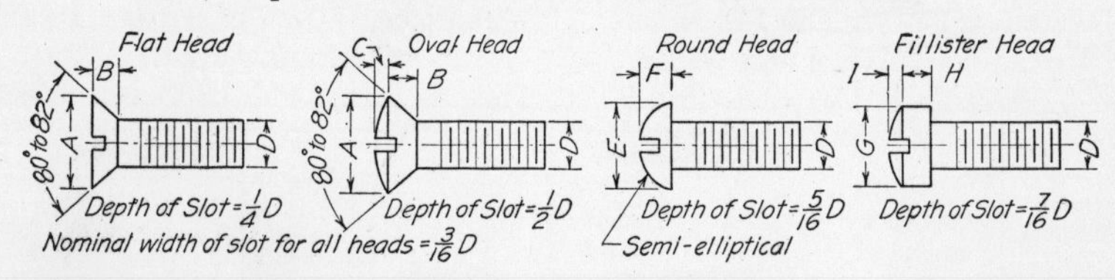

Nominal size	2	3	4	5	6	8	10	12	1/4	5/16	3/8
D = Diam.	.086	.099	.112	.125	.138	.164	.190	.216	.250	.3125	.375
Thds. per in. (coarse)	56	48	40	40	32	32	24	24	20	18	16
Thds. per in. (Fine)	64	56	48	....	40	36	32	28	28	24	24
A	.164	.190	.216	.242	.268	.320	.372	.424	.492	.618	.742
B	.046	.054	.061	.069	.076	.092	.107	.122	.142	.179	.215
C	.041	.048	.054	.061	.067	.080	.094	.107	.124	.156	.186
E	.154	.178	.202	.227	.250	.298	.346	.395	.458	.574	.689
F	.065	.073	.081	.089	.097	.113	.130	.146	.168	.207	.247
G	.132	.153	.175	.198	.217	.260	.303	.344	.402	.505	.606
H	.050	.058	.066	.075	.083	.099	.115	.132	.153	.193	.232
I	.023	.027	.030	.033	.037	.043	.049	.056	.064	.080	.096

Dimensions of Wood Screws
Compiled from ASA B18c 1930

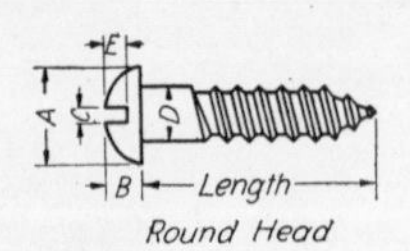

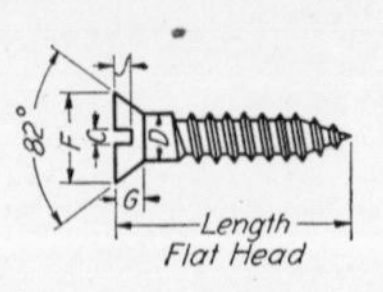

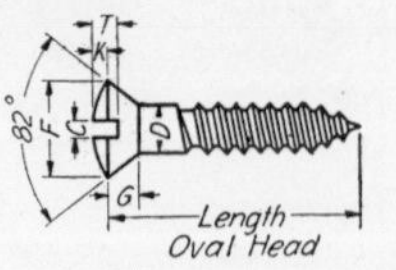

Screw No.	Diameter, *D*	*A*	*B*	*C*	*E*	*F*	*G*	*J*	*K*	*T*
0	.060	.106	.047	.025	.034	.112	.030	.012	.018	.027
1	.073	.130	.056	.027	.038	.138	.038	.015	.022	.034
2	.086	.154	.064	.030	.042	.164	.045	.019	.025	.041
3	.099	.178	.072	.032	.046	.190	.053	.022	.029	.047
4	.112	.202	.080	.034	.050	.216	.061	.025	.033	.054
5	.125	.228	.089	.037	.054	.242	.068	.028	.037	.061
6	.138	.250	.097	.039	.058	.268	.076	.031	.040	.067
7	.151	.274	.105	.041	.062	.294	.083	.034	.044	.073
8	.164	.298	.113	.043	.066	.320	.092	.037	.048	.080
9	.177	.322	.121	.045	.070	.346	.100	.040	.051	.086
10	.190	.346	.130	.048	.075	.371	.107	.043	.055	.093
11	.203	.370	.138	.050	.078	.398	.114	.046	.059	.100
12	.216	.395	.146	.052	.083	.424	.123	.049	.063	.116
14	.242	.443	.162	.057	.091	.476	.137	.056	.069	.120
16	.268	.491	.178	.061	.099	.528	.152	.062	.077	.133
18	.294	.539	.195	.066	.107	.580	.167	.068	.085	.146
20	.320	.587	.212	.070	.116	.632	.183	.074	.092	.159
24	.372	.683	.244	.079	.132	.736	.213	.087	.107	.186

Dimensions of Washers

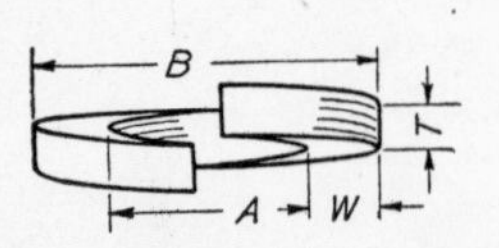

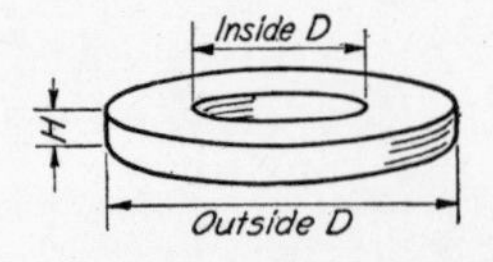

Nominal size	Lock washers[1] S.A.E. Standard						Plain washers S.A.E. Standard		
	A	*B*	*W*	*T*, Thickness			Inside diameter	Outside diameter	Thickness, *H*
				Regular	Light	Heavy			
1/4	0.265	0.453	3/32	1/16	3/64	5/64	9/32	5/8	1/16
5/16	0.328	0.578	1/8	1/16	3/64	3/32	11/32	11/16	1/16
3/8	0.390	0.640	1/8	3/32	1/16	1/8	13/32	13/16	1/16
7/16	0.453	0.767	5/32	1/8	1/16	5/32	15/32	15/16	1/16
1/2	0.515	0.859	11/64	1/8	1/16	11/64	17/32	1 1/16	3/32
9/16	0.593	0.968	3/16	1/8	3/32	3/16	19/32	1 3/16	3/32
5/8	0.655	1.062	13/64	5/32	3/32	13/64	21/32	1 5/16	3/32
11/16	0.718	1.155	7/32	3/16	1/8	7/32	23/32	1 3/8	3/32
3/4	0.780	1.280	1/4	3/16	1/8	1/4	13/16	1 1/2	1/8
7/8	0.905	1.437	17/64	3/16	5/32	17/64	15/16	1 3/4	1/8
1	1.030	1.655	5/16	1/4	3/16	5/16	1 1/16	2	1/8
1 1/8	1.155	1.905	3/8	1/4	3/16	5/16	1 3/16	2 1/4	1/8
1 1/4	1.280	2.155	7/16	1/4	3/16	5/16	1 5/16	2 1/2	5/32
1 3/8	1.405	2.280	7/16	5/16	1/4	3/8	1 7/16	2 3/4	5/32
1 1/2	1.530	2.530	1/2	5/16	1/4	3/8	1 9/16	3	5/32

[1] Lock-washer sizes should be designated by giving the nominal size, the width, and thickness in the order given, as 1 × 5/16 × 1/4.

Dimensions of Standard Steel and Wrought-iron-Pipe

Nominal inside diameter, inches	Actual outside diameter, inches	Actual inside diameter, inches	Internal area, square inches	Thr'ds per inch	Dist. pipe enters, inches	Actual inside diam., inches	
						Extra heavy	Double extra
1/8	.405	.270	.057	27	3/16	.205	
1/4	.540	.364	.104	18	9/32	.294	
3/8	.675	.494	.191	18	19/64	.421	
1/2	.840	.623	.304	14	3/8	.542	.244
3/4	1.05	.824	.533	14	13/32	.736	.422
1	1.315	1.048	.861	11 1/2	1/2	.951	.587
1 1/4	1.66	1.38	1.496	11 1/2	35/64	1.272	.885
1 1/2	1.9	1.61	2.036	11 1/2	9/16	1.494	1.088
2	2.375	2.067	3.356	11 1/2	37/64	1.933	1.491
2 1/2	2.875	2.468	4.78	8	7/8	2.315	1.755
3	3.5	3.067	7.383	8	15/16	2.892	2.284
3 1/2	4	3.548	9.887	8	1	3.358	2.716
4	4.5	4.026	12.73	8	1 1/16	3.818	3.136
4 1/2	5	4.508	15.961	8	1 7/64	4.28	3.564
5	5.563	5.045	19.986	8	1 5/32	4.813	4.063
6	6.625	6.065	28.89	8	1 1/4	5.751	4.875
7	7.625	7.023	38.738	8	1 3/8	6.625	5.875
8	8.625	7.982	50.027	8	1 7/16	7.625	6.875
9	9.625	8.937	62.72	8	1 9/16	8.625	
10	10.75	10.019	78.823	8	1 11/16	9.75	

American Standard Cast Iron Screwed Fittings

For Maximum Working Saturated Steam Pressure of 125 Lbs. per Sq. In.
Approved by American Standards Association, Dec. 1927

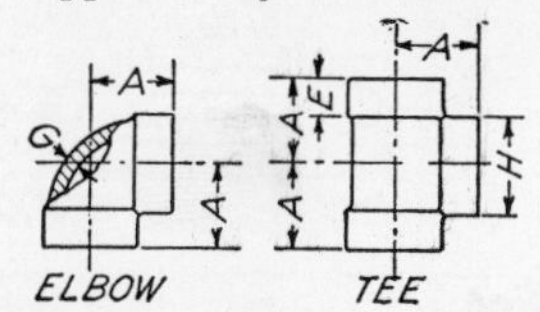

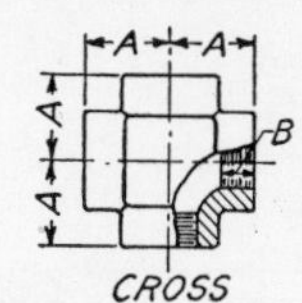

Nominal pipe size	A	B	C	E	F		G	H
		Min		Min	Min	Max	Min	Min
1/4	0.81	0.32	0.73	0.38	0.540	0.584	0.110	0.93
3/8	0.95	0.36	0.80	0.44	0.675	0.719	0.120	1.12
1/2	1.12	0.43	0.88	0.50	0.840	0.897	0.130	1.34
3/4	1.31	0.50	0.98	0.56	1.050	1.107	0.155	1.63
1	1.50	0.58	1.12	0.62	1.315	1.385	0.170	1.95
1 1/4	1.75	0.67	1.29	0.69	1.660	1.730	0.185	2.39
1 1/2	1.94	0.70	1.43	0.75	1.900	1.970	0.200	2.68
2	2.25	0.75	1.68	0.84	2.375	2.445	0.220	3.28
2 1/2	2.70	0.92	1.95	0.94	2.875	2.975	0.240	3.86
3	3.08	0.98	2.17	1.00	3.500	3.600	0.260	4.62
3 1/2	3.42	1.03	2.39	1.06	4.000	4.100	0.280	5.20
4	3.79	1.08	2.61	1.12	4.500	4.600	0.310	5.79
5	4.50	1.18	3.05	1.18	5.563	5.663	0.380	7.05
6	5.13	1.28	3.46	1.28	6.625	6.725	0.430	8.28
8	6.56	1.47	4.28	1.47	8.625	8.725	0.550	10.63
10	8.08	1.68	5.16	1.68	10.750	10.850	0.690	13.12
12	9.50	1.88	5.97	1.88	12.750	12.850	0.800	15.47

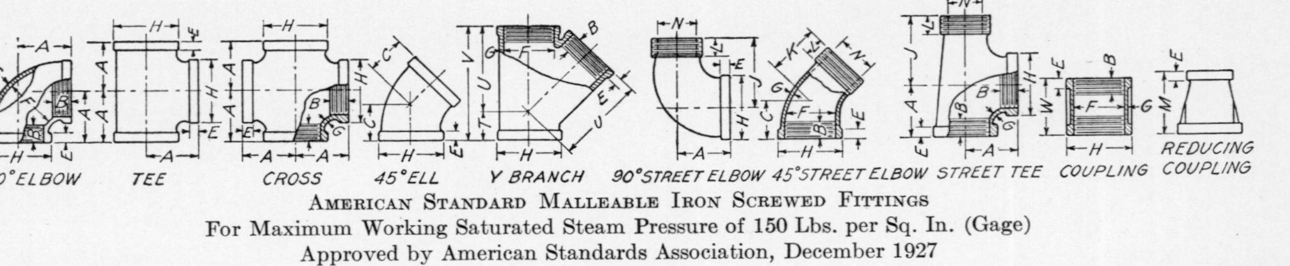

AMERICAN STANDARD MALLEABLE IRON SCREWED FITTINGS

For Maximum Working Saturated Steam Pressure of 150 Lbs. per Sq. In. (Gage)

Approved by American Standards Association, December 1927

Nominal pipe size	A	B	C	E	F		G	H	J	K	L	M	N	T	U	V	W	Thickness of ribs couplings
		Min.		Min.	Min.	Max.	Min.	Min.			Min.		Max.					
1/8	0.69	0.25	0.68	0.200	0.405	0.435	0.090	0.693	1.00	0.84	0.2638	....	0.15	0.34	0.97	1.31	0.96	0.090
1/4	0.81	0.32	0.73	0.215	0.540	0.584	0.095	0.844	1.19	0.94	0.4018	1.00	0.26	0.43	1.19	1.62	1.06	0.095
3/8	0.95	0.36	0.80	0.230	0.675	0.719	0.100	1.015	1.44	1.03	0.4078	1.13	0.37	0.50	1.43	1.93	1.16	0.100
1/2	1.12	0.43	0.88	0.249	0.840	0.897	0.105	1.197	1.63	1.15	0.5337	1.25	0.51	0.61	1.71	2.32	1.34	0.105
3/4	1.31	0.50	0.98	0.273	1.050	1.107	0.120	1.458	1.89	1.29	0.5457	1.44	0.69	0.72	2.05	2.77	1.52	0.120
1	1.50	0.58	1.12	0.302	1.315	1.385	0.134	1.771	2.14	1.47	0.6828	1.69	0.91	0.85	2.43	3.28	1.67	0.134
1 1/4	1.75	0.67	1.29	0.341	1.660	1.730	0.145	2.153	2.45	1.71	0.7068	2.06	1.19	1.02	2.92	3.94	1.93	0.145
1 1/2	1.94	0.70	1.43	0.368	1.900	1.970	0.155	2.427	2.69	1.88	0.7235	2.31	1.39	1.10	3.28	4.38	2.15	0.155
2	2.25	0.75	1.68	0.422	2.375	2.445	0.173	2.963	3.26	2.22	0.7565	2.81	1.79	1.24	3.93	5.17	2.53	0.173
2 1/2	2.70	0.92	1.95	0.478	2.875	2.975	0.210	3.589	3.86	2.57	1.1375	3.25	2.20	1.52	4.73	6.25	2.88	0.210
3	3.08	0.98	2.17	0.548	3.500	3.600	0.231	4.285	4.51	3.00	1.2000	3.69	2.78	1.71	5.55	7.26	3.18	0.231
3 1/2	3.42	1.03	2.39	0.604	4.000	4.100	0.248	4.843	5.09	3.35	1.2500	4.00	3.24	1.85	6.25	8.10	3.43	0.248
4	3.79	1.08	2.61	0.661	4.500	4.600	0.265	5.401	5.69	3.70	1.3000	4.38	3.70	2.01	6.97	8.98	3.69	0.265
5	4.50	1.18	3.05	0.780	5.563	5.663	0.300	6.583	6.86	4.44	1.4063	5.12	4.69	2.34	8.43	10.77	4.22	0.300
6	5.13	1.28	3.46	0.900	6.625	6.725	0.336	7.767	8.03	5.18	1.5125	5.86	5.67	2.66	9.81	12.47	4.75	0.336
8	....	1.47	....	1.125	8.625	8.725	0.403	9.995	....	....	1.7125	7.25	7.53	....	....	.....	5.75	0.403

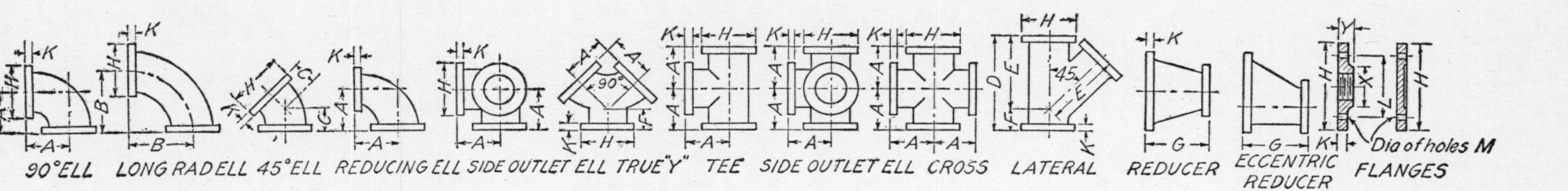

American Standard Cast Iron Pipe Flanges and Flanged Fittings
For Maximum Working Saturated Steam Pressure of 125 lbs. per sq. in. (Gage)
Approved by American Standards Association, February 1928

Nominal pipe size	A	B	C	D	E	F	G	H	K Min.	L	M	Number of bolts	Dia. of bolts	Length of bolts	X Min.	Y Min.
1	3½	5	1¾	7½	5¾	1¾	....	4¼	7/16	3⅛	⅝	4	½	1½	1 15/16	0.68
1¼	3¾	5½	2	8	6¼	1¾	....	4⅝	½	3½	⅝	4	½	1½	2 5/16	0.76
1½	4	6	2¼	9	7	2	....	5	9/16	3⅞	⅝	4	½	1¾	2 9/16	0.87
2	4½	6½	2½	10½	8	2½	5	6	⅝	4¾	¾	4	⅝	2	3 1/16	1.09
2½	5	7	3	12	9½	2½	5½	7	11/16	5½	¾	4	⅝	2¼	3 9/16	1.14
3	5½	7¾	3	13	10	3	6	7½	¾	6	¾	4	⅝	2¼	4 ¼	1.20
3½	6	8½	3½	14½	11½	3	6½	8½	13/16	7	¾	8	⅝	2½	4 13/16	1.25
4	6½	9	4	15	12	3	7	9	15/16	7½	¾	8	⅝	2¾	5 5/16	1.30
5	7½	10¼	4½	17	13½	3½	8	10	15/16	8½	⅞	8	¾	2¾	6 7/16	1.41
6	8	11½	5	18	14½	3½	9	11	1	9½	⅞	8	¾	3	7 9/16	1.51
8	9	14	5½	22	17½	4½	11	13½	1 ⅛	11¾	⅞	8	¾	3¼	9 11/16	1.71
10	11	16½	6½	25½	20½	5	12	16	1 3/16	14¼	1	12	⅞	3½	11 15/16	1.93
12	12	19	7½	30	24½	5½	14	19	1 ¼	17	1	12	⅞	3½	14 1/16	2.13

TABLE OF LIMITS FOR CYLINDRICAL FITS
Compiled from American Tentative Standard A.S.A. B4a.

Size		Limits															
		Class 1 Loose fit				Class 2 Free fit				Class 3 Medium fit				Class 4 Snug fit			
From	Up to and incl.	Hole or external member		Shaft or internal member		Hole or external member		Shaft or internal member		Hole or external member		Shaft or internal member		Hole or external member		Shaft or internal member	
		+		−	−	+		−	−	+		−	−	+			−
0	3/16	0.001	0.000	0.001	0.002	0.0007	0.0000	0.0004	0.0011	0.0004	0.0000	0.0002	0.0006	0.0003	0.0000	0.0000	0.0002
3/16	5/16	0.002	0.000	0.001	0.003	0.0008	0.0000	0.0006	0.0014	0.0005	0.0000	0.0004	0.0009	0.0004	0.0000	0.0000	0.0003
5/16	7/16	0.002	0.000	0.001	0.003	0.0009	0.0000	0.0007	0.0016	0.0006	0.0000	0.0005	0.0011	0.0004	0.0000	0.0000	0.0003
7/16	9/16	0.002	0.000	0.002	0.004	0.0010	0.0000	0.0009	0.0019	0.0006	0.0000	0.0006	0.0012	0.0005	0.0000	0.0000	0.0003
9/16	11/16	0.002	0.000	0.002	0.004	0.0011	0.0000	0.0010	0.0021	0.0007	0.0000	0.0007	0.0014	0.0005	0.0000	0.0000	0.0003
11/16	13/16	0.002	0.000	0.002	0.004	0.0012	0.0000	0.0012	0.0024	0.0007	0.0000	0.0007	0.0014	0.0005	0.0000	0.0000	0.0004
13/16	15/16	0.002	0.000	0.002	0.004	0.0012	0.0000	0.0013	0.0025	0.0008	0.0000	0.0008	0.0016	0.0006	0.0000	0.0000	0.0004
15/16	1 1/16	0.003	0.000	0.003	0.006	0.0013	0.0000	0.0014	0.0027	0.0008	0.0000	0.0009	0.0017	0.0006	0.0000	0.0000	0.0004
1 1/16	1 3/16	0.003	0.000	0.003	0.006	0.0014	0.0000	0.0015	0.0029	0.0008	0.0000	0.0010	0.0018	0.0006	0.0000	0.0000	0.0004
1 3/16	1 3/8	0.003	0.000	0.003	0.006	0.0014	0.0000	0.0016	0.0030	0.0009	0.0000	0.0010	0.0019	0.0006	0.0000	0.0000	0.0004
1 3/8	1 5/8	0.003	0.000	0.003	0.006	0.0015	0.0000	0.0018	0.0033	0.0009	0.0000	0.0012	0.0021	0.0007	0.0000	0.0000	0.0005
1 5/8	1 7/8	0.003	0.000	0.004	0.007	0.0016	0.0000	0.0020	0.0036	0.0010	0.0000	0.0013	0.0023	0.0007	0.0000	0.0000	0.0005
1 7/8	2 1/8	0.003	0.000	0.004	0.007	0.0016	0.0000	0.0022	0.0038	0.0010	0.0000	0.0014	0.0024	0.0008	0.0000	0.0000	0.0005
2 1/8	2 3/8	0.003	0.000	0.004	0.007	0.0017	0.0000	0.0024	0.0041	0.0010	0.0000	0.0015	0.0025	0.0008	0.0000	0.0000	0.0005
2 3/8	2 3/4	0.003	0.000	0.005	0.008	0.0018	0.0000	0.0026	0.0044	0.0011	0.0000	0.0017	0.0028	0.0008	0.0000	0.0000	0.0005
2 3/4	3 1/4	0.004	0.000	0.005	0.009	0.0019	0.0000	0.0029	0.0048	0.0012	0.0000	0.0019	0.0031	0.0009	0.0000	0.0000	0.0006
3 1/4	3 3/4	0.004	0.000	0.006	0.010	0.0020	0.0000	0.0032	0.0052	0.0012	0.0000	0.0021	0.0033	0.0009	0.0000	0.0000	0.0006
3 3/4	4 1/4	0.004	0.000	0.006	0.010	0.0021	0.0000	0.0035	0.0056	0.0013	0.0000	0.0023	0.0036	0.0010	0.0000	0.0000	0.0006
4 1/4	4 3/4	0.004	0.000	0.007	0.011	0.0021	0.0000	0.0038	0.0059	0.0013	0.0000	0.0025	0.0038	0.0010	0.0000	0.0000	0.0007
4 3/4	5 1/2	0.004	0.000	0.007	0.011	0.0022	0.0000	0.0041	0.0063	0.0014	0.0000	0.0026	0.0040	0.0010	0.0000	0.0000	0.0007
5 1/2	6 1/2	0.005	0.000	0.008	0.013	0.0024	0.0000	0.0046	0.0070	0.0015	0.0000	0.0030	0.0045	0.0011	0.0000	0.0000	0.0007
6 1/2	7 1/2	0.005	0.000	0.009	0.014	0.0025	0.0000	0.0051	0.0076	0.0015	0.0000	0.0033	0.0048	0.0011	0.0000	0.0000	0.0008
7 1/2	8 1/2	0.005	0.000	0.010	0.015	0.0026	0.0000	0.0056	0.0082	0.0016	0.0000	0.0036	0.0052	0.0012	0.0000	0.0000	0.0008

TABLE OF LIMITS FOR CYLINDRICAL FITS
Compiled from American Tentative Standard A.S.A. B4a

Size		Limits															
		Class 5 Wringing fit				Class 6 Tight fit				Class 7 Medium force fit				Class 8 Heavy force and shrink fit			
From	Up to and incl.	Hole or external member		Shaft or internal member		Hole or external member		Shaft or internal member		Hole or external member		Shaft or internal member		Hole or external member		Shaft or internal member	
		+		+		+		+	+	+		+	+	+		+	+
0	3/16	0.0003	0.0000	0.0002	0.0000	0.0003	0.0000	0.0003	0.0000	0.0003	0.0000	0.0004	0.0001	0.0003	0.0000	0.0004	0.0001
3/16	5/16	0.0004	0.0000	0.0003	0.0000	0.0004	0.0000	0.0005	0.0001	0.0004	0.0000	0.0005	0.0001	0.0004	0.0000	0.0007	0.0003
5/16	7/16	0.0004	0.0000	0.0003	0.0000	0.0004	0.0000	0.0005	0.0001	0.0004	0.0000	0.0006	0.0002	0.0004	0.0000	0.0008	0.0004
7/16	9/16	0.0005	0.0000	0.0003	0.0000	0.0005	0.0000	0.0006	0.0001	0.0005	0.0000	0.0008	0.0003	0.0005	0.0000	0.0010	0.0005
9/16	11/16	0.0005	0.0000	0.0003	0.0000	0.0005	0.0000	0.0007	0.0002	0.0005	0.0000	0.0008	0.0003	0.0005	0.0000	0.0011	0.0006
11/16	13/16	0.0005	0.0000	0.0004	0.0000	0.0005	0.0000	0.0007	0.0002	0.0005	0.0000	0.0009	0.0004	0.0005	0.0000	0.0013	0.0008
13/16	15/16	0.0006	0.0000	0.0004	0.0000	0.0006	0.0000	0.0008	0.0002	0.0006	0.0000	0.0010	0.0004	0.0006	0.0000	0.0015	0.0009
15/16	1 1/16	0.0006	0.0000	0.0004	0.0000	0.0006	0.0000	0.0009	0.0003	0.0006	0.0000	0.0011	0.0005	0.0006	0.0000	0.0016	0.0010
1 1/16	1 3/16	0.0006	0.0000	0.0004	0.0000	0.0006	0.0000	0.0009	0.0003	0.0006	0.0000	0.0012	0.0006	0.0006	0.0000	0.0017	0.0011
1 3/16	1 3/8	0.0006	0.0000	0.0004	0.0000	0.0006	0.0000	0.0009	0.0003	0.0006	0.0000	0.0012	0.0006	0.0006	0.0000	0.0019	0.0013
1 3/8	1 5/8	0.0007	0.0000	0.0005	0.0000	0.0007	0.0000	0.0011	0.0004	0.0007	0.0000	0.0015	0.0008	0.0007	0.0000	0.0022	0.0015
1 5/8	1 7/8	0.0007	0.0000	0.0005	0.0000	0.0007	0.0000	0.0011	0.0004	0.0007	0.0000	0.0016	0.0009	0.0007	0.0000	0.0025	0.0018
1 7/8	2 1/8	0.0008	0.0000	0.0005	0.0000	0.0008	0.0000	0.0013	0.0005	0.0008	0.0000	0.0018	0.0010	0.0008	0.0000	0.0028	0.0020
2 1/8	2 3/8	0.0008	0.0000	0.0005	0.0000	0.0008	0.0000	0.0014	0.0006	0.0008	0.0000	0.0019	0.0011	0.0008	0.0000	0.0031	0.0023
2 3/8	2 3/4	0.0008	0.0000	0.0005	0.0000	0.0008	0.0000	0.0014	0.0006	0.0008	0.0000	0.0021	0.0013	0.0008	0.0000	0.0033	0.0025
2 3/4	3 1/4	0.0009	0.0000	0.0006	0.0000	0.0009	0.0000	0.0017	0.0008	0.0009	0.0000	0.0024	0.0015	0.0009	0.0000	0.0039	0.0030
3 1/4	3 3/4	0.0009	0.0000	0.0006	0.0000	0.0009	0.0000	0.0018	0.0009	0.0009	0.0000	0.0027	0.0018	0.0009	0.0000	0.0044	0.0035
3 3/4	4 1/4	0.0010	0.0000	0.0006	0.0000	0.0010	0.0000	0.0020	0.0010	0.0010	0.0000	0.0030	0.0020	0.0010	0.0000	0.0050	0.0040
4 1/4	4 3/4	0.0010	0.0000	0.0007	0.0000	0.0010	0.0000	0.0021	0.0011	0.0010	0.0000	0.0033	0.0023	0.0010	0.0000	0.0055	0.0045
4 3/4	5 1/2	0.0010	0.0000	0.0007	0.0000	0.0010	0.0000	0.0023	0.0013	0.0010	0.0000	0.0035	0.0025	0.0010	0.0000	0.0060	0.0050
5 1/2	6 1/2	0.0011	0.0000	0.0007	0.0000	0.0011	0.0000	0.0026	0.0015	0.0011	0.0000	0.0041	0.0030	0.0011	0.0000	0.0071	0.0060
6 1/2	7 1/2	0.0011	0.0000	0.0008	0.0000	0.0011	0.0000	0.0029	0.0018	0.0011	0.0000	0.0046	0.0035	0.0011	0.0000	0.0081	0.0070
7 1/2	8 1/2	0.0012	0.0000	0.0008	0.0000	0.0012	0.0000	0.0032	0.0020	0.0012	0.0000	0.0052	0.0040	0.0012	0.0000	0.0092	0.0080

Widths and Heights of Standard Square and Flat Stock Keys with Corresponding Shaft Diameters

Approved by American Standards Association

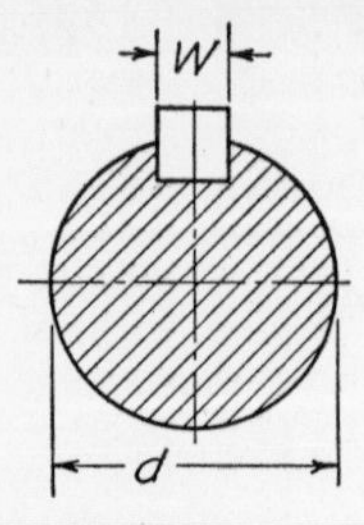

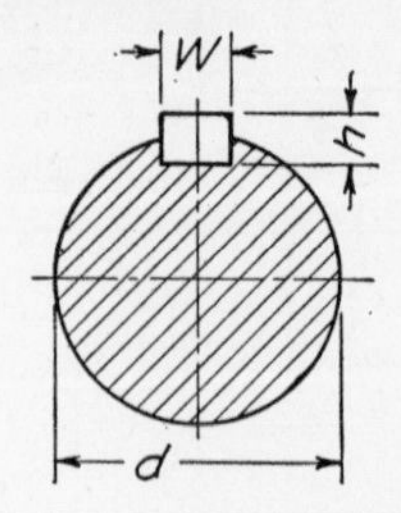

Shaft dia. d (inclusive)	Square stock keys—W	Flat stock keys W × L	Shaft dia. d (inclusive)	Square stock keys—W	Flat stock keys W × L
1/2 to 9/16	1/8	1/8 × 3/32	2 7/8 to 3 1/4	3/4	3/4 × 1/2
5/8 to 7/8	3/16	3/16 × 1/8	3 3/8 to 3 3/4	7/8	7/8 × 5/8
15/16 to 1 1/4	1/4	1/4 × 3/16	3 7/8 to 4 1/2	1	1 × 3/4
1 5/16 to 1 3/4	3/8	3/8 × 1/4	4 3/4 to 5 1/2	1 1/4	1 1/4 × 7/8
1 13/16 to 2 1/4	1/2	1/2 × 3/8	5 3/4 to 6	1 1/2	1 1/2 × 1
2 5/16 to 2 3/4	5/8	5/8 × 7/16			

Dimensions of Standard Gib Head Keys, Square and Flat

Approved by American Standards Association

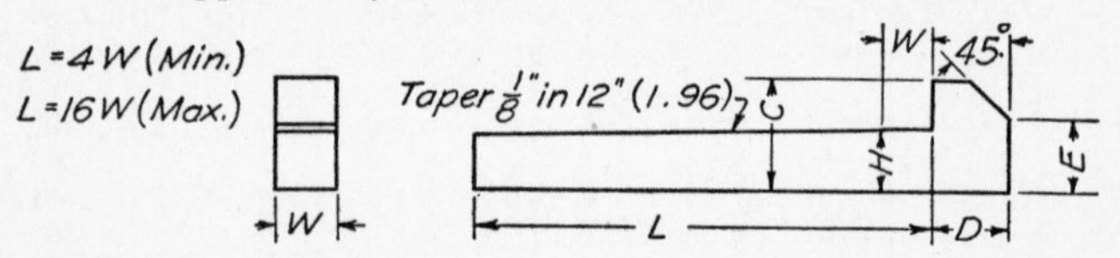

Dias. of shafts (incl.)	Square type					Flat type				
	Key		Gib head			Key		Gib head		
	W	H	C	D	E	W	H	C	D	E
1/2 to 9/16	1/8	1/8	1/4	7/32	5/32	1/8	3/32	3/16	1/8	1/8
5/8 to 7/8	3/16	3/16	5/16	9/32	7/32	3/16	1/8	1/4	3/16	5/32
15/16 to 1 1/4	1/4	1/4	7/16	11/32	11/32	1/4	3/16	5/16	1/4	3/16
1 5/16 to 1 3/4	3/8	3/8	11/16	15/32	15/32	3/8	1/4	7/16	3/8	5/16
1 13/16 to 2 1/4	1/2	1/2	7/8	19/32	5/8	1/2	3/8	5/8	1/2	7/16
2 5/16 to 2 3/4	5/8	5/8	1 1/16	23/32	3/4	5/8	7/16	3/4	5/8	1/2
2 7/8 to 3 1/4	3/4	3/4	1 1/4	7/8	7/8	3/4	1/2	7/8	3/4	5/8
3 3/8 to 3 3/4	7/8	7/8	1 1/2	1	1	7/8	5/8	1 1/16	7/8	3/4
3 7/8 to 4 1/2	1	1	1 3/4	1 3/16	1 3/16	1	3/4	1 1/4	1	13/16
4 3/4 to 5 1/2	1 1/4	1 1/4	2	1 7/16	1 7/16	1 1/4	7/8	1 1/2	1 1/4	1
5 3/4 to 6	1 1/2	1 1/2	2 1/2	1 3/4	1 3/4	1 1/2	1	1 3/4	1 1/2	1 1/4

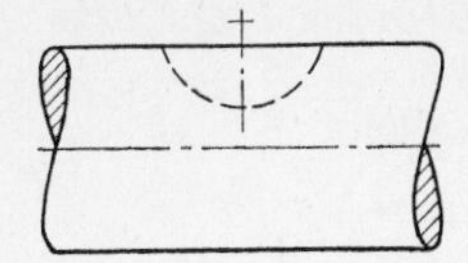
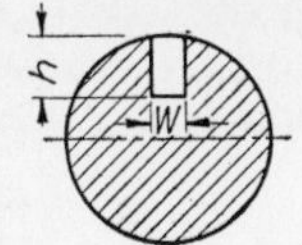

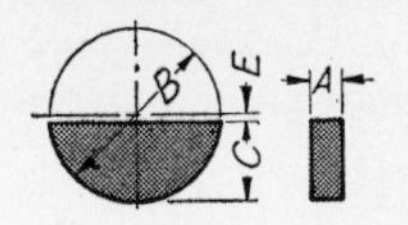

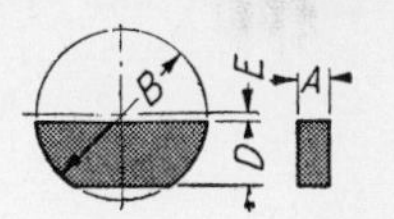

Woodruff Key and Key Slot Dimensions[1]

Key[2] No.	Nominal size	Maximum width of key	Maximum diameter of key	Maximum height of key		Distance below center	Key slot	
		A	*B*	*C*	*D*	*E*	*W*	*H*
204	1/16 × 1/2	0.0635	0.500	0.203	0.194	3/64	0.0630	0.1718
304	3/32 × 1/2	0.0948	0.500	0.203	0.194	3/64	0.0943	0.1561
305	3/32 × 5/8	0.0948	0.625	0.250	0.240	1/16	0.0943	0.2031
404	1/8 × 1/2	0.1260	0.500	0.203	0.194	3/64	0.1255	0.1405
405	1/8 × 5/8	0.1260	0.625	0.250	0.240	1/16	0.1255	0.1875
406	1/8 × 3/4	0.1260	0.750	0.313	0.303	1/16	0.1255	0.2505
505	5/32 × 5/8	0.1573	0.625	0.250	0.240	1/16	0.1568	0.1719
506	5/32 × 3/4	0.1573	0.750	0.313	0.303	1/16	0.1568	0.2349
507	5/32 × 7/8	0.1573	0.875	0.375	0.365	1/16	0.1568	0.2969
606	3/16 × 3/4	0.1885	0.750	0.313	0.303	1/16	0.1880	0.2193
607	3/16 × 7/8	0.1885	0.875	0.375	0.365	1/16	0.1880	0.2813
608	3/16 × 1	0.1885	1.000	0.438	0.428	1/16	0.1880	0.3443
609	3/16 × 1 1/8	0.1885	1.125	0.484	0.475	5/64	0.1880	0.3903
807	1/4 × 7/8	0.2510	0.875	0.375	0.365	1/16	0.2505	0.2500
808	1/4 × 1	0.2510	1.000	0.438	0.428	1/16	0.2505	0.3130
809	1/4 × 1 1/8	0.2510	1.125	0.484	0.475	5/64	0.2505	0.3590
810	1/4 × 1 1/4	0.2510	1.250	0.547	0.537	5/64	0.2505	0.4220
811	1/4 × 1 3/8	0.2510	1.375	0.594	0.584	3/32	0.2505	0.4690
812	1/4 × 1 1/2	0.2510	1.500	0.641	0.631	7/64	0.2505	0.5160
1008	5/16 × 1	0.3135	1.000	0.438	0.428	1/16	0.3130	0.2818
1009	5/16 × 1 1/8	0.3135	1.125	0.484	0.475	5/64	0.3130	0.3278
1010	5/16 × 1 1/4	0.3135	1.250	0.547	0.537	5/64	0.3130	0.3908
1011	5/16 × 1 3/8	0.3135	1.375	0.594	0.584	3/32	0.3130	0.4378
1012	5/16 × 1 1/2	0.3135	1.500	0.641	0.631	7/64	0.3130	0.4848
1210	3/8 × 1 1/4	0.3760	1.250	0.547	0.537	5/64	0.3755	0.3595
1211	3/8 × 1 3/8	0.3760	1.375	0.594	0.584	3/32	0.3755	0.4065
1212	3/8 × 1 1/2	0.3760	1.500	0.641	0.631	7/64	0.3755	0.4535

[1] From A.S.A B17f, 1930.

[2] Key numbers indicate the nominal key dimensions. The last two digits give the nominal diameter (B) in eighths of an inch and the digits preceding the last two give the nominal width (A) in thirty-seconds of an inch. Thus, 204 indicates a key 2/32 by 4/8, or 1/16 by 1/2 inch.

Dimensions of Pratt and Whitney Keys

Pratt and Whitney round-end feather keys are in extensive use. The length L may vary but should never be less than $2W$.

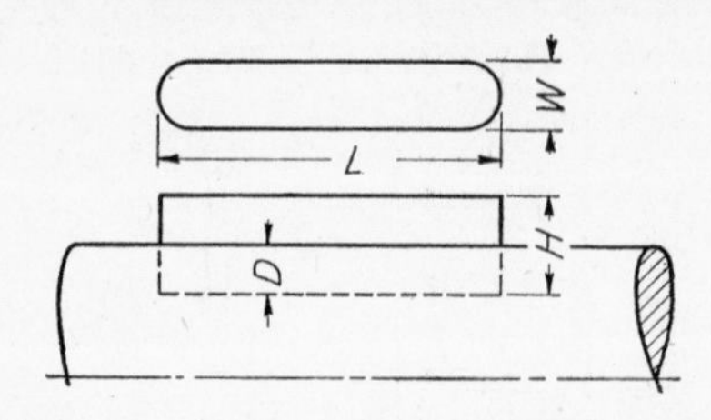

Key No.	L	W	H	D	Key No.	L	W	H	D
1	1/2	1/16	3/32	1/16	22	1 3/8	1/4	3/8	1/4
2	1/2	3/32	9/64	3/32	23	1 3/8	5/16	15/32	5/16
3	1/2	1/8	3/16	1/8	F	1 3/8	3/8	9/16	3/8
4	5/8	3/32	9/64	3/32	24	1 1/2	1/4	3/8	1/4
5	5/8	1/8	3/16	1/8	25	1 1/2	5/16	15/32	5/16
6	5/8	5/32	15/64	5/32	G	1 1/2	3/8	9/16	3/8
7	3/4	1/8	3/16	1/8	51	1 3/4	1/4	3/8	1/4
8	3/4	5/32	15/64	5/32	52	1 3/4	5/16	15/32	5/16
9	3/4	3/16	9/32	3/16	53	1 3/4	3/8	9/16	3/8
10	7/8	5/32	15/64	5/32	26	2	3/16	9/32	3/16
11	7/8	3/16	9/32	3/16	27	2	1/4	3/8	1/4
12	7/8	7/32	21/64	7/32	28	2	5/16	15/32	5/16
A	7/8	1/4	3/8	1/4	29	2	3/8	9/16	3/8
13	1	3/16	9/32	3/16	54	2 1/4	1/4	3/8	1/4
14	1	7/32	21/64	7/32	55	2 1/4	5/16	15/32	5/16
15	1	1/4	3/8	1/4	56	2 1/4	3/8	9/16	3/8
B	1	5/16	15/32	5/16	57	2 1/4	7/16	21/32	7/16
16	1 1/8	3/16	9/32	3/16	58	2 1/2	5/16	15/32	5/16
17	1 1/8	7/32	21/64	7/32	59	2 1/2	3/8	9/16	3/8
18	1 1/8	1/4	3/8	1/4	60	2 1/2	7/16	21/32	7/16
C	1 1/8	5/16	15/32	5/16	61	2 1/2	1/2	3/4	1/2
19	1 1/4	3/16	9/32	3/16	30	3	3/8	9/16	3/8
20	1 1/4	7/32	21/64	7/32	31	3	7/16	21/32	7/16
21	1 1/4	1/4	3/8	1/4	32	3	1/2	3/4	1/2
D	1 1/4	5/16	15/32	5/16	33	3	9/16	27/32	9/16
E	1 1/4	3/8	9/16	3/8	34	3	5/8	15/16	5/8

Wire & Sheet-metal Gages

Dimensions in Decimal Parts of an Inch

Number of gage	1 American or Brown & Sharpe	2 Washburn & Moen or American Steel & Wire Co.	3 Birmingham or Stubs iron wire	4 Music wire	5 Twist drill sizes	6 Imperial wire gage	7 U. S. Std. for plate	Number of gage
0000000	.....	.4900	....	....	.....	.5000	.5000	0000000
000000	.5800	.4615	....	.004	.....	.4640	.4688	000000
00000	.5165	.4305	.500	.005	.....	.4320	.4375	00000
0000	.4600	.3938	.454	.006	.....	.4000	.4063	0000
000	.4096	.3625	.425	.007	.....	.3720	.3750	000
00	.3648	.3310	.380	.008	.....	.3480	.3438	00
0	.3249	.3065	.340	.009	.....	.3240	.3125	0
1	.2893	.2830	.300	.010	.2280	.3000	.2813	1
2	.2576	.2625	.284	.011	.2210	.2760	.2656	2
3	.2294	.2437	.259	.012	.2130	.2520	.2500	3
4	.2043	.2253	.238	.013	.2090	.2320	.2344	4
5	.1819	.2070	.220	.014	.2055	.2120	.2188	5
6	.1620	.1920	.203	.016	.2040	.1920	.2031	6
7	.1443	.1770	.180	.018	.2010	.1760	.1875	7
8	.1285	.1620	.165	.020	.1990	.1600	.1719	8
9	.1144	.1483	.148	.022	.1960	.1440	.1563	9
10	.1019	.1350	.134	.024	.1935	.1280	.1406	10
11	.0907	.1205	.120	.026	.1910	.1160	.1250	11
12	.0808	.1055	.109	.029	.1890	.1040	.1094	12
13	.0720	.0915	.095	.031	.1850	.0920	.0938	13
14	.0641	.0800	.083	.033	.1820	.0800	.0781	14
15	.0571	.0720	.072	.035	.1800	.0720	.0703	15
16	.0508	.0625	.065	.037	.1770	.0640	.0625	16
17	.0453	.0540	.058	.039	.1730	.0560	.0563	17
18	.0403	.0475	.049	.041	.1695	.0480	.0500	18
19	.0359	.0410	.042	.043	.1660	.0400	.0438	19
20	.0320	.0348	.035	.045	.1610	.0360	.0375	20
21	.0285	.0317	.032	.047	.1590	.0320	.0344	21
22	.0253	.0286	.028	.049	.1570	.0280	.0313	22
23	.0226	.0258	.025	.051	.1540	.0240	.0281	23
24	.0201	.0230	.022	.055	.1520	.0220	.0250	24
25	.0179	.0204	.020	.059	.1495	.0200	.0219	25
26	.0159	.0181	.018	.063	.1470	.0180	.0188	26
27	.0142	.0173	.016	.067	.1440	.0164	.0172	27
28	.0126	.0162	.014	.071	.1405	.0148	.0156	28
29	.0113	.0150	.013	.075	.1360	.0136	.0141	29
30	.0100	.0140	.012	.080	.1285	.0124	.0125	30
31	.0089	.0132	.010	.085	.1200	.0116	.0109	31
32	.0080	.0128	.009	.090	.1160	.0108	.0102	32
33	.0071	.0118	.008	.095	.1130	.0100	.0094	33
34	.0063	.0104	.007	.100	.1110	.0092	.0086	34
35	.0056	.0095	.005	.106	.1100	.0084	.0078	35
36	.0050	.0090	.004	.112	.1065	.0076	.0070	36
37	.0045	.0085	....	.118	.1040	.0068	.0066	37
38	.0040	.0080	....	.124	.1015	.0060	.0063	38
39	.0035	.0075	....	.130	.0995	.0052	.....	39
40	.0031	.0070	....	.138	.0980	.0048	.....	40

1. Recognized standard in U. S. for wire and sheet metal of copper and other metals except steel and iron.
2. Recognized standard for steel and iron wire. Called the U. S. Steel Wire Gage.
3. Formerly much used, now nearly obsolete.
4. American Steel & Wire Company's music (or piano) wire gage. Recommended by U. S. Bureau of Standards.
5. Known as the "Manufacturers' Standard."
6. Official British Standard.
7. Legalized U. S. Standard for iron and steel plate, although plate is now always specified by its thickness in decimals of an inch.

A committee of the American Standards Association is at present working on the "standardization of a method of designating the diameter of metal and metal alloy wire . . . and the establishment of standard series of nominal sizes . . ."

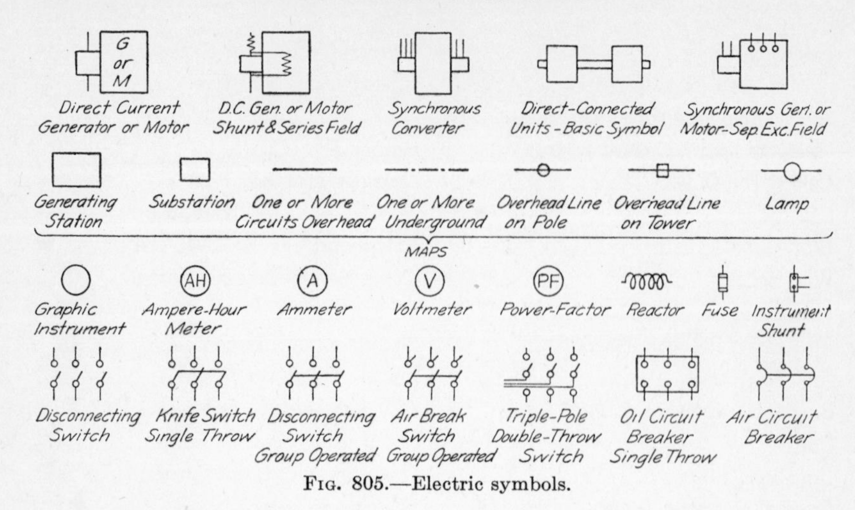

Fig. 805.—Electric symbols.

Electric Symbols.—Symbols for the diagrammatic representation of electric apparatus and construction have not been fully standardized. Figure 805 gives the basic symbols which are in general use in electrical drawing.

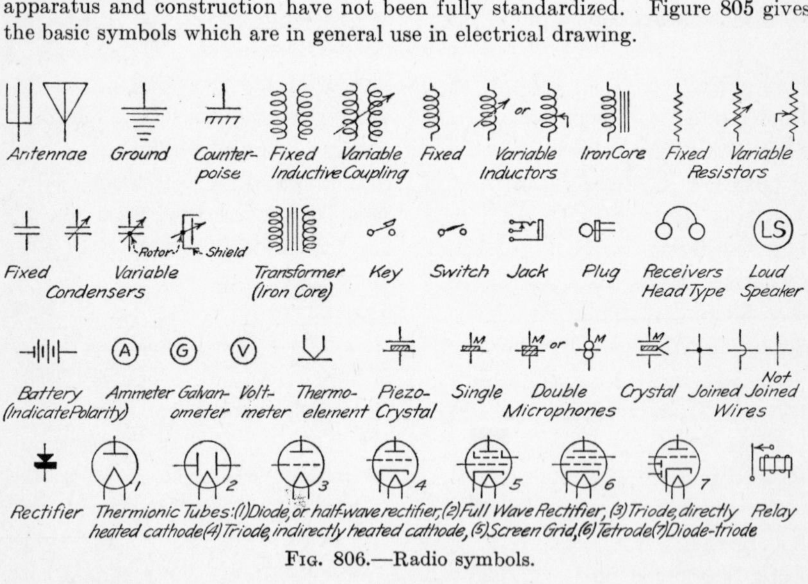

Fig. 806.—Radio symbols.

Radio Symbols.—Figure 806 gives the radio symbols in present general use. Most of these are approved as American Tentative Standard but certain symbols have not yet been approved because of conflicts with those for the same device as used in the electric power and electric traction fields.

For patent drawings the set of symbols specified in the "Rules of Practice" should be followed.

The American Standard wiring symbols, Fig. 807 are in universal use by architects and electricians.

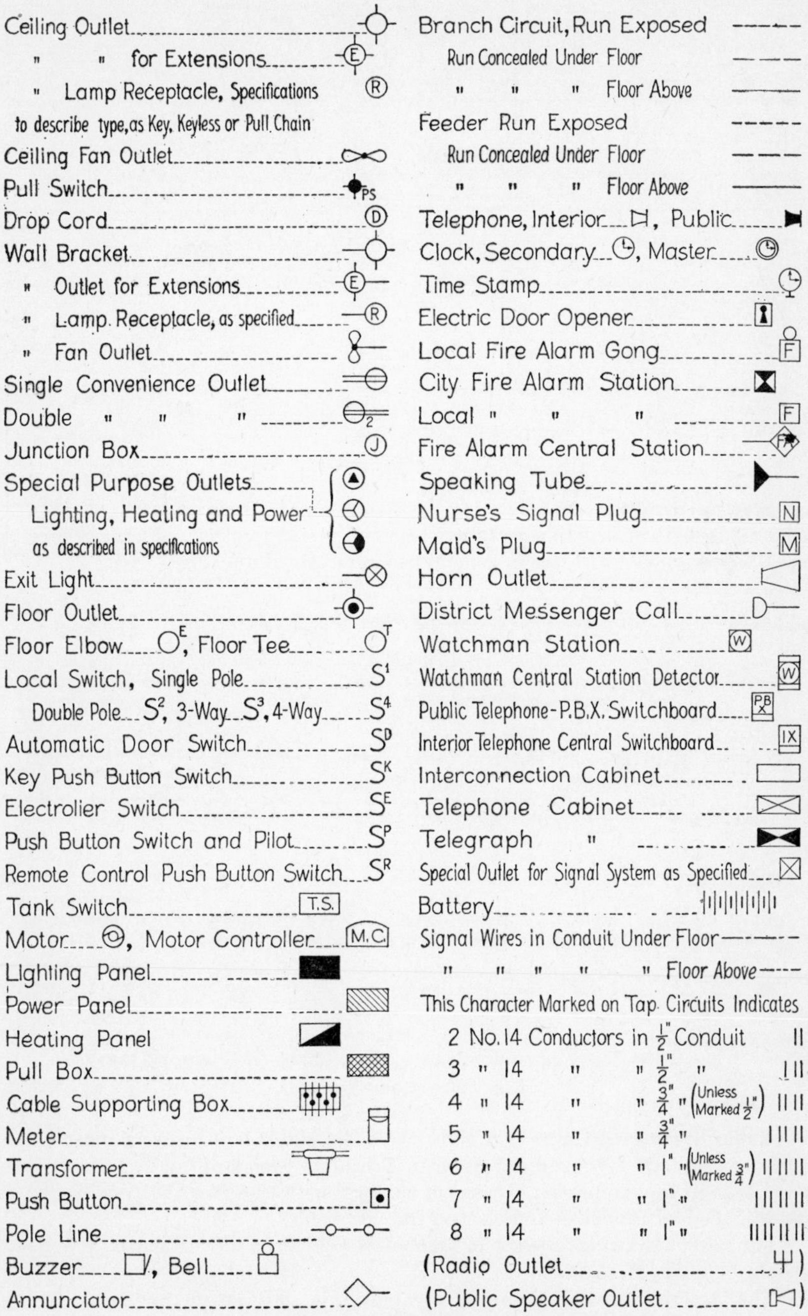

Ceiling Outlet
" " for Extensions (E)
" Lamp Receptacle, Specifications (R)
to describe type, as Key, Keyless or Pull Chain
Ceiling Fan Outlet
Pull Switch (PS)
Drop Cord (D)
Wall Bracket
" Outlet for Extensions (E)
" Lamp Receptacle, as specified (R)
" Fan Outlet
Single Convenience Outlet
Double " " " (2)
Junction Box (J)
Special Purpose Outlets
Lighting, Heating and Power
as described in specifications
Exit Light
Floor Outlet
Floor Elbow O^E, Floor Tee O^T
Local Switch, Single Pole S^1
Double Pole S^2, 3-Way S^3, 4-Way S^4
Automatic Door Switch S^D
Key Push Button Switch S^K
Electrolier Switch S^E
Push Button Switch and Pilot S^P
Remote Control Push Button Switch S^R
Tank Switch (T.S.)
Motor, Motor Controller (M.C.)
Lighting Panel
Power Panel
Heating Panel
Pull Box
Cable Supporting Box
Meter
Transformer
Push Button
Pole Line
Buzzer, Bell
Annunciator

Branch Circuit, Run Exposed
Run Concealed Under Floor
" " " Floor Above
Feeder Run Exposed
Run Concealed Under Floor
" " " Floor Above
Telephone, Interior, Public
Clock, Secondary, Master
Time Stamp
Electric Door Opener
Local Fire Alarm Gong (F)
City Fire Alarm Station
Local " " " (F)
Fire Alarm Central Station (FA)
Speaking Tube
Nurse's Signal Plug (N)
Maid's Plug (M)
Horn Outlet
District Messenger Call
Watchman Station (W)
Watchman Central Station Detector (W)
Public Telephone-P.B.X. Switchboard (PBX)
Interior Telephone Central Switchboard (IX)
Interconnection Cabinet
Telephone Cabinet
Telegraph "
Special Outlet for Signal System as Specified
Battery
Signal Wires in Conduit Under Floor
" " " " " Floor Above
This Character Marked on Tap Circuits Indicates
2 No. 14 Conductors in $\frac{1}{2}''$ Conduit
3 " 14 " " $\frac{1}{2}''$ "
4 " 14 " " $\frac{3}{4}''$ " (Unless Marked $\frac{1}{2}''$)
5 " 14 " " $\frac{3}{4}''$ "
6 " 14 " " 1" " (Unless Marked $\frac{3}{4}''$)
7 " 14 " " 1" "
8 " 14 " " 1" "
(Radio Outlet)
(Public Speaker Outlet)

Fig. 807.—American Standard wiring symbols.

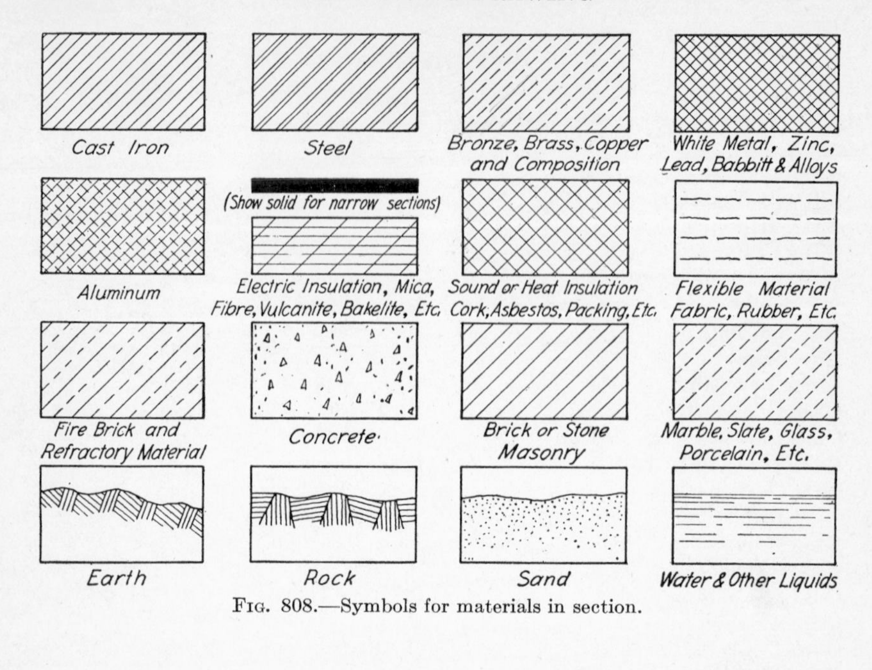

Fig. 808.—Symbols for materials in section.

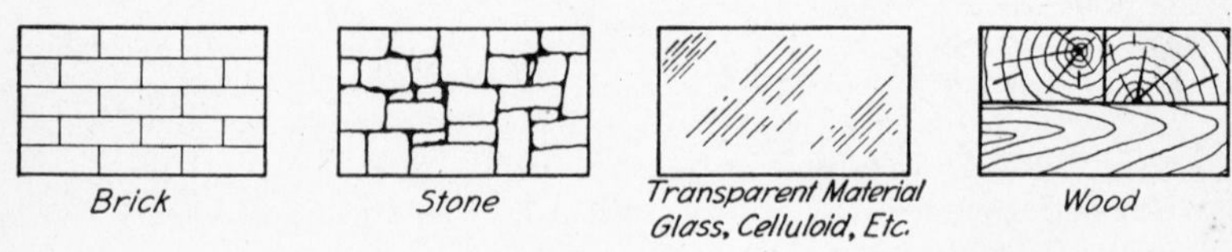

Fig. 809.—Symbols for materials exterior.

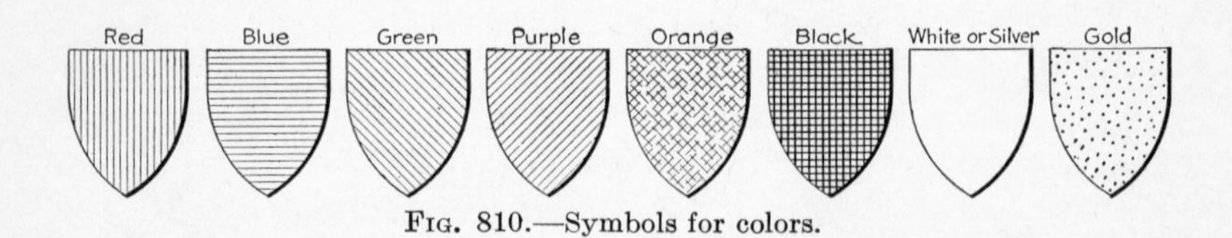

Fig. 810.—Symbols for colors.

Symbols for Colors.—Line symbols for the representation of colors were first used in heraldry, under the heraldic names of *gules*—red, *azure*—blue, *vert*—green, *purpure*—purple, *sable*—black, *tenny*—tawny, *sanguine*—dark red, *argent*—silver, and *or*—gold, and these have become the universal standard in all kinds of drawing. It is occasionally necessary on a black and white drawing to indicate the required colors of a fabric or design, as in the device illustrated in Fig. 52. This is notably true in patent office drawing, as mentioned on page 417. The symbols of Fig. 811 are the patent office standards, and, with the exception of orange, those used in heraldry.

ABBREVIATIONS

A. C.—Alternating current
A.S.A.—Am. Standards Assn.
A.W.G.—American wire gage (B & S)
B.B.—Ball bearings
B.C.—Bolt circle
B.H.P.—Brake horsepower
B.W.G.—Birmingham wire gage
B & S—Brown & Sharpe gage
Bab.—Babbitt metal
Br.—Brass
Bz. or Bro.—Bronze
C'bore—Counterbore
C.I.—Cast iron
℄ or C.L.—Center line
cm.—Centimeter (s)
⊔—Channel
Cop.—Copper
C.P.—Circular pitch
C.R.S.—Cold rolled steel
Csk.—Countersink
C to C—Center to center
Cyl.—Cylinder
D.—Diameter
D.C.—Direct current
Deg. or (°)—Degree (s)
D. Forg. or D.F.—Drop forging
D.P.—Diametral pitch
Drg. or Dwg.—Drawing
EF—Extra fine (threads)
f—Finish
ff.—File finish
Fil.—Fillister
ft. or (')—Feet
Ga.—Gage
G.I.—Galvanized iron
Gr.—Grind
Hd.—Head
H.D.G.—Hot dipped galvanized
Hex.—Hexagonal
H.P. or HP—Horsepower
Hrd. & Gr.—Harden and grind
I—I-beam
I.H.P.—Indicated horsepower
in. or (")—Inch (es)
K.W.—Kilowatt
∟ or ang.—Angle
L.H.—Left hand
m.—Meters
mm.—Millimeters
Mal. I.—Malleable iron
Min. or (')—Minutes
M.S.—Machine steel
N.—National (Am.) Std.
NC—National Coarse (Th'ds)
NF—National Fine (Th'ds)
No. or #—Number
O.D.—Outside diameter
P—Pitch
Pat.—Pattern
Pcs.—Pieces
P. D.—Pitch diameter
⊥—Perpendicular to
Phos. Bro.—Phosphor bronze
Pl.—Plate
lb. or #—Pounds
#/sq.in.—Pounds per square inch
R—Radius
Rd.—Round
Req.—Required
R.H.—Right hand
r.p.m.—Revolutions per minute
S. or St.—Mild steel
S.A.E.—Society of Automotive Engineers
S.C.—Steel casting
Sc.—Screw
S.Forg.—Steel forging
Sq.—Square
Sq.in. or □"—Square inch (es)
Sq.ft. or □'—Square feet
Std.—Standard
S.Tube—Steel tubing
T—Teeth
Thd.—Thread
Thds.—Threads
T.S.—Tool steel
U.S.F.—United States form (threads) (old)
U.S.S.—United States Standard (old)
WF—Wide flange
W. I.—Wrought iron

Weights of Materials

Material	Weight	Material	Weight
Commercial bronze, 95 per cent	0.320 lb./cu. in.	Steel, cold drawn	0.283 lb./cu. in.
Commercial bronze, 90 per cent	0.318 lb./cu. in.	Steel, machine steel	0.282 lb./cu. in.
Red brass, 85 per cent	0.316 lb./cu. in.	Steel, tool	0.272 lb./cu. in.
Red brass, 80 per cent	0.313 lb./cu. in.	Tin	0.263 lb./cu. in.
Drawing or spinning brass	0.306 lb./cu. in.	Zinc	0.254 lb./cu. in.
Muntz metal	0.303 lb./cu. in.	Glass, common	0.094 lb./cu. in.
Tobin bronze	0.304 lb./cu. in.	Glass, plate	0.093 lb./cu. in.
Everdur	0.308 lb./cu. in.	Duralumin	0.103 lb./cu. in.
Cast aluminum S.A.E. No. 30	0.102 lb./cu. in.	Copper	0.318 lb./cu. in.
Cast aluminum S.A.E. No. 321	0.097 lb./cu. in.	Gold	0.697 lb./cu. in.
Iron, gray cast	0.260 lb./cu. in.	Silver	0.380 lb./cu. in.
Iron, wrought	0.283 lb./cu. in.	Water	62.4 lb./cu. ft.
Babbitt metal	0.267 lb./cu. in.	Sandstone	144.0 lb./cu. ft.
Aluminum	0.092 lb./cu. in.	Limestone	163.0 lb./cu. ft.
Lead	0.411 lb./cu. in.	Fire brick	17.5 lb./cu. ft.
Mercury	0.490 lb./cu. in.	Cypress	30.0 lb./cu. ft.
Nickel	0.318 lb./cu. in.	Maple (hard)	33.0 lb./cu. ft.
Monel metal	0.322 lb./cu. in.	Pine (yellow, long leaf)	44.0 lb./cu. ft.
		Pine (white)	26.0 lb./cu. ft.
		Oak (white)	46.0 lb./cu. ft.
		Redwood	26.0 lb./cu. ft.
		African teak	62.0 lb./cu. ft.

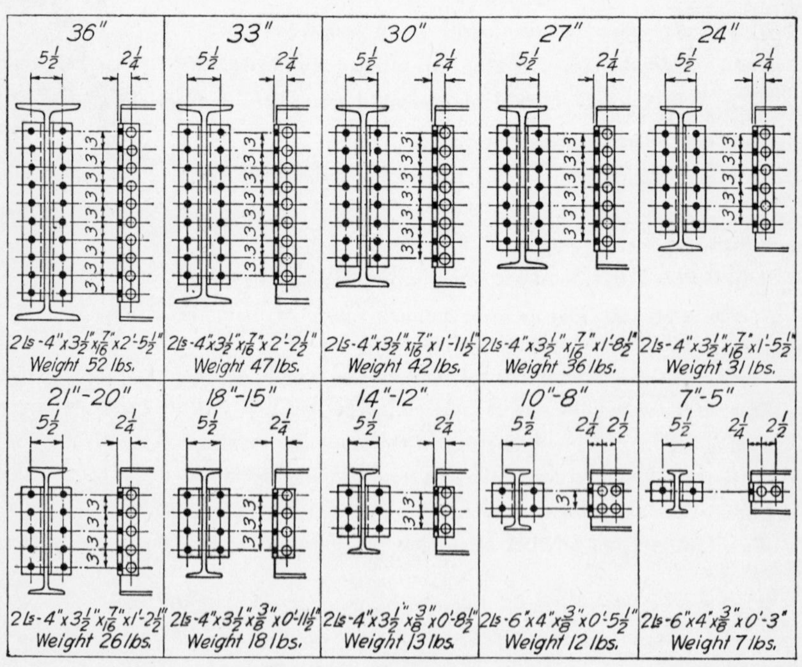

Fig. 811.—Beam connections.

Commercial Sizes.—The following notes give the commercial methods of specifying sizes of the items in the list. The material must, of course, always be specified.

Ball Bearings and *Roller Bearings.*—Give type, manufacturer's name and serial number.

Belting.—Give width, and thickness or ply.

Chain.—Give diameter of rod used.

Electrical Conduit.—Same as pipe.

Expansion Bolts.—Give diameter of bolt, not of casing.

Keys-Woodruff.—Specify by number. *Pratt and Whitney*, specify by number. *Square* and *flat*, give width, thickness and length.

Leather Fillets (for patterns).—Designated by numbers corresponding to the radii in sixteenths, thus No. 2 is ⅛-inch radius.

Lock Washers.—Give type, nominal size, width and thickness.

Machine Chains.—Give pitch, c. to c. of rivets, and width, inside for block or roller type and outside for rocker-joint type.

Nails (common).—Give size by number with letter *d*, as 10*d* (tenpenny = 10 lb. per thousand).

Pipe.—Give nominal inside diameter.

Pipe Fittings.—Give nominal size of pipe, material, and finish.

R. R. Rails.—Give height of section and weight per yard.

Rivets.—Give diameter, length, type of head, and material.

Rolled Steel Shapes.—Give name, essential dimensions, and weight per foot.

Rope.—Give largest diameter.

Shafting.—The best practice is to give the actual diameter.

Sheet Metal.—Give thickness by gage number, or preferably in thousandths of an inch (for 3/16 inch and over, give thickness in fractions).

Split Cotter.—Give diameter and length of straight part.

Springs.—Helical, give outside diameter, gage or diameter of wire in thousandths, length and coils per inch when free.

Taper Pins.—Give number or diameter at large end, and length.

Tapered Pieces.—Give size at large end, taper per foot, and length.

Tubing.—Give outside diameter and thickness.

Washers.—Give in order, nominal size, width and thickness.

Wire.—Give diameter by gage number or preferably in thousandths of an inch.

Wire Cloth.—Give number of meshes per lineal inch, and gage or diameter of wire.

Wood Screws.—Give length, diameter by number, and kind of head.

Special.—Manufactured articles or fittings, give manufacturer's name and catalogue number.

GLOSSARY OF SHOP TERMS FOR DRAFTSMEN

Anneal—To soften a metal piece and remove internal stresses by heating to its critical temperature and allowing to cool very slowly.

Arc weld (*v*)—To weld by electric arc process.

Bore (*v*)—To enlarge a hole with a boring tool as in a lathe or boring mill. Distinguished from *drill.*

Boss—A projection of circular cross section, as on a casting or forging.

Braze—To join by the use of hard solder.

Broach (*v*)—To finish the inside of a hole to a shape usually other than round. (*n*) A tool with serrated edges, pushed or pulled through a hole to enlarge it to a required shape.

Buff—To polish with abrasive on a cloth wheel or other soft carrier.

Burnish—To smooth or polish by a rolling or sliding tool under pressure.

Bushing—A removal sleeve or liner for a bearing.

Carburize—To prepare a low-carbon steel for heat treatment by packing in a box with carbonizing material, such as wood charcoal, and heating to about 2000° F. for several hours, then allowing to cool slowly.

Case-harden—To harden the surface of carburized steel by heating to critical temperature and quenching, as in an oil or lead bath.

Castellate—To form into a shape resembling a castle battlement, as castellated nut. Often applied to a shaft with multiple integral keys milled on it.

Chamfer—To bevel a sharp external edge.

Chase (*v*)—To cut threads in a lathe, as distinguished from cutting threads with a die. (*n*) A slot or groove.

Chill (*v*)—To harden the surface of cast iron by sudden cooling against a metal mold.

Chip (*v*)—To cut or clean with a chisel.

Color-harden—To case-harden to a very shallow depth, chiefly for appearance.

Core (*v*)—To form the hollow part of a casting, using a solid form made of sand, shaped in a core box, baked and placed in the mold. After cooling the core is easily broken up leaving the casting hollow.

Counterbore (*v*)—To enlarge a hole to a given depth. (*n*) The cylindrical enlargement of the end of a drilled or bored hole. 2. A cutting tool for counterboring, having a piloted end of the size of the drilled hole.

Countersink (*v*)—To form a depression to fit the conical head of a screw, or the thickness of a plate, so the face will be level with the surface. (*n*) A conical tool for countersinking.

Crown—Angular or rounded contour, as on the face of a pulley.

Die—One of a pair of hardened metal blocks for forming, impressing or cutting out a desired shape. 2. (thread) A tool for cutting external threads. Opposite of tap.

Die casting (*n*)—A very accurate and smooth casting made by pouring a molten alloy (or composition, as Bakelite) usually under pressure into a metal mold or die. Distinguished from a casting made in sand.

Die Stamping (*n*)—A piece, usually of sheet metal, formed or cut out by a die.

Draw (*v*)—To form by a distorting or stretching process. 2. To temper steel by gradual or intermittent quenching.

Drill (*v*)—To sink a hole with a drill, usually a twist drill. (*n*) A pointed cutting tool rotated under pressure.

Drop Forging (*n*)—A wrought piece formed hot between dies under a drop hammer, or by pressure.

Face (*v*)—To machine a flat surface perpendicular to the axis of rotation on a lathe. Distinguished from *turn.*

Feather—A flat sliding key, usually fastened to the hub.

Fettle—To remove fins and smooth the corners on unfired ceramic products.

File (*v*)—To finish or trim with a file.

Fillet (*n*)—A rounded filling of the internal angle between two surfaces.

Fin—A thin projecting rib. Also, excess ridge of material.

Fit (*n*)—The kind of contact between two machined surfaces, as (1) *drive, force* or *press*—when the shaft is slightly larger than the hole and must be forced in with sledge or power press.

(2) *shrink*—when the shaft is slightly larger than the hole, the piece containing the hole is heated, thereby expanding the hole sufficiently to slip over the shaft. On cooling the shaft will be seized firmly if the fit allowances have been correctly proportioned.

(3) *running or sliding*—when sufficient allowance has been made between sizes of shaft and hole to allow free running without seizing or heating.

(4) *wringing*—when the allowance is smaller than a running fit and the shaft will enter the hole by twisting it by hand.

Flange—A projecting rim or edge for fastening or stiffening.

Forge (*v*)—To shape metal while hot and plastic by a hammering or forcing process either by hand or by machine.

Galvanize (*v*)—To treat with a bath of lead and zinc to prevent rusting.

Graduate (*v*)—To divide a scale or dial into regular spaces.

Grind (*v*)—To finish or polish a surface by means of an abrasive wheel.

Kerf (*n*)—The channel or groove cut by a saw or other tool.

Key (*n*)—A small block or wedge inserted between shaft and hub to prevent circumferential movement.

Keyway, or keyseat—A groove or slot cut to fit a key. A key fits into a keyseat and slides in a keyway.

Knurl (*v*)—To roughen or indent a turned surface, as a knob or handle.

Lap (*n*)—A piece of soft metal, wood or leather charged with abrasive material, used for obtaining an accurate finish. (*v*) To finish by lapping.

Lug—A projecting "ear" usually rectangular in cross section. Distinguished from *boss.*

Malleable casting (*n*)—An ordinary casting toughened by annealing. Applicable to small castings, with uniform metal thicknesses.

Mill (*v*)—To machine with rotating toothed cutters on a milling machine.

Pack-harden—To carburize and case-harden.

Pad—A shallow projection. Distinguished from *boss* by shape or size.

Peen (*v*)—To stretch, rivet or clinch over by strokes with the peen of a hammer. (*n*) The end of a hammer-head opposite the face, as **ball peen.**

Pickle (*v*)—To clean castings or forgings in a hot weak sulphuric acid bath.

Plane (*v*)—To machine work on a planer, having a fixed tool and reciprocating bed.

Planish (*v*)—To finish sheet metal by hammering with polished-faced hammers.

Polish (*v*)—To make smooth or lustrous by friction with a very fine abrasive.

Profile (*v*)—To machine an outline with a rotary cutter usually controlled by a master cam or die.

Punch (*v*)—To perforate by pressing a non-rotating tool through the work.

Ream (*v*)—To finish a drilled or punched hole very accurately with a rotating fluted tool of the required diameter.

Relief (*n*)—The amount one plane surface of a piece is set below or above another plane, usually for clearance or for economy in machining.

Rivet (*v*)—To fasten with rivets. 2. To batter or upset the headless end of a pin used as a permanent fastening.

Sand blast (*v*)—To clean castings or forgings by means of sand driven through a nozzle by compressed air.

Shape (*v*)—To machine with a shaper, a machine tool differing from a planer in that the work is stationary and the tool reciprocating.

Shear (*v*)—To cut off sheet or bar metal between two blades.

Sherardize (*v*)—To galvanize with zinc by a dry heating process.

Shim (*n*)—A thin spacer of sheet metal for adjusting.

Spin (*v*)—To shape sheet metal by forcing it against a form as it revolves.

Spline (*n*)—A long keyway. Sometimes, also a flat key.

Spot-face (*v*)—To finish a round spot on a rough surface, usually around a drilled hole, to give a good seat to a screw or bolt head. Cut, usually 1/16″ deep, by a rotating milling cutter.

Spot weld (*v*)—To weld in spots by means of the heat of resistance to an electric current. Not applicable to sheet copper or brass.

Steel casting (*n*)—Material used in machine construction. Is ordinary cast iron into which varying amounts of scrap steel have been added in the melting.

Swage (*v*)—To shape metal by hammering or pressure with the aid of a form or anvil called a swage block.

Sweat (*v*)—To join metal pieces by clamping together with solder between, and applying heat.

Tack weld (*v*)—To join at the edge by welding in short intermittent sections.

Tap (*v*)—To cut threads in a hole with a tapered tool called a tap, having threads on it and fluted to give cutting edges.

Temper (*v*)—To change the physical characteristics of steel by a process of heat treatment.

Templet—A flat pattern for laying out shapes, location of holes, etc.

Trepan (*v*)—To cut an outside annular groove around a hole.

Tumble (*v*)—To clean, smooth or polish castings or forgings in a rotating barrel or drum by friction with each other, assisted by added mediums, as scraps, "jacks," balls, sawdust, etc.

Turn (*v*)—To machine on a lathe. Distinguished from *face*.

Upset (*v*)—To forge a larger diameter or shoulder on a bar.

Weld (*v*)—To join two pieces by heating them to the fusing point and pressing or hammering together.

GLOSSARY OF STRUCTURAL TERMS FOR DRAFTSMEN

Batten Plate—A small plate used to hold two parts in their proper position when made up as one member.

Batter—A deviation from the vertical in upright members.

Bay—The distance between two trusses or transverse bents.

Beam—A horizontal member forming part of the frame of a building or structure.

Bent—A vertical framework usually consisting of a truss or beam supported at the ends on columns.

Brace—A diagonal member used to stiffen a frame work.

Buckle Plate—A flat plate with dished depression pressed into it to give transverse strength.

Built-up Member—A member built from standard shapes to give one single stronger member.

Camber—Slight upward curve given to trusses and girders to avoid effect of sag.

Cantilever—A beam, girder or truss overhanging one or both supports.

Chord—The principal member of a truss on either the top or bottom.

Clearance—Rivet driving clearance is distance from center of rivet to obstruction. Erection clearance is amount of space left between members for ease in assembly.

Clevis—U-shaped shackle for connecting a rod to a pin.

Clip Angle—A small angle used for fastening various members together.

Column—A vertical compression member.

Cope—To cut out top or bottom of flanges and web so that one member will frame into another.

Coping—A projecting top course of concrete or stone.

Counters—Diagonal members in a truss to provide for reversal of shear due to live load.

Cover Plate—A plate used in building up flanges in a built-up member to give greater strength and area, or for protection.

Crimp—To offset the end of a stiffener to fit over the leg of an angle.

Diagonals—Diagonal members used for stiffening and wind bracing.

Dowel—An iron or wooden pin extending into but not through two timbers to connect them.

Drift Pin—A tapered steel pin used to bring rivet holes fair in assembling steel work.

Edge Distance—The distance from center of rivet to edge of plate or flange.

Fabricate—To cut, punch and sub-assemble members in the shop.

Fillers—Either plate or ring fills used to take up space in riveting two members where a gusset is not used.

Flange—The projecting portion of a beam, channel or column.

Gage Line—The center line for rivet holes.

Gin Pole—A guyed mast with block at the top for hoisting.

Girder—A horizontal member, either single or built up, acting as a principal beam.

Girt—A beam usually bolted to columns to support the side covering or serve as window lintels.

Gusset Plate—A plate used to connect various members, such as in a truss.

Hip—The intersection between two sloping surfaces forming an exterior angle.

Knee Brace—A corner brace used to prevent angular movement.

Lacing or Lattice Bars—Bars used diagonally to space and stiffen two parallel members, such as in a built-up column.

Laterals—Members used to prevent lateral deflection.

Lintel—A horizontal member used to carry a wall over an opening.

Louvres—Metal slats either movable or fixed, as in a monitor ventilator.

Monitor Ventilator—A frame work at the top of the roof, that carries fixed or movable louvres.

Muntin—Parting strip in sash.

Panel—The space between adjacent floor supports, or purlins in a roof.

Pitch—Center distance between rivets parallel to axis of member. Also for roofs, the ratio of rise to span.

Purlins—Horizontal members extending between trusses, used as beams for supporting the roof.

Rafters—Beams or truss members supporting the purlins.

Sag Ties—Tie rods between purlins in the plane of the roof to carry the component of the roof load parallel to the roof.

Separator—Either a cast-iron spacer or wrought-iron pipe on bolt for the purpose of holding members a fixed distance apart.

Shim—A thin piece of wood or steel placed under a member to bring it to a desired elevation.

Sleeve Nut—A long nut with right and left threads for connecting two rods to make an adjustable member.

Span—Distance between centers of supports of a truss, beam or girder.

Splice—A longitudinal connection between the parts of a continuous member.

Stiffener—Angle, plate or channel riveted to a member to prevent buckling.

Stringer—A longitudinal member used to support loads directly.

Strut—A compression member in a framework.

Truss—A rigid framework for carrying loads, formed in a series of triangles.

Turnbuckle—A coupling, threaded right and left or swiveled on one end, for adjustably connecting two rods.

Valley—The intersection between two sloping surfaces, forming a reentrant angle.

Web—The part of a channel, I-beam or girder between the flanges.

INDEX